THE AMERICAN MIDLAND NATURALIST

Monograph No. 7

THE AMERICAN MIDLAND NATURALIST

Monograph Series

EDITORIAL STAFF

THE AMERICAN MIDLAND NATURALIST

Monograph No. 7

Edited by Robert E. Gordon
Published by the University of Notre Dame
Notre Dame, Indiana

FLORA OF ILLINOIS

Containing keys for identification of
flowering plants and ferns

By GEORGE NEVILLE JONES
Professor of Botany and Curator of the Herbarium
University of Illinois

Reprint of the Third Edition, June 1971
American Midland Naturalist
Department of Biology
University of Notre Dame
Notre Dame, Indiana

THIRD EDITION

The University of Notre Dame Press
Notre Dame, Indiana
1963

ADDENDA ET CORRIGENDA

Third Edition, Flora of Illinois, 1963

Page

4, line 25; for *rhombipetata* read *rhombipetala*

4, line 26; for *Lithospermum croceum* read *L. caroliniense*

5, line 30; for *Stylisma pickeringii* read *S. pattersoni*

15, delete the first four lines and substitute:

    35. Ovary inferior.

        36. Stamens 3; leaves equitant; flowers blue or white . . . . 136. Iridaceae

        36. Stamens 6; leaves not equitant; flower white or yellow . . . .

        . . . . .135. Amaryllidaceae

        35. Ovary Superior . . . . 130. Liliaceae

18, couplet 35(b): Leaves without stipules . . . . Caprifoliaceae
Valerianella in VALERIANACEAE may key out here also.
Plants are annual or biennial herbs; flowers small, whitish, in terminal cymes.

21, line 31; after purplish, insert: or minute, greenish

22, couplet 26(a): *Mertensia* in BORAGINACEAE also often has large flowers, 2 cm or longer, but the fruits are 4 nutlets, not capsules.

23, couplet 8(a): . . . . Proserpinaca in 84. HALORAGACEAE (not 119)

31, line 13 from bottom; after stamens 5 insert: *Parthenocissus* in 52. Vitaceae

37, couplet 8(b): after "Branches not prickly" add: rarely with thorns: (this applies to some Rosaceae).

37, couplet 15(a): Note that Oleaceae basically do not belong in this category, because the leaves and leaf-scars are alternate above, but usually opposite below.

47, line 6; for *A. rhizophyllus* read *A. rhizophyllum*

50, line 35: for 14. *Hepatica* read 15. *Hepatica*

58, under Cabomba add: also Vermilion Co.

61, couplet 3(b): Leaves merely crenate-serrate, not lobed (except *V. sagittata*).

64, line 10 from bottom; for leaves prickly read leaves not prickly

67, line 40 (under Cristatella) after counties add: also Whiteside Co., V. H. Chase.

79, line 5; for leaves subulate read leaves subulate to linear.

82, another common name for Hibiscus trionum is: Venus Mallow.

86, line 35; after occasional, insert: introd. from Eur.

91, line 2 from bottom; delete: also Kankakee Co.

97, couplet 22(a): Leaves 5-15 cm long, etc.; stems 1-2.5 m tall (not cm!)

106, line 13 from bottom; for *Aesculus glabra* L., read *A. glabra* Willd.

115, line 19; for *G. verum* read *G. vernum*

122, line 4 from bottom; transfer calyx lobes usually glandular-serrulate to end of bottom line after pubescent.

127, couplet 24(b): the genus *Lotus* may key out here also, as follows:
Flowers in racemes, umbels, or solitary.

    25. Flowers in racemes; stamens distinct; pods stipitate, turgid or inflated; plants tending to turn back in drying . . . . .8. Baptisia

    25. Flowers in umbels or solitary; stamens diadelphous: pods linear, somewhat compressed, notstipitate; plants not turning black in drying.

        25' Flowers pink, solitary . . . . 15. *Hosackia*

        25' Flowers yellow, in umbels . . . . 11. *Lotus*

132, *Medicago*, couplet 2(a): Pods curved but not spirally coiled (instead of "straight") . . . . (M. lupulina)

132, line 7 from bottom; for Pods straight read Pods 1-seeded, reniform, reticulate

133, line 4; after 1904; insert: more recently in Peoria Co. by V. H. Chase

136, line 14 from bottom; after scabrous insert above

150, under Juglandaceae: 1(b) . . . . husk splitting into 4 valves (not halves)

167, line 21; after Jackson, insert Peoria,

188, line 12; for Peoria read Tazewell

188, line 7 from bottom; delete and

189, under Convolvulaceae: 2. Styles 2, each 2-cleft, the stigmas 4 . . . . . 1. *Stylisma*
                    2. Style 1, the stigmas 2.

191, last line: cross out "on short pedicels" (they are really rather long; the statement is superfluous anyway)

197, line 9, for 15. read 18.

199, line 20; delete: apparently the only 111. collection; add: collected by J. K. Bouseman in 1961.

203, *Gerardia:* 2. Pedicels less than twice the length of the fruiting calyx.

        3.

        3.

           4.

           4.

      2. Pedicels more than twice the length of the fruiting calyx.

217, *Agastache;* 1 . . . calyx-lobes oval, obtusish, 1-1.5 mm long; etc. (not ovate, acutish) . . . . *A. nepetoides*

   1 . . . . calyx-lobes lanceolate, acuminate, 2.5-3 mm long; (not 2-2,5)
   . . . . *A. scrophulariaefolia*

219, couplet 4(a): Calyx smooth etc.; leaves usually lanceolate (cross out the linear)
   . . . . for *S. tenuifolia*

225, line 11; for 4. Leaves 2-8 mm long read cm.

231, line 2 from bottom; for Peoria read Tazewell

237, line 5; after columnar insert: 31. *Echinacea*

237, line 8; for 18. Boltonia read 18. *Boltonia*

247, line 14 from bottom; after Marshall, insert Bureau,

254, line 30; for Daily read Daisy

264, in Compositae: Tribe 9, Anthemidae is missing; should go between *Dyssodia* and *Achillae*

270, line 29 (under Krigia) insert:

   1. Plants annual; pappus of 5-7 short rounded scales and an equal number of longer bristles; scrapes slender, each with one head; leaves basal; involucre 6-8 mm high; dry soil in fields and open woods, chiefly in the valleys of the Illinois and Wabash rivers. May-July . . . . .K. virginica (L.) Willd.

273, line 5; for light yellow read whitish

274, line 6 in the key to Alismaceae, after base insert: or leaves linear-lanceolate;

282, *line* 5 from bottom; delete Peoria Co.: *Schoenbeck.*

289, *Tradescantia virginiana* L., instead of *T. virginica* L.

309, line 10; for Nutt. read Honck.

323, line 2 from bottom; after spikelets several-flowered add: (except *Hordeum* and some *Chlorideae*).

328, line 10; for 4. Glumes 3. read 4. Glumes apparently 3.

337, line 8; delete Marshall Co.

338, line 13; after spontaneous. insert: native of Eurasia.

346, couplet 7(a): Spikelets 2.8-3.1 mm long, instead of 3-3.2 mm for *P. geminum*

Glossary: axial: in the axil

   axile: belonging to the axis (i.e., with the placentae on the axis)

Index: Anthemidae, p. 264

Index To Plant Names

CONTENTS

FIGURES

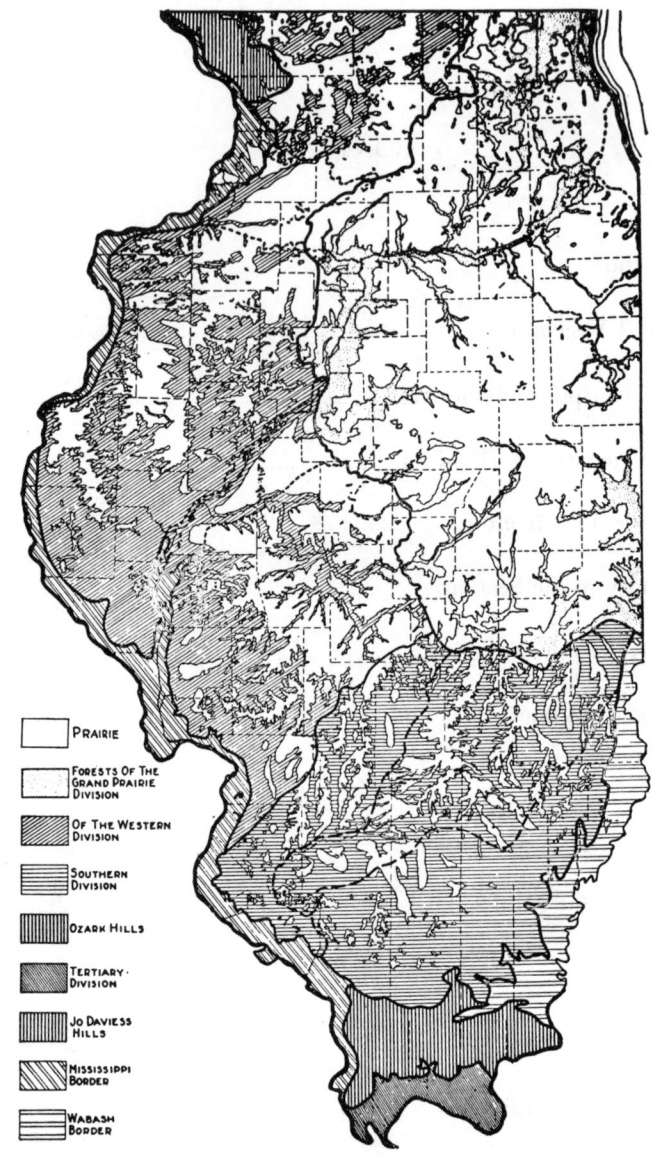

□	PRAIRIE
▨	FORESTS OF THE GRAND PRAIRIE DIVISION
▨	OF THE WESTERN DIVISION
▤	SOUTHERN DIVISION
▥	OZARK HILLS
▨	TERTIARY· DIVISION
▥	JO DAVIESS HILLS
▨	MISSISSIPPI BORDER
▤	WABASH BORDER

VEGETATIONAL MAP OF ILLINOIS. The boundaries of the principal geographical divisions of the state are indicated by solid lines, and their subdivisions by broken lines. Shading, as shown in the key, indicates approximately the areas that formerly were forested. (Reproduced by permission from A. G. Vestal's map of 1930, which was based on C. J. Telford's map in Illinois Nat. Hist. Surv. Bull. vol. 16, 1926.)

Flora of Illinois

Introduction

As the second edition (1950) has been out-of-print for more than two years, continued demand seems to warrant publication of a revised third edition. Thanks largely to the activities of several botanists in various parts of the state, many additional data are now at hand, particularly regarding the occurrence and distribution of species.

The preparation of a third edition of this book has afforded opportunity to make certain revisions. A number of rearrangements and corrections have been made in the analytical keys. Many of the keys have been rewritten entirely. Some species have been added, some others have been deleted, and a few nomenclatural changes have been made. New monographs and taxonomic revisions during the past decade have necessitated revisionary treatment in some groups. The main objective of this work is that of the previous editions, to afford a ready means of identification of the approximately 2400 species of flowering plants and fernworts growing without cultivation in Illinois.

The keys to species include, in addition to diagnostic characters, a statement of habitat, frequency and distribution, time of flowering, and some relevant synonymy, the intention having been to correlate the valid name of the species with other names that may be found in the older manuals. Suitable popular names have been provided for many species. For rare plants, specimens are often cited by collector and number or date.

When the first edition of *Flora of Illinois* was published in 1945, two of the standard botanical manuals of eastern United States were between thirty and forty years old. Five years later when the second edition appeared in 1950, these manuals were still in use, although the eighth edition of *Gray's Manual* appeared somewhat later in the same year, and H. A. Gleason's *New Britton & Brown Illustrated Flora of Northeastern United States and Adjacent Canada* was published in 1952. Publication in 1955 of *Vascular Plants of Illinois,* with its extensive synonymy, 1375 distributional maps, and a bibliography of several thousand entries, has rendered largely unnecessary the repetition in this edition of the extensive 27-page bibliography of the second edition. Moreover, there is a list by R. H. Mohlenbrock (Rhodora 63: 19-24, 1961) comprising 51 publications on the Illinois flora since 1955 by more than a dozen different authors.

All species of vascular plants regarded by the writer as growing spontaneously in Illinois have been included, provided there is evidence that they are established and maintain themselves year after year without cultivation. Further study may reveal the presence of additional species. With few exceptions, no species has been admitted, unless authentic specimens from Illinois have been examined. Known or suspected hybrids often are mentioned, or keyed out when practicable,

1

when they constitute a part of the recognizable flora. Stray plants or waifs, and especially those that have not been collected within the past half century in Illinois, and which presumably no longer occur spontaneously, and species reported for the state for which no reliable voucher specimens have been found, usually have been excluded. Uncritical acceptance of all published records is not a satisfactory basis for dealing with the species of a flora.

In this edition the taxonomy has been extensively reviewed, not only in the treatment of genera and species, but especially in the sequence of families by breaking away from the familiar but partly outmoded Englerian system which as early as 1893 was characterized by C. E. Bessey as "a makeshift maintained by conservatism." The stimulus of Bessey, and later of the great modern botanical phylogenist, John Hutchinson of Kew, whose *Families of Flowering Plants,* one of the most important botanical works of its kind produced in the twentieth century, has influenced not only the study of phylogenetic botany but other related fields, such as systematic plant anatomy. Although we are unable to accept Hutchinson's system in its entirety, we have adopted many of the principles and practices so ably expounded by him. The sequence of families followed herein will be more or less familiar to those botanists who are acquainted with Hutchinson's *British Flowering Plants,* Metcalfe & Chalk's *Anatomy of the Dicotyledons,* and Clapham, Tutin & Warburg, *Flora of the British Isles.*

According to theories of Bentham & Hooker, Bessey, Hallier, Wieland, Arber & Parkin, Hutchinson, and their many followers, Dicotyledons beginning with Ranales are placed first, and Monocotyledons follow as a derived subclass. The orders of the Archichlamydeae of Engler are extensively rearranged, but those of the Metachlamydeae, considered to comprise a polyphyletic series that has reached a similar evolutionary level, have been retained largely as Engler left them. Monocotyledons show two evolutionary divergent lines, the first largely entomophilous from Alismales to Orchidales, the second progressively anemophilous from Arales to Graminales.

This study is based mainly upon material contained in the herbarium of the University of Illinois, including more than 400,000 specimens from various parts of the earth. Of these approximately one-fourth were collected in Illinois. Directly or indirectly ten other institutional herbaria in Illinois have been drawn upon, particularly Chicago Natural History Museum, Illinois State Natural History Survey, Southern Illinois University, and Illinois State Museum, representing a total of more than 150,000 Illinois collections of vascular plants.

Acknowledgments

I am under obligation to so many persons for assistance that it is scarcely practical here to mention all, but I should like to express cordial thanks to Dr. Virginius Heber Chase of Peoria Heights, Illinois, for his continued collaboration, and for reference to his magnificent herbarium of nearly 50,000 specimens recently purchased by the University of Illinois; to Professor R. H. Mohlenbrock of Southern Illinois University for initial assistance in organizing the manuscript, for the key to Cyperus, and for data concerning some plants in southern Illinois; to my colleague Professor Dale M. Smith for advice concerning *Asplenium* and *Helianthus;* to Mr. E. H. Daubs on Lemnaceae; and finally to my wife for help in proofreading and preparation of specimens.

FLORA AND VEGETATION

DESCRIPTION OF THE AREA

Illinois is part of the Great Central Plain of North America, and is situated between 37° and 42° N. lat., and 87° and 91° W. long. It is bounded on the north by Wisconsin, on the east by Indiana, on the west by Iowa and Missouri, and on the south by Kentucky. The maximum length is 380 miles, and the width more than 200 miles. Its area is approximately 57,926 square miles. Physiographically, most of this state except the southern portion lies in the Till Plains Section of the Central Lowland Province. Biogeographically, almost all of Illinois lies in the Austral Zone. The great majority of native species of plants are therefore of southern affinities, and the boreal element is extremely small. The Austroriparian Province enters the state only at its extreme southern end. The average elevation above sea level is about 600 feet. The highest point is 1241 feet altitude at Charles Mound in Jo Daviess County along the Wisconsin-Illinois boundary. Although most of the area has a low elevation and comparatively level surface there is a good drainage system with more than 275 streams, which may be grouped in two river systems, one having the Mississippi River, and the other the Wabash and Ohio rivers as its outlet. The soils of Illinois are remarkable for their fertility, and agriculture is one of the important occupations. The better agricultural districts are characterized by a black loam, and the alluvial soil of the river valleys is especially fertile. On many of the river bluffs the soil is loess. Nearly all the rocks of Illinois are sedimentary and belong to the Paleozoic era. Igneous rocks are found only in a few places, and metamorphic rocks are almost unknown.

During the Glacial period there were four advances of the ice-sheet into Illinois. The ice of the third, or Illinoian, stage covered approximately nine-tenths of the state, and extended southward to the Ozark Ridge, the most southerly latitude reached by the North American ice-sheet. Hence, there are only three districts in Illinois that may have remained untouched by the Pleistocene glaciation. These are 1) the seven southernmost counties of the state, 2) an area between the Mississippi and Illinois rivers in Calhoun County, and 3) Jo Daviess County and a small portion of Carroll County. The second and third districts are part of a much larger nonglaciated region known as the Driftless Area, which occupies adjacent portions of Wisconsin, Minnesota, and Iowa.

The flora and fauna of Illinois are similar to those of adjacent states. Extensive forests and grasslands formerly covered the entire region. In the northern part there were large prairies with tongues of forest extending along the principal watercourses. At the present time, although the vegetation has been greatly disturbed, the flora is still rich and varied, with a large number of species of grasses, as well as other herbs and ligneous plants. The more extensive forested areas are chiefly in the southern counties, especially on the flood plains of the principal rivers, and in the Ozark Hills. These forests are composed almost entirely of hardwoods. Oak, hickory, maple, elm, and ash are among the more common kinds of trees.

Formerly one of the most remarkable features of the state of Illinois was its great stretches of prairies covered with rich growth of tall grasses and several hundred species of other herbaceous flowering plants. The most extensive of these prairies occurred in northern and central Illinois, and were interspersed with numerous swamps and shallow ponds which have long since disappeared. However, the original prairie has all but vanished from the Illinois landscape, and no typical area of upland prairie remains for botanical study. Extensive tracts of these upland prairies were swampy, but almost all have been drained and their natural vegetation has since disappeared except from roadsides and along the railroads. Other areas are covered chiefly with sand or sandy loam, and support a flora of psammophilous species, including *Leptoloma cognatum, Tephrosia virginiana, Helianthemum canadense, Oenothera rhombipetata, Phlox bifida, Lithospermum croceum,* and *Chrysopsis villosa.* The principal sand-areas are in the northern half of the state.

VEGETATIONAL DIVISIONS

The spontaneous flora of Illinois comprises a vegetation that is rather sharply differentiated into prairie and forest. Each of these two types of vegetation includes a number of communities or associations, reflecting the transitions in temperature and rainfall, as well as the topographic and edaphic conditions. On the accompanying map the ecological divisions are based principally upon the broader topographical features, including the effects of glacial geology. The area affected by the recent (Wisconsin) glaciation is mostly treeless, and extensive areas of upland prairie formerly occurred in the western division. It will be noted that the botanical areas are correlated with the various agricultural districts, and are thus intimately connected with various phases of human geography. Moreover, it is obvious that faunal areas parallel the natural botanical divisions, and thus these divisions are useful to zoologists, as well as to students of the applied branches of biology, including plant pathology, agriculture, etc. The biotic divisions now recognized are as follows:

Grand Prairie Division	Southern Division
Western Division	Wabash Border
Jo Daviess Hills	Ozark Hills
Mississippi Border	Tertiary Division

GRAND PRAIRIE DIVISION

The term is applied to the eastern portion of Illinois, and includes all the area of recent or Wisconsin glaciation which is for the most part treeless. This area has the youngest soils of the state, in which leaching of dissolved materials has not progressed to any great extent. Characteristic prairie-plants, including *Silphium terebinthinaceum, Eryngium yuccifolium, Sorghastrum nutans, Andropogon furcatus,* and *Sporobolus heterolepis,* are frequent in these areas of black prairie soil. The morainal country of Lake and McHenry counties is hilly, and was formerly extensively forested. Small tracts of timber still remain. *Quercus macrocarpa* is one of the conspicuous trees. *Tilia americana* and *Quercus rubra* are frequent in drier habitats. Many of the lower areas are occupied by marshes, bogs, and lakes, and in these places colonies of *Larix laricina* are to be found.

The counties near Lake Michigan contain a number of northern species, including *Larix laricina, Pinus banksiana, Scheuchzeria americana, Carex aurea, Eriophorum angustifolium, Betula pumila, Ribes hirtellum, Shepherdia canadensis, Cornus canadensis, Andromeda glaucophylla,* and *Chamaedaphne calyculata.* The beach area of Lake Michigan has numerous sand-ridges and dunes, with intervening sand-prairies and sloughs. Several species are peculiar to this area, such as: *Juniperus canadensis, J. horizontalis, Ammophila breviligulata, Calamovilfa longifolia, Salix adenophylla, Cakile edentula, Potentilla anserina, Prunus pumila, Lathyrus maritimus, Chamaesyce polygonifolia, Arctostaphylos uva-ursi,* and *Artemisia caudata.*

WESTERN DIVISION

This division includes most of the western part of Illinois. Much of the area is covered by relatively old glacial drift (Illinoian) with recent deposits of loess. These prairie areas contain several xerophytic western species, including *Bouteloua gracilis, Stylisma pickeringii, Lesquerella argentea, Amorpha canescens, Opuntia rafinesquii,* and *Synthyris bullii.* Areas of lower elevation include prairie sloughs. Southwest of the Grand Prairie, and west of the Illinois River, more than half the area is occupied by forest, and only a few flat upland prairies of fair size, such as the Bushnell and Carthage prairies occur. This condition has been brought about by the extensive dissection of the country near the larger rivers.

JO DAVIESS HILLS

The Driftless Area in Jo Daviess County has served as a refuge for preglacial plants. At the present time there are several species of limited distribution within the state, including *Adoxa moschatellina, Dodecatheon amethystinum, Primula mistassinica, Ranunculus rhomboideus, Anemone ludoviciana, Hackelia americana* and others. Much of the terrain is maturely dissected, and consists of steep, forested slopes. The tops of the plateaus are treeless or only sparsely forested. Along the cliffs of the larger streams there are several northern species of trees and shrubs, including *Pinus strobus, Taxus canadensis,* and *Betula papyrifera,* as well as a number of herbaceous plants.

MISSISSIPPI BORDER

The dry western-exposed bluffs of the Mississippi River and of the lower Illinois River have intermittent areas of grassland vegetation containing western prairie species. Sand-prairies are present in the Hancock and Oquawka areas. In a few places sand has been carried by the wind from the river valley to the uplands. Along the northern and central river bluffs the terrain has been deeply eroded, with resultant interruptions of the mantle of loess, and are thus at present not continuously forested. The American beech, *Fagus grandifolia,* and the tulip tree, *Liriodendron tulipifera,* extend northward to Randolph and Jackson counties. The common trees of the northern part of the river bottoms of the Mississippi River are *Acer saccharinum, Ulmus americana, Betula nigra, Quercus palustris,* and *Fraxinus americana.* In the southern part of this area *Liquidambar styraciflua* and *Quercus lyrata* are common.

SOUTHERN DIVISION

The Southern Division is the area of oldest Illinoian Drift. Later depositions of loess with subsequent weathering have complicated the soil profiles. With the exception of the bottomlands, which have a vegetation similar to that of the alluvial soils of the Mississippi Border, the soils throughout the Southern Division are generally poor for plant growth on account of their fine texture and impervious subsoil. Thus they prevent good drainage and aeration, with the result that there is too much water in spring and early summer, and too little in late summer. The principal upland species of woody plants are *Quercus palustris, Q. imbricaria, Q. stellata,* and *Gleditsia triacanthos. Sassafras albidum* and *Diospyros virginiana* are of not infrequent occurrence.

WABASH BORDER

This division includes the bottomlands and bluffs of the Wabash and Ohio rivers, as well as the adjoining upland areas. A great variety of species of ligneous plants is to be found in the forested areas, including *Celtis laevigata, Acer saccharum, Tilia americana, Nyssa aquatica,* and *Liriodendron tulipifera.* Three species of oak, *Quercus falcata, Q. prinus,* and *Q. shumardii,* as well as *Catalpa speciosa,* are characteristic species of this part of the state. The sweet gum, *Liquidambar styraciflua,* extends northward to Crawford County, and the mistletoe, *Phoradendron flavescens,* parasitic principally on elm and other bottomland trees, is known to occur as far north as Lawrence and Crawford counties. This bottomland vegetation extends many miles up the tributaries of the Wabash River.

OZARK HILLS

The Ozark Ridge of southern Illinois is the most conspicuous topographic feature in the state. The axis of the ridge lies along an east-west line across the southern part of the state from Jackson and Union counties to Gallatin and Hardin counties. The highest point is Williams Hill in Pope County, with an elevation of 1065 feet. The flora of the Ozark Hills has been little affected by the Illinois ice-sheet, which apparently did not reach beyond the northern edge of the area. There are several species of vascular plants which have not extended their ranges northward in Illinois and are therefore peculiar to this part of the state. Some of these plants are: *Polypodium polypodioides, Pinus echinata, Smilax bona-nox, Ulmus alata, Magnolia acuminata, Sedum pulchellum, Rhododendron roseum,* and *Vaccinium arboreum.*

TERTIARY DIVISION

The Mississippi Embayment of the Coastal Plain of the south Atlantic and Gulf states extends into Illinois as far as the southern base of the Ozark Hills. The tertiary deposits in the bottomlands of Alexander, Pulaski, and Massac counties contain a number of austro-riparian species that have not migrated northward into the glaciated areas. Some of these are: *Taxodium distichum, Arundinaria gigantea, Quercus phellos, Planera aquatica, Itea virginica, Wisteria macrostachya, Nyssa aquatica, Bumelia lycioides,* and *Bignonia capreolata.*

SYSTEMATIC TREATMENT

Key to the Sections

GROUP I. Seed Plants. Plants normally reproducing by seeds containing an embryo. Gymnosperms and Angiosperms.

A. Herbaceous Plants

1. Plants grasses, sedges, or rushes; perianth green or brownish or absent ....SECTION 1, p. 9
1. Plants not grasses, sedges, or rushes.
  2. Terrestrial plants, not floating on or submerged in water; sometimes growing at the edge of water but then usually erect.
    3. Leaves compound, composed of few or many leaflets, or divided to the midrib or base ....SECTION 2, p. 9
    3. Leaves simple, sometimes lobed, but the lobes usually not extending to the midrib or base (leaves rarely absent or reduced to spines or scales).
      4. Stems not climbing or twining; tendrils absent; plants never cacti or cactus-like.
        5. Plants green, normally possessing chlorophyll, not parasitic or saprophytic or noticeably so.
          6. Plants without a leafy stem, or the stem underground, the flower-stalks leafless, or with a single leaf or a pair or whorl of leaves subtending the inflorescence ....SECTION 3, p. 12
          6. Plants with leafy stems, the leaves sometimes reduced to scales; stem sometimes with only a single leaf, but this borne far below the inflorescence.
            7. Leaves evidently parallel-veined; mostly Monocotyledons (except *Eryngium* and *Tragopogon*) with the floral parts, or some of them in threes, not in fives; stem in cross-section showing the vascular bundles irregularly distributed throughout the pith or around a central cavity; cotyledon 1 ....SECTION 4, p. 15
            7. Leaves not evidently parallel-veined, almost always net-veined (or sometimes apparently only 1-veined); mostly Dicotyledons (except *Trillium* and *Smilax*) with the floral parts often in fives or fours, only exceptionally in threes; stem in cross-section showing a central pith (or, in hollow stems, a cavity) surrounded by a circle of vascular bundles; cotyledons 2.
              8. Leaves, or at least some of them, opposite or whorled.
                9. Leaves entire ....SECTION 5, p. 15
                9. Leaves more or less toothed or lobed ....SECTION 6, p. 19
              8. Leaves alternate.
                10. Leaves entire ....SECTION 7, p. 20
                10. Leaves toothed (or sinuate) or lobed, sometimes cordate at base ....SECTION 8, p. 23
        5. Plants parasitic or saprophytic, without chlorophyll; leaves reduced to scales; fruit a capsule ....SECTION 9, p. 25

8

4. Stems either twining or climbing (tendrils sometimes present); or else cactus plants with conspicuously jointed, succulent, spiny stems ....SECTION 10, p. 26
2. Aquatic plants, floating on or submerged in water (sometimes growing on muddy or sandy shores) ....SECTION 11, p. 27

B. Trees and Shrubs (Including Woody Climbers and Trailers)

11. Gymnosperms. Leaves needle-like (acicular), linear, scale-like, or subulate, evergreen (deciduous in *Larix* and *Taxodium*) ....SECTION 19, p. 39
11. Angiosperms. Leaves not as above: "broadleaf" trees and shrubs (except *Hudsonia*).
    12. Flowers appearing with or after the leaves.
        13. Leaves opposite or whorled ....SECTION 12, p. 28
        13. Leaves alternate.
            14. Leaves compound ....SECTION 13, p. 31
            14. Leaves simple.
                15. Leaves entire ....SECTION 14, p. 32
                15. Leaves toothed or lobed, not entire.
                    16. Leaves lobed ....SECTION 15, p. 34
                    16. Leaves toothed, but not lobed ....SECTION 16, p. 35
    12. Flowers on leafless or almost leafless twigs, appearing before the leaves (or in autumn when they are falling, in *Hamamelis*) ....
    ....SECTION 17, p. 37
GROUP II. Fern and Fern-allies. Plants without flowers or seeds, reproducing by spores borne in sporangia ....SECTION 18, p. 38

Key to the Families

Section 1.   Grasses, Sedges, and Rushes

1. Flowers enclosed by chaffy scales; perianth none, or of bristles; fruit a grain or an achene.
    2. Stem cylindrical and usually hollow except at the nodes; leaves in 2 rows on the stem, the sheaths usually split; fruit a grain ....146. GRAMINEAE
    2. Stem cylindrical or triangular, solid, the nodes usually not conspicuous; sheaths not split; fruit an achene ....145. CYPERACEAE
1. Flowers not enclosed by chaffy scales; perianth 6-parted; stems terete; fruit a capsule ....131. JUNCACEAE

Section 2. Herbs With Compound (or Deeply Divided) Leaves

1. Plants without leafy stems, the leaves all basal.
    2. Leaves 2-cleft; flowers white; fruit a capsule opening by a lid ....
    ....9. PODOPHYLLACEAE
    2. Leaflets 3 or more; fruit not opening by a lid.
        3. Flowers on a spadix surrounded by a spathe; fruit a berry ....
        ....*Arisaema* in 141. ARACEAE
        3. Flowers in racemes or umbels.
            4. Leaflets 3.
                5. Leaflets entire; flowers regular; stamens 10 ....38. OXALIDACEAE
                5. Leaflets not entire.
                    6. Flowers papilionaceous; stamens 10 ....54. LEGUMINOSAE
                    6. Flowers regular; stamens numerous ....53. ROSACEAE
            4. Leaflets numerous; flowers irregular ....14. FUMARIACEAE

1. Plants with stems bearing 1 or more leaves.
  7. Flowers borne in a dense head on a common receptacle surrounded or subtended by an involucre of bracts; fruit an achene; stipules none ......
    ....125. COMPOSITAE
  7. Flowers not borne in a dense head on a common receptacle surrounded or subtended by an involucre.
    8. Flowers on a spadix surrounded by a spathe; fruit a berry ....
    ....*Arisaema* in 141. ARACEAE
    8. Flowers not borne on a spadix surrounded by a spathe.
      9. Flowers in umbels; petals 5; stamens 5; ovary inferior.
        10. Fruit dry, composed of 2 carpels; styles 2 ....92. UMBELLIFERAE
        10. Fruit a berry; styles 5, or 3, or 2 ....91. ARALIACEAE
      9. Flowers not in umbels, or if so, the flowers not as above in all respects.
        11. Corolla papilionaceous; fruit a legume or loment; leaves alternate, usually stipulate ....×....54. LEGUMINOSAE
        11. Corolla not papilionaceous.
          12. Stem bearing only a single leaf or a pair or whorl of leaves.
            13. Pistil 1.
              14. Style or stigma 1.
                15. Sepals and petals each 4; fruit a pod; leaflets 3 or 5, toothed ....*Dentaria* in 18. CRUCIFERAE
                15. Sepals 6; petals small, gland-like; seeds berry-like ....9. PODOPHYLLACEAE
              14. Styles 4 or 5; fruit a drupe ....64. ADOXACEAE
            13. Pistils several to many, separate, simple; fruit achenes or follicles ....3. RANUNCULACEAE
          12. Stems with usually 2 or more alternate leaves, or 2 or more pairs of leaves.
            16. Leaves, or some of them, opposite.
              17. Leaves pinnate or pinnately lobed.
                18. Sepals 4, purple, petaloid; petals none; stamens numerous; plants climbing; achenes with persistent styles ....*Clematis* in 3. RANUNCULACEAE
                18. Sepals not as above; corolla present; stamens few; plants not climbing.
                  19. Flowers blue or white; fruit a capsule.
                    20. Corolla regular; stamens 5 ....
                    ....106. HYDROPHYLLACEAE
                    20. Corolla 2-lipped; stamens 4 ....
                    ....108. SCROPHULARIACEAE
                  19. Flowers yellow or pink.
                    21. Flowers yellow; stamens 10; fruit 5-angled, spiny ......*Tribulus* in 40. ZYGOPHYLLACEAE
                    21. Flowers pink; stamens 3; fruit 1-seeded ....
                    ....123. VALERIANACEAE
              17. Leaves palmately lobed, or digitate, or trifoliolate; petals none; fruit an achene.
                22. Flowers small, green, unisexual; leaves digitately divided into 5-11 serrate, acuminate divisions ....72. CANNABINACEAE
                22. Flowers not green; sepals petal-like ....
                ....3. RANUNCULACEAE

16. Leaves alternate.
    23. Stems climbing; flowers purple (or white); leaves ovate or hastate, often 3-lobed or 3-divided ....107. Solanaceae
    23. Stems not climbing.
      · 24. Corolla of united petals, blue, white or red; leaves pinnate or pinnately lobed; fruit a capsule.
        25. Leaflets entire; style 1 ....104. Polemoniaceae
        25. Leaflets toothed or lobed; styles 2, or style 2-cleft ....106. Hydrophyllaceae
      24. Corolla of separate or nearly separate petals, or petals none, or only one.
        26. Flowers spurred.
          27. Stamens numerous; fruit of follicles ....3. Ranunculaceae
          27. Stamens 6; fruit a capsule ....14. Fumariaceae
        26. Flowers not spurred.
          28. Leaflets 3, obcordate, otherwise entire; flowers yellow; fruit a capsule ....38. Oxalidaceae
          28. Leaflets not obcordate.
            29. Leaves with stipules.
              30. Flowers small, green, unisexual; leaves digitately divided into 5-11, serrate, acuminate divisions ....72. Cannabinaceae
              30. Flowers pink, yellow, white, or purple.
                31. Flowers small, pink; leaves pinnate, the leaflets incised; plants annual, pubescent ....*Erodium* in 36. Geraniaceae
                31. Flowers yellow, white, or purple.
                  32. Leaflets entire; fruit a legume ....54. Leguminosae
                  32. Leaflets toothed or lobed; fruit not a legume.
                    33. Stamens and petals perigynous ....53. Rosaceae
                    33. Stamens and petals hypogynous, or flowers unisexual and the plants dioecious ....3. Ranunculaceae
            29. Leaves without stipules.
              34. Petals and sepals each 3; flowers very small, axillary; annual plants with pinnate leaves ....39. Limnanthaceae

34. Petals and sepals 4 or more, or absent; or the sepals united, sometimes only 2.
35. Sepals 2, caducous (falling as
the flower opens) ; plants with
milky or yellowish juice; stamens numerous, hypogynous;
fruit a capsule ....
........................13. Papaveraceae
35. Sepals 4 or 5; plants with
watery juice.
36. Petals and sepals each 4,
fruit a pod.
37. Leaves trifoliolate; stamens 6 or more, ex-
serted ....
........17. Capparidaceae
37. Leaves not trifoliolate;
stamens 6, four long
and two short ....
..............18. Cruciferae
36. Petals 5 or none; sepals
usually 5, sometimes 4;
fruit an achene or follicle,
or rarely a berry.
38.Stamens and petals hy-
pogynous; sepals free
........3. Ranunculaceae
38. Stamens and petals perigynous; sepals united
at base ....53. Rosaceae

Section 3. Herbs Without Leafy Stems; Leaves Simple

1. Leaves either pitcher-like or covered with glandular appendages; petals 5;
fruit a capsule; insectivorous plants growing in bogs.
2. Leaves large, pitcher-like; flower solitary, nodding ....21. Sarraceniaceae
2. Leaves small, covered with glandular appendages; flowers in a raceme
....15. Droseraceae
1. Leaves not as above; plants not insectivorous.
3. Flowers sessile in dense heads, or in spikes.
4. Flowers in heads.
5. Leaves parallel-veined, grass-like, stiff, flat, linear, twisted; flowers
yellow, perfect; capsule many-seeded ....132. Xyridaceae
5. Leaves net-veined, or rarely apparently only 1-veined.
6. Involucre of 4 white bracts; leaves whorled at the summit of the
stem; calyx minutely 4-toothed; petals 4; stamens 4; drupe red
....Cornus canadensis in 90. Cornaceae
6. Involucral bracts otherwise; calyx in the form of a pappus; stamens 5, inserted on the corolla, their anthers united into a
tube; fruit an achene ....125. Compositae
4. Flowers in spikes (or on a spadix).

7. Flowers crowded on a cylindrical apparently lateral spadix 6-8 cm long; petals 0; sepals 0; stamens 6; leaves linear; rhizomes thick, aromatic; plants of swampy ground ....*Acorus* in 141. ARACEAE

7. Flowers not as above.
  8. Ovary superior.
    9. Stamens 6; leaves cordate; flowers blue or white, 2-lipped; fruit 1-seeded ....134. PONTEDERIACEAE
    9. Stamens 4, or rarely 2; flowers greenish; corolla 4-lobed; calyx of 4 persistent sepals ....111. PLANTAGINACEAE
  8. Ovary inferior; flowers irregular; stamens 1 or 2 ....
    ....140. ORCHIDACEAE

3. Flowers not sessile in dense heads or spikes.
  10. Scapes with more than 1 flower.
    11. Leaves terete or nearly so.
      12. Flowers green, small, numerous, in elongated, bractless, spike-like racemes; perianth 6-parted ....127. JUNCAGINACEAE
      12. Flowers pink, not in racemes.
        13. Flowers in umbels; perianth 6-parted; stamens 6; plants with onion flavor and odor ....*Allium* in 130. LILIACEAE
        13. Flowers in cymes; petals 5; sepals 2; plants inodorous ......
        ....*Talinum* in 25. PORTULACACEAE
    11. Leaves not terete.
      14. Corolla irregular, 2-lipped, often spurred; stamens 2 or 1; fruit a capsule.
        15. Ovary superior; leaves absent, or dissected and bladder-bearing ....112. LENTIBULARIACEAE
        15. Ovary inferior; leaves entire, parallel-veined ....
        ....140. ORCHIDACEAE
      14. Corolla regular.
        16. Flowers on branches of the inflorescence in several or many whorls; achenes numerous, flattened; petals 3, white; leaves oval, cordate, hastate, or sagittate ....
        ....126. ALISMACEAE
        16. Flowers not whorled; fruit a capsule.
          17. Leaves evidently parallel-veined, narrow; petals 3, or perianth 6-parted.
            18. Leaves 2-ranked (equitant); flowers usually blue, sometimes white, rarely reddish brown; stamens 3; ovary inferior ....136. IRIDACEAE
            18. Leaves not 2-ranked.
              19. Flowers 4 or fewer (except *Aletris*), yellow or white; leaves sometimes pubescent; ovary inferior ....135. AMARYLLIDACEAE
              19. Flowers numerous, or if few, orange or pink; leaves glabrous; ovary superior (or ½ inferior) ....130. LILIACEAE
          17. Leaves net-veined; petals 5 or 4.
            20. Flowers in an umbel, or 1-3 on slender pedicels; petals and stamens each 5 (rarely 6); calyx 5-lobed ....97. PRIMULACEAE
            20. Flowers in cymes, panicles or racemes.
              21. Corolla of 4 petals; sepals 4; stamens 6 ....
              ....18. CRUCIFERAE
              21. Corolla of 5 petals.

22. Sepals 2 ....*Claytonia* in 25. PORTULACACEAE
22. Sepals 5.
    23. Styles 2; anthers opening longitudinally; leaves not evergreen; fruit 1-loculed ....62.   SAXIFRAGACEAE
    23. Style 1; anthers opening by terminal pores; leaves evergreen; fruit a 5-loculed capsule ....93.   ERICACEAE
10. Scapes or peduncles 1-flowered.
  24. Leaves toothed or lobed; petals separate, or absent.
    25. Leaves large, peltate, palmately 7-9-lobed; petals 6-8, white; sepals 6, petaloid, fugacious; fruit a yellowish green berry ....9.   PODOPHYLLACEAE
    25. Leaves not peltate.
      26. Fruit an achene; flowers yellow, bluish or white; petals sometimes absent, the sepals then petal-like; juice watery ....3.   RANUNCULACEAE
      26. Fruit a capsule; petals present.
        27. Plants with red juice; leaves thickish; petals 4-15 (usually 8), white; flower regular; capsule acute ....*Sanguinaria* in 13. PAPAVERACEAE
        27. Plants with colorless juice; leaves thin; petals 5; flowers irregular, blue, yellow, or white; capsule obtuse ....11.   VIOLACEAE
  24. Leaves entire.
    28. Leaves reniform, cordate, or ovate; fruit a capsule.
      29. Leaves pubescent beneath, reniform; flowers brownish purple; calyx 3-lobed; petals none; stamens 12; ovary inferior; woodland plants ....*Asarum* in 87. ARISTOLOCHIACEAE
      29. Leaves glabrous; flowers blue or white.
        30. Petals, sepals, stamens each 5; staminodia present; stigmas 4; plants of bogs and springy places ....63.   PARNASSIACEAE
        30. Perianth 6-parted; staminodia none; stamens 3; stigmas 3; plants of muddy shores ....*Heteranthera* in 134. PONTEDERIACEAE
    28. Leaves not as above.
      31. Flowers on a spadix surrounded by a spathe; fruit a berry ....141.   ARACEAE
      31. Flowers not on a spadix; spathe none; fruit not a berry.
        32. Leaves orbicular, peltate; flowers 10-25 cm in diameter, pale yellow; petals and stamens numerous ....6.   NELUMBONACEAE
        32. Leaves not peltate; flowers smaller.
          33. Flowers irregular; ovary inferior; stamens 1 or 2 ....140.   ORCHIDACEAE
          33. Flowers regular.
            34. Pistils numerous, simple, borne on a slender spike-like receptacle; stamens 5-20; sepals 5, minutely spurred at base; petals 5; leaves all basal, linear-spatulate ....*Myosurus* in 3. RANUNCULACEAE
            34. Pistil 1, compound.

35. Leaves equitant; flowers blue or white; ovary inferior; stamens 3 ......136. IRIDACEAE
35. Leaves not equitant; ovary superior; stamens 6 ....130. LILIACEAE

Section 4. Mostly Monocotyledonous Herbs (Except Grasses, Sedges, and Rushes) With Leafy Stems

1. Flowers in dense heads or spikes.
   2. Leaves cordate; flowers blue, 2-lipped; stamens 6 ....
   ....*Pontederia* in 134. PONTEDERIACEAE
   2. Leaves not cordate.
      3. Plants growing in wet places; flowers greenish.
         4. Spikes cylindrical, the upper part staminate, the lower pistillate; plants 2-3 m tall ....143. TYPHACEAE
         4. Heads spherical; plants not so tall ....144. SPARGANIACEAE
      3. Plants of dry ground; flowers not green.
         5. Leaves spiny- or bristly-margined; plants with watery juice ....
         ....*Eryngium* in 92. UMBELLIFERAE
         5. Leaves smooth-margined; plants with milky juice ....
         ....*Tragopogon* in 125. COMPOSITAE
1. Flowers not in dense heads.
   6. Ovary or ovaries superior.
      7. Ovaries 3 or 6, nearly separate; stamens 3 ....127. JUNCAGINACEAE
      7. Ovary 1, compound.
         8. Flowers irregular, blue, enclosed or subtended by a small spathe; petals 3, unequal ....*Commelina* in 133. COMMELINACEAE
         8. Flowers regular.
            9. Flowers blue or purple; filaments pubescent; juice mucilaginous
            ....*Tradescantia* in 133. COMMELINACEAE
            9. Flowers not blue (sometimes lavender); filaments glabrous or nearly so.
               10. Stamens 3 ....131. PONTEDERIACEAE
               10. Stamens 6..130. LILIACEAE
   6. Ovary inferior, compound.
      11. Stamens 3; flowers regular; leaves equitant ....136. IRIDACEAE
      11. Stamens 1 or 2; flowers irregular; leaves not equitant ....
      ....140. ORCHIDACEAE

Section 5. Dicotyledonous Herbs (Except Trillium) With Opposite or Whorled Entire Leaves

1. Flowers sessile in dense heads on a common receptacle surrounded or subtended by an involucre of bracts; fruit an achene. [*Pycnanthemum* (Labiatae), with flowers in dense head-like clusters, might also be sought here.]
   2. Stem with small prickles; chaff of the receptacle (among the flowers) with long rigid spine-like tips; stamens 4, distinct ......124. DIPSACACEAE
   2. Stem not prickly; chaff of the receptacle not as above, sometimes absent; stamens 5, united by their anthers (syngenesious) ....125. COMPOSITAE
1. Flowers not sessile in dense heads on a common receptacle surrounded or subtended by an involucre of bracts.
   3. Corolla of separate petals (or apparently so), or corolla absent (the calyx sometimes petal-like).

4. Leaves with black or pellucid dots, opposite, entire; flowers yellow or pink.
    5. Styles 2-6; stamens more numerous than the petals ....19. Hypericaceae
    5. Style 1; stamens as many as the corolla-lobes ....97. Primulaceae
4. Leaves not punctate.
    6. Leaves with stipules; petals minute or absent; stigmas 2-4.
        7. Petals 2 or 3; capsule several-seeded, the seeds reticulated; leaves oblanceolate or obovate; small plants of wet ground ....20. Elatinaceae
        7. Petals none; fruit a 1-seeded utricle ....29. Illecebraceae
    6. Leaves without stipules.
        8. Plants with milky juice; capsule deeply 3-lobed; upper leaves usually whorled; flowers small, white or greenish ....43. Euphorbiaceae
        8. Plants with colorless juice.
            9. Flowers solitary; stamens 6; ovary superior, 3-loculed ....genera in 130. Liliaceae
            9. Flowers not as above in all respects.
                10. Flowers irregular, in spikes or racemes; sepals 5, three of them small, and two larger and colored like the 3 petals; fruit flattened ....42. Polygalaceae
                10. Flowers regular.
                    11. Leaves in whorls.
                        12. Flowers axillary; leaves in fives or sixes; petals none; sepals 5; fruit a small 3-valved capsule; plants annual, prostrate ....26. Aizoaceae
                        12. Flowers in cymes or panicles; petals 5; plants perennial.
                            13. Leaves (at least the lower) in threes; flowers in cymes; petals entire; fruit a follicle ....Sedum in 60. Crassulaceae
                            13. Leaves mostly in fours, acuminate; inflorescence paniculate; petals laciniate; fruit a capsule ....Silene in 24. Caryophyllaceae
                    11. Leaves not whorled (or if so, not thick and succulent).
                        14. Calyx and corolla absent; flowers small, green, solitary, axillary; leaves spatulate or linear; styles 2, filiform; fruit notched; small plants of wet soil ....85. Callitrichaceae
                        14. Calyx present; corolla present or absent.
                            15. Sepals separate.
                                16. Petals none; flowers crowded into an interrupted spike; calyx woolly; bracts scarious; leaves lanceolate, sessile ....
                                  ....28. Amaranthaceae
                              16. Petals usually present; inflorescence not as above.
                                  17. Sepals 2; stamens 5; style 3-cleft ....
                                  .... Claytonia in 25. Portulacaceae
                                17. Sepals 5; leaves more than 1 pair.
                                    18. Sepals equal or nearly so.

19. Petals white (sometimes absent); leaves with ordinary flat blades; stems usually soft ....
.................24. CARYOPHYLLACEAE

19. Petals yellow; leaves small, scale-like or subulate, appressed or nearly erect ....19. HYPERICACEAE

18. Sepals unequal, the 2 outer much narrower than the 3 inner ones; petals yellow, greenish, or purplish; stems rigid and almost woody ....
...................................12. CISTACEAE

15. Sepals united at least below.

20. Flowers surrounded by a calyx-like involucre, the calyx blue or pink, corolla-like; stamens 3-5, exserted ....31. NYCTAGINACEAE

20. Flowers not surrounded by an involucre; calyx green.

21. Petals and stamens hypogynous, or the flowers without a pistil ....
................................24. CARYOPHYLLACEAE

21. Stamens inserted on the calyx.

22. Stigma capitate; style 1; petals present (absent in *Peplis*); fruit a capsule ....75. LYTHRACEAE

22. Stigmas 2, sessile or nearly so; petals none; fruit a utricle ....
......*Scleranthus* in 29. ILLECEBRACEAE

3. Corolla sympetalous (petals united, at least below).

23. Corolla irregular (flowers zygomorphic).

24. Fruit of 4 small nutlets; ovary 4-lobed; stem 4-angled; leaves usually glandular-punctate; plant usually with mint odor ....
....118. LABIATAE

24. Fruit a capsule; ovary not 4-lobed; plants without mint odor.

25. Seeds few, borne on hooks in the elastically dehiscent capsule
....110. ACANTHACEAE

25. Seeds numerous, not borne on hooks; capsule not elastically dehiscent.

26. Ovary 1-loculed with 2 parietal placentae; corolla 3-5 cm long, gibbous, campanulate, 5-lobed and somewhat 2-lipped; capsule 10-15 cm long, the beak longer than the body; odoriferous glandular annuals ....
....114. MARTYNIACEAE

26. Ovary 2-loculed; placentae axial ....108. SCROPHULARIACEAE

23. Corolla regular or nearly so (flowers actinomorphic).

27. Leaves whorled.

28. Flowers in a head surrounded by 4 white bracts; petals 4; stamens 4; drupe red ....90. CORNACEAE

28. Flowers not as above.

29. Flowers in a pyramidal panicle 30-60 cm long; fruit a compressed, 2-valved capsule; corolla greenish yellow with brownish purple dots ....
....*Frasera* in 102. GENTIANACEAE

29. Inflorescence otherwise.

30. Flowers in umbels; corolla with 5 reflexed lobes; fruit a
    many-seeded follicle; seeds with a tuft of silky hairs;
    plants with milky juice ....100. Asclepiadaceae
30. Flowers not in umbels.
    31. Flowers yellow (or white); fruit a capsule ....
        ....97. Primulaceae
    31. Flowers white or greenish, axillary or cymose; fruit
        of 2 united indehiscent 1-seeded nutlets ....
        ....119. Rubiaceae
27. Leaves not whorled.
    32. Leaves evergreen, opposite; stems trailing; flowers axillary;
        plants glabrous.
        33. Leaf-base narrowed; corolla blue, 5-lobed, 1.5-3 cm long;
            calyx 5-parted; stamens 5; stigma annular, its apex
            penicillate ....Vinca in 99. Apocynaceae
        33. Leaf-base rounded or cordate; corolla white or pink, usual-
            ly 4-lobed, 1-1.5 cm long; calyx 4-toothed; stamens 4,
            stigmas 4; fruit a red double drupe ....
            ....Mitchella in 119. Rubiaceae
    32. Leaves rarely evergreen; plants not as above in all respects.
        34. Ovary inferior.
            35. Leaves with stipules, or the petioles connected by a
                (sometimes bristle-bearing) stipular membrane or
                line ....119. Rubiaceae
            35. Leaves without stipules ....120. Caprifoliaceae
        34. Ovary or ovaries superior.
            36. Ovaries 2, or if 1, deeply lobed; fruit usually of 2 fol-
                licles; seeds with a tuft of silky hairs; plants usually
                with milky juice.
                37. Flowers in cymes, or solitary ....99. Apocynaceae
                37. Flowers in umbels ....100. Asclepiadaceae
            36. Ovary 1; fruit a capsule or drupe; plants with watery
                juice.
                38. Stamens opposite the corolla-lobes; corolla tube
                    short or none; flowers bright yellow, or solitary
                    in the axils ....97. Primulaceae
                38. Stamens alternate with the lobes of the corolla;
                    flowers not yellow (rarely yellowish white).
                    39. Corolla-tube long and slender.
                        40. Stamens 5.
                            41. Stigmas 3; pistils 3-carpellate; capsules
                                3-loculed, 3-seeded ....
                                ....Phlox in 104. Polemoniaceae
                            41. Stigmas 3; pistils 3-carpellate; capsules
                                2-loculed; flowers red ....
                                ....101. Loganiaceae
                        40. Stamens 4; stigma simple or two-lobed, the
                            apex of the style recurved; pistils 2-
                            carpellate; capsule 6-20-seeded ....
                            ....Ruellia in 110. Acanthaceae
                    39. Corolla tube short or none, (or more than 3
                        mm thick).
                        42. Stamens 5 or 4; capsule 1-loculed ....
                            ....102. Gentianaceae

42. Stamens 2; capsule 2-loculed ....
...............................108. Scrophulariaceae

Section 6. Dicotyledonous Herbs With Toothed or Lobed Opposite or Whorled Leaves

1. Flowers sessile in dense heads on a common receptacle surrounded by an involucre of bracts.
    2. Stem with small prickles; chaff of the receptacle (among the flowers) with long rigid spine-like tips; stamens 4, distinct ......124. Dipsacaceae
    2. Stem not prickly; chaff of the receptacle not as above, sometimes absent; stamens 5, united by their anthers (syngenesious) ....125. Compositae
1. Flowers not sessile in dense heads on a common receptacle surrounded or subtended by an involucre of bracts.
    3. Corolla of separate petals, or absent.
        4. Leaves deeply lobed.
            5. Plants glabrous; leaves 2, peltate; flower solitary; petals 6-9, white ....9. Podophyllaceae
            5. Plants (at least the stem) pubescent; leaves 2 or more, not peltate; flowers usually more than 1.
                6. Petals present; stamens 10; styles 5; fruit of 5 carpels ....
                ....36. Geraniaceae
                6. Petals none, but the sepals colored and petal-like; stamens more than 10; fruit of numerous achenes ....3. Ranunculaceae
        4. Leaves merely toothed.
            7. Plants with milky juice (or if with watery juice, the pubescence stellate); the fruit deeply 3-lobed; corolla none, but the flowers surrounded by an often corolla-like involucre ....43. Euphorbiaceae
            7. Plants with watery juice; fruit not 3-lobed.
                8. Flowers green, without petals; fruit 1-seeded.
                    9. Plants scurfy with minute whitish scales; stipules none ....
                    ....Atriplex in 27. Chenopodiaceae
                    9. Plants glabrous, or pubescent with slender, sometimes stinging hairs, never scurfy or scaly; leaves stipulate ....73. Urticaceae
                8. Flowers with white or colored petals; fruit usually with more than 1 seed.
                    10. Petals large (1 cm or more in length), pink or purplish; leaves 3-4-ribbed; plants bristly-hairy ....82. Melastomaceae
                    10. Petals small (less than 1 cm in length); leaves not ribbed; plants not bristly-hairy.
                        11. Ovary inferior; seeds with a tuft of soft hairs, or else the fruit with short, hooked hairs ....83. Onagraceae
                        11. Ovary superior; seeds without hairs; fruit never bristly ....
                        ....62. Saxifragaceae
    3. Corolla sympetalous, the petals united, at least below.
        12. Leaves evergreen, small, oval or obovate, crenate above the middle; stems slender, trailing; flowers in pairs, nodding, pink, fragrant, about 1 cm long ....Linnaea in 120. Caprifoliaceae
        12. Leaves not evergreen; plants not as above.
            13. Fruit of 2 or 4 nutlets; stems usually 4-angled.
                14. Ovary not lobed, the style terminal on it; plants lacking a mint odor; corolla usually nearly regular ....116. Verbenaceae

14. Ovary deeply 4-lobed, the style arising between the lobes;
plants usually with a mint odor; corolla usually bilabiate,
rarely nearly regular ....118. LABIATAE
13. Fruit of only 1 nutlet, or else a capsule with many seeds.
15. Flowers reflexed and becoming appressed to the stem in fruit;
fruit a single nutlet in the bottom of the calyx; calyx-teeth
hooked at the tip; corolla purplish; median and lower
leaves slender-petioled ....117. PHRYMACEAE
15. Flowers not reflexed and appressed to the stem; calyx-teeth
not hooked.
16. Ovary inferior; stamens 3 ....123. VALERIANACEAE
16. Ovary superior; stamens usually 2, or 4, rarely 5 ....
....108. SCROPHULARIACEAE

Section 7. Dicotyledonous Herbs (Except Smilax) With Alternate Leaves
1. Flowers sessile in dense heads on a common receptacle surrounded by an
involucre of bracts ....125. COMPOSITAE
1. Flowers not sessile in dense heads on a common receptacle surrounded or
subtended by an involucre of bracts.
2. Stem-leaves reduced to minute scales; corolla irregular, spurred; plants
small, growing in wet soil ....112. LENTIBULARIACEAE
2. Stem-leaves not all reduced to scales.
3. Leaves with stipules, these sometimes united to form a sheath (sometimes fugacious).
4. Stipules united and forming a membranous sheath at the nodes;
fruit an achene ....32. POLYGONACEAE
4. Stipules not sheathing; fruit a several-seeded capsule or pod.
5. Petals none; fruit a small 3-loculed capsule ......43. EUPHORBIACEAE
5. Petals present; plants pubescent; fruit a 1-loculed pod.
6. Leaves sessile or nearly so; flowers yellow, papilionaceous ....
....*Crotalaria* in 54. LEGUMINOSAE
6. Leaves petioled; flowers greenish white ....
....*Hybanthus* in 11. VIOLACEAE
3. Leaves without stipules, or stipules minute.
7. Petals separate, or none; calyx sometimes petal-like.
8. Plants with milky juice; stem umbellately branched above; uppermost leaves whorled; involucres with white petal-like appendages ....43. EUPHORBIACEAE
8. Plants without milky juice; stems and leaves not as above.
9. Calyx and corolla absent; flowers in spikes; leaves cordate,
petioled ....33. SAURURACEAE
9. Calyx present; corolla present or absent.
10. Flowers small, green.
11. Flowers in umbels; perianth 6-parted; fruit a berry ....
....*Smilax* in 130. LILIACEAE
11. Flowers not in umbels; perianth not 6-parted; fruit not
a berry.
12. Plants perennial, pubescent; fruit a capsule, with
more than 1 seed; leaves small and narrow ....
....12. CISTACEAE
12. Plants annual, glabrous or pubescent; fruit an
achene, or a 1-seeded capsule.
13. Flowers all in loose cymose axillary clusters; style

1, not branched; plants pubescent ....
......................................*Parietaria* in 73. URTICACEAE
13. Flowers all or mostly in spikes or terminal cymes
or panicles, or else all in dense, sessile, axillary
clusters; styles 2 or 3, or 1 and branched.
14.Flowers subtended by scarious bracts, the
sepals sharp-pointed; leaves not linear or
with spiny tips; plants never white-mealy
....28. AMARANTHACEAE
14. Flowers not subtended by scarious bracts;
sepals not awn-pointed; leaves linear and
with spiny tips; or the plants whitish-mealy
at least about the inflorescence or the
lower surface of the leaves ....
....27. CHENOPODIACEAE
10. Flowers not green; petals present, or the calyx colored and
petal-like.
15. Leaves cordate, velvety-pubescent; petals yellow; carpels
10-17, pubescent, dehiscent at the apex ....
....*Abutilon* in 23. MALVACEAE
15. Leaves not cordate, or if so, not velvety-pubescent.
16. Sepals 2 ....25. PORTULACACEAE
16. Sepals more than 2 (rarely cohering in pairs).
17. Flowers borne on the lower part of the stem near
the ground; calyx S-shaped; petals none;
leaves petioled, cordate or halberd-shaped ......
................*Aristolochia* in 87. ARISTOLOCHIACEAE
17. Flowers borne on the upper part of the stem;
calyx never curved.
18. Ovary inferior.
19. Petals yellow or purplish; fruit a several-
seeded capsule ....83. ONAGRACEAE
19. Petals none, the sepals whitish and petal-
like; fruit 1-seeded, indehiscent; plants
glabrous, glaucous ....88. SANTALACEAE
18. Ovary superior.
20. Petals none, the 5 sepals petal-like; flowers in racemes; fruit a juicy dark purple
berry ....30. PHYTOLACCACEAE
20. Petals 4-6; fruit a capsule or pod.
21. Flowers regular; anthers opening longitudinally.
22. Style 1, or stigma sessile.
23. Petals and stamens hypogynous.
24. Sepals, petals, and stamens
each 5; fruit a 5-loculed
capsule ....37. LINACEAE
24. Sepals and petals each 4;
stamens 6, four long and
two short; fruit a 1- or
2-loculed capsule ....
..................18. CRUCIFERAE

23. Petals and stamens inserted on the calyx; branches usually more or less angled ....75. LYTHRACEAE

22. Styles 2; petals 5; sepals 5, reflexed; stamens 10; leaves chiefly basal ....62. SAXIFRAGACEAE

21. Flowers irregular; anthers opening by terminal pores ......42. POLYGALACEAE

7. Petals united (the corolla sympetalous).

25. Corolla regular (actinomorphic).

26. Flowers large (1.5-6 cm long); fruit a capsule.

27. Plants with milky juice, often climbing; capsules few-seeded ....105. CONVOLVULACEAE

27. Plants with watery juice, never climbing; capsules many-seeded ....107. SOLANACEAE

26. Flowers smaller.

28. Plants with milky juice; fruit of 1 or 2 large pods, the seeds with a tuft of silky hairs.

29. Flowers in umbels; filaments united into a tube enclosing the pistil ....100. ASCLEPIADACEAE

29. Flowers in cymes, purplish blue; stamens free ....*Amsonia* in 99. APOCYNACEAE

28. Plants with watery juice.

30. Fruit of 4 (or sometimes fewer) nutlets; plants rough-hairy, often bristly, or glabrous and with blue flowers ....115. BORAGINACEAE

30. Fruit a capsule or berry.

31. Flowers blue; fruit a capsule.

32. Ovary superior; styles 2 ....106. HYDROPHYLLACEAE

32. Ovary inferior; style 1 ......121. CAMPANULACEAE

31. Flowers not blue.

33. Style 3-cleft ....104. POLEMONIACE. E

33. Style not 3-cleft.

34. Flowers in umbels ....100. ASCLEPIADACEAE

34. Flowers not in umbels.

35. Plants climbing or twining; flowers purple (rarely white) in small cymes; berries ovoid, red ....*Solanum dulcamara* in 107. SOLANACEAE

35. Plants not climbing or twining.

36. Flowers white or pink or yellow; fruit a capsule; calyx not enlarged in fruit ....97. PRIMULACEAE

36. Flowers yellowish or whitish, often with a dark center; fruit a berry, enclosed by the 5-lobed, 10-ribbed, often 5-10-angled, reticulated, inflated calyx ....*Physalis* in 107. SOLANACEAE

25. Corolla irregular (zygomorphic).

37. Ovary superior.

38. Ovary 2-loculed, with numerous ovules; fruit a many-seeded capsule ....108. SCROPHULARIACEAE
38. Ovary deeply 4-lobed; fruit of 4 nutlets; stamens 5, exserted, unequal; plants pubescent, biennial; flowers 1.5-2 cm in diameter, bright blue ....
....*Echium* in 115. BORAGINACEAE
37. Ovary inferior; capsule 2-loculed, many-seeded, opening at the top; stamens 5, the anthers cohering in a tube around the style ....122. LOBELIACEAE

Section 8. Dicotyledonous Herbs With Toothed or Lobed Alternate Leaves

1. Flowers sessile, small, in dense heads on a common receptacle surrounded or subtended by an involucre of bracts; fruit an achene ....125. COMPOSITAE
1. Flowers not as above.
   2. Fruit and ovary covered with hooked bristles; corolla minute, greenish yellow; leaves deeply lobed; flowers in small compact head-like umbels ....*Sanicula* in 92. UMBELLIFERAE
   2. Fruit and ovary never with hooked bristles.
      3. Leaves conspicuously lobed.
         4. Corolla of united petals (sympetalous).
            5. Corolla irregular ....108. SCROPHULARIACEAE
            5. Corolla regular.
               6. Stems usually twining; plants with milky juice ....
               ....105. CONVOLVULACEAE
               6. Stems not climbing; plants with watery juice.
                  7. Styles 2 ....106. HYDROPHYLLACEAE
                  7. Style 1 ....107. SOLANACEAE
         4. Corolla of separate petals, or petals absent.
            8. Calyx lobes 3; flowers small, sessile, axillary, greenish, apetalous; upper leaves toothed, the lower ones deeply pinnately lobed; plants of wet habitats; fruit sharply angled ....
            ,,,,,, ...*Proserpinaca* in 119. HALORAGACEAE
            8. Calyx-lobes or sepals more than 3.
               9. Sepals and petals each 4.
                  10. Ovary superior; stamens 6; capsule 2-valved ....
                  ....18. CRUCIFERAE
                  10. Ovary inferior; stamens 8; capsule 4-valved ....
                  ....83. ONAGRACEAE
               9. Sepals 5 or 6 (or 0 in sp. of *Atriplex*).
                  11. Petals none; flowers small, green or greenish; fruit an achene or utricle.
                     12. Leaves stipulate; sepals 6; stamens 6; fruit an achene ....32. POLYGONACEAE
                     12. Leaves without stipules; sepals 5 (or 0 in sp. of *Atriplex*); stamens 5; fruit a utricle ....27. CHENOPODIACEAE
                  11. Petals usually present.
                     13. Flowers regular.
                        14. Ovary inferior; stamens numerous; fruit a capsule ....80. LOASACEAE
                        14. Ovary superior.
                           15. Stamens 10 (rarely 5), free or nearly so; ovary 5-lobed, each lobe becoming a 1-seeded nutlet ....36. GERANIACEAE

15. Stamens more than 10.
    16. Stamens monadelphous; anthers 1-loculed; fruit a capsule, or of 5 or more carpels arranged in a ring ....23. MALVACEAE
    16. Stamens free; anthers 2-loculed; fruit an achene.
        17. Stamens perigynous ....53. ROSACEAE
        17. Stamens hypogynous ....3. RANUNCULACEAE
13. Flowers irregular.
    18. Leaves with stipules; stamens 5; fruit a capsule ....11. VIOLACEAE
    18. Leaves without stipules; stamens many; fruit an achene or a follicle ....3. RANUNCULACEAE
3. Leaves not lobed, merely toothed, or sinuate.
  19. Petals more or less united; fruit a capsule or berry.
    20. Ovary inferior; corolla blue or red (rarely white).
      21. Corolla split down one side, irregular; stamens united by their anthers ....122. LOBELIACEAE
      21. Corolla not split, regular; stamens free ....121. CAMPANULACEAE
    20. Ovary superior; flowers not red or blue.
      22. Stamens 5.
        23. Calyx spurred, petal-like; flowers axillary; leaves exstipulate; plants smooth and succulent ....41. BALSAMINACEAE
        23. Calyx not spurred or petal-like.
          24. Flowers in spikes or racemes; fruit a smooth capsule ....*Verbascum* in 108. SCROPHULARIACEAE
          24. Flowers axillary or in cymes; fruit a berry or a spiny capsule ....107. SOLANACEAE
      22. Stamens 4 or 2.
        25. Low branching odoriferous glandular annuals with cordate oblique leaves; calyx 5-cleft; corolla 5-lobed; capsule 8-15 cm long, the curved beak longer than the body ....114. MARTYNIACEAE
        25. Erect perennials; sepals 4; corolla campanulate, 2-3-lobed; stamens 2; capsule short, emarginate ....*Synthyris* in 108. SCROPHULARIACEAE
  19. Petals separate or none.
    26. Petals none.
      27. Plants with stinging hairs; leaves petioled, serrate, stipulate; flowers in axillary cymes, unisexual; sepals 5; stamen 1; style 1; fruit an achene ....*Laportea* in 73. URTICACEAE
      27. Plants without stinging hairs.
        28. Stamens numerous; petals 0; sepals petal-like, bright yellow; pistils 3-12; plants glabrous, succulent, with hollow stems and cordate or reniform leaves ....*Caltha* in 3. RANUNCULACEAE
      28. Stamens fewer.
        29. Styles 5 or 6; stamens twice the number of the sepals; flowers perfect, in 1-sided spikes or cymes; stipules none; fruit many-seeded, dehiscent ....*Penthorum* in 60. CRASSULACEAE
        29. Styles 1-3.

30. Fruit a 3-lobed capsule; stigmas fringed; leaves
with small stipules ....
.........................*Acalypha* in 43. EUPHORBIACEAE

30. Fruit a 1-seeded utricle; stipules none.
    31. Flowers with scarious bracts ....🔾......................
    ....28. AMARANTHACEAE
    31. Flowers bractless ....27. CHENOPODIACEAE

26. Petals present.
    32. Ovary inferior; stamens usually twice as many (rarely the
same number) as the petals and calyx-lobes; fruit a capsule, rarely indehiscent ....83. ONAGRACEAE

    32. Ovary or ovaries superior.
        33. Corolla irregular.
            34. One of the petals spurred.
                35. Stipules present; ovary 1-loculed ......11. VIOLACEAE
                35. Stipules none; ovary 5-loculed; plants smooth
and succulent ....41. BALSAMINACEAE
            34. Flowers not spurred; stipules none; ovary 2-loculed
....42. POLYGALACEAE

        33. Corolla regular or nearly so, not spurred.
            36. Sepals and petals each 4; stamens 6 (rarely 2); fruit
a pod; stipules none ....18. CRUCIFERAE
            36. Sepals 5; petals usually 5, rarely 1-3.
                37. Sepals separate; petals yellow; fruit achenes ......
                ....3. RANUNCULACEAE
                37. Sepals united, at least below.
                    38. Leaves mostly basal, more or less hairy, the
blades roundish, cordate at the base;
flowers paniculate ....
.....................*Heuchera* in 62. SAXIFRAGACEAE
                    38. Leaves mostly on the stem.
                        39. Stipules none; leaves thickish; plants
glabrous; stamens free ....
....60. CRASSULACEAE
                        39. Stipules present; leaves not succulent;
plants usually more or less pubescent.
                        40. Stamens monadelphous; plants often
with stellate hairs ....23. MALVACEAE
                        40. Stamens free, perigynous; pubescence
not stellate ....*Geum* in 53. ROSACEAE

Section 9.   Parasitic or Saprophytic Herbs; Stems Not Climbing or Twining

1. Flowers regular.
    2. Ovary superior; stamens 6-12; plant waxy-white or reddish, drying black
....*Monotropa* in 93. ERICACEAE
    2. Ovary inferior; plants annual, very small ....139. BURMANNIACEAE
1. Flowers irregular.
    3. Ovary inferior; petals and sepals each 3, distinct ....140. ORCHIDACEAE
    3. Ovary superior; corolla 2-lipped ....113. OROBANCHACEAE

Section 10. Plants Twining or Climbing; or Cacti

1. Cactus plants, with conspicuously jointed stems, the internodes flattened, succulent, bristly or spiny; leaves none, or reduced to bristles; flowers perfect, regular, solitary, showy; sepals, petals, and stamens numerous ....79. CACTACEAE
1. Not cactus plants; stems twining or climbing; plants sometimes with tendrils.
    2. Plants with tendrils.
        3. Leaves entire.
            4. Flowers in umbels; perianth 6-parted; stamens 6; stigmas thick, almost sessile; fruit a berry; leaves with 3 or more principal veins from the base ....*Smilax* in 130. LILIACEAE
            4. Flowers in slender axillary and terminal racemes; calyx 5-parted; stamens 8; styles 3; fruit an obtusely triangular achene enclosed in the indurated calyx; leaves with 1 main vein ....
            ....*Brunnichia* in 32. POLYGONACEAE
        3. Leaves lobed or toothed, or compound.
            5. Flowers solitary, perfect; petals separate; stipules present ....
            ....78. PASSIFLORACEAE
            5. Flowers unisexual, in racemes or corymbs.
                6. Petals united; fruit a pepo...................................81. CUCURBITACEAE
                6. Petals separate; fruit an inflated capsule ....45. SAPINDACEAE
    2. Plants without tendrils.
        7. Leaves somewhat peltate, the petiole attached on the underside of the blade near the margin, the blades usually angled or lobed; fruit juicy, 1-seeded; flowers small, in axillary panicles ....
        ....10. MENISPERMACEAE
        7. Leaves not peltate.
            8. Leaves opposite or whorled.
                9. Leaves entire.
                    10. Plants with milky juice; petals 5, united; fruit a follicle; seeds with silky hairs.
                        11. Stamens distinct; flowers cymose ....99. APOCYNACEAE
                        11. Filaments united into a tube enclosing the pistil, the anthers adnate to the stigma, and the pollen cohering in masses ....100. ASCLEPIADACEAE
                    10. Plants without milky juice.
                        12. Sepals 4, petal-like; petals 0; stamens numerous; style persistent on the achene, often pubescent ....
                        ....*Clematis* in 3. RANUNCULACEAE
                        12. Flowers otherwise.
                            13. Perianth 6-parted; stamens 6; plants dioecious; fruit a 3-angled capsule ....137. DIOSCOREACEAE
                            13. Sepals 5; petals 5; stamens 5; flowers perfect; fruit a follicle; seeds with a tuft of hairs ....
                            ....*Ampelamus* in 100. ASCLEPIADACEAE
                9. Leaves toothed or lobed.
                    14. Leaves triangular-hastate; flowers pink, in small heads ....
                    ....*Mikania* in 125. COMPOSITAE
                    14. Leaves not triangular-hastate; flowers green, unisexual, in catkins or panicles ....72. CANNABINACEAE
            8. Leaves alternate, or reduced to inconspicuous scales.
                15. Plants with chlorophyll, not parasitic; leaves not reduced to scales.

16. Leaves with sheathing stipules; corolla none; calyx 5-lobed; flowers perfect; fruit an achene ....32. POLYGONACEAE
16. Leaves without sheathing stipules.
   17. Plants dioecious; perianth 6-parted; stamens 6.
      18. Flowers in drooping racemes or panicles; styles 3, distinct; fruit a 3-angled or -winged capsule ....
      ....137. DIOSCOREACEAE
      18. Flowers in umbels; stigmas thick, almost sessile; fruit a small bluish black berry ......*Smilax* in 130. LILIACEAE
   17. Flowers perfect; corolla sympetalous; stamens 5.
      19. Corolla funnelform; fruit a capsule; plants often with milky juice ....105. CONVOLVULACEAE
      19. Corolla rotate, purple or blue (or white); anthers yellow, connivent around the style, opening by apical pores; berries red; juice watery ....
      ....*Solanum dulcamara* in 107. SOLANACEAE
15. Plants bright yellow or orange, parasitic on other plants and lacking chlorophyll; leaves reduced to scales; fruit a capsule
   ....*Cuscuta* in 105. CONVOLVULACEAE

Section 11. Aquatic Plants, Floating on or Submerged in Water

1. Plants very small, free-floating, thalloid, without stems and leaves ....
   ....142. LEMNACEAE
1. Plants larger, normally with leaves and usually with stems.
   2. Leaves entire or finely toothed.
      3. Blades roundish, cordate at base, or peltate; flowers large, solitary.
         4. Leaves peltate; carpels immersed in a fleshy turbinate receptacle ......
         ....6. NELUMBONACEAE
         4. Leaves and carpels otherwise ....5. NYMPHAEACEAE
      3. Blades neither cordate nor peltate
         5. Floating leaves spatulate; leaves opposite, small; flowers minute, unisexual, sessile, 1-3 in the axils; stamen 1; styles 2, filiform; fruit 4-lobed, notched at the apex ....85. CALLITRICHACEAE
         5. Leaves never spatulate.
            6. Plants acaulescent; leaves long, linear; fertile flowers on long slender scapes; fruit many-seeded ....
            ....*Vallisneria* in 138. HYDROCHARITACEAE
            6. Plants with stems.
               7. Leaves alternate, or all basal, or imperfectly opposite.
                  8. Flowers green, in spikes; sepals 4; stamens 4; carpels usually 4; stipules present, membranous; fruit 1-seeded ....
                  ....129. POTAMOGETONACEAE
                  8. Flowers not green.
                     9. Leaves mostly parallel-veined.
                        10. Ovary or ovaries superior.
                           11. Ovaries several or many, simple, 1-ovuled, forming achenes ....126. ALISMACEAE
                         11. Ovary one, compound; fruit several-seeded ....
                         ....134. PONTEDERIACEAE
                      10. Ovary inferior ....138. HYDROCHARITACEAE
                    9. Leaves net-veined.

      12. Ovary 1-ovuled; fruit 1-seeded; flowers rose-pink, in a
spike-like panicle; stipules united to form a cylindrical membranous sheath ....
....*Polygonum* in 32. POLYGONACEAE

      12. Ovary with 2 or more ovules; fruit a capsule.

        13. Ovary superior ....*Neobeckia* in 18. CRUCIFERAE

        13. Ovary inferior ....83. ONAGRACEAE

  7. Leaves opposite or whorled.

    14. Aquatic monocotyledons.

      15. Perianth 3- or 6-parted; fruit several-seeded; leaves 5-15
mm long, minutely spinulose-toothed ....
...............................*Elodea* in 138. HYDROCHARITACEAE

      15. Perianth none; fruit 1-seeded.

        16. Leaves spinulose-toothed; carpel 1 ....128. NAIADACEAE

        16. Leaves entire; carpels 2-5 ....129. POTAMOGETONACEAE

    14. Dicotyledons; stamens 4.

      17. Corolla absent or of separate petals ....83. ONAGRACEAE

      17. Corolla sympetalous ....*Bacopa* in 108. SCROPHULARIACEAE

2. Leaves, or most of them, deeply lobed or divided.

  18. Leaves finely dissected (or sometimes root-like), often bearing small
bladders; flowers (in our species) yellow, bilabiate; fruit a capsule
....112. LENTIBULARIACEAE

  18. Leaves not bladder-bearing, all or most of them finely dissected.

    19. Flowers white or yellow, solitary.

      20. Floating leaves peltate, narrowly elliptical, 1.5-2 cm long; sub-
merged leaves opposite or verticillate; petals 3; sepals 3;
pistils 3 ....4. CABOMBACEAE

      20. Floating leaves, if any, not peltate.

        21. Leaves alternate; petals 5; sepals 5; pistils more than 3
....*Ranunculus* in 3. RANUNCULACEAE

        21. Leaves opposite, the upper lanceolate, serrate; heads soli-
tary, radiate; rays 6-10, yellow; achenes 1-1.5 cm long,
with 3-6 slender awns ....*Bidens* in 125. COMPOSITAE

    19. Flowers small, green or whitish.

      22. Flowers green, minute; leaves alternate or whorled.

        23. Leaves simple, entire.................................86. HIPPURIDACEAE

        23. Leaves not entire.

          24. Leaves all dissected into rather rigid divisions; fruit 1-
seeded ....CERATOPHYLLACEAE

          24. Upper leaves sometimes merely pectinate; fruit 4-lobed
....84. HALORAGACEAE

      22. Flowers whitish, whorled at the nodes of the erect, hollow, in-
inflated, almost leafless flowering stem; corolla 5-lobed;
sepals 5, linear; stamens 5, included; fruit a many-seeded
capsule ....*Hottonia* in 97. PRIMULACEAE

Section 12.   Trees or Shrubs (Including Woody Climbers)
With Opposite or Whorled Leaves

1. Leaves compound.

  2. Leaflets 3 or 2.

    3. Stems climbing or trailing.

4. Leaflets 2, ovate, cordate, acuminate, entire, dark green; tendrils branched; cymes 2-4-flowered; corolla red, 4-5 cm long; stamens 4; capsules linear, 10-20 cm long; seeds winged, elliptical; cross-section of wood showing a cross ....*Bignonia* in 109. BIGNONIACEAE

4. Leaflets 3, coarsely toothed; tendrils none; plants dioecious, the flowers white, numerous in panicles; stamens numerous; achenes pubescent, plumose ....*Clematis* in 3. RANUNCULACEAE

3. Stems not climbing or trailing.
  5. Leaflets coarsely toothed; flowers greenish, unisexual; fruit a pair of samaras ....*Acer negundo* in 50. ACERACEAE
  5. Leaflets finely serrate; flowers whitish, perfect; fruit an inflated, 3-lobed capsule ....46. STAPHYLEACEAE

2. Leaflets 5-11 (rarely 3-5).
  6. Leaves palmately compound, the leaflets serrate, straight-veined; flowers irregular, in large panicles, most of them sterile; capsule leathery, smooth or spiny, usually with a single large glossy seed ....47. HIPPOCASTANACEAE
  6. Leaves pinnately compound.
    7. Plants climbing or trailing; leaflets 9-11, serrate, 3-6 cm long; flowers perfect, the corolla red, 5-lobed, somewhat 2-lipped, 6-9 cm long; capsules cylindrical, 8-12 cm long ....*Campsis* in 109. BIGNONIACEAE
    7. Erect trees or shrubs.
      8. Branches with a large pith; fruit a drupe; flowers regular, perfect, numerous, small, whitish, cymose; stamens 5; ovary inferior ....*Sambucus* in 120. CAPRIFOLIACEAE
      8. Branches with a small pith; fruit a samara; flowers small, greenish, unisexual, appearing before the leaves.
        9. Leaflets 3-5 (rarely 7-9), at least some of them usually coarsely toothed; samaras in pairs; stamens 4-6 ....*Acer negundo* in 50. ACERACEAE
        9. Leaflets 5-11, entire to shallowly serrate; samaras single; stamens 2 ....*Fraxinus* in 98. OLEACEAE

1. Leaves simple.
  10. Margins toothed or lobed.
    11. Margins toothed, not lobed; shrubs.
      12. Young branchlets often somewhat quadrangular; leaves serrulate; flowers perfect, axillary, greenish or purplish; petals 4-6; calyx 4-5-cleft; stamens 4-5, inserted on the disk; fruit deeply 3-5-lobed ....*Euonymus* in 44. CELASTRACEAE
      12. Branchlets terete or nearly so.
        13. Leaves evergreen, small, oval, crenate above the middle; stems slender, trailing; flowers in pairs, nodding, pink, fragrant, about 1 cm long ......*Linnaea* in 120. CAPRIFOLIACEAE
        13. Leaves otherwise.
          14. Margins dentate or sharply serrate; ovary inferior.
            15. Principal lateral veins 1-5 pairs; corolla of 4 separate petals; stamens more than 5; capsule many-seeded ....55. HYDRANGEACEAE
            15. Principal lateral veins 5-10 pairs; corolla sympetalous, 5-lobed or 2-lipped, the 5 stamens inserted in the tube; fruit a 1-seeded drupe or a many-seeded capsule ....120. CAPRIFOLIACEAE

14. Margins crenate; ovary superior; stamens 4-5, inserted
with the petals and opposite them; fruit a drupe ....
....*Rhamnus* in 51. RHAMNACEAE
11. Margins lobed and often toothed.
  16. Lobes acute, toothed.
    17. Trees; styles 2; fruit a pair of samaras ....50. ACERACEAE
    17. Shrubs; style 3-lobed; fruit a 1-seeded drupe ....
    ....*Viburnum* in 120. CAPRIFOLIACEAE
  16. Lobes obtuse, entire; shrubs; stamens 5, inserted on the pink
sympetalous corolla; fruit a 2-seeded drupe ....
......................................*Symphoricarpos* in 120. CAPRIFOLIACEAE
10. Margins entire, or merely undulate or slightly crenulate or denticulate.
  18. Plants parasitic on the branches of trees; leaves thick, leathery; fruit
a berry ....89. LORANTHACEAE
  18. Not parasitic.
    19. Leaves beneath, and branchlets covered with minute silvery
scales; flowers small, axillary, unisexual; calyx 4-parted; corolla 0; stamens 8; fruit a drupe ....77. ELAEAGNACEAE
    19. Leaves not silvery.
      20. Leaves with small black dots; low shrubs; flowers yellow,
cymose; sepals and petals each 4 or 5; stamens numerous;
fruit a capsule ....19. HYPERICACEAE
      20. Leaves not black dotted.
        21. Leaves large (15-50 cm long), ovate or cordate.
          22. Leaves usually in whorls of 3; flowers whitish, marked
with yellow and purple; anther-bearing stamens 2;
capsules cylindrical ....
....*Catalpa* in 109. BIGNONIACEAE
          22. Leaves opposite; flowers purple; anther-bearing sta-
mens 4; capsules ovoid ....
....................................*Paulownia* in 109. BIGNONIACEAE
        21. Leaves usually smaller.
          23. Twining or climbing shrubs; flowers perfect; corolla
sympetalous.
            24. Follicles 2, slender, many-seeded; seeds comose;
calyx glandular inside; corolla regular ....
.................*Trachelospermum* in 99. APOCYNACEAE
            24. Fruit a few-seeded berry; corolla irregular ....
.......................*Lonicera* in 120. CAPRIFOLIACEAE
          23. Erect shrubs or small trees.
            25. Leaves slightly crenate near the middle, lanceo-
late, acuminate at each end; plants dioecious
or polygamous, the flowers apetalous, or petals
small and deciduous; stamens 2-4; drupe with
1, or rarely 2 seeds ....*Forestiera* in 98. OLEACEAE
            25. Leaves entire, not acuminate.
              26. Leaves short-petioled.
                27. Bark of stems and branches more or less
loose and shreddy; ovary inferior; calyx
and corolla 5-lobed ....
....................................120. CAPRIFOLIACEAE

27. Bark smooth; ovary superior; corolla and calyx 4-lobed; stamens 2; flowers small, white, regular, in terminal panicles; fruit a 2-loculed, 1-2-seeded, black, berry-like drupe ....
..........................*Ligustrum* in 98. OLEACEAE
26. Leaves with petioles usually 1 cm or more in length; calyx and corolla each 4-lobed; stamens 4.
    28. Leaves glabrous, or sparsely pubescent along the midvein, at least the upper ones usually in whorls of three; flowers in globose heads ....
    ....*Cephalanthus* in 119. RUBIACEAE
    28. Leaves pubescent, at least on the lower surface, never whorled; flowers in cymes
    ....90. CORNACEAE

Section 13. Trees or Shrubs With Alternate, Compound Leaves

1. Leaves once compound, i.e., not decompound.
  2. Leaflets 3.
    3. Prickles present.
      4. Flowers rose; carpels enclosed in a hypanthium ("hip") which becomes red and succulent in fruit; achenes bony ....
      ....*Rosa* in 53. ROSACEAE
      4. Flowers white; fruit of several or many fleshy drupelets inserted on a convex receptacle .... *Rubus* in 53. ROSACEAE
    3. Prickles none.
      5. Leaflets silky-pubescent; stipules present; flowers yellow, perfect; achenes densely pubescent ....*Potentilla* in 53. ROSACEAE
      5. Leaflets not silky-pubescent, either glabrous or only short-pubescent, stipules absent; flowers greenish, plants polygamous or dioecious.
        6. Leaflets sessile, pellucid-punctate; fruit a suborbicular samara, 1.5-3 cm in diameter ....*Ptelea* in 34. RUTACEAE
        6. Leaflets, at least the terminal one, petiolulate; fruit a drupe
        ....49. ANACARDIACEAE
  2. Leaflets more than 3.
    7. Leaves palmately compound.
      8. Stems prickly; tendrils none; stamens numerous ....
      ....*Rubus* in 53. ROSACEAE
      8. Stems not prickly; tendrils present; stamens 5.
    7. Leaves pinnately compound.
      9. Leaflets entire or undulate, or remotely denticulate.
        10. Leaflets 3-7, silky-pubescent, revolute-margined; flowers yellow; fruit an achene; shrub 30-100 cm tall ....
        ....*Potentilla* in 53. ROSACEAE
        10. Leaflets 5-51.
          11. Leaflets with pellucid dots; flowers greenish yellow in small axillary cymes, appearing before the leaves; branches often with sharp stout stipular prickles; fruit ellipsoid, 4-6 mm long, 1-seeded, spicy flavored ....
          ....*Zanthoxylum* in 34. RUTACEAE
          11. Leaflets without pellucid dots.

12. Fruit a pod; flowers often papilionaceous ....
....54. LEGUMINOSAE
12. Fruit a drupe; flowers never papilionaceous ....
....49. ANACARDIACEAE
9. Leaflets more or less toothed.
13. Leaflets 11-41, entire except for two or more coarse teeth at the
base, lanceolate, 7-15 cm long; leaves 20-90 cm long, ill-
scented; flowers small, greenish, polygamous, in erect panicles
10-30 cm long; samaras 3-4 cm long, twisted, with the compressed seed in the middle ....35. SIMARUBACEAE
13. Leaflets with numerous teeth.
14. Stipules none; flowers greenish.
15. Trees; staminate flowers in catkins; fruit a nut ....
....67. JUGLANDACEAE
15. Shrubs; flowers in panicles; fruit a drupe ....
....49. ANACARDIACEAE
14. Stipules present (sometimes soon disappearing); flowers not
green or in catkins ....53. ROSACEAE
1. Leaves 2-3-compound.
16. Petioles and midribs often with small prickles; leaflets ovate, acute, serrate to entire; flowers small, white, in umbels; drupes numerous,
small, black, ovoid; shrub or small tree with prickly branches ....
....*Aralia spinosa* in 91. ARALIACEAE
16. Petioles and midribs never spiny; fruit a legume.
17. Leaflets 12-28, obtuse, 2-3.5 cm long, remotely denticulate; trees,
usually with spines on the trunk and branches ....
....*Gleditsia* in 54. LEGUMINOSAE
17. Leaflets 30-60, acute, 4-8 cm long, entire; trees without spines ....
....*Gymnocladus* in 54. LEGUMINOSAE

Section 14. Trees or Shrubs (Including Woody Climbers) With Alternate Simple Entire Leaves

1. Branches or stems more or less prickly or spiny.
2. Leaves usually with a pair of tendrils at the base of the petiole ....
....*Smilax* in 130. LILIACEAE
2. Tendrils absent.
3. Leaves ovate or ovate-lanceolate, acuminate; twigs with sharp spines;
flowers small, greenish, unisexual; fruit yellow, as large as a grape-
fruit; trees with milky juice ....*Maclura* in 71. MORACEAE
3. Leaves oblanceolate or lanceolate, often fascicled on short lateral
branchlets.
4. Trailing or climbing shrubs with arching or spreading light gray angular branches; flowers greenish purple; berries red, many-seeded
....*Lycium* in 107. SOLANACEAE
4. Erect shrubs or small tree; flowers white; drupe black, 1-seeded ......
....96. SAPOTACEAE
1. Plants without spines or prickles.
5. Plants prostrate or climbing.
6. Stems prostrate; tendrils none ....93. ERICACEAE
6. Stems climbing or twining.
7. Tendrils usually present at base of petioles; flowers in umbels, greenish; fruit a berry ....*Smilax* in 130. LILIACEAE
7. Tendrils none.

8. Flowers axillary; leaves cordate; fruit a capsule ....
....87. ARISTOLOCHIACEAE
8. Flowers in small cymes, purple (or rarely white); berries ovoid,
red ....*Solanum dulcamara* in 107. SOLANACEAE
5. Plants erect; trees or shrubs.
  9. Leaves cordate, palmately veined; pods 6-8 cm long; shrub or small
tree ....'.......................................*Cercis* in 54. LEGUMINOSAE
  9. Leaves not cordate.
    10. Leaves bristle-tipped ....*Quercus* in 65. FAGACEAE
    10. Leaves not bristle-tipped.
      11. Stipules usually present.
        12. Flowers large, greenish yellow, white, or purplish, solitary;
trees ....1. MAGNOLIACEAE
        12. Flowers not as above.
          13. Flowers in catkins; fruit a capsule ....69. SALICACEAE
          13. Flowers axillary; fruit a drupe ....51. RHAMNACEAE
      11. Stipules none.
        14. Leaves somewhat palmately veined with 3 principal veins
from near the base, often with one or more lateral lobes;
leaves and bark spicy-aromatic ....
....*Sassafras* in 74. LAURACEAE
        14. Leaves pinnately veined or 1-veined.
          15. Pith of the twigs chambered, or divided by woody
plates; trees with imperfect flowers.
            16. Leaves crowded towards the ends of the branches;
twigs soon glabrous; drupe ovoid or ellipsoid, 1-
seeded; flowers 5-merous ....*Nyssa* in 90. CORNACEAE
            16. Leaves not crowded; young twigs pubescent; berry
large, globose, 4-12-seeded, reddish yellow and
sweet when ripe, astringent when green ....
....94. EBENACEAE
          15. Pith continuous; flowers perfect.
            17. Leaves large, 15-40 cm long at maturity, oblanceo-
late; buds naked, reddish-pubescent; flowers axillary, dark purple or green, 2-4 cm in diameter;
sepals 3; petals 6; stamens numerous, in a globose
mass surrounding the pistils ....2. ANNONACEAE
            17. Leaves smaller.
              18. Leaves evergreen.
                19. Leaves scale-like, numerous, 1-2 mm long,
closely imbricated, hoary-pubescent; flow-
ers yellow; fruit an ovoid, 3-angled, glabrous 1-2-seeded capsule; heath-like shrubs
10-30 cm tall ....12. CISTACEAE
                19. Leaves larger, fewer; flowers not yellow; cap-
sules many-seeded ....93. ERICACEAE
              18. Leaves deciduous.
                20. Base of petiole hollow, covering the lateral
buds; terminal bud absent; leaves oval;
bark tough and fibrous; flowers pale yellow, appearing before the leaves; fruit an
ellipsoid drupe ....
........................*Dirca* in 76. THYMELAEACEAE
              20. Petioles otherwise; terminal bud present.

21. Leaves glabrous or more or less pubescent, but not strigillose beneath.
    22. Leaves minutely resinous-dotted beneath, elliptical-obovate, ciliolate; flowers in axillary drooping racemes; corolla ellipsoid, greenish or pink ....
    ....*Gaylussacia* in 93. ERICACEAE
    22. Leaves not resinous-dotted.
        23. Petioles usually 1 cm or more in length; ovary superior.
            24. Bark spicy-aromatic; buds scaly; drupe red, 1 cm long at maturity ....
            ......*Lindera* in 74. LAURACEAE
            24. Bark not aromatic; winter buds naked; drupe 6-8 mm in diameter, dark purple when ripe ....
            Rhamnus in 51. RHAMNACEAE
        23. Petioles shorter; buds scaly; ovary inferior; fruit a several-seeded berry ....
        ....*Vaccinium* in 93. ERICACEAE
21. Leaves strigillose and pale green beneath; lateral veins running parallel to the margins, the upper ones ending in the apex; petals 4; sepals 4; flowers white, cymose; fruit a bluish black drupe 6-8 mm in diameter ....
    ......*Cornus alternifolia* in 90. CORNACEAE

Section 15. Trees and Shrubs With Alternate, Simple, Lobed Leaves

1. Leaves palmately veined and lobed.
  2. Plants climbing by tendrils ....52. VITACEAE
  2. Plants not climbing; tendrils none.
    3. Some of the leaves usually 3-lobed, not serrate, aromatic ....
    ....*Sassafras* in 74. LAURACEAE
    3. Leaves usually serrate or sinuate-dentate as well as lobed.
      4. Trees.
        5. Leaf-lobes not serrate or sinuate; blades white-tomentose beneath at first; flowers and fruits in catkins ....*Populus* in 69. SALICACEAE
        5. Leaf-lobes serrate or sinuate-toothed.
          6. Flowers and fruits in dense, globose heads.
            7. Leaf-lobes serrate; leaves glabrous or pubescent, never white-tomentose; 2-year-old branchlets often corky-ridged ....
            ....*Liquidambar* in 58. HAMAMELIDACEAE
            7. Leaf-lobes sinuate-toothed; blades white-tomentose beneath when young, becoming nearly glabrous at maturity; branchlets terete; bark exfoliating ....59. PLATANACEAE
          6. Staminate flowers in catkins; pistillate flowers ripening into a succulent multiple fruit (a mulberry); leaf-lobes serrate-dentate ....*Morus* in 71. MORACEAE

4. Shrubs.
    8. Stamens 5; ovary inferior; fruit a berry; branches sometimes spiny
      or prickly ....57. GROSSULARIACEAE
    8. Stamens numerous; ovaries superior, separate, or united at the
      base, becoming follicles or drupelets; branches never spiny ......
      ....53. ROSACEAE
1. Leaves pinnately veined.
  9. Lobes of the leaves serrate or crenate.
    10. Fruit of 2-5 follicles; bark shreddy; flowers in corymbs; branches
       never spiny ....*Physocarpus* in 53. ROSACEAE
    10. Fruit a pome; branches often spiny.
      11. Flowers in cymes; styles united below the middle; pome large, the
        carpels papery or leathery; branches (but not the twigs) some-
        times with rather blunt spines ....*Malus* in 53. ROSACEAE
      11. Flowers in corymbs; pomes small, the carpels bony; branches (and
        twigs) often with sharp spines ....*Crataegus* in 53. ROSACEAE
  9. Lobes of the leaves not serrate.
    12. Leaves with a truncate apex and two broad lateral lobes; buds cov-
       ered by the membranous stipules; flowers large ....
       ....*Liriodendron* in 1. MAGNOLIACEAE
    12. Leaves not truncate at apex; flowers small.
      13. Leaves pinnatifid with many rounded lobes on each side of the
        midvein; monoecious shrub with fragrant foliage; flowers in
        erect catkins; fruit an ovoid nutlet surrounded by subulate
        bracts ....68. MYRICACEAE
      13. Leaves with few lobes.
        14. Leaves with three principal veins from the base, aromatic;
          flowers yellow, 6-8 mm broad, in racemes 3-5 cm long ....
          ....*Sassafras* in 74. LAURACEAE
        14. Leaves with one vein from the base, not aromatic; flowers
          greenish, the staminate in catkins; fruit an acorn ....
          ....*Quercus* in 65. FAGACEAE

Section 16. Trees and Shrubs With Alternate, Simple Leaves, the Blades Toothed but Not Lobed

1. Base of blade symmetrical or nearly so.
  2. Flowers, at least the staminate (except *Fagus*) in catkins.
    3. Fruit a small several-seeded capsule, the seeds with a tuft of silky
      hairs; both staminate and pistillate flowers in catkins; stigmas 2,
      often 2-lobed (sometimes 3); dioecious shrubs or trees ....
      ....69. SALICACEAE
    3. Fruit not a capsule; seeds without a tuft of silky hairs; styles 2 or 3.
      4. Fruit a 1-loculed, 1-seeded nut; plants monoecious.
        5. Styles 3 ....65. FAGACEAE
        5. Styles 2-cleft, or stigmas 2 ....66. BETULACEAE
      4. Fruit a juicy multiple fruit; plants often with milky juice; styles 2
      ....71. MORACEAE
  2. Flowers never in catkins.
    6. Leaves with 1 principal vein from the base.
      7. Leaves with 15-25 pairs of nearly straight, conspicuous lateral veins;
        margins sharply double-serrate; fruit a samara ....70. ULMACEAE
      7. Leaves with fewer, less conspicuous veins; fruit not a samara.
        8. Stamens fewer than 15.

9. Anthers opening by apical pores; pith of the branches solid ......
....93. ERICACEAE
9. Anthers opening lengthwise; flowers white or greenish.
  10. Pith chambered, or separated by woody plates.
    11. Leaves stellate-pubescent beneath; flowers perfect, white,
       nodding, on slender pedicels; calyx 4-toothed; petals
       4, united below; fruit dry, bony within, 1-seeded, 4-
       winged ....*Halesia* in 95. STYRACACEAE
    11. Leaves not stellate-pubescent.
      12. Flowers greenish, unisexual; fruit a drupe ....
        ....*Nyssa* in 90. CORNACEAE
      12. Flowers white, perfect; fruit a 2-valved, ellipsoid, 2-
        loculed, several-seeded capsule tipped with the 2
        styles ....56. ESCALLONIACEAE
  10. Pith solid.
    13. Stems climbing, twining or trailing; leaves elliptical to
       roundish, finely serrate, glabrous; flowers in terminal
       racemes; capsules subglobose, yellow, with crimson
       seeds ....*Celastrus* in 44. CELASTRACEAE
    13. Stems erect.
      14. Flowers solitary or clustered in the axils; fruit a
        small, berry-like drupe with 4-8 bony nutlets ....
        ....48. AQUIFOLIACEAE
      14. Flowers in small dense panicles or corymbs; fruit a 3-
        loculed capsule, or drupaceous ......51. RHAMNACEAE
  8. Stamens 15 or more; fruit a drupe, pome, or follicle ....
    ....53. ROSACEAE
6. Leaves with 3 or more principal veins from the base.
  15. Leaves cordate, slender-petioled, abruptly acuminate, sharply
    serrate; trees ....22. TILIACEAE
  15. Leaves not cordate.
    16. Low shrub; pith continuous; flowers white; fruit a capsule;
      leaves ovate or elliptic-lanceolate, short-petioled, finely
      toothed ....*Ceanothus* in 51. RHAMNACEAE
    16. Trees or shrubs; pith of branches chambered; flowers greenish,
      apetalous; fruit a red drupe; leaves ovate-lanceolate or lance-
      olate, acuminate, scabrous ....*Celtis* in 70. ULMACEAE
1. Base of blade noticeably asymmetrical.
  17. Leaves sinuately or obtusely toothed, obovate or oval; flowers appearing
    in autumn when the leaves are falling; petals 4, yellow, linear; calyx
    4-parted; stamens 8, short; styles 2; fruit a capsule ....
    ....*Hamamelis* in 58. HAMAMELIDACEAE
  17. Leaves serrate; flowers appearing in spring; fruit not a capsule.
    18. Leaves cordate, glabrous, or the lower surface pubescent or with
      tufts of hairs in the axils of the veins; flowers appearing after the
      leaves, in drooping cymes, small, fragrant, the peduncle united
      with the membranous bract; fruit small, globose indehiscent ....
      ....22. TILIACEAE
    18. Leaves scabrous or hispidulous; flowers apetalous, appearing with or
      before the leaves.
      19. Flowers in catkins; leaf-buds acute ....*Ostrya* in 66. BETULACEAE
      19. Flowers not in catkins; leaf-buds obtuse ....70. ULMACEAE

Section 17. Flowers on Leafless (or Almost Leafless) Twigs

1. Leaf-buds and leaf-scars opposite.
  2. Flowers perfect, large, violet, in terminal panicles; leaves large, cordate, petioled, pubescent; fruit a capsule with numerous small winged seeds ....*Paulownia* in 109. BIGNONIACEAE
  2. Flowers unisexual (rarely perfect), the plants dioecious, polygamous, or monoecious; styles or stigmas 2; fruit of samaras.
    3. Bud-scales scurfy brown or black; bundle-scars forming a crescent-shaped line; calyx small, 4-cleft or obsolete; stamens usually 2; fruit a single samara ....*Fraxinus* in 98. OLEACEAE
    3. Bud-scales not scurfy, paler; bundle-scars not forming a curved line; calyx usually 5-lobed; stamens 4-10, usually 8; fruit a pair of samaras ....50. ACERACEAE
1. Leaf-buds and leaf-scars alternate.
  4. Flowers (at least the staminate) in catkins, apetalous.
    5. Style 2-cleft, or stigmas 2 (or 3 or 4).
      6. Perianth none.
        7. Fruit a many-seeded capsule; plants dioecious ....69. SALICACEAE
        7. Fruit a 1-seeded nut; plants monoecious ....66. BETULACEAE
      6. Perianth of 4 sepals; fruit a syncarp ....71. MORACEAE
    5. Style or stigmas 3 (or 4); fruit a 1-seeded nut ....65. FAGACEAE
  4. Flowers not in catkins.
    8. Branches with sharp stipular prickles; plants dioecious; sepals 0; petals 4-5, greenish yellow; stamens 4 or 5; pistils 2-5; leaves pinnate ....*Zanthoxylum* in 34. RUTACEAE
    8. Branches not prickly; leaves simple.
      9. Flowers white (or pink), perfect; petals 5; sepals 5.
        10. Style 1 ....*Prunus* in 53. ROSACEAE
        10. Styles 5 ....*Amelanchier* in 53. ROSACEAE
      9. Flowers not white.
        11. Corolla papilionaceous, red-purple; flowers perfect, in umbel-like clusters; stamens 10; fruit a legume ....
        ....*Cercis* in 54. LEGUMINOSAE
        11. Corolla not papilionaceous; fruit not a legume.
          12. Flowers with 4 linear yellow petals; calyx 4-parted; stamens 8, short; styles 2; fruit a capsule; flowers appearing in autumn when the leaves are falling ....
          ....*Hamamelis* in 58. HAMAMELIDACEAE
          12. Flowers greenish, purplish, or yellowish, appearing in spring.
            13. Flowers greenish or purple.
              14. Stamens numerous; petals 6; sepals 3; leaves entire, alternate ....2. ANNONACEAE
              14. Stamens 2-9; petals 0.
                15. Stamens 2-4; calyx 0; leaves opposite ....
                ....*Forestiera* in 98. OLEACEAE
                15. Stamens 4-9, inserted on the calyx; calyx 4-9 cleft; trees with serrate alternate leaves ....
                ....70. ULMACEAE
            13. Flowers yellowish or yellow; leaves entire or lobed.
              16. Sepals 5; petals 5; stamens 5 ....49. ANACARDIACEAE
              16 Sepals 6 or 4.

17. Calyx 6-parted; stamens 9; anthers opening by valves; flowers fragrant, in small clusters; twigs with spicy odor and flavor ....74. Lauraceae

17. Calyx tubular, corolla-like, obscurely 4-toothed ....
....76. Thymelaeaceae

Section 18. Ferns and Fern-Allies (Lycosphens)

1. Plants attached to the substratum by roots, either growing on land or submerged in water, but not free-floating.
   2. Leaves not quadrifoliolate or clover-like.
     3. Leaves narrow, sessile, 1-veined, subulate or linear or oval, simple, not "fern-like."
       4.Leaves not whorled; stem solid, not conspicuously jointed.
         5. Stems elongated, leafy.
           6. Cones terete (or in some species the sporangia borne in the axils of ordinary leaves); spores of only one kind; leaves without a ligule ....1. Lycopodiaceae
           6. Cones more or less 4-angled; spores of two kinds, large (megaspores), and small (microspores), borne in different sporangia in the same cone; ligule present ....2. Selaginellaceae
         5. Stem short, thick, corm-like; leaves rush-like, in a basal tuft; plants aquatic or growing in wet soil ....3. Isoetaceae
       4. Leaves whorled, united to form toothed sheaths at the conspicuous nodes on grooved, usually hollow stems; sporangia in a terminal cone ....4. Equisetaceae
     3. Leaves usually broad and "fern-like" in most species, petiolate, often compound, with numerous or several free (rarely netted) veins.
       7. Small delicate ferns with filmy translucent leaves usually consisting of a single layer of cells; sporangia sessile on a filiform receptacle within a tubular or urceolate indusium ....6. Hymenophyllaceae
       7. Larger ferns with the leaves membranous to coriaceous, consisting of several layers of cells; sporangia not as above.
         8. Sporangia large, sessile, opening by a transverse slit, borne in a stalked terminal spike or loose panicle, the sterile blade appearing lateral; vernation erect or inclined ....5. Ophioglossaceae
         8. Sporangia small, stalked, borne in clusters (sori) on the back of ordinary or modified foliar leaves, or in pod-like divisions of modified leaves; vernation usually coiled.
           9. Sporangia covering some or all divisions of the fertile leaves, densely crowded, short-stalked, globose, opening by a longitudinal slit into two valves; annulus none; veins free ....
....7. Osmundaceae
           9. Sporangia in sori on the back or margin of ordinary or modified leaves, long-stalked, opening by a nearly complete vertical ring (annulus) ....8. Polypodiaceae
   2. Leaves quadrifoliolate, clover-like, long-stalked; sporocarps ovoid, borne at the base of the stalks and containing both megaspores and microspores; plants perennial with slender rhizomes ....9. Marsileaceae
1. Plants not attached by roots, minute (5-25 mm broad), free-floating; leaves imbricated, 2-lobed; sporocarps in pairs beneath the stem ....
....10. Salviniaceae

Section 19. Gymnosperms

1. Leaves (and cone-scales) spirally arranged, i.e., fascicled or alternate, never opposite or whorled.
    2. Fruit berry-like, red, 1-seeded, the seed nearly enclosed by the pulpy aril; microsporophylls with 3-8 pollen-sacs; cotyledons 2; leaves linear, evergreen ....1. TAXACEAE
    2. Fruit a woody cone.
        3. Cone-scales subtended by distinct bracts; microsporophylls with 2 pollen-sacs; branchlets not deciduous ....2. PINACEAE
        3. Cone-scales without distinct bracts; microsporophylls with 3-8 pollen-sacs; lateral branchlets (in our species) deciduous, the leaves light green, flattened, 2-ranked; bark fibrous ....3. TAXODIACEAE
1. Leaves and cone-scales opposite or whorled, the leaves small, scale-like or subulate ....4. CUPRESSACEAE

KEYS TO GENERA AND SPECIES

Division I. **Pteridophyta.** Ferns and Fern-allies

1. **Lycopodiaceae** Rich. — Clubmoss Family

1. **Lycopodium** L. — Clubmoss

1. Sporangia borne in the axils of foliar leaves, not in distinct terminal cones.
2. Leaves linear-oblanceolate, glossy, widest above the middle, erose-denticulate toward the apex; cool moist woods, rare ....*L. lucidulum* Michx.
2. Leaves lanceolate-linear, widest at the base, nearly or quite entire; cool woods, rare; Cook, La Salle, and Ogle counties ....*L. porophilum* Lloyd & Underw.
1. Sporangia borne in terminal cones; sporophylls similar to the foliar leaves.
3. Sterile branches creeping; Cook Co., *L. N. Johnson* in 1890; *J. A. Steyermark* in 1947 ....*L. inundatum* L.
3. Sterile branches erect; shaded sandstone ledges; Pope Co., *J. W. Voigt & J. R. Swayne 1170* ....
....*L. flabelliforme* (Fern.) Blanch.

2. Selaginellaceae Warming

1. **Selaginella** Beauv. — Selaginella

1. Leaves numerous, uniformly imbricated, many-ranked, subulate, short-awned; dry sandstone rocks, local; n. Ill., extending southward to Henderson and La Salle counties; also Pope Co. Rock Selaginella ....*S. rupestris* (L.) Spring
1. Leaves of two kinds, 4-ranked, spreading in two planes, ovate, acute or cuspidate; moist soil, local. Creeping Selaginella ....
....*S. apoda* (L.) Morren

3. Isoetaceae Warming — Quillwort Family

1. **Isoetes** L. — Quillwort

1. Megaspores 0.3-0.4 mm in diameter, nearly smooth, or with low tubercles; microspores finely spinulose, ashy-gray; wet meadows or shallow ponds, rare; has been reported from Cook, Fulton, Madison, McHenry, Menard, St. Clair and Stark counties ....
....*I. melanopoda* Gay & Dur.
1. Megaspores 0.4-0.6 mm in diameter, honeycomb-reticulate; microspores smooth or nearly so; ponds, rare. St. Clair Co. ....
....*I. engelmanni* A.Br.

40

4. Equisetaceae Rich. — Horsetail Family

1. Equisetum L.

1. Stems all alike, usually simple; stomata in regular rows in the grooves.
    2. Stems usually tall, 10- to 50-angled, hollow; teeth of the sheaths soon deciduous.
        3. Sheaths about as long as broad, short-cylindrical, appressed, ashy-gray, with a black band near the base; stems dark green, perennial, rough-tuberculate; cones rigidly apiculate; moist sandy soil, common. Tall Scouring-rush [*E. prealtum* Raf.]* ....*E. hyemale* L.
        3. Sheaths slightly longer than broad, dilated upward and somewhat funnelform, green, and usually with a narrow black rim; stems pale, annual, smooth or nearly so; cones blunt or with a small apiculus; sandy soil, common. Smooth Scouring-rush [*E. kansanum* Schaffner] ....*E. laevigatum* A.Br.
    2. Stems low, slender, 5- to 10-angled; teeth of the sheaths persistent; cones apiculate.
        4. Stems 15-30 cm tall, 1-3 mm thick, 5- to 10-angled; central cavity one-third the diameter of the stem; sheaths 5- to 10-toothed; cones 5-10 mm long; moist sandy soil in the n. half of the state. Variegated Scouring-rush [*E. nelsoni* (A.A.Eaton) Schaffner] ....*E. variegatum* Schleich.
        4. Stems 5-15 cm tall, 0.5-1 mm thick, 6-angled; central cavity absent; sheaths mostly 3-toothed; cones 3-5 mm long; moist ground, rare, Lake and McHenry counties. Dwarf Scouring-rush ....*E. scirpoides* Michx.
1. Stems annual, flexible; stomata scattered; cones blunt.
    5. Stems all alike, green, usually branched at maturity.
        6. Stems 10- to 30-grooved; central cavity one-half or more the diameter of the stem; sheaths tight; along ditches or in marshes or shallow water in the n. half of the state. Water Horsetail ....*E. fluviatile* L.
        6. Stems 5- to 10-angled; central cavity about one-sixth the diameter of the stem; sheaths loose; wet soil, rare. Peoria and Tazewell counties. Marsh Horsetail ....*E. palustre* L.
    5. Stems of two kinds, the sterile green and branched, the fertile whitish or brownish, appearing in early spring and soon withering; moist sandy soil, common, particularly on railroad embankments. Field Horsetail ....*E. arvense* L.

5. Ophioglossaceae Presl — Adder's-tongue Family

1. Sterile blade pinnately divided; venation free; sporangia in a panicle ....1. *Botrychium*
1. Sterile blade simple, entire; venation reticulate; sporangia in two rows in a simple slender spike ....2. *Ophioglossum*

---

* Synonyms appear in brackets.

1. Botrychium Sw. — Grape Fern

1. Sterile blade stalked, attached near the base of the plant; lateral veins of the leaf-segments forked; epidermal cells with straight walls.
    2. Leaf-segments incised; woods, locally throughout Ill. ....*B. dissectum* Spreng.
    2. Leaf-segments merely crenate or serrulate.
        3. Blades thin; segments acutish; woods, locally throughout Ill. ....*B. obliquum* Muhl.
        3. Blades thick, somewhat coriaceous; segments obtuse; woods, rare, n. Ill. ....*B. multifidum* (S.G.Gmel.) Rupr.
1. Sterile blade nearly or quite sessile, attached near the middle of the plant, thin, membranous, the segments unbranched; epidermal cells with flexuous walls; moist woods, common ....*B. virginianum* (L.) Sw.

2. Ophioglossum L. — Adder's-Tongue

1. Sterile blades usually 2-5, oval, apiculate, the principal veins 13 or more, forming broad areolae containing numerous included veinlets; spores pitted; hillsides, banks, thickets, chiefly on limestone, rare; known from Hardin, Jersey, and Randolph counties ....*O. engelmanni* Prantl
1. Sterile blades usually solitary, or sometimes 2, oval, obtuse, the principal veins 7-11, forming narrow areolae containing few included veinlets; spores reticulate; meadows, open woods, swamps, moist thickets, rare; Jackson and Union counties. [*O pusillum* Raf.] ....*O. vulgatum* L.

6. Hymenophyllaceae Gaud. — Filmy Fern Family

1. Trichomanes L. — Filmy Fern

T. boschianum Sturm. On sandstone near a spring, Jackson Hollow, Pope Co. First collected Aug. 2, 1923, by *Mary M. Steagall 37;* several subsequent collections from near the same locality.

7. Osmundaceae R.Br. — Royal Fern Family

1. Osmunda L.

1. Leaves twice pinnate, some of them fertile at the apex and forming an erect terminal panicle; swampy ground or wet woods, local. Royal Fern ....*O. regalis* L.
1. Leaves once pinnate.
    2. Leaves of two kinds, the fertile and sterile ones separate; sterile leaves longer than the fertile, each pinna with a tuft of tomentum at base; swampy ground; chiefly in the n. part of the state; also Pope Co. Cinnamon Fern ......*O. cinnamomea* L.

2. Sterile and fertile leaves similar, the latter bearing 2-6 pairs of fertile pinnae near the middle; pinnae of the sterile leaves lacking tufts of tomentum at base; moist ground in woods, local. Interrupted Fern ....*O. claytoniana* L.

8. Polypodiaceae S.F.Gray — Fern Family

1. Sporangia enclosed in globose or necklace-like brownish portions of the contracted and modified fertile leaves; fertile and sterile leaves dissimilar.
  2. Sterile leaves 1-pinnatifid, the veins reticulate; fertile leaves 2-pinnate; rhizome horizontal, the leaves therefore solitary ....1. *Onoclea*
  2. Sterile leaves 2-pinnatifid, the veins free; fertile leaves 1-pinnate; rhizome short, erect, the leaves therefore tufted ....2. *Matteuccia*
1. Sporangia on the margin or back of ordinary foliar or modified leaves.
  3. Indusium inferior or partly so (often evanescent).
    4. Sori dorsal.
      5. Indusium partly inferior, delicate, hood-like, attached by its base at one side ....3. *Cystopteris*
      5. Indusium wholly inferior, roundish at first, soon splitting ....4. *Woodsia*
    4. Sori marginal, in minute cup-like inferior indusia at the ends of the veins; leaves bipinnate, delicate, fragrant, sparsely glandular-pubescent ....5. *Dennstaedtia*
  3. Indusium superior or none.
    6. Sori dorsal, *i.e.,* on the back of the leaves away from the margin, or if apparently near the margin not covered by the revolute edge of the leaf-segments.
      7. Sori roundish.
        8. Stipes not jointed to the rhizome; indusium (if present) conspicuous, but often soon deciduous.
          9. Indusium orbicular, peltate; leaves (in our species) 1-pinnate, the stipe and rachis scaly, the pinnules spinulose-serrate, auriculate at the base of the upper margin ....6. *Polystichum*
          9. Indusium (lacking in some species) reniform, attached at its sinus; leaves 1-3-pinnately compound ....7. *Dryopteris*
        8. Stipes jointed to the rhizome; blades pinnately lobed; indusium none ....8. *Polypodium*
      7. Sori elongated, oval to oblong or linear, straight or curved, two or more times as long as wide.
        10. Leaves simple, entire, 5-30 cm long, lanceolate, tapering from a truncate or cordate or even hastate base, rooting at the tip and thus giving rise to new plants; veins forking and anastomosing ....9. *Camptosorus*
        10. Leaves pinnate or pinnatifid.
          11. Leaves evergreen, coriaceous, small (5-40 cm long); stipes firm, slender, wiry, brown or black ....10. *Asplenium*
          11. Leaves not evergreen, herbaceous; stipes soft, stoutish, stramineous (when dry).
            12. Sori in chain-like rows parallel to the midveins; veins united to form a series of narrow areolae along the midrib, elsewhere free ....12. *Woodwardia*
            12. Sori and venation otherwise ....11. *Athyrium*
      6. Sori marginal, *i.e.,* borne at the edges of the lobes or segments of the leaves, either in definite sori or in a conspicuous line and covered by the revolute leaf-margin.

13. Leaves pedate, the stipe forked at the summit, dark brown or black, smooth, glossy; pinnules flabellate; sori several, distinct ....15. *Adiantum*
13. Leaves not pedate, the stipe simple; sori apparently continuous along the margin of the pinnules.
   14. Sori borne near the tips of separate veins; rhizomes scaly; chiefly small, rupestral ferns.
     15. Leaves delicate, strongly dimorphic; stipe straw-colored or pale brown ....13. *Cryptogramma*
     15. Leaves firm, nearly or quite uniform; stipes dark brown or blackish.
       16. Leaf-blades glabrous ....14. *Pellaea*
       16. Leaf-blades pubescent ....16. *Cheilanthes*
   14. Sori borne on a heavy marginal vein extending around the lobes; leaves coarse, ternate; rhizomes horizontal, black, not scaly ....17. *Pteridium*

1. **Onoclea** L. — Sensitive Fern

O. sensibilis L. Moist woods, or edges of meadows, common.

2. **Matteuccia** Todaro — Ostrich Fern

M. struthiopteris (L.) Todaro. Wet ground, not common; n. Ill., southward to Peoria Co. [*Pteretis struthiopteris* (L.) Nieuwl.].

3. **Cystopteris** Bernh.

1. Leaves broadly lanceolate, acute, 20-40 cm long, the basal pair of pinnae usually slightly shorter; bulblets none; moist soil in woods, common; the most abundant fern in Ill. Brittle Fern ....*C. fragilis* (L.) Bernh.
1. Leaves narrowly lanceolate, 30-120 cm long when mature; axils of some of the upper pinnae usually bearing small bulblets on the lower surface; basal pair of pinnae the largest; on moist cliffs in shaded ravines, not uncommon. Bulblet Fern ....*C. bulbifera* (L.) Bernh.

4. **Woodsia** R.Br.

1. Leaves 20-50 cm long, minutely glandular; petiole not jointed; indusium ample, with few broad spreading jagged lobes; cliffs, not common. Cliff Fern ....*W. obtusa* (Spreng.) Torr.
1. Leaves 5-15 cm long, rusty-chaffy beneath; petiole jointed a short distance above its base; indusium inconspicuous, the divisions filiform; cliffs, rare; Ogle Co. Rock Woodsia ....*W. ilvensis* (L.) R.Br.

5. **Dennstaedtia** Bernh.

D. punctilobula (Michx.) Moore. Hay-scented Fern. Sandstone cliffs in wooded ravines, rare; Wabash Co., *Schneck;* Lusk Creek, Pope Co., *Bailey & Swayne 2759.*

6. **Polystichum** Roth — Christmas Fern

P. acrostichoides (Michx.) Schott. In wooded ravines, common.

7. **Dryopteris** Adans.

1. Indusium none; leaves triangular; rhizome slender, horizontal.
  2. Leaves ternate, glabrous, the three divisions stalked; rachis not winged; wooded ravines, rare; Ogle and St. Clair counties. Oak Fern [*Phegopteris dryopteris* (L.) Fée] ....*D. disjuncta* (Ledeb.) Morton
  2. Leaves twice pinnatifid, pubescent or glandular beneath, the pinnae all sessile, adnate to the rachis.
    3. Rachis terete and wingless above the lowest pair of pinnae; moist ravines, cliffs, and woods, rare; Henderson, La Salle, Menard, Ogle and Pulaski counties. Long Beech Fern ....*D. phegopteris* (L.) C.Chr.
    3. Rachis winged above the lowest pair of pinnae by their adnate bases; rich woods and ravines, not uncommon. Broad Beech Fern ....*D. hexagonoptera* (Michx.) C.Chr.
1. Indusium present.
  4. Leaves membranous, not evergreen; vascular bundles of the stipe two, free or united; rhizomes slender, almost without scales.
    5. Lowest pinnae reduced in length, widely spaced, deflexed, the blade therefore conspicuously narrowed toward the base; margins of the pinnules flat; indusium glandular; veins mostly simple; woods and thickets, rare. New York Fern ....*D. noveboracensis* (L.) A.Gray
    5. Lowest pinnae only slightly reduced; margins of the pinnules revolute; indusium ciliate; veins of the sterile blades forked; marshes, common, except in the southern counties. Marsh Fern ....*D. thelypteris* (L.) A.Gray
  4. Leaves of firm texture, often evergreen; vascular bundles of the stipe five or more; rhizome stout, conspicuously scaly.
    6. Leaves 1-pinnate, or rarely 2-pinnate.
      7. Sori on the margin of the obscurely crenate or entire pinnules; leaves coriaceous; sandstone cliffs and wooded ravines, not uncommon. Marginal Wood Fern ....*D. marginalis* (L.) A.Gray
      7. Sori near the midvein; pinnules toothed.
        8. Leaf-blades 20-40 cm wide, ovate in outline, scarcely narrowed below; pinnae broadest near the middle; rich woods in ravines, rare; known from Fulton, Grundy, La Salle, McLean, Peoria, and Will counties. Goldie's Fern ....*D. goldiana* (Hook.) A.Gray
        8. Leaf-blades narrower, elliptical in outline, narrowed at the base; lower pinnae broadest at the base; swampy

woods, rare; n. Ill., known from Boone, Cook, Kankakee, Lake, La Salle, Ogle, and Winnebago counties. Crested Wood Fern ....*D. cristata* (L.) A.Gray
6. Leaves 2-3 pinnate, the pinnae spinulose-toothed.
   9. Pinnae at right angles to the rachis; inner pinnules of the basal row equalling or shorter than the next outer ones; leaves (at least the rachis) usually with a few small scattered stipitate glands; indusium with marginal glands; moist woods, locally throughout Ill., except the eastern and central counties. Common Wood Fern ....
   ....*D. intermedia* (Muhl.) A.Gray
   9. Pinnae oblique to the rachis; inner pinnules of the basal row longer than the next outer ones; leaves and indusia not glandular; woods, local; n. Ill.; also Pope and Union counties. Spinulose Wood Fern ....
   ....*D. spinulosa* (O.F.Muell.) Watt

8. **Polypodium** L. — Polypody

1. Leaves glabrous on both sides; rocky ledges, locally abundant. [*P. vulgare* of auth., non L.] ....*P. virginianum* L.
1. Leaves copiously scaly-scurfy beneath; on rocks, rarely on trees; s. Ill. ....*P. polypodioides* (L.) Watt

9. **Camptosorus** Link

C. rhizophyllus (L.) Link. Walking Fern. Moist rocky ledges, not rare.

10. **Asplenium** L. — Spleenwort

1. Stipe green at least above; rachis green throughout, flat.
   2. Leaves pinnatifid, or pinnate below, lanceolate, tapering to a long narrow tip, the segments obtuse, crenate; sandstone cliffs, rare, s. Ill. Pinnatifid Spleenwort ....*A. pinnatifidum* Nutt.
   2. Leaves 2- to 3-pinnate, rhombic in outline, the segments cuneate, finely toothed at the apex; usually on calcareous cliffs; s. Ill.; without definite locality, *Brendel.* Rue Spleenwort [*A. cryptolepis* Fern.] ....*A. ruta-muraria* L.
1. Stipe dark; rachis black or brown, or green on upper part, terete.
   3. Rachis brown on lower half, green above.
      4. Blades with 3-6 pairs of doubly serrate to subentire not lobed pinnae; stipes dark brown or black, not glossy; sandstone cliffs, very rare; "s. Ill.", *F. S. Earle* about 1890. Kentucky Spleenwort ....*A. kentuckiense* T.N.McCoy
      4. Blades with 8-18 pairs of lobed (or with pinnules), sharply toothed pinnae; stipes chestnut-brown, glossy; sandstone cliffs, s. Ill.; known from Jackson, Randolph, and Union counties. Cliff Spleenwort ....*A. bradleyi* D.C.Eaton
   3. Rachis black or brown throughout.

5. Leaves pinnatifid, the apex caudate, the segments lanceolate, sessile, variable in size, more or less auriculate at the base; on a rocky, wooded hillside along the Mississippi R., near McClure, Alexander Co., *E. J. Palmer* in 1919; Jackson Co., *J. McCree* in 1941. Scott's Spleenwort. [*Asplenium platyneuron* × *A. rhizophyllus; Asplenosorus* × *ebenoides* (R.R.Scott) Wherry] ....× *A. ebenoides* R.R.Scott
5. Leaves pinnate, with 15-40 pairs of pinnae.
6. Pinnae auriculate on upper side near base, serrate.
7. Leaves uniform, all fertile; pinnae mostly opposite, elliptical; rachis black; limestone cliffs, rare; Jackson and Union counties. Black Spleenwort ......*A. resiliens* Kunze
7. Leaves dimorphous, the sterile smaller, spreading; pinnae alternate, lanceolate; rachis chestnut-brown; rocky woods, not common. Ebony Spleenwort ....
....*A. platyneuron* (L.) Oakes
6. Pinnae crenate, oval, obtuse, not auriculate; sandstone cliffs, southern Ill., local. Maidenhair Spleenwort ....
....*A. trichomanes* L.

11. **Athyrium** Roth

1. Leaves bipinnate or bipinnatifid.
2. Leaves bipinnate; pinnules sharply serrate or incised; woods, local. Lady Fern. [*A. filix-femina* ex p. of Am. auth., non L. ....*A. angustum* (Willd.) Presl
2. Leaves bipinnatifid; segments crenate-serrate; woods, not infrequent. Silvery Spleenwort ....*A. thelypterioides* (Michx.) Desv.
1. Leaves 1-pinnate; pinnae entire or crenulate, linear-lanceolate, acuminate; moist woods, common. Glade Fern ....
....*A. pycnocarpon* (Spreng.) Tidestr.

12. **Woodwardia** Sm. — Chain Fern

W. virginica (L.) Sm. Tamarack bog near Antioch, Lake Co.

13. **Cryptogramma** R.Br.

C. stelleri (S.G.Gmel.) Prantl. Rock-brake. On damp, usually calcareous rocks, rare; n. Ill.

14. **Pellaea** Link — Cliff-brake Fern

1. Stipes and rachises glabrous or nearly so; leaves 5-25 cm long, pale bluish-green; chiefly calcareous rocks, local ....*P. glabella* Mett.
1. Stipes and rachises with numerous jointed hairs; leaves 10-50 cm long, grayish-green; dry calcareous rocks, not common; s. Ill. ....*P. atropurpurea* (L.) Link

15. **Adiantum** L. — Maidenhair Fern

A. pedatum L. Moist woods, fairly common throughout Ill.

16. Cheilanthes Sw. — Lip Fern

1. Leaves 3-10 cm long, 1-2 cm wide, densely tomentose beneath; stipes becoming nearly or quite glabrous; indusia continuous; among rocks, principally limestone, not common; chiefly in the western and southern counties ....*C. feei* Moore
1. Leaves 10-30 cm long, 2-6 cm wide, hirsute-villosulous beneath; stipes persistently hirsute; indusia discontinuous; chiefly on non-calcareous rocks in the southern counties ....*C. lanosa* (Michx.) D.C.Eaton

17. Pteridium Gled. ex Scop. — Bracken

P. latiusculum (Desv.) Hieron. Open woods, common. [*Pteris aquilina* and *Pteridium aquilinum* of auth., non L.].

9. Marsileaceae R.Br.

1. Marsilea L.

M. quadrifolia L. European Marsilea. Ponds, etc., introd. from eastern U.S.; native of Europe. Known from Jackson, McDonough, and Vermilion counties.

10. Salviniaceae Reichenb.

1. Azolla Lam.

A. mexicana Presl. Mosquito Fern. Floating on still water, not uncommon; of local distribution, but chiefly in the western counties.

Division II. Spermatophyta. Seed Plants

Subdivision I. Gymnospermae. Gymnosperms

1. Taxaceae Lindl. — Yew Family

1. Taxus L. — Yew

T. canadensis Marsh. Canada Yew. Ground-hemlock. Wooded hillsides near streams, rare; n.w. Ill., extending southeastward to La Salle and Kankakee counties.

2. Pinaceae Lindl. — Pine Family

1. Leaves evergreen, in fascicles of 2-5, surrounded at the base by a sheath; cones usually maturing the second year ....1. *Pinus*
1. Leaves deciduous, in clusters of 20-40 on short lateral spurs; cones maturing the first year ....2. *Larix*

1. Pinus L. — Pine

1. Leaves five in each fascicle, slender, bluish-green, 6-12 cm long; each leaf with one vascular bundle; cones cylindrical, often curved, pendent, 10-15 cm long; n. Ill., known from Carroll, Cook, Jo Daviess, Lake, La Salle, Lee, Ogle and Winnebago counties. Eastern White Pine ....*P. strobus* L.
1. Leaves two or three in a fascicle; each leaf with two vascular bundles.

2. Leaves 2-4 cm long, rigid, twisted, spreading; cone-scales spineless; n. Ill., in Cook and Lake counties, and formerly in Ogle
Co. Jack Pine ....*P. banksiana* Lamb.
2. Leaves 7-12 cm long, straight; cone-scales with a sharp prickle
about 1 mm long; s. Ill., Jackson, Randolph, and Union
counties. Shortleaf Pine ....*P. echinata* Mill.

2. Larix Mill.

L. laricina (DuRoi) K.Koch. Tamarack or American Larch. Bogs
in Cook, Lake, and McHenry counties.

3. Taxodiaceae Schimper
1. Taxodium Rich.

T. distichum (L.) Rich. Bald Cypress. Swampy ground, s. Ill.,
extending northward to Lawrence and Marion counties.

4. Cupressaceae Horan.

1. Branchlets flattened in one plane; leaves all scale-like; cones woody ....
.... 1. *Thuja*
1. Branchlets not flattened; some or all of the leaves usually subulate; cones
berry-like or drupe-like, bluish, glaucous ....2. *Juniperus*

1. Thuja L. — Arbor-vitae. White Cedar

T. occidentalis L. Chiefly on cliffs and bluffs of St. Peter sandstone; also in tamarack bogs; known from Cook, Kane, Lake, and La
Salle counties; also Peoria, *Brendel* in 1853, but now extinct there.

2. Juniperus L. — Juniper

1. Leaves all subulate, sharp-pointed, mostly in threes, 7-15 mm
long; low shrub with spreading or decumbent branches; sand
dunes near Lake Michigan; Cook and Lake counties. Low
Juniper [*J. communis* var. *depressa* Pursh; *J. communis* of
auth., non L.] ....*J. canadensis* Burgsd.
1. Leaves of two kinds, scale-like on the mature branchlets, subulate
on the young growth, mostly opposite.
2. Tree 10-25 m tall; cones on straight peduncles; locally abundant on bluffs and wooded slopes. Eastern Red Cedar [*J.
virginiana* var. *crebra* Fern. & Grisc.] ....*J. virginiana* L.
2. Prostrate shrub; cones on recurved peduncles; sand dunes near
Waukegan and Lake Bluff, Lake Co., the most southerly
stations for this species. Trailing Juniper ....
....*J. horizontalis* Moench

Subdivision II. Angiospermae. Flowering Plants

Class I. Dicotyledoneae (Juss.) DC.
1. Magnoliaceae J.St.Hil. — Magnolia Family

1. Leaves entire, acute or acuminate; buds pubescent ....1. *Magnolia*
1. Leaves with a truncate apex and two broad lateral lobes; buds glabrous
....2. *Liriodendron*

1. **Magnolia** L. — Cucumber Tree

M. acuminata L. Woods, s. Ill., as far north as Jackson, Johnson, and Pope counties. May.

2. **Liriodendron** L. — Tulip Tree

L. tulipifera L. Woods, local; s. Ill., extending northeastward to Vermilion Co. May.

2. **Annonaceae** R.Br. — Custard-apple Family
1. **Asimina** Adans. — Pawpaw

A. triloba (L.) Dunal. Woods, nearly throughout Ill., extending northward to Cook and Lee counties. Apr.-May.

3. **Ranunculaceae** Juss. — Buttercup Family

1. Flowers yellow.
  2. Petals none; sepals petal-like, yellow, deciduous; leaves crenate; carpels several-ovuled, becoming follicles ....1. *Caltha*
  2. Petals present; sepals green; carpels 1-ovuled, becoming achenes ....9. *Ranunculus*
1. Flowers not wholly yellow.
  3. Flowers white to pink.
    4. Stems climbing; leaves opposite; flowers in panicles ....16. *Clematis*
    4. Stems not climbing; leaves not opposite.
      5. Flowers zygomorphic, spurred; leaves palmately divided or cleft; inflorescence a raceme ....7. *Delphinium*
      5. Flowers actinomorphic, spurless.
        6. Aquatic plants with finely dissected leaves; sepals 5, green; petals 5, white; carpels 1-ovuled, becoming achenes ....9. *Ranunculus*
        6. Not aquatic, mostly woodland plants.
          7. Flowers racemose; petals small, stamen-like or none; leaves ternately compound.
            8. Racemes simple, short; fruit red or white, berry-like, poisonous ....5. *Actaea*
            8. Racemes paniculate, elongate; fruit a follicle ....6. *Cimicifuga*
          7. Flowers solitary or in pairs, or 3 or 4 in an umbel, not racemose.
            9. Flowers with an involucre of 3 sepal-like bracts immediately beneath the calyx; leaves 3-lobed ....14. *Hepatica*
            9. Flowers without an involucre, or the involucre similar to the leaves, and remote from the flowers.
              10. Sepals 3, petaloid, evanescent; petals none; carpels 2-ovuled, becoming berries; leaves reniform, palmately lobed ....2. *Hydrastis*
              10. Sepals 5 or more, petal-like; petals none; fruit of achenes or follicles.
                11. Leaves palmately lobed or cleft, the segments usually sessile; fruit of achenes; plants with a rhizome or caudex ....12. *Anemone*
                11. Leaves ternately compound, the leaflets stalked.

12. Flowers solitary; leaflets mucronulate; carpels 3-4, each 2- to 3-ovuled, becoming divaricate, slender-beaked follicles 5 mm long; style present; roots not at all or only slightly thickened ....3. *Isopyrum*

12. Flowers usually 3 or 4 in an umbel; leaflets not mucronulate; carpels 4-15, each 1-ovuled, becoming ribbed achenes 8-12 mm long at maturity; stigma sessile; roots tuberous-thickened ....13. *Anemonella*

3. Flowers red, blue-purple, or greenish.

13. Leaves entire, basal, linear; sepals minutely spurred at base; receptacle becoming conspicuously elongated ....8. *Myosurus*

13. Leaves lobed, parted, or compound.

14. Flowers red, spurred, nodding so that the five spurs point upward; stamens exserted; anthers yellow ....4. *Aquilegia*

14. Flowers not red.

15. Flowers spurred, blue; leaves alternate ....7. *Delphinium*

15. Flowers spurless.

16. Leaves pedate; flowers solitary, nodding ....14. *Helleborus*

16. Leaves not pedate; flowers usually not solitary.

17. Leaves alternate.

18. Leaves simple, palmately lobed; flowers all perfect.

19. Flowers solitary, subtended by 3 small sessile bracts simulating a calyx; sepals 6-12 ....15. *Hepatica*

19. Flowers corymbose; involucres none; sepals 3-5, usually 4 ....11. *Trautvetteria*

18. Leaves ternately compound; flowers polygamous or plants dioecious ....10. *Thalictrum*

17. Leaves not alternate; flowers solitary.

20. Leaves (of the stem) whorled, dissected ....12. *Anemone*

20. Leaves opposite ....16. *Clematis*

1. Caltha L. — Marsh-marigold

C. palustris L. Wet ground, n. and central Ill., southward to Christian, Shelby, and Coles counties. Apr.-May.

2. Hydrastis Ellis — Goldenseal

H. canadensis L. Woods, not common. Apr.-May.

3. Isopyrum L. — False Rue Anemone

I. biternatum (Raf.) Torr. & Gray. Moist woods, common throughout Ill. Mar.-May.

4. Aquilegia L. — Columbine

1. Flowers scarlet and yellow; spurs straight; wooded ravines, throughout Ill. Apr.-June. [*A. coccinea* Small] ....*A. canadensis* L.

1. Flowers blue, purple, pink, or white; spurs strongly hooked; sometimes escaped from cultivation, but not established in Ill. Garden Columbine ....*A. vulgaris* L.

5. **Actaea** L. — Baneberry

1. Pedicels in fruit nearly as thick as the peduncle; petals usually truncate at apex; fruit greenish-white, tipped with the sessile purple stigma; seeds 3-10, each 4-5 mm long; rich woods, common. Apr.-June. White Baneberry. Doll's Eyes [*A. pachypoda* Ell.] ....*A. alba* (L.) Mill.
1. Pedicels slender; petals spatulate, tapering to the tip; fruit red [white in f. *neglecta* (Gillman) Robins.] seeds 10-16, each 3-4 mm long; woods; n. Ill. Apr.-June. Red Baneberry ....
....*A. rubra* (Ait.) Willd.

6. **Cimicifuga** L.

1. Leaflets oval or ovate, truncate to subcordate at base; racemes puberulent; woods, very rare; St. Clair and Wabash counties. June-July. Black Cohosh ....*C. racemosa* (L.) Nutt.
1. Leaflets broadly ovate to suborbicular, at least the terminal one deeply cordate at base; racemes pilosulous; rich woods, rare; Pope Co. July-Aug. Bugbane ....*C. cordifolia* Pursh

7. **Delphinium** L. — Larkspur

1. Carpel 1; follicle erect, pubescent; flowers blue, pink, or white; annual, nat. from Eur., frequently cult. and occasionally escaped to roadsides, fields, and waste places. June-Aug. ....*D. ajacis* L.
1. Carpels 3; native perennials.
  2. Follicles erect, puberulent; roots elongate; racemes 10-20 cm long.
    3. Flowers whitish; racemes virgate; prairies and open woods, w. Ill., rare; Augusta, Hancock Co., *S. B. Mead*. May-June. Prairie Larkspur [*D. albescens* Rydb.; *D. penardi* of auth., non Huth] ....*D. virescens* Nutt.
    3. Flowers bluish or white; racemes lax; Henderson, Macon, Mercer, and Moultrie counties. Blue Larkspur [*D. azureum* Michx.] ....*D. carolinianum* Walt.
  2. Follicles widely divergent; roots short, tuberous; racemes lax; flowers bluish-purple (rarely white); woods, locally throughout central and s. Ill., extending northward to Henry, McLean, and Iroquois counties. Apr.-June. Dwarf Larkspur ....*D. tricorne* Michx.

8. **Myosurus** L. — Mousetail

M. minimus L. Moist ground in woods or fallow fields, local; chiefly in the s. half of Ill., extending northward to La Salle Co. Apr.-June.

9. **Ranunculus** L. — Buttercup
(*Batrachium* S.F.Gray)

1. Petals white; mature achenes transversely wrinkled; plants aquatic.

2. Beak of achene 0.5-1 mm long; leaves rigid, sessile or nearly so, usually 1-1.5 cm long, not collapsing when withdrawn from the water; ponds and slow streams, not common. May-July. [*R. circinatus* sensu auth., non Sibth.] ....
....*R. longirostris* Godr.

2. Beak of achene minute; leaves soft, mostly petioled, 2-2.5 cm long, usually collapsing when withdrawn from the water; ponds and slow streams; absent from the s. counties. May-July. [*R. aquatilis* L. var. *capillaceus* DC.] ....
....*R. trichophyllus* Chaix

1. Petals yellow; achenes not transversely wrinkled.

3. Achenes thin-walled, distinctly striate or ribbed, minutely apiculate, in ellipsoid heads 5-15 mm long; plants stoloniferous, the cordate or reniform crenate glabrous leaves basal and at the nodes of the stolons; flowers 6-8 mm in diameter, the 5-8 petals slightly shorter than the oval sepals; wet sandy soil, not common; Cook, Du Page, Henry, Kane, and McHenry counties. May-July ....*R. cymbalaria* Pursh

3. Achenes not thin-walled or striate.

4. Plants aquatic, immersed in water or creeping on mud, the leaves palmately lobed or divided, or finely dissected.

5. Submersed leaves divided into linear-filiform segments; petals 7-15 mm long; ponds and ditches. Apr.-June [*R. delphinifolius* Torr.] ....*R. flabellaris* Raf.

5. Submersed leaves orbicular with 3-5 lobes; petals 4-7 mm long; ponds, rare; Cook Co., *Munroe* in 1877 ....
....*R. purshii* Richards.

4. Plants not floating; if stems creeping in mud and rooting at the nodes, the leaves not finely dissected.

6. Basal leaves merely denticulate or crenate (rarely lobed).

7. Leaves lanceolate or linear, or the basal ovate.

8. Achenes turgid, 0.7-1 mm long, apiculate; head of achenes 2-4 mm in diameter; annuals with linear or linear-lanceolate stem-leaves.

9. Petals 1-3, pale yellowish, not more than 1-1.5 mm long; stamens 3-10; wet ground, s. Ill., not common, extending northward to Macoupin Co. May-June. [*R. oblongifolius* Ell.]...*R. pusillus* Poir.

9. Petals 5-7, bright yellow, 3-7 mm long; stamens 20-25; wet ground, chiefly in s. Ill., but extending northward to Fulton Co. May-June. [*R. texensis* Engelm.] ....
...........................*R. laxicaulis* (Torr. & Gray) Darby

8. Achenes compressed, the body 2 mm long, the subulate beak 1 mm long; head of achenes 5-8 mm in diameter; petals 5-7 mm long; stamens 30-50;

leaves lanceolate; plants perennial; swamps or
ditches, local, chiefly in s. Ill. June-Aug. ....
....*R. ambigens* Wats.

7. Basal leaves reniform or cordate, merely crenate (some
of the later ones often lobed or cleft) ; stem-leaves
cleft or lobed; achenes minutely beaked, in globose
heads.

10. Petals much longer than the sepals.

11. Basal leaves oval or ovate, not cordate; stamens in
3-5 series; sepals long-villous; prairies, n. Ill.;
rare, Jo Daviess, McHenry, and Winnebago
counties. May. Prairie Buttercup [*R. ovalis*
Raf.] ....*R. rhomboideus* Goldie

11. Basal leaves reniform or orbicular, cordate;
stamens in 1-2 series; sepals sparsely pilosulous;
sandstone ravines, rare, s. Ill.; Jackson and
Randolph counties, *R. H. Mohlenbrock* in 1954
and 1957. April-May. ....
...................................*R. harveyi* (A.Gray) Britt.

10. Petals somewhat shorter than the sepals; flowers less
than 1 cm in diameter; plant glabrous or nearly so;
moist ground, very common. Apr.-May. Small-
flowered Buttercup ....*R. abortivus* L.

6. Leaves all or nearly all lobed or divided.

12. Achenes muriculate; flowers axillary; waste ground;
native of Eur.; Jackson Co., *R. H. Mohlenbrock*
2437 in 1954 ....*R. parviflorus* L.

12. Achenes smooth (or sparsely tuberculate in *R. sardous*) ;
flowers mostly terminal.

13. Petals not longer than the sepals; flowers less than
1 cm in diameter.

14. Stem glabrous or nearly so, hollow; achenes
merely apiculate, in ellipsoid heads; along
ditches, locally nearly throughout Ill. May-
July ....*R. sceleratus* L.

14. Stem usually pubescent.

15. Basal leaves usually 3-lobed; woods, not com-
mon; chiefly s. Ill., n. to Shelby and
Cumberland counties. Apr.-May ....
..............................*R. micranthus* Nutt.

15. Basal leaves deeply parted or divided.

16. Leaf-divisions merely serrate; heads of
achenes globose, the achenes with
slender, hooked beaks; woods. Apr.-
June ....*R. recurvatus* Poir.

16. Leaf-divisions cleft or incised; heads of achenes ellipsoid, the achenes with short, nearly straight beaks; wet ground, not common. July-Aug. ....
...............................*R. pennsylvanicus* L.f.
13. Petals longer than the sepals; flowers 1.5-2.5 cm in diameter.
   17. Beak of the mature achene less than 1 mm long, recurved.
      18. Stem more or less cormose-thickened at base; leaves with the terminal division stalked; sepals reflexed; fields and roadsides, occasional; nat. from Eur.; May-July. Bulbous Buttercup. ....*R. bulbosus* L.
      18. Stem not swollen at base.
         19. Sepals reflexed; achenes usually low tuberculate; terminal leaflet often petiolulate; pastures, wet fields, and roadsides; adv. from Eur.; s. Ill. May ....
....*R. sardous* Crantz
         19. Sepals spreading; achenes smooth; terminal leaflet sessile; roadsides and fields; nat. from Eur. May-July. Tall Buttercup ....*R. acris* L.
   17. Beak of the mature achene 1 mm or more in length.
      20. Petals broadly obovate; plants stoloniferous.
         21. Beak of the achene curved; mature achene 2-2.5 mm in diameter; roadsides and fields, common; adv. from Eur. Apr.-June. Creeping Buttercup ....*R. repens* L.
         21. Beak nearly straight; mature achene 3-4 mm in diameter; wet woods, common. Apr.-June. Marsh Buttercup ....
...............................*R. septentrionalis* Poir.
      20. Petals oval, oblong, or narrowly obovate; achenes 2-2.5 mm in diameter; plants not stoloniferous.
         22. Stem strigose; leaf-lobes narrow; some of the roots tuberous-thickened; woods and meadows. Apr.-May. Tufted Buttercup [*R. illinoensis* Greene] ....
...............................*R. fascicularis* Muhl.
         22. Stem villous; leaf-lobes oval to oblanceolate; roots scarcely thickened; woods or roadsides; chiefly in s. Ill., but extending northward to Hancock, McLean,

and Champaign counties. Apr.-May.
Bristly Buttercup ....*R. hispidus* Michx.

10. Thalictrum L. — Meadow-rue

1. Leaflets glabrous on both surfaces.
   2. Leaflets thin, suborbicular in outline, obtusely 5- to 9-lobed;
      stem-leaves slender-petioled; rich woods. Apr.-May. Early
      Meadow-rue ....*T. dioicum* L.
   2. Leaflets thick, oval, sharply 3-lobed, revolute-margined; stem-
      leaves sessile or nearly so; moist thickets and hedge-rows.
      June-July ....*T. hypoglaucum* Rydb.
1. Leaflets glandular or short-pubescent beneath; stem-leaves sessile.
   3. Leaflets finely glandular with short-stipitate or sessile glands on
      the lower surface; woods and roadsides, local. May-June.
      Waxy Meadow-rue ....*T. revolutum* DC.
   3. Leaflets finely short-pubescent on the lower surface, not glandu-
      lar; moist ground, local. May-June. Purplish Meadow-rue
      ....*T. dasycarpum* Fisch. & Lall.

11. Trautvetteria Fisch. & Meyer — False Bugbane

T. caroliniensis (Walt.) Vail. Near Beardstown, Cass Co., *C. A.
Geyer* in 1842. June-July.

12. Anemone L.
(*Pulsatilla* Adans.)

1. Styles elongate, plumose; plant silky-villous; leaf-segments linear;
   sepals 5-7, bluish-purple to white, 2-3.5 cm long; prairie soil;
   n. Ill. Mar.-Apr. Pasque Flower [*A. patens* var. *wolfgangiana*
   sensu A.Gray, non (Besser) W.J.D. Koch] ......*A. ludoviciana* Nutt.
1. Styles shorter, glabrous or pubescent, not plumose; sepals white to
   purplish.
   2. Sepals 10-20, linear-elliptical, pubescent outside; stem 8-20 cm
      tall, arising from a small tuber; prairie soil, gravelly slopes,
      rocky banks or bluffs in the n. part of the state, extending
      southward to Pike, Menard, and Macon counties. Apr.-May.
      Carolina Anemone ....*A. caroliniana* Walt.
   2. Sepals 5 or 6; plants with a rhizome.
      3. Stem usually branched, several-flowered, 30-90 cm tall; sepals
         pubescent.
         4. Stem-leaves sessile; sepals 12-17 mm long, white; fruiting
            heads globose; achenes flat, wing-margined, orbicular,
            sparsely pubescent, the style 3 mm long; roadsides and
            open woods, common; s. to Jackson Co. May-July.
            Meadow Anemone [*A. pennsylvanica* L.] ..*A. canadensis* L.
         4. Stem-leaves stalked; sepals 8-10 mm long, greenish-white;
            achenes densely villous.

5. Fruiting heads cylindrical, more than twice as long as wide; style 1 mm long; leaf-divisions narrow, cuneate; roadsides and open woods in the n. half of the state, s. to Macoupin and Coles counties. May-July. Long-fruited Anemone ....*A. cylindrica* A.Gray

5. Fruiting heads ellipsoid, about twice as long as wide; style 1.5-2 mm long; leaf-divisions ovate or ovate-lanceolate; woods throughout Ill. June-Aug. Tall Anemone ....*A. virginiana* L.

3. Stem simple, one-flowered, 10-30 cm tall, from a slender rhizome; stem-leaves stalked; basal leaf solitary, appearing later than the flower; sepals glabrous; achenes pubescent, fusiform, the hooked beak 1-2 mm long; rich woods in n. Ill., extending southward to Kankakee and La Salle count-ties. Apr.-May. Wood Anemone [*A. nemorosa* of auth., non L.; *A. quinquefolia* var. *interior* Fern.] ....
....*A. quinquefolia* L.

13. **Anemonella** Spach

A. thalictroides (L.) Spach. Rue-anemone. Dry open woods, local. Apr.-May. Plants with petaloid stamens are found occasionally.

14. **Helleborus** L. — Hellebore

H. viridis L. A garden escape; native of Europe.

15. **Hepatica** Hill

1. Leaf-lobes acute or acutish; flowers varying from purplish to white; woods, not uncommon. Mar.-May. [*H. acuta* (Pursh) Britt.] ....*H. acutiloba* DC.

1. Leaf-lobes rounded at the apex; woods, n.e. Ill.; Cook, Du Page, Lake, McHenry, and Winnebago counties. [*H. triloba* sensu auth., non Chaix] ....*H. americana* (DC.) Ker

16. **Clematis** L.
(*Viorna* Reichenb.; *Atragene* L.)

1. Flowers solitary, nodding; sepals purplish.

2. Leaves conspicuously reticulate beneath; sepals thick, leathery, the tips recurved, marginless or only narrowly margined; fruiting styles glabrous or nearly so; moist woods and thickets, common. June-Aug. Leather-flower ....*C. pitcheri* Torr. & Gray

2. Leaves thin, not conspicuously reticulate.

3. Sepals thick, leathery, 1.5-2.5 cm long; fruiting styles plumose; thickets and stream banks, rare; Richland Co., *R. Ridgway* in 1910. June-July. [*Viorna ridgwayi* Standl.] ....*C. viorna* L.

3. Sepals thin, 3-4.5 cm long, with wide undulate or crisped
   margins; fruiting styles pubescent but not plumose; wet
   woods, not common; known from Alexander, Pulaski, and
   St. Clair counties ....*C. crispa* L.
1. Flowers panicled; sepals white, thin, spreading.
   4. Leaflets usually 3, thin, toothed or lobed; sepals 9-11 mm long;
      moist ground, locally nearly throughout Ill. July-Aug.
      Virgin's Bower ....*C. virginiana* L.
   4. Leaflets 5, entire, coriaceous; sepals 10-17 mm long; roadsides
      and borders of woods, occasional; known from Crawford,
      Jackson, and Peoria counties; native of e. Asia. Aug.-Oct.
      ....*C. dioscoreifolia* Lévl. & Van.

4. Cabombaceae A.Gray — Watershield Family

1. Leaves all peltate, entire, floating; stamens 12-18; carpels 4-18 ......1. *Brasenia*
1. Submersed leaves dissected; stamens 6; carpels 2-3 ....2. *Cabomba*

1. Brasenia Schreb. — Watershield

B. schreberi Gmel. Ponds and slow streams, rare. June-July.

2. Cabomba Aubl.

C. caroliniana A.Gray. Carolina Watershield. Ponds, rare; s. Ill.;
Mt. Carmel, Wabash Co., Oct. 12, 1876, *Schneck 40;* LaRue Swamp,
Union Co. May-Sept.

5. Nymphaeaceae DC. — Waterlily Family

1. Leaves oval; flowers yellow; sepals 5-7; petals 10-20, small filament-like
   ....1. *Nuphar*
1. Leaves orbicular; flowers white; sepals 4; petals numerous ....2. *Nymphaea*

1. Nuphar Sm.

1. Petioles round in cross-section; ponds and slow streams, occasional.
   June-Aug. Yellow Pond-lily ....*N. advena* Ait.
1. Petioles flattened; ponds, rare; n. Ill., Cook and Lake counties.
   June-Aug. Variegated Pond-lily ....*N. variegatum* Engelm.

2. Nymphaea L. — Waterlily

1. Flower not fragrant, 10-25 cm in diameter; petals spatulate;
   rhizome with numerous self-detaching tubers; seeds 3-4.5 mm
   long, globose-ovoid; ponds and slow streams, rare. June-Aug.
   White Waterlily ....*N. tuberosa* Paine
1. Flower very fragrant, 6-12 cm in diameter; petals elliptical; rhizome without tubers; seeds 1.5-2.5 mm long, ellipsoid; lakes and
   shallow ponds, rare. June-Sept. Fragrant Waterlily ....
   ....*N. odorata* Ait.

6. Nelumbonaceae Lindl. — Lotus Family

1. Nelumbo Adans. — American Lotus

(*Nelumbium* Juss.)

N. lutea (Willd.) Pers. Shallow water and muddy shores, local. July-Aug.

7. Ceratophyllaceae A.Gray — Hornwort Family

1. Ceratophyllum L. — Hornwort

1. Leaf-divisions linear, rather rigid, flattened, serrate; achenes with a spine on each side at the base; ponds and slow streams, not uncommon ....*C. demersum* L.
1. Leaf-divisions filiform, flaccid, entire or with a few short bristles; achenes with 3-5 spines on each side; ponds and slow streams, local; Hancock, Henderson, Kankakee, and Ogle counties ....*C. echinatum* A.Gray

8. Berberidaceae Torr. & Gray — Barberry Family

1. Berberis L. — Barberry

1. Leaves entire; flowers usually solitary, or 2-4; spines usually simple; petals notched; commonly cultivated and occasionally escaped to waste ground and woodlands; native of Japan. Apr.-May. Japanese Barberry ....*B. thunbergii* DC.
1. Leaves spinulose-serrate; flowers in pendulous racemes.
    2. Leaves with 2-10 teeth on each side; twigs brownish or purplish; racemes few-flowered; petals notched; fruit 7-8 mm long; Spring Lake, Tazewell Co., *G. C. Curran* in 1924. American Barberry ....*B. canadensis* Mill.
    2. Leaves with 13-25 teeth on each side; twigs gray; racemes many-flowered; petals entire; fruit 8-12 mm long; escaped from cult. to pastures, edges of woods and waste places, occasional; native of Eur. Apr.-May. European Barberry ....*B. vulgaris* L.

9. Podophyllaceae DC. — Mayapple Family

1. Leaves simple; flowers solitary, white; petals 6-8.
    2. Leaves 7- 9-lobed; berry yellowish-green, pulpy, 4-5 cm long ....1. *Podophyllum*
    2. Leaves 2-cleft; capsule obconical, 1.5-2 cm long, opening at the top by a lid ....2. *Jeffersonia*
1. Leaf ternately compound; flowers yellowish-green, in a terminal panicle; sepals 6; petals 6, small, thick, spatulate, gland-like; seeds bluish-black, berry-like, about 8 mm in diameter ....3. *Caulophyllum*

1. Podophyllum L. — Mayapple

P. peltatum L. Woods, common. Apr.-May.

2. **Jeffersonia** Bart. — Twinleaf

J. diphylla (L.) Pers. Woods, local. Apr.-May.

3. **Caulophyllum** Michx. — Blue Cohosh

C. thalictroides (L.) Michx. Woods, common. Apr-May.

10. Menispermaceae DC. — Moonseed Family

1. Leaf-blades usually as broad as or broader than long; petioles 3-20 cm long; drupe black.
  2. Leaf-blades reniform in outline, slightly peltate near the base, palmately 3- to 7-angled or shallowly lobed, dark green and glabrous above, paler and sparsely pilosulous along the veins beneath; panicles 2-6 cm long; petals 6-9; sepals 4-10; stigma flabellate; stamens 12-18, or 24; drupe bluish-black, about 1 cm in diameter ....1. *Menispermum*
  2. Leaf-blades deeply palmately lobed, cordate at the base, the lobes acuminate; panicles 10-20 cm long; sepals 9; petals 0; stamens 9 or 12; stigma radiate; drupe black, ovoid, 2-2.5 cm long ....2. *Calycocarpum*
1. Leaf-blades usually somewhat longer than broad, ovate or deltoid, sinuately lobed or entire, softly pubescent beneath; petioles 1-5 cm long; petals, sepals, and stamens each 6, or the stamens in the pistillate flowers reduced or lacking; stigma subulate; drupe red, 6-8 mm long ....
....3. *Cocculus*

1. Menispermum L. — Moonseed

M. canadense L. In alluvial soil in woods, thickets, or along fences, common. May-June.

2. Calycocarpum Nutt.

C. lyoni (Pursh) Nutt. Cupseed. Moist thickets, rich woods, and river banks, s. Ill., rare. June-July.

3. Cocculus DC.

C. carolinus (L.) D.C. Carolina Snailseed. Banks of streams, s. Ill., rare. July-Aug.

11. Violaceae DC. — Violet Family

1. Corolla merely gibbous at the base; sepals not auricled; stamens united into a sheath ....1. *Hybanthus*
1. Corolla spurred; sepals more or less auricled at the base; stamens distinct or slightly cohering ....2. *Viola*

1. Hybanthus Jacq. — Green Violet

H. concolor (Forst.) Spreng. Moist ravines and rich woods, rare; generally distrib. throughout Ill., except the northern counties. Apr.-June. [*Cubelium concolor* (Forst.) Raf.].

2. Viola L. — Violet

1. Plants acaulescent, or without manifest stems at flowering time, the leaves and pedicels arising directly from the rhizome or from stolons.

2. Rhizome short, thick, stout (3-10 mm in diameter); petals violet to white.
   3. Leaves more or less lobed or dissected.
      4. Leaves dissected into narrow divisions.
         5. Petals all glabrous within, lilac, or the upper two dark violet; style clavate, beakless, oblique at apex; plants without cleistogamous flowers; prairies and borders of woods, locally throughout Ill. Apr.-June. Bird-foot Violet ....*V. pedata* L.
         5. Lateral petals hirsute within; corolla violet; style capitate, with a conical beak on the lower side; plants producing cleistogamous flowers; prairies or dry open woods, locally throughout Ill., except the southern counties. May. Prairie Violet [*V. delphinifolia* Nutt.] ....*V. pedatifida* Don
      4. Leaves usually lobed or cleft; plants producing cleistogamous flowers.
        6. Leaves all 5- to 11-lobed or -parted.
          7. Plants glabrous or nearly so; gravelly areas; Peoria Co., *V. H. Chase* ....*V. viarum* Pollard
          7. Plants pubescent; woods and prairie soil in the n. half of the state. Apr.-May ....*V. bernardi* Greene
        6. Leaves usually of two kinds, the earliest and latest not lobed, the other 5- to 7-parted; woods, locally throughout Ill. Apr.-May. [*V. triloba* var. *dilatata* (Ell.) Brainerd] ....*V. falcata* Greene
   3. Leaves merely crenate-serrate, not lobed.
      8. Leaves ovate-cordate to reniform or deltoid.
        9. Leaves glabrous or nearly so.
         10. Hairs of the lateral petals not clavate; cleistogamous flowers on short prostrate or ascending pedicels.
          11. Leaves ovate-cordate to reniform, acute or obtuse; flowers violet-purple (except albinos).
           12. Leaf-blades obtuse or obtusish, broadly cordate or reniform at maturity; spurred petal glabrous or nearly so within; cleistogamous flowers on short prostrate pedicels; capsules 10-15 mm long; seeds dark brown.
            13. Flowers violet-purple; capsules green; woods and roadsides, the common species throughout Ill. Apr.-May. Butterfly Violet ....*V. papilionacea* Pursh
            13. Flowers grayish white with violet veins on the lower petals; capsules purplish; occasional in disturbed ground; a recent migrant from s.e. U.S., now known to

occur in Ill. as far north as Bureau Co.
Apr.-May. Confederate Violet ....
....*V. priceana* Pollard

12. Leaf-blades acutish, narrowly cordate, usually
longer than broad; spurred petal hirsute
within; cleistogamous flowers on ascending
pedicels; seeds light brown; moist soil, not
common. May-June. Woodland Blue Violet
....*V. affinis* LeConte

11. Leaves deltoid, acuminate; petals lilac; spurred
petal glabrous within; open woods. Apr.-May
....*V. missouriensis* Greene

10. Hairs of the lateral petals conspicuously clavate-
capitate; cleistogamous flowers on slender erect
pedicels; wet ground, not common. May-June.
Marsh Blue Violet ....*V. cucullata* Ait.

9. Leaves decidedly pubescent; petals violet or lavender,
rarely white; sepals ciliolate; woods, common throughout Ill. Apr.-May. Downy Blue Violet ....
....*V. sororia* Willd.

8. Leaves sagittate-lanceolate.

14. Leaves glabrous or nearly so, rather long-petioled,
lanceolate, often dilated and incised at base; open
woods. Apr.-May. Arrow-leaved Violet ....
....*V. sagittata* Ait.

14. Leaves pubescent, mostly short-petioled, ovate, crenate;
hillsides, not common; chiefly in the n. half of the
state. Apr.-May. Sand Violet [*V. ovata* Nutt.] ....
....*V. fimbriatula* Sm.

2. Rhizome slender (1-2 mm in diameter); plants usually stoloniferous.

15. Flowers small, white, the lower petals purple-veined; style
not hooked; seeds brown or black; native species.

16. Leaves tapering or truncate at base.

17. Leaves lanceolate or elliptical-lanceolate, several times
as long as broad and usually less than 2 cm wide,
tapering at the base; borders of swamps, local; s.
to Wabash Co. May-June. Lance-leaved Violet
....*V. lanceolata* L.

17. Leaves ovate, not more than twice as long as wide,
usually more than 2 cm broad, truncate at base;
borders of swamps; Kankakee Co. May-June.
Primrose Violet ....*V. primulifolia* L.

16. Leaves cordate, glabrous; pedicels usually somewhat
longer than the leaves; springy ground, rare; Cook,
Lake, Ogle, and Winnebago counties. Apr.-May.
Smooth White Violet [*V. blanda* sensu auth., non
Willd.] ....*V. pallens* (Banks) Brainerd

15. Flowers large (1-2 cm broad), violet, or sometimes white, very fragrant; style hooked; leaves broadly ovate, cordate, crenate, finely pubescent; stolons rooting at the nodes; seeds cream colored; roadsides and waste places, occasional; introd. from Eur. and often cultivated. Apr.-June. Sweet Violet ....*V. odorata* L.
1. Plants caulescent at flowering time; flowers axillary.
  18. Plants perennial; stipules toothed or entire, bract-like.
    19. Petals yellow.
      20. Plants nearly glabrous; basal leaves usually present at flowering time; seeds 2-2.5 mm long; woods, common. Apr.-May. Common Yellow Violet [*V. pensylvanica* Michx.; *V. scabriuscula* Schw.] ....*V. eriocarpa* Schw.
      20. Plants decidedly pubescent; basal leaves usually absent at flowering time; seeds 2.6-3 mm long; moist woods; chiefly n. Ill.; also Pulaski Co. Apr.-May. Downy Yellow Violet ....*V. pubescens* Ait.
    19. Petals violet or white.
      21. Stipules entire, scarious; petals violet or white; woods, rare. Apr.-June. Canada Violet [*V. canadensis* sensu auth., non L.] ....*V. rugulosa* Greene
      21. Stipules dentate or fimbriate.
        22. Petals creamy-white; sepals ciliolate; upper leaves acute; stipules 1.5-2.5 cm long; alluvial soil, common; apparently absent from the n.w. counties. Apr.-June. Cream Violet ....*V. striata* Ait.
        22. Petals pale violet; sepals glabrous; leaves obtuse; stipules usually less than 1.5 cm long; woods, rare; Cook Co., A. Chase. Apr.-May. Dog Violet ....*V. conspersa* Reichenb.
  18. Plants annual; stipules large, pectinate; sandy soil in fields and open woods, common. Apr.-June. Wild Pansy. Johnny-jump-up ....*V. rafinesquii* Greene

12. **Cistaceae** Horan. — Rockrose Family

1. Low shrubs; leaves scale-like; petals 5, yellow, fugacious; styles slender, elongate ....1. *Hudsonia*
1. Herbs; leaves not scale-like.
  2. Petals 5, yellow, fugacious; style short; pubescence stellate ....2. *Helianthemum*
  2. Petals 3, greenish or red, persistent; style none; pubescence not stellate ....3. *Lechea*

1. **Hudsonia** L.

H. tomentosa Nutt. Sandy soil, local; Fulton, Jo Daviess, and Lee counties. May-July.

2. Helianthemum Mill. — Frostweed

1. Petaliferous flowers 5-12, pale yellow, in a short terminal cymose raceme, their capsules 3-5 mm in diameter; seeds reticulate; sandy soil in open woods, local. June-July. [*H. majus* sensu Bickn., non (L.) BSP.] ....*H. bicknellii* Fern.
1. Petaliferous flowers solitary (or rarely 2), bright yellow, their capsules 6-9 mm in diameter; seeds papillose; in similar habitats. June. [*Lechea major* L.; *Cistus canadensis* L.; *H. majus* (L.) BSP.] ....*H. canadense* (L.) Michx.

3. Lechea L. — Pinweed

1. Stem with spreading (villous) pubescence; leaves of the basal shoots oval; stem leaves oval, 10-25 mm long, 6-12 mm wide; sandy soil. July-Aug. ....*L. villosa* Ell.
1. Stem with appressed (strigose) pubescence, or sometimes nearly glabrous.
    2. The narrow outer sepals equalling or exceeding the inner ones.
        3. Stems 25-70 cm tall; leaves narrowly elliptical; sandy soil. July-Aug. ....*L. minor* L.
        3. Stems usually 10-20 cm tall; leaves linear; sandy or sterile soil in woods. July-Aug. [*L. tenuifolia* var. *occidentalis* Hodgdon] ....*L. tenuifolia* Michx.
    2. The narrow outer sepals shorter than or equalling the inner ones.
        4. Plants pale green, finely canescent; panicle strict, virgate; sandy soil; n. Ill. July-Aug. ....*L. stricta* Leggett
        4. Plants dark green, more or less pubescent, but not canescent.
            5. Panicle strict, virgate; capsules globose, 2-3 mm in diameter; sandy soil, rare. July-Aug. ....*L. intermedia* Leggett
            5. Panicle-branches spreading; capsules ellipsoid, 1-1.5 mm in diameter; sandy soil, known from Cook, Iroquois, Kankakee, Lake, Will, and Winnebago counties. July-Aug. [*L. moniliformis* Bickn.] ....*L. leggettii* Britt. & Hollick

13. Papaveraceae B. Juss. — Poppy Family

1. Flowers white or whitish.
    2. Petals none; sepals 2, cream-colored ....1. *Macleaya*
    2. Petals 4-15, white; sepals 2 or 3.
        3. Petals usually 8 or more, fugacious; leaves prickly; juice red ....
        ....2. *Sanguinaria*
        3. Petals 4-6; leaves with prickly teeth; juice yellow ....3. *Argemone*
1. Flowers not white.
    4. Leaves ternately dissected; capsules long and slender ....4. *Eschscholtzia*
    4. Leaves pinnatifid; capsules linear, ovoid, or ellipsoid.
        5. Leaves prickly; capsules ellipsoid, prickly ....3. *Argemone*
        5. Leaves not prickly; capsules not ellipsoid, glabrous or bristly-hirsute.
            6. Flowers yellow; leaves pinnatifid; capsules dehiscent from the base; juice yellow.

7. Petals 18-25 mm long; buds erect, ovoid; capsules ovoid, acute
   at each end, bristly-hirsute ....5. *Stylophorum*
7. Petals 8-13 mm long; buds nodding, obovoid; capsules linear,
   glabrous ....6. *Chelidonium*
6. Flowers red or pink; juice milky; capsules globose or pyriform,
   opening by 4-20 tooth-like lids under the margin of the discoid
   stigma ....7. *Papaver*

1. **Macleaya** R.Br. — Plume Poppy

M. cordata (Willd.) R.Br. Introd. from e. Asia; cult. and rarely
persistent; has been collected in Cook and Henry counties.

2. **Sanguinaria** L. — Bloodroot

S. canadensis L. Woods, common. Mar.-Apr.

3. **Argemone** L. — Prickly Poppy
1. Flowers sessile; petals orange, yellow, or creamy; sparingly escaped
   from gardens to roadsides and waste places; Henderson and
   Mason counties. June-Sept. Mexican Poppy ....*A. mexicana* L.
1. Flowers pedunculate; petals white.
   2. Peduncles leafy; adv. from w. U.S.; Lawrence, Morgan, and
      Whiteside counties. June-Sept. ....*A. intermedia* Sweet
   2. Peduncles leafless; adv. in Ill.; cultivated and occasionally spon-
      taneous. White Prickly Poppy ....*A. alba* Lestib. f.

4. **Eschscholtzia** Cham. — California Poppy

E. californica Cham. Cult., and rarely spontaneous; native of California; Kane and Wabash counties.

5. **Stylophorum** Nutt. — Celandine Poppy

S. diphyllum (Michx.) Nutt. Woods, not common; s. Ill. Apr.-
June.

6. **Chelidonium** L. — Celandine

C. majus L. Occasionally found in waste places, roadsides, and
woods, usually near towns; nat. from Eur. May-Aug.

7. **Papaver** L. — Poppy
1. Plants glaucous, glabrous; leaves lobed, clasping the stem; capsules
   globose; waste places; introd. from Eur. June-Aug. Opium
   Poppy ....*P. somniferum* L.
1. Plants hirsute, not glaucous; leaves pinnate, tapering to the peti-
   oled base; capsules obovoid, turbinate, or clavate.
   2. Capsules obovoid or turbinate; waste places; introd. from Eur.
      May-July. Corn Poppy ....*P. rhoeas* L.
   2. Capsules clavate; introd. from Eur.; Wabash Co. ......*P. dubium* L.

14. **Fumariaceae** DC. — Fumitory Family

1. Corolla with each of the two outer petals spurred or saccate at the base; capsules several-seeded ....1. *Dicentra*
1. Corolla with only one petal spurred.
    2. Flowers yellow or pinkish; capsules linear, several-seeded, dehiscent; style persistent ....2. *Corydalis*
    2. Flowers deep purple, tipped with crimson; pods globose, 1-seeded, indehiscent, glabrous, minutely tuberculate; style deciduous ......3. *Fumaria*

1. **Dicentra** Bernh.

1. Corolla with 2 divergent spurs; inner petals minutely crested; flowers not fragrant; stem from a bulb-like corm; woods, common. Mar.-May. Dutchman's-breeches ....
   ....*D. cucullaria* (L.) Bernh.
1. Corolla heart-shaped, the spurs short and rounded; crests of the inner petals conspicuous, projecting; flowers fragrant; stem from a short horizontal rhizome bearing small whitish or yellowish corms; woods, usually less common than the preceding species, beginning to flower a week or ten days later. Squirrel-corn ....
   ....*D. canadensis* (Goldie) Walp.

2. **Corydalis** Vent.

1. Flowers rose, tipped with yellow, 12-15 mm long; spur short, rounded, less than ¼ the length of the corolla; capsules 3-4 cm long, the pedicels 6-10 mm long; rocky woods, Cook, La Salle, and Ogle counties. May-Aug. Pink Corydalis ....
   ....*C. sempervirens* (L.) Pers.
1. Flowers yellow throughout; plants 10-30 cm tall.
    2. Flowers 5-9 mm long; outer petals crested on the back.
        3. Outer petals dentate; capsules pendulous, on slender pedicels 1-1.5 cm long; seeds puncticulate, sharp-margined; moist woods, local. Apr.-May. Pale Corydalis [*C. aurea* of auth., not Willd.] ....*C. flavula* (Raf.) DC.
        3. Outer petals entire; capsules erect or ascending, the pedicels 2-3 mm long; seeds smooth, round-margined; woods, local. May-July. Small-flowered Corydalis ....
        ....*C. micrantha* (Engelm.) A.Gray
    2. Flowers 12-16 mm long; outer petals not crested.
        4. Capsules spreading or pendent, torulose; bracts lanceolate; seeds smooth; gravelly soil, rare; Cook, La Salle, Ogle, and Winnebago counties. May-Aug. Golden Corydalis ....
        ....*C. aurea* Willd.
    4. Capsules erect or ascending.
        5. Bracts ovate-lanceolate; seeds smooth; rocky woods, Cook, Henderson, Kankakee, Lee, and Peoria counties. Apr.-May ....*C. montana* Engelm.

5. Bracts lanceolate; seeds finely pitted; Meredosia, Morgan
Co., *D. H. Thompson* in 1928 ....
...................................*C. campestris* (Britt.) Buchh. & Palmer

3. Fumaria L. — Fumitory

F. officinalis L. Waste places, occasional; native of Eur. May-Aug.

15. Droseraceae S.F.Gray — Sundew Family

1. Drosera L. — Sundew

1. Leaf-blades suborbicular; seeds fusiform, striate, glossy, 1-1.5 mm
long; bogs, Lake and Ogle counties. July-Sept. Round-
leaved Sundew ....*D. rotundifolia* L.
1. Leaf-blades linear-spatulate; seeds ellipsoid, papillose, 0.7-1 mm
long; bogs, rare; Cook and Kankakee counties. July-Sept.
Long-leaved Sundew [*D. longifolia* of auth.] ....
....*D. intermedia* Hayne

16. Resedaceae S.F.Gray — Mignonette Family

1. Reseda L. — Mignonette

R. alba L. Rarely escaped from gardens; native of Europe.

17. Capparidaceae Lindl. — Caper Family

1. Petals entire, or notched at the apex.
2. Petals notched; pod sessile or nearly so on its pedicel; stamens more
than 6 ....1. *Polanisia*
2. Petals entire; pod long-stipitate on its pedicel; stamens 6 ....2. *Cleome*
1. Petals laciniate, unequal; stamens 6-14; pod long-stipitate on its pedicel
....3. *Cristatella*

1. Polanisia Raf.

1. Petals whitish, 4-5 mm long; stamens 9-12; sandy soil, often along
railroads. July-Aug. Clammyweed [*P. graveolens* Raf.] ....
....*P. dodecandra* (L.) DC.
1. Petals pale yellow, 8-10 mm long; stamens 12-16; sandy soil, not
common; probably spread eastward into Ill. along railroads.
June-Aug. ....*P. trachysperma* T. & G.

2. Cleome L.

1. Plants glabrous; dry soil; adv. from w. U.S.; Fayette, Henderson,
Henry, Jackson, Sangamon, and Wabash counties. July-Sept.
[*C. integrifolia* T. & G.] ....*C. serrulata* Pursh
1. Plants pubescent; escaped from gardens; Jackson Co. ....
....*C. speciosissima* Deppe

3. Cristatella Nutt.

C. jamesii T. & G. Sandy soil; Jo Daviess and Mason counties.
June-Aug.

18. Cruciferae B.Juss. — Mustard Family

1. Petals yellow, yellowish, or cream (sometimes fading whitish).
  2. Pods several times longer than wide.
    3. Pubescence of simple hairs or plants glabrous.
      4. Pods with a distinct beak.
        5. Seeds in a single row in each locule; pods terete or slightly angular.
          6. Racemes leafy-bracted; leaves pinnatifid with obtuse lobes; seeds oval ....4. *Erucastrum*
          6. Racemes bractless; seeds subglobose ....5. *Brassica*
        5. Seeds more or less in two rows in each locule; leaves mostly basal, oblanceolate, sinuate-dentate or pinnatifid; pods flattened, 2.5-4 cm long, 2 mm wide ....6. *Diplotaxis*
      4. Pods merely tipped with the style or stigma.
        7. Leaves lobed to pinnatifid; petals yellow.
          8. Pods 4-angled; seeds in 1 row in each locule; valves of the pod 1-nerved ....7. *Barbarea*
          8. Pods terete or nearly so.
            9. Valves nerveless; seeds in 2 rows in each locule ....8. *Rorippa*
            9. Valves of the pod with 1-3 nerves; seeds in 1 row in each locule ....9. *Sisymbrium*
        7. Leaves entire, cordate-clasping the stem, glabrous, glaucous; petals cream, 8-10 mm long; pods linear, ascending, 8-10 cm long ....11. *Conringia*
    3. Pubescence (at least of the leaves) of branched hairs.
      10. Leaves entire to dentate; pubescence of appressed, 2-branched hairs which appear as if attached by the middle; petals more than 3 mm long; pods 4-angled ....13. *Erysimum*
      10. Leaves bipinnatifid or tripinnatifid, usually finely dissected, sparsely pubescent with short, branched hairs; petals 2-3 mm long; pods terete or nearly so ....14. *Descurainia*
  2. Pods short, not more than three times as long as wide.
    11. Pods flattened parallel to the broad septum, orbicular, 3 mm broad, shallowly notched at the apex; leaves linear-spatulate, entire, densely stellate-canescent ....24. *Alyssum*
    11. Pods turgid, not compressed, or only slightly so, ellipsoid, obovoid, or globose.
      12. Leaves pinnately parted or lobed; pods ellipsoid ....8. *Rorippa*
      12. Leaves entire or toothed, and except in *Lesquerella*, sagittate-clasping the stem.
        13. Pods globose ....27. *Lesquerella*
        13. Pods obovoid ....28. *Camelina*
1. Petals white, pink, or purple (rarely absent), never yellow.
  14. Pods several times longer than wide (a silique).
    15. Pods indehiscent, cylindrical, several-seeded, with pith between the seeds but no true partitions, breaking at maturity into 1-seeded segments; petals purple or white.
      16. Upper part of fruit thicker and longer than lower.
        17. Pods 2-seeded, 2-jointed ....1. *Cakile*
        17. Pods several-seeded, several-jointed ....2. *Raphanus*
      16. Upper part of fruit consisting of a flattened beak ....3. *Eruca*
    15. Pods dehiscent by 2 valves, without transverse partitions.
      18. Pods more or less flattened parallel to the septum.

19. Leaves palmately cleft and divided ....16. *Dentaria*
19. Leaves otherwise.
  20. Pubescence of simple hairs or none; leaves simple or pinnately divided; valves of the pod nerveless, elastically dehiscent and recurving at maturity ....
    ....18. *Cardamine*
  20. Pubescence, at least in part, of branched hairs.
    21. Pods strongly flattened, 2-15 mm long; leaves chiefly basal (except *D. brachycarpa*) ....15. *Draba*
    21. Pods slightly flattened, or nearly terete, more than 1.5 cm long; stem leafy ....19. *Arabis*
18. Pods terete or tetragonal, not flattened.
  22. Valves of the pod conspicuously keeled, 3-nerved; leaves deltoid-cordate, dentate, petiolate; plant with garlic odor
    ....10. *Alliaria*
  22. Valves of the pod rounded or flat.
    23. Leaves simple, pinnately lobed to entire.
      24. Petals 1.5-2 cm long, purple, or rarely white; leaves ovate-lanceolate, denticulate ....12. *Hesperis*
      24. Petals less than 1.5 cm long.
        25. Petals purple; plant glabrous; lower leaves sometimes pinnatifid at the base, dentate, the upper ones lanceolate, dentate, tapering to an auriculate base; pods 2-3 cm long; stigma entire ....
        ....17. *Iodanthus*
        25. Petals white; plant sparsely pubescent with forked hairs; pods 1-1.5 cm long; stigma 2-lobed ....
        ....20. *Arabidopsis*
    23. Leaves odd-pinnate with 1-11 roundish or oval leaflets; petals white; mature pods 1-2 cm long, somewhat curved; aquatic glabrous perennial ....21. *Nasturtium*
14. Pods short, usually not more than three times as long as wide (a silicle).
  26. Pubescence, if any, of simple hairs.
    27. Pods terete, ellipsoid, or subglobose, not flattened. plants glabrous.
      28. Basal leaves smaller, often finely divided (if in water); pods 1-loculed, the style 2-3 mm long ....22. *Neobeckia*
      28. Basal leaves 15-30 cm long, oval or ovate, crenate; root large, thick, pungent; pods 2-loculed, seldom maturing, the style 0.5 mm long ....23. *Armoracia*
    27. Pods more or less compressed or flattened.
      29. Plants grayish-pubescent; upper leaves ovate, clasping, dentate, the lower oblanceolate; pods broadly ovate, indehiscent, papillose, 4 mm broad, notched at the base, the style 1-2 mm long ....29. *Cardaria*
      29. Plants green; pubescent or glabrous; pods suborbicular, dehiscent, notched at the apex.
        30. Pods 2-seeded, less than 5 mm broad; branches puberulent ....30. *Lepidium*
        30. Pods several-seeded, 1-1.5 cm broad; plants glabrous ......
        ....31. *Thlaspi*
26. Pubescence of forked or stellate hairs, at least on the stem.

31. Petals deeply bifid; pods ellipsoid to nearly globose, scarcely
  flattened; seeds several in each locule, winged ....26. *Berteroa*
31. Petals entire or nearly so; pods strongly flattened.
  32. Pods triangular ....32. *Capsella*
  32. Pods rounded or nearly so.
    33. Plants densely stellate-pubescent ....24. *Alyssum*
    33. Plants with 2-pointed hairs ....25. *Lobularia*

1. **Cakile** Mill. — Sea Rocket

C. edentula (Bigel.) Hook. Shore of L. Michigan, not common.
July-Sept. [*C. americana* Nutt.]

2. **Raphanus** L. — Radish

1. Pods conspicuously torulose and longitudinally ridged when dry,
  3-4 mm thick; petals yellowish, spatulate, clawed, veiny, fading
  whitish or purplish; fields and waste ground; nat. from Eur.
  June-Aug. Wild Radish ....*R. raphanistrum* L.
1. Pods smooth, not torulose, 5-9 mm thick; petals purple, less commonly white, 1.5-2 cm long, conspicuously veined; fields and
  waste ground; escaped from cult. May-Sept. Radish ....
  ....*R. sativus* L.

3. **Eruca** Adans. — Rocket Salad

E. sativa Mill. Nat. from Eur.; Peoria Co. *F. E. McDonald* in
1907.

4. **Erucastrum** (DC.) Presl — Dog Mustard

E. gallicum (Willd.) O. E. Schulz. Waste ground; adv. from Eur.
June-Oct.

5. **Brassica** L.

1. Leaves not clasping the stem.
  2. Pods hispid, 3 cm long, with a flattened beak half the length of
    the pod; fields and waste places; nat. from Eur. Apr.-Aug.
    White Mustard [*B. alba* sensu auth., non Gilib.; *Sinapis alba*
    L.]...*B. hirta* Moench
  2. Pods glabrous.
    3. Pods ascending at maturity, 3-5 cm long, 2-3 mm thick, the
      beak 4-8 mm long; pedicels ascending, 6-10 mm long.
      4. Beak of the mature pod flattened, nearly as wide as the
        body, usually containing one seed in the basal part;
        pedicels stout, 4-6 mm long; fields and waste places; nat.
        from Eur. May-Sept. Field Mustard [*B. arvensis*
        Rabenh., non L.] ....*B. kaber* (DC.) L. C. Wheeler
      4. Beak of the mature pod terete, seedless; pedicels slender,
        7-10 mm long; fields and waste places; nat. from Eur-
        asia. July-Sept. Indian Mustard ......*B. juncea* (L.) Cosson
    3. Pods erect, 1-1.5 cm long, 1-1.5 mm thick; beak terete, 1.5-2
      mm long; pedicels erect, 3-5 mm long; fields and waste
      places; nat. from Eur. Apr.-Sept. Black Mustard ....
      ....*B. nigra* (L.) Koch

1. Upper leaves sessile and clasping by the auriculate base.
  5. Plants glaucous, usually partly hispid when young.
    6. Roots slender; leaves not fleshy; fields and waste places; nat.
      from Eur. Apr.-Oct. Yellow Mustard ....*B. campestris* L.
    6. Roots thicker; leaves fleshy; fields and waste places; introd.
      from Eur. Cabbage ....*B. oleracea* L.
  5. Plants not glaucous; roots thickened; persisting occasionally
    from cult. Turnip ....*B. rapa* L.

6. **Diplotaxis** DC. — Sand Rocket

D. muralis (L.) DC. Waste places, occasional; adv. from Eur.
June-Aug.

7. **Barbarea** R.Br. — Wintercress

1. Petals bright yellow, 6-8 mm long; basal leaves with 2-8 lateral
  leaflets; mature pods 1.5-2.5 cm long, the pedicel not as thick
  as the pod; roadsides, fields, and waste places, very common;
  nat. from Eur. Apr.-June. Common Wintercress [*B. stricta*
  sensu auth., non Andrz.] ....*B. vulgaris* R.Br.
1. Petals pale yellow, 4-6 mm long; basal leaves with 8-16 lateral
  leaflets; mature pods 5-6 cm long; pedicels about as thick as
  the pods; waste places; nat. from Eur. Early Wintercress [*B.
  praecox* R.Br.] ....*B. verna* (Mill.) Aschers.

8. **Rorippa** Scop. — Yellow Cress

1. Petals 3-5 mm. long; perennials with rhizomes.
  2. Leaves pinnately divided, not auriculate at base; pods linear,
    the style 0.5 mm long; moist ground; nat. from Eur. May-
    Sept. ....*R. sylvestris* (L.) Besser
  2. Leaves pinnately lobed, auriculate at base; mature pods cylin-
    drical, the style 2-3 mm long; river banks. Apr.-Aug. ....
    ....*R. sinuata* (Nutt.) Hitchc.
1. Petals 1-2 mm long; leaves with small auricles at base; style on
  mature pods 0.5-1 mm long; annual or biennial native species.
  3. Pedicels short, not more than 1-2 mm long; pods 6-10 mm long,
    ellipsoid; stem glabrous; median and upper leaves shallowly
    toothed or sinuate; muddy creek banks, or in fields, common.
    May-Oct. ....*R. sessiliflora* (Nutt.) Hitchc.
  3. Pedicels and pod usually 3-5 mm long; leaves usually pinnatifid,
    especially toward the base.
    4. Stem and leaves hirsutulous; pods 1-2 times as long as wide
      and slightly shorter than the pedicel; wet ground, rare;
      Cook Co., *E. J. Hill, A. Chase;* McHenry Co., *W. A. Nason*
      ....*R. hispida* (Desv.) Britt.
    4. Stem and leaves glabrous; pods about twice as long as wide,
      and longer than the pedicels; wet ground or in water,
      common throughout Ill. May-Oct. [*R. palustris* (L.)
      Besser] ....*R. islandica* (Oeder) Borbás

9. Sisymbrium L.

1. Pods 1-1.5 cm long, on very short pedicels closely appressed to the stem; petals 3 mm long; stem divaricately branched above; leaves pinnatifid into 5-13 lobes; waste ground, common; nat. from Eur. May-Sept. Hedge Mustard ......*S. officinale* (L.) Scop.
1. Pods 3-10 cm long, spreading or ascending on slender pedicels; petals 5-8 mm long.
    2. Lower part of stem spreading-hirsute; upper leaves with linear divisions; petals pale yellow, 6-8 mm long; pods 7-10 cm long, the ascending pedicels 5-8 mm long; a common weed in fields and waste places; nat. from Eur. May-Aug. Tumble Mustard ....*S. altissimum* L.
    2. Lower part of the stem retrorsely hirsute; upper leaves with lanceolate divisions; petals bright yellow, 5-6 mm long; pods 3 cm long, on spreading pedicels 1-1.5 cm long; fields and waste places; adv. from Eur. May-Nov. ....*S. loeselii* L.

10. Alliaria B.Ehrh. — Garlic Mustard

A. officinalis Andrz. Roadsides, waste places, and in woods; nat. from Eur.; known to occur in Carroll, Piatt, Sangamon, Tazewell, and Winnebago counties. May-June.

11. Conringia Adans. — Hare's-ear Mustard

C. orientalis (L.) Dum. Waste places, occasional; adv. from Eur. May-July.

12. Hesperis L. — Rocket

H. matronalis L. Roadsides, waste places, cultivated ground; escaped from cult.; introd. from Eur. June-July.

13. Erysimum L.

1. Petals 1.5-2 cm long; pods 4-8 cm long, 2 mm thick; sandy soil; Cass, Fulton, Hancock, La Salle, Mason, and Menard counties. May-June. Western Wallflower [*E. arkansanum* Nutt.] ....
....*E. asperum* (Nutt.) DC.
1. Petals 4-8 mm long.
    2. Fruiting pedicels 3-8 mm long; petals 6-8 mm long.
        3. Pods 6-8 cm long, divaricately spreading; leaves mostly repand-dentate or denticulate; waste places, roadsides, or fields; adv. from Eur. Apr.-June ....*E. repandum* L.
        3. Pods 3.5-4.5 cm long, nearly erect; leaves entire; dry ground, not common; chiefly in the northern half of Ill. [*E. parviflorum* Nutt., non Pers.] ......*E. inconspicuum* (Wats.) MacM.
    2. Fruiting pedicels slender, 1 cm long; pods ascending, 1.5-2.5 cm long, 1-1.5 mm wide; petals 4-5 mm long; leaves entire or nearly so; fields and waste places; chiefly in the n. half of the state. June-Aug. Wormseed Mustard ....*E. cheiranthoides* L.

14. **Descurainia** Webb & Berth. — Tansy Mustard

1. Pods clavate, 7-10 mm long; sandy soil or roadsides, common. Apr.-June ....*D. brachycarpa* (Richards.) O. E. Schulz
1. Pods linear, about 2 cm long; waste places, not common; adv. from Eur. ....*D. sophia* (L.) Webb

15. **Draba** L. — Whitlowcress

1. Stem leafy-branched; pods narrowly oval, acute, 2-3 mm long, 1 mm wide, glabrous, 6- to 16-seeded, equalling or exceeding the pedicels; petals entire, whitish, sometimes minute or none; dry soil, s. Ill., extending northward to Coles Co. Apr.-May ....*D. brachycarpa* Nutt.
1. Stem scapose, the leaves chiefly basal; pods 15- to 60-seeded.
    2. Petals entire or emarginate, 3-5 mm long; pods mostly longer than the pedicels.
        3. Pods linear, 8-12 mm long, 1-2 mm wide, glabrous or hispidulous; rachis and pedicels glabrous; leaves entire or nearly so; sandy soil, locally abundant; Apr.-May ....*D. reptans* (Lam.) Fern.
        3. Pods oval to linear-elliptical, 6-15 mm long, 2 mm wide, pubescent; rachis and pedicels pubescent; leaves dentate above the middle; sandy soil, s. Ill., Monroe and Randolph counties. Mar.-May ....*D. cuneifolia* Nutt.
    2. Petals deeply 2-cleft; pods oval, glabrous, 4-10 mm long, shorter than the pedicels; cultivated ground and waste places, occasional; nat. from Eurasia. Mar.-May ....*D. verna* L.

16. **Dentaria** L. — Toothwort

D. laciniata Muhl. Woods, common throughout Ill. Mar.-May. [*D. laciniata* var. *integra* (O.E.Schulz) Fern.].

17. **Iodanthus** T. & G.

I. pinnatifidus (Michx.) Steud. Woods, especially near streams, local. May-July.

18. **Cardamine** L. — Bittercress

1. Leaves toothed or entire; petals 7-12 mm long; plants perennial; stem with a tuberous base.
    2. Petals white; stem 15-50 cm tall, puberulent at base, otherwise glabrous; basal leaves oval; cauline leaves 4-8; wet ground. May-June ....*C. bulbosa* (Schreb.) BSP.
    2. Petals pale lavender; stem 10-25 cm tall, sparsely hirsute, varying to glabrous; basal leaves orbicular; cauline leaves 2-6; woods. Apr.-May ....*C. douglassii* (Torr.) Britt.
1. Leaves pinnate or pinnatifid; petals white, 2-3 mm long; plants annual.
    3. Leaves nearly all basal, more or less pubescent; stamens 4; an occasional weed in cultivated ground and greenhouses; nat. from Eur. Apr.-May ....*C. hirsuta* L.

3. Stem more or less leafy, the leaves glabrous; stamens usually 6; native plants.
   4. Leaflets or leaf-segments of the median and upper leaves oblong to oval, often toothed, the terminal one larger; rachis narrowly winged; wet soil. Apr.-Aug. ....
....*C. pensylvanica* Muhl.
   4. Leaflets or leaf-segments of the median and upper leaves linear, entire, not decurrent, the terminal one similar; rachis not winged; moist soil. Apr.-May ....*C. arenicola* Britt.

19. Arabis L. — Rockcress

1. Pods erect or ascending.
   2. Stem-leaves and basal leaves pinnatifid; pods ascending, 2-2.5 cm long; petals 1.5-3 mm long; rocky woods and waste ground; in the southern half of the state, extending to Hancock and Fulton counties. Apr.-May. [*Sibara virginica* (L.) Rollins] ....*A. virginica* (L.) Poir.
   2. Stem-leaves entire or dentate.
      3. Stem-leaves not auricled at the base, spatulate or linear, 1-3 cm long; basal leaves pinnatifid; pods ascending, 2-3.5 cm long; petals 6-8 mm long; rocky or sandy soil; n. third of Ill., extending southward to Henderson and Kankakee counties. May-July ....*A. lyrata* L.
      3. Stem-leaves auricled at the base; basal leaves entire or dentate.
         4. Mature pods erect or appressed, not more than 1 mm wide.
            5. Pods 5-9 cm long, nearly terete; seeds almost wingless, in two distinct rows; petals 3-4 mm long, cream or pale yellowish; waste places; nat. from Eur. May-July. Tower Mustard ....*A. glabra* (L.) Bernh.
            5. Pods 4-5 cm long; flat; seeds winged, in only 1 row; petals 4-5 mm long, white or pale pink; among rocks near streams; s. to Hancock and De Witt counties. May-June. [*A. hirsuta* of Am. auth.; *A. ovata* (Pursh) Poir. (?)] ....*A. pycnocarpa* Hopkins
         4. Mature pods spreading or ascending, 1.5-2 mm wide, flat; seeds winged, in two rows; petals 5-8 mm long, pink; river banks, rare; Kane and Lee counties. June-July, [*A. drummondii* sensu auth., non Gray; *A. divaricarpa* sensu auth., non A. Nels.] ....*A. confinis* Wats.
1. Pods divaricately spreading, or arcuate-recurved or pendulous at maturity.
   6. Leaves not auricled at base, lanceolate or oblong-lanceolate, 3-12 cm long; pods pendulous, falcate, 5-7 cm long, 2-3 mm wide; seeds winged; petals 5-6 mm long, greenish-white; sepals pilosulous; wooded slopes. May-July. Sicklepod ....
....*A. canadensis* L.

6. Leaves, at least the median and lower, auriculate at base; mature pods less than 2 mm wide.
7. Mature pods 2-2.5 cm long, straight, spreading; seeds wingless; petals white or pale lavender, 2-3 mm long; stemleaves oblanceolate, obtusish, unequally dentate; moist woods near streams, common. Apr.-June. [*A. dentata* T. & G., homonym] ....*A. shortii* (Fern.) Gleason
7. Mature pods 4-9 cm long, arcuate-recurved; seeds winged; petals greenish-white, 4-6 mm long; plant glabrous throughout; gravelly soil in woods. Apr.-June. Smooth Rockcress ....*A. laevigata* (Muhl.) Poir.

20. Arabidopsis Heynh. — Mouse-ear Cress

A. thaliana (L.) Heynh. Waste places, chiefly in the s. counties; nat. from Eur. Apr.-June.

21. Nasturtium R.Br. — Watercress

N. officinale R.Br. In clear water, especially in or near springs; nat. from Eurasia. May-Sept.

22. Neobeckia Greene

N. aquatica (A. Eaton) Greene. Ditches, ponds, or slow streams, not common. June-Aug. [*Armoracia aquatica* (A. Eaton) Wieg.].

23. Armoracia Gaertn. — Horseradish

A. rusticana (Lam.) Gaertn. Waste places, ditches, roadsides; escaped from cult.; native of Eur. May-June. [*A. lapathifolia* Gilib., *nom. invalid.*]

24. Alyssum L.

A. alyssoides L. Fields and waste places, occasional; nat. from Eur. May-June.

25. Lobularia Desv. Sweet Alyssum

L. maritima (L.) Desv. Occasionally spontaneous after cult.; introd. from Eur.

26. Berteroa DC. — Hoary Alyssum

B. incana (L.) DC. Waste places, locally abundant; nat. from Eur. June-Sept.

27. Lesquerella Wats. — Bladder-pod

1. Pods, as well as the whole plant, densely stellate-pubescent; plants perennial; in sand or sandy soil, rare; Havana, Mason Co., Aug. 22, 1904, *H. A. Gleason* [*L. argentea* (Pursh) MacM., non (Schauer) Wats.] ....*L. ludoviciana* (Nutt.) Wats.
1. Pods glabrous; plants annual, sparsely stellate-pubescent; "by the Chicago & Alton R.R. near Rock Bridge, s. of Willow Springs, June 9, 1894," *Hill;* east of Sag Bridge, June 9, 1894, *Moffatt 172* ("only two plants found; fruit immature.") ; native in Okla. and Tex. [*L. nuttallii* Wats.] ....*L. gracilis* (Hook.) Wats.

28. Camelina Crantz

1. Stem glabrous; leaves auriculate at base; petals yellow, 5-6 mm
   long; pods 6-9 mm long, 5-6 mm broad; pedicels 12-25 mm
   long; an occasional weed in fields and waste places; adv. from
   Eur. June-July ....*C. sativa* (L.) Crantz
1. Stem hirsute below; leaves sagittate at base; petals pale yellow,
   3-4 mm long; pods 4-6 mm long, 4-5 mm broad; pedicels 8-15
   mm long; fields and roadsides; nat. from Eur. May-July ....
   ....*C. microcarpa* Andrz.

29. Cardaria Desv. — Hoary Cress

C. draba (L.) Desv. Fields and waste places; nat. from Eur. Apr.-
June. [*Lepidium draba* L.].

30. Lepidium L. — Peppercress

1. Stem-leaves sessile, not sagittate.
   2. Pods 2-4 mm long.
      3. Petals conspicuous, white, spatulate, longer than the sepals;
         waste places, very common. May-Nov. Common Pepper-
         cress ....*L. virginicum* L.
      3. Petals absent, or minute, linear, much shorter than the sepals;
         waste places, occasional; nat. from Eurasia. May-July. [*L.
         intermedium* A. Gray; *L. apetalum* sensu auth., non L.]
         ....*L. densiflorum* Schrad.
   2. Pods 5-7 mm long; introd. from Eur.; Cook Co. Garden Cress
      ....*L. sativum* L.
1. Stem-leaves sagittate or clasping at base.
   4. Stem-leaves lanceolate, denticulate, grayish puberulent; petals
      white; pods 5-6 mm long; fields and waste places, common;
      nat. from Eur. May-July. Field Peppercress ....
      ....*L. campestre* (L.) R.Br.
   4. Stem-leaves ovate, entire, glabrous, clasping; basal leaves bipin-
      nate, with linear divisions; petals yellow; pods 4 mm long;
      waste places, occasional; nat. from Eur. May-June. Clasping
      Peppercress ....*L. perfoliatum* L.

31. Thlaspi L.

T. arvense L. Field Pennycress. Fields and waste places; nat. from
Eur. May-Aug.

32. Capsella Medic. — Shepherd's Purse

C. bursa-pastoris (L.) Medic. Fields and waste places, very common; nat. from Eur. Mar.-Oct.

19. Hypericaceae Lindl. — St. John's-wort Family

1. Petals yellow, convolute in the bud; hypogynous glands absent.
   2. Sepals 4, in unequal pairs, the outer pair larger, bract-like; petals 4 ....
      ....1. *Ascyrum*

2. Sepals 5; petals 5 ....2. *Hypericum*
1. Petals pink or greenish-purple, imbricate in the bud; sepals 5; hypogynous
glands 3; leaves oval ....3. *Triadenum*

1. Ascyrum L. — St. Andrew's Cross

A. hypericoides L. Wooded slopes or ridges, locally in southern
Illinois. July-Aug. [*A. crux-andreae* sensu auth., non L.; *A. multicaule*
Michx.].

2. Hypericum L. — St. John's-wort

1. Leaves with ordinary flat blades.
  2. Flowers large, the petals 0.8-2.5 cm long; stamens numerous.
    3. Petals not at all black-dotted or streaked.
      4. Styles 5; capsules 5-loculed.
        5. Capsules 2-2.5 cm long; flowers 4-5 cm in diameter;
          stems herbaceous, 0.5-1.5 m tall; leaves lanceolate or
          ovate-lanceolate, sessile, partly clasping; banks of
          streams, locally nearly throughout Ill. July-Aug.
          Giant St. John's-wort. [*H. ascyron* of auth., non L.]
          ....*H. pyramidatum* Ait.
        5. Capsules 3-9 mm long; flowers 2-3 cm in diameter;
          shrubs to 1.5 m tall; leaves linear or oblanceolate or
          elliptical.
          6. Sepals 5-30 mm long; capsules 7-15 mm long; sandy
            or rocky soil, rare, Cook and Lake counties. June-
            Aug. Kalm's St. John's-wort ....*H. kalmianum* L.
          6. Sepals 2-5 mm long; capsules 3-7 mm long; low, wet
            ground, rare; s. Ill., Massac Co., *J. R. Swayne 1104*
            and *1163* in 1950. [*H. densiflorum* var. *lobocar-*
            pum (Gattinger) Svenson] ....
            ....*H. lobocarpum* Gattinger
      4. Styles 3 (rarely 4), free, or united into a beak.
        7. Capsules 10-13 mm long, 3-loculed; flowers 1.5-2 cm
          in diameter; branched shrubs to 1 meter tall; moist
          woods; principally in the s. half of the state. July-Aug.
          Shrubby St. John's-wort ....*H. prolificum* L.
        7. Capsules 4-7 mm long; flowers 1-1.5 cm in diameter.
          8. Capsules 3- to 4-loculed; stamens persistent, forming a
            mass at base of capsule; wet ground, rare; St. Clair
            Co., *Brendel* in 1850; Wabash Co., *Schneck* ....
            ....*H. adpressum* Bart.
          8. Capsules 1-loculed; stamens not persistent.
            9. Styles united below; stigmas elongate; plants not
              virgate.
              10. Stems somewhat woody at base; inflorescence
                many-flowered; seeds rugulose and pitted;
                roadsides, open woods, river banks, common
                throughout Ill. June-Aug. Round-fruited St.
                John's-wort. [*H. cistifolium* sensu auth., non
                Lam.]...................*H. sphaerocarpum* Michx.

10. Stems herbaceous throughout, simple or nearly
so, from a slender, creeping, stoloniferous
base; inflorescence few-flowered; seeds striate;
wet ground, rare; Fulton and St. Clair counties.. July-Aug. ....*H. ellipticum* Hook.
9. Styles free to base; stigmas ovoid; plants virgate;
moist woods, rare, Jackson and Pope counties ......
....*H. denticulatum* Walt.
3. Petals black-lined or black-dotted, at least along the margin;
styles separate; capsules 3-loculed.
11. Petals dotted only along the margin; leaves linear or
oblong, 1-2 cm long, 2-8 mm wide, numerous; stem
much branched, often with basal sterile shoots; roadsides and fields, common; nat. from Eur. June-Aug.
Common St. John's-wort ....*H. perforatum* L.
11. Petals marked with black lines and dots; leaves elliptical
to ovate.
12. Leaves elliptical, obtuse or acute; petals 5-7 mm long;
capsules 4-6 mm long; roadsides and open woods.
July-Aug. Spotted St. John's-wort ....
....*H. punctatum* Lam.
12. Leaves lanceolate or ovate, acuminate; petals 10-15
mm long; capsules 6-8 mm long; open woods, local.
May-June. Large Spotted St. John's-wort ....
....*H. pseudomaculatum* Bush
2. Flowers small, the petals 3-6 mm long; stamens few (5-20).
13. Capsules 3-3.5 mm long; sepals linear, obtusish; leaves oval
or elliptical, obtuse, 5-veined from the base; plants often
diffusely branched; moist soil, local. July-Sept. Dwarf
St. John's-wort ....*H. mutilum* L.
13. Capsules 4-6 mm long; sepals narrowly lanceolate, acumi-
nate; branching strict, erect, or stem simple.
14. Leaves oval to elliptic-lanceolate, clasping, 3- to 7-
veined from the base.
15. Leaves firm, ovate, acute, often distant; stem simple;
sepals lanceolate, acuminate; wet sandy barrens,
local ....*H. gymnanthum* Engelm. & Gray
15. Leaves elliptic-lanceolate, acutish, somewhat rounded
at the clasping base, 3-10 mm wide; sepals 5-6
mm long, nearly equalling the capsule; moist
ground, rare, n.e. Ill., extending southwestward to
Tazewell Co. July-Aug. Larger Canadian St.
John's-wort ....*H. majus* (Gray) Britt.
14. Leaves lanceolate, obtuse, tapered at the sessile base, 1-3
mm wide; sepals 2.5-3 mm long, noticeably shorter
than the capsule; moist sandy soil, in the northern half
of Ill. July-Sept. Canadian St. John's-wort ....
....*H. canadense* L.

1. Leaves scale-like or subulate.
   16. Leaves scale-like, 2-3 mm long; capsules much longer than the sepals; flowers 4-8 mm in diameter, nearly sessile; sandy soil, local. Aug.-Oct. ....*H. gentianoides* (L.) BSP.
   16. Leaves subulate, 5-20 mm long; capsules about as long as the sepals; flowers 10-12 mm in diameter, pedicelled; sterile soil in fields or on thinly wooded ridges in the southern half of the state. July-Sept. ....

   ....*H. drummondii* (Grev. & Hook.) T. & G.

3. Triadenum Raf. — Marsh St. John's-wort

1. Leaves 2-5 cm long, copiously glandular beneath, sessile or partly clasping at the base, broadest below the middle; swamps or bogs in the northern half of Ill. July-Sept. [*T. virginicum* sensu auth., non (L.) Raf.] ....*T. fraseri* (Spach) Gleason
1. Leaves 5-15 cm long, elliptical or oblanceolate, thin.
   2. Leaves sessile, glandless or nearly so; swampy ground in woods; Alexander, Massac, and Pulaski counties. [*T. longifolium* Small] ....*T. tubulosum* (Walt.) Gleason
   2. Leaves short-petioled, narrowed at the base, glandular beneath; cypress swamps, and wet ground in woods in southern Illinois. July-Aug. [*T. petiolatum* (Walt.) Britt.] ....
   ....*T. walteri* (Gmel.) Gleason

20. Elatinaceae Lindl. — Waterwort Family

1. Plants glabrous; flowers 2- to 4-merous; sepals obtuse ....1. *Elatine*
1. Plants puberulent; petals, sepals, and stamens 5; sepals acuminate ....2. *Bergia*

1. Elatine L. — Waterwort

E. brachysperma A. Gray. Shallow water, rare; Springfield, Sangamon Co., *Bebb;* Athens, Menard Co., *Hall.*

2. Bergia L.

B. texana (Hook.) Seub. Shores, rare; near Cahokia, Madison Co., *H. Eggert* in 1874; St. Clair Co., *Eggert* in 1878. Aug.-Oct.

21. Sarraceniaceae LaPylie — Pitcher-plant Family

1. Sarracenia L. — Pitcher-plant

S. purpurea L. Peat bogs; Cook, Lake, and McHenry counties. May-June.

22. Tiliaceae Juss. — Linden Family

1. Tilia L. — Linden

1. Leaves of the flowering branches glabrous beneath except for tufts of hairs in the axils of the lateral veins, coarsely serrate, abruptly short-acuminate; woods, common. June-July. American Linden. Basswood. [*T. glabra* Vent.] ....*T. americana* L.

1. Leaves of the flowering branches tomentose beneath, finely serrate,
gradually short-acuminate; woods, Hardin and Pope counties.
June-July. White Basswood ....*T. heterophylla* Vent.

23. **Malvaceae** Necker — Mallow Family

1. Pistil consisting of several carpels united in a ring around a central axis,
   but usually separating at maturity; stamen-column anther-bearing at
   the top.
   2. Carpels 1-ovuled and 1-seeded.
      3. Plants with perfect flowers.
         4. Calyx subtended by an involucre of 6-9 connate bracts; tall plants
            with showy flowers ....1. *Althaea*
         4. Calyx subtended by usually 3 separate bracts, or these sometimes
            lacking.
            5. Stigmas linear, on the inner side of the style-branches; petals
               rose, purple, or white.
               6. Petals obcordate; carpels beakless ....2. *Malva*
               6. Petals truncate, sometimes dentate or fimbriate; carpels beaked
                  ....3. *Callirhoe*
            5. Stigmas capitate, terminal; petals yellow, small.
               7. An involucel present at the base of the calyx; leaves linear ......
                  ....4. *Malvastrum*
               7. Involucels absent; leaves ovate-lanceolate.
                  8. Flowers yellow; leaves with a short spine at base ....5. *Sida*
                  8. Flowers pale blue; leaves without spines ....6. *Anoda*
      3. Plants dioecious; petals white; carpels rugose-reticulate; leaves
         palmately 5- to 11-lobed ....7. *Napaea*
   2. Carpels 2- to several-seeded; stigmas capitate or truncate, terminal.
      9. Petals yellow; involucre none; carpels 10-17; leaves long-petioled,
         velvety-pubescent, cordate, acuminate, 6-30 cm broad ....8. *Abutilon*
      9. Petals pink or rose; involucre of 3 narrow bracts; leaves palmately
         lobed ....9. *Iliamna*
1. Pistil consisting of 3-5 united carpels, becoming in fruit a loculicidal
   several-seeded capsule; stamen-column anther-bearing below the summit;
   flowers large, showy.
   10. Bractlets six or more, linear ....10. *Hibiscus*
   10. Bractlets three, broadly cordate ....11. *Gossypium*

1. **Althaea** L. — Hollyhock

A. rosea (L.) Cav. Roadsides and waste ground, occasional; native
of China.

2. **Malva** L. — Mallow

1. Petals not more than twice as long as the sepals.
   2. Leaves crisped on the margins; carpels reticulate; stem stout,
      erect, 0.5-2 m tall; escaped from cult.; native of Eur. July-
      Sept. ....*M. crispa* L.
   2. Leaves not crisped.
      3. Stems erect; petals 5 mm long; carpels 8-11, more or less
         pubescent and rugose on the back; weed in waste places;

native of Eur.; Champaign and Peoria counties. July-Aug. Round-leaved Mallow. [*M. pusilla* With.] ....
....*M. rotundifolia* L.

3. Stems prostrate or ascending; petals 10-12 mm long; carpels 12-15, pubescent; waste places; very common; nat. from Eur. May-Sept. [*M. rotundifolia* sensu auth., non L.] ....
....*M. neglecta* Wallr.

1. Petals 3-8 times as long as the sepals.

4. Leaves 3- to 7-lobed; petals purple; carpels wrinkled; occasional in waste places as a garden escape; introd. from Eur. Aug.-Sept. ....*M. sylvestris* L.

4. Leaves deeply dissected; petals pink; carpels pubescent; road-sides, escaped from cult.; native of Eur. June. Musk Mallow ....*M. moschata* L.

3. Callirhoe Nutt. — Poppy Mallow

1. Petals usually white or pinkish, 1-1.5 cm long, flowers without subtending bracts; carpels pubescent; roadsides and waste places, occasional. May-June. [*C. digitata* sensu auth., non Nutt.] ....*C. alcaeoides* (Michx.) A.Gray

1. Petals purple.

2. Leaves roundish in outline, palmately 5- to 7-parted; stems procumbent; peduncles 1-flowered; plants hispid-pubescent; carpels rugose-reticulate; cultivated ground and roadsides; occasionally adv. from west of the Mississippi R. May-Aug. ....*C. involucrata* (T. & G.) A.Gray

2. Leaves mostly triangular or halberd-shaped, crenate; stem erect; peduncles several-flowered; plants stellate-pubescent; carpels pubescent, not rugose; sandy soil, chiefly in the northern counties. June-Sept. ....*C. triangulata* (Leavenw.) A.Gray

4. Malvastrum A. Gray — Globe Mallow

M. angustum A. Gray. Dry ground, rare; La Salle and Rock Island counties. July-Aug. [*Sidopsis hispida* (Pursh) Rydb.; *Sphaeralcea angusta* (A. Gray) Fern.].

5. Sida L.

S. spinosa L. Fields and waste ground, common; native of trop. Am. July-Oct.

6. Anoda Cav.

A. cristata (L.) Schlecht. Escaped from cult.; Hancock Co.

7. Napaea L. — Glade Mallow

N. dioica L. Alluvial soil, locally throughout the northern half of Ill. July-Aug.

8. Abutilon Mill. — Indian Mallow

A. theophrasti Medic. Butterprint. Velvet-leaf. Fields and road-sides, common; native of India. Aug.-Oct.. [*A. avicennae* Gaertn.; *A. abutilon* (L.) Rusby].

9. Iliamna Greene

I. remota Greene. On an island in the Kankakee R., the type locality; plants on Peters Mt., Va., belong to a separate species. June-July. [*Sphaeralcea acerifolia* sensu auth., non Nutt.; *S. remota* (Greene) Fern.; *Phymosia remota* (Greene) Britt.].

10. Hibiscus L. — Rose Mallow

1. Stems 1-2 m tall; native perennial species.
    2. Stem, leaves, and capsules glabrous; seeds pubescent; muddy shores of streams and ponds nearly throughout Ill. July-Oct. ....*H. militaris* Cav.
    2. Stem and lower surface of leaves pubescent; seeds glabrous.
        3. Upper surface of leaves glabrous or essentially so; bracts canescent but not ciliate; capsules glabrous; swampy ground; Cook, Douglas, La Salle, Woodford, and William-son counties. July-Sept. [*H. moscheutos* of auth., not L.] ....*H. palustris* L.
        3. Upper surface of leaves velvety-pubescent; bracts canescent, and ciliate with long simple hairs; capsules stellate-pubescent; shores of ponds and streams; chiefly in the s. half of the state. Aug.-Oct. [*H. grandiflorus* sensu auth., non Michx.] ....*H. lasiocarpus* Cav.
1. Stem 10-40 cm tall; leaves 3- to 7-lobed; plants annual.
    4. Calyx inflated, 5-winged; seeds finely verrucose; roadsides, fields, and waste places; nat. from Eur. Aug.-Oct. Flower-of-an-hour ....*H. trionum* L.
    4. Calyx spathiform; seeds mucilaginous; rarely persisting after cult.; introd. from Afr. Okra ....*H. esculentus* L.

11. Gossypium L. — Cotton

G. hirsutum L. Native of trop. Am.; cultivated in s. Ill. and south-ward; occasionally apparently spontaneous.

24. Caryophyllaceae Reichenb. — Pink Family

1. Sepals separate or nearly so; petals without claws or appendages.
    2. Petals deeply 2-cleft or 2-parted.
        3. Capsules cylindrical, commonly curved, opening by a row of 10 (rare-ly 8) apical teeth; styles 5 ....1. *Cerastium*
        3. Capsules ovoid or ellipsoid, splitting into usually 6 (rarely 8 or 10) valves; styles 3-5 ....2. *Stellaria*
    2. Petals entire or emarginate, or absent.
        4. Leaves with scarious stipules.
            5. Leaves whorled; styles 5 ....3. *Spergula*
            5. Leaves opposite; styles 3 ....4. *Spergularia*

4. Leaves without stipules.
  6. Styles as many as the sepals ....5. *Sagina*
  6. Styles fewer than the sepals.
    7. Stamens 10; capsule ovoid ....6. *Arenaria*
    7. Stamens 3-5; capsule cylindrical ....7. *Holosteum*
1. Sepals united into a tubular calyx; petals clawed.
  8. Calyx without bracts at base.
    9. Calyx-teeth much longer than the calyx-tube; styles 5 ......8. *Agrostemma*
    9. Calyx-teeth much shorter than the calyx-tube.
      10. Styles 5 or 3 (0 in the staminate flowers of *Lychnis*).
        11. Styles 3, rarely 4; flowers perfect; capsule opening by 6 teeth
        ....9. *Silene*
        11. Styles 5 (or 0); capsule opening by 10 teeth ....
        ....10. *Lychnis*
      10. Styles 2 (occasionally 3, rarely 4); calyx terete or 5-angled ....
      ....11. *Saponaria*
  8. Calyx subtended by 1-4 bracts, cylindrical; styles 2.
    12. Calyx with 30-40 nerves ....12. *Dianthus*
    12. Calyx with 5-15 nerves ....13. *Tunica*

1. **Cerastium** L. — Mouse-ear Chickweed

1. Petals much longer than the sepals.
  2. Flowers 1.2-2 cm broad; fruiting calyx 6-7 mm long; capsule
    12-14 mm long; seeds 1 mm in diameter; plants perennial;
    in thin soil, chiefly in limestone areas. May-June. Field
    Mouse-ear Chickweed. [*C. arvense* sensu auth., non L.; *C.
    arvense* var. *oblongifolium* (Torr.) Hollick & Britt.] ....
    ....*C. velutinum* Raf
  2. Flowers 5-8 mm broad; fruiting calyx 4-5 mm long; capsule
    9-11 mm long; seeds 0.4-0.8 mm in diameter; plants annual.
    3. Pedicels 15-40 mm long, hooked at tip; moist ground, com-
      mon. Apr.-May. Nodding Mouse-ear Chickweed ....
      ....*C. nutans* Raf.
    3. Pedicels 2-10 mm long, not hooked at tip; adv. from the
      West; occasional in Ill. Apr.-May ....
      ....*C. brachypodum* (Engelm.) B.L.Robins.
1. Petals equalling or only slightly longer than the sepals.
  4. Pedicels scarcely longer than the sepals, the cyme therefore
    compact; plants annual; moist ground, rare; nat. from Eur.
    Apr.-May ....*C. viscosum* L.
  4. Pedicels two to five times longer than the sepals, the cyme
    therefore rather loose.
    5. Bracts terminating in long tufts of hairs; plants annual; adv.
      from Eur.; Pulaski and Union counties. Apr.-May ....
      ....*C. brachypetalum* Pers.
    5. Bracts without long tufts of hairs at tips; plants perennial;
      waste ground, lawns, fields, common; nat. from Eur. May-
      Aug. Common Mouse-ear Chickweed ....*C. vulgatum* L.

2. **Stellaria** L. — Chickweed

(*Alsine* L. ex p., non Wahl.)

1.Leaves oval or ovate.
  2. Petals longer than the sepals; plants perennial.
    3. Stems glandular-puberulent above, glabrous below; leaves ovate; styles 5; waste places, occasional; adv. from Eur. Water Chickweed ....*S. aquatica* (L.) Scop.
    3. Stems with two lines of hairs; leaves elliptical; styles 3; wooded slopes and ravines, rare; Cook and Du Page counties. June-July ....*S. pubera* Michx.
  2. Petals shorter than the sepals; stem terete, with a single median line of hairs; stamens 3-7; styles 3-4; plants annual; waste ground and fields, very common; nat. from Eur. Jan.-Dec. Common Chickweed ....*S. media* (L.) Vill.
1. Leaves linear or narrowly lanceolate.
  4. Leaves narrowly elliptical-lanceolate, widest at or above the middle, the margin microscopically papillate; seeds essentially smooth; moist ground. May-June ....*S. longifolia* Muhl.
  4. Leaves linear-lanceolate, broadest below the middle; margin often sparsely ciliolate; seeds coarsely rugulose-tuberculate; moist ground; adv. from Eur. May-June ....*S. graminea* L.

3. **Spergula** L. — Spurrey

S. arvensis L. Fields and waste places, occasional; nat. from Eur.

4. **Spergularia** J. & C. Presl — Sand Spurrey

S. rubra (L.) J. & C. Presl. Found once in Cook Co., by *W. S. Moffatt* in 1893.

5. **Sagina** L. — Pearlwort

S. decumbens (Ell.) Torr. & Gray. Dry ground, occasional. Apr.-May.

6. **Arenaria** L. — Sandwort

(*Moehringia* L.)

1.Leaves oval or ovate; valves of the capsules 2-toothed or 2-cleft.
  2. Leaves oval, obtuse, 1-3 cm long; sepals obtuse, shorter than the petals; seeds smooth; woods in the n. half of the state. May-June ....*A. lateriflora* L.
  2. Leaves ovate, acute, 2-8 mm long; sepals acuminate, longer than the petals; seeds rough; waste ground; adv. from Eur. Apr.-June. Thyme-leaved Sandwort ....*A. serpyllifolia* L.
1. Leaves linear-filiform or subulate; valves of the capsule entire.
  3. Leaves rigid, subulate, evergreen, with others fascicled in the axils; plant perennial, glabrous; dry wooded bluffs, and on rocks, northern Ill., rare. May-July. [*A. michauxii* (Fenzl) Hook.f.] ....*A. stricta* Michx.
  3. Leaves soft, linear-filiform; plant annual; pedicels glandular-puberulent; wooded slopes along streams, rare; Cook, Kan-

kakee, St. Clair, and Will counties. May-June. [*A. patula* f.
media Steyerm.] .... *A. patula* Michx.

7. Holosteum L. — Jagged Chickweed

H. umbellatum L. Roadsides, fields, and waste places; nat. from
Eur. Apr.-May.

8. Agrostemma L. — Corn Cockle

A. githago L. An occasional weed in fields and waste ground; nat.
from Eur. May-July. The seeds are poisonous.

9. Silene L. — Catchfly

1. Leaves opposite, not whorled.
2. Calyx ovoid or clavate, not becoming inflated in fruit or constricted at the mouth.
3. Stems glabrous or nearly so, or the upper internodes glutinous.
4. Flowers 12-17 mm in diameter in flat-topped cymes; calyx
clavate, 1-1.5 cm long; leaves ovate-lanceolate; waste
places; adv. from Eur. June-July. Sweet William
Catchfly ....*S. armeria* L.
4. Flowers 3-4 mm in diameter, paniculate; calyx ovoid, 5-8
mm long; upper leaves linear to lanceolate; roadsides
and fields, not uncommon. May-July. Sleepy Catchfly
....*S. antirrhina* L.
3. Stem puberulent.
5. Petals white or pink.
6. Calyx 12-16 mm long; roadsides and fields, rare; adv.
from Eur. June-July. Forked Catchfly ....
....*S. dichotoma* Ehrh.
6. Calyx 15-25 mm long; cultivated ground or roadsides;
adv. from Eur. June-July. Night-flowering Catchfly
....*S. noctiflora* L.
5. Petals crimson or scarlet; calyx 15-25 mm long.
7. Leaves ovate-lanceolate; petals mostly undivided; roadsides and prairie soil, s. Ill., rare. July-Aug. Royal
Catchfly ....*S. regia* Sims
7. Leaves spatulate or oblanceolate; petals 2-cleft; woods,
local. May-July. Firepink ....*S. virginica* L.
2. Calyx inflated in fruit, more or less constricted at the mouth.
8. Flowers in loose, terminal panicles; plants glaucous.
9. Calyx campanulate, 12-16 mm long, conspicuously veiny,
rounded at base; seeds 1.2-1.5 mm long; fields or roadsides, occasional; nat. from Eur. May-July. Bladder
Catchfly ....*S. cucubalus* Wibel
9. Calyx ellipsoid, 10-12 mm long, not conspicuously veined,
tapering at base; seeds 0.8-1 mm long; roadsides and
waste places, occasional; nat. from Eurasia. June-Aug.
....*S. cserei* Baumg.

8. Flowers few, usually solitary; plants not glaucous; calyx sub-
cylindrical; wooded ravines, infrequent; June-July ....
....*S. nivea* (Nutt.) Otth
1. Leaves mostly in whorls of four, acuminate; petals white, 1.5-2
cm long; calyx campanulate, 1-1.5 cm long; woods throughout
Ill. June-Aug. Almost all Ill. plants are more or less puberulent [var. *scabrella* (Nieuwl.) Steyerm.] Occasionally specimens
from s. Ill. are glabrous or nearly so ....*S. stellata* (L.) Ait.f.

10. Lychnis L. — Campion
(*Melandrium* Roehl)

1. Flowers white, red, or pink; plant viscid-pubescent or hirsute.
  2. Flowers white, opening in the morning; plants viscid-pubescent;
  fields and roadsides; nat. from Eur. May-Aug. Evening
  Campion ....*L. alba* Mill.
  2. Flowers red, opening in the evening; plants puberulent to
  hirsute; waste places; adv. from Eur. June-Aug. Red
  Campion ....*L. dioica* L.
1. Flowers crimson; plants white-woolly throughout; waste places,
occasional; introd. from Eur. June-Aug. Mullein Pink ....
....*L. coronaria* (L.) Desr.

11. Saponaria L.
(*Vaccaria* Medic.)

1. Calyx terete; flowers 2-3 cm in diameter (sometimes double), in
dense corymbiform cymes; plants perennial; roadsides, common; adv. from Eur. June-Sept. Bouncing Bet ......*S. officinalis* L.
1. Calyx sharply 5-angled; flowers 6-8 mm in diameter, few, in a
loose cyme; plants annual; roadsides and fields; adv. from Eur.
June-Aug. Cow-herb. [*Vaccaria segetalis* (Necker) Garcke]
....*S. vaccaria* L.

12. Dianthus L. — Pink

1. Flowers numerous.
  2. Leaves 10-20 mm wide; plants perennial; introd. from Eur.;
  Jackson Co. Sweet William ....*D. barbatus* L.
  2. Leaves 2-8 mm wide; plants annual; along roads or in pastures,
  occasional. June-Aug. Deptford Pink ....*D. armeria* L.
1. Flowers solitary; adv. from Eurasia; known from Piatt and Vermilion counties. ....*D. deltoides* L.

13. Tunica Scop. — Saxifrage Pink

T. saxifraga (L.) Scop. Roadsides and waste places; adv. from
Eur.

25. Portulacaceae Reichenb. — Purslane Family

1. Leaves several, clustered at the base of the stem, terete; petals rose;
capsule papery, opening by 3 valves ....1. *Talinum*
1. Leaves not all clustered at the base of the stem.

2. Leaves 2, linear-lanceolate; petals pink or white; capsule 3- to 6-seeded, opening by 3 valves ....2. *Claytonia*
2. Leaves numerous, thick, spatulate; capsules circumscissile, many-seeded ....3. *Portulaca*

1. Talinum Adans. — Rock-pink

1. Stamens 12-30 or more; petals 7-13 mm long.
  2. Stamens 12-25; petals 7-8 mm long; seeds rugose; sandy soil, rare; Henderson, Jo Daviess, Lake, La Salle, Lee, Ogle, and Winnebago counties. June-Sept. ....*T. rugospermum* Holz.
  2. Stamens 30 or more; petals 10-13 mm long; seeds smooth; exposed sandstone bluffs, rare; Randolph Co. *R. H. Mohlenbrock* in 1955. June-Sept. ....*T. calycinum* Engelm.
1. Stamens 4-8; petals 5-6 mm long; rocky ledges, rare; Johnson, Pope, and Union counties. June-Sept. ....*T. parviflorum* Nutt.

2. Claytonia L. — Spring Beauty

C. virginica L. Woods and waysides, abundant throughout the state. Mar.-May.

3. Portulaca L.

1. Leaves obovate, spatulate; stamens 6-10; fields and waste ground, common; nat. from Eur. July-Sept. ....*P. oleracea* L.
1. Leaves terete; stamens about 40; occasional garden escape. Portulaca ....*P. grandiflora* Hook.

26. Aizoaceae A.Br. — Carpetweed Family

1. Mollugo L. — Carpetweed

M. verticillata L. Fields, roadsides, and waste places, common; nat. from the southern states. June-Oct.

27. Chenopodiaceae Dum. — Goosefoot Family

1. Leaves alternate.
  2. Leaves not spine-tipped or subulate.
    3. Flowers perfect, not enclosed in a pair of triangular bracts; perianth present.
      4. Flowers in clusters; fruit enclosed in the calyx.
        5. Calyx not horizontally winged ....1. *Chenopodium*
        5. Calyx becoming horizontally winged.
          6. Leaves sinuate-dentate; flowers paniculate ....2. *Cycloloma*
          6. Leaves linear or narrowly lanceolate, entire, yellowish-green; flowers spicate ....3. *Kochia*
      4. Flowers solitary, axillary; calyx of a single sepal ....4. *Corispermum*
    3. Flowers unisexual, the pistillate enclosed by a pair of triangular bracts; leaves narrowly lanceolate to hastate ....5. *Atriplex*
  2. Leaves subulate, spinescent; stems branched, striate; flowers 1-3 in the axils ....6. *Salsola*
1. Leaves scale-like, opposite; branches terete, succulent, jointed ......7. *Salicornia*

1. **Chenopodium** L. — Goosefoot. Pigweed

1. Plants more or less glandular and aromatic, not at all farinose.
  2. Leaves sinuate-pinnatifid; pericarp not gland-dotted; fruit only partly enclosed by the calyx; roadsides, waste ground, occasional; nat. from Eur. July-Sept. Jerusalem Oak ....*C. botrys* L.
  2. Leaves repand-dentate to subentire; pericarp gland-dotted; fruit completely enclosed by the calyx; waste ground, common; nat. from trop. Am. July-Oct. Mexican Tea ....*C. ambrosioides* L.
1. Plants not glandular or aromatic, but sometimes farinose.
  3. Flowers in globose clusters 1 cm or more in diameter, forming an interrupted spike, the calyx becoming red, succulent, and strawberry-like at maturity; leaves triangular to lanceolate; seeds horizontal, dull, 0.8 mm in diameter; sandy soil; McHenry and Peoria counties. May-Aug. Strawberry Pigweed ....*C. capitatum* (L.) Aschers.
  3. Flowers in smaller glomerules; calyx not succulent.
    4. Leaves sinuately dentate or entire.
      5. Sepals more or less prominently keeled in fruit.
        6. Pericarp loose, readily separating from the seed; leaves thin; seeds horizontal.
          7. Leaves green and glabrous or nearly so on both surfaces when mature, slender-petioled, lanceolate to ovate, entire, or the lower ones sinuate-dentate; woods, common. June-Oct. [*C. standleyanum* Aellen] ....*C. boscianum* Moq.
          7. Leaves densely farinose at least beneath, rather short-petioled, linear or lanceolate, often somewhat hastately toothed; sandy soil, occasional; native west of the Mississippi R.; adv. in Ill. July-Sept. Narrow-leaved Goosefoot. [*C. leptophyllum* sensu auth., non Nutt.] ....*C. pratericola* Rydb.
        6. Pericarp firmly adherent to the seed.
          8. Leaves more or less sinuately dentate.
            9. Leaves commonly densely farinose on the lower surface; seeds 1-1.5 mm in diameter; cultivated ground and waste places, common; nat. from Eur. July-Sept. Lamb's Quarter. [*C. viride* L.; *C. missouriense* Aellen; *C. bushianum* Aellen; *C. paganum* Reichenb.] ....*C. album* L.
            9. Leaves green and glabrous on both surfaces, triangular-ovate or somewhat deltoid-hastate, often truncate at base; seeds 1 mm in diameter; stem 30-90 cm tall; waste places, occasional; nat. from Eur. July-Sept. City Goosefoot ....*C. urbicum* L.

8. Leaves small, entire or hastately toothed, the upper ones smaller, elliptical, cuspidate; seeds puncticulate, 1 mm in diameter; dry soil, locally throughout Ill. July-Sept. ....*C. berlandieri* Moq.
5. Sepals only slightly or not at all keeled.
  10. Leaves bright green on both surfaces; seeds 1-1.5 mm in diameter.
    11. Leaves entire, ovate to elliptical; flowers in much-branched axillary panicles; along railroads; nat. from Eur.; Murphysboro, Jackson Co., *R. H. Mohlenbrock* ....*C. polyspermum* L.
    11. Leaves sagittate, hastate, or deltoid; flowers usually in terminal paniculate glomerules; seeds all horizontal; leaves very coarsely toothed; waste places; nat. from Eur.. July-Oct. Nettle-leaved Goosefoot ....*C. murale* L.
  10. Leaves pale green, sinuate-margined, 1-3 cm long, the lower surface whitish-mealy; stem low, spreading or prostrate; seeds 0.6-0.8 mm in diameter, sharp-edged; waste places; nat. from Eur. July-Sept. Oak-leaved Goosefoot ....*C. glaucum* L.
4. Leaves sharply divaricately lobed or coarsely few-toothed, thin, large, green, glabrous; sepals slightly keeled, incompletely covering the seed; pericarp firmly adherent; seeds 1.5-2 mm in diameter; fields, woods, or waste ground; nat. from Eur. July-Sept. [*C. gigantospermum* Aellen] ....
............................*C. hybridum* L.

2. Cycloloma Moq. — Winged Pigweed

C. atriplicifolium (Spreng.) Coult. Sandy soil, local. July-Aug.

3. Kochia Roth

K. scoparia (L.) Roth. A weed in waste places about towns; nat. from Eurasia. July-Oct. — The var. *culta* Farw. [*K. trichophylla* Voss], summer-cypress or burning bush, with compact symmetrical ovoid habit, the foliage turning purple-red in autumn, is occasionally apparently spontaneous, but not established.

4. Corispermum L. — Bugseed

C. hyssopifolium L. Sandy soil, local; Cook, Lake, Mason, and Menard counties. July-Sept. [Incl. *C. nitidum* sensu auth., non Kit.].

5. Atriplex L.

1. Bracts enclosing the fruit somewhat succulent.
  2. Bracts triangular, not conspicuously veined.
    3. Leaves lanceolate; bracts cuneate at base; waste ground; nat. from Eur. July-Aug. ....*A. patula* L.

    3. Lower leaves hastate; bracts truncate at base; waste ground;
        nat. from Eur. Aug.-Oct. ....*A. hastata* L.
   2. Bracts oval, conspicuously net-veined; waste ground; nat. from
      Asia; Du Page, Lake, and Vermilion counties ......*A. hortensis* L.
1. Bracts enclosing the fruit hard and bony.
    4. Bracts ovate, acute, longer than broad; stem terete or nearly so;
       leaves oval to ovate; waste ground, occasional; native of
       Eurasia ....*A. rosea* L.
    4. Bracts suborbicular, as broad as long; stem angular; leaves
       triangular-ovate to deltoid; waste ground, adv. from the
       western states. Silverscale ....*A. argentea* Nutt.

6. Salsola L. — Saltwort

   S. pestifer A. Nels. Russian-thistle. Sandy soil, chiefly in the n.
half of Ill.; nat. from Asia. July-Sept. [*S. kali* var. *tenuifolia* Tausch.].

7. Salicornia L. — Glasswort

   S. europaea L. Muddy banks, Harvey, Cook Co., Sept. 2, 1948,
G. S. Winterringer 1588, 1599.

28. Amaranthaceae J.St.Hil. — Amaranth Family

1. Leaves alternate; filaments separate and distinct; anthers 2-loculed.
   2. Both staminate and pistillate flowers with 3-5 sepals ....1. *Amaranthus*
   2. Pistillate flowers without a calyx; staminate flowers with 5 conspicuous
      mucronate sepals longer than the bracts ....2. *Acnida*
1. Leaves opposite; anthers 1-loculed.
   3. Flowers in axillary glomerules; pistillate calyx not woolly ......3. *Tidestromia*
   3. Flowers in terminal spikes or panicles; at least the pistillate calyx woolly.
     4. Flowers perfect, in dense spikes on long peduncles; plants woolly-
       pubescent; filaments united into a tube ....4. *Froelichia*
     4. Flowers unisexual, paniculate; plants glabrous or nearly so; filaments
       united at base ....5. *Iresine*

1. Amaranthus L. — Amaranth

1. Flowers in dense terminal and axillary panicles; plants tall, erect.
   2. Leaves with a pair of rigid axillary spines; waste ground, com-
      mon; nat. from trop. Am. June-Oct. Spiny Pigweed ....
      ....*A. spinosus* L.
   2. Leaves without spines; utricle circumscissile.
     3. Plants monoecious; both staminate and pistillate flowers in
       the same or different spikes.
       4. Sepals of the pistillate flowers about 1.5 mm long.
         5. Panicle purple; bracts merely awn-pointed, shorter than
          or equalling the obtuse sepals; utricle longer than the
          calyx; occasionally escaped from gardens; native of
          China; Cook Co., *Moffatt* ....*A. cruentus* L.

5. Panicle green; bracts long-awned, about twice the length of the acute sepals; utricle shorter than to about equalling the calyx; common weed in waste ground and fields. Aug.-Oct. ....*A. hybridus* L.
4. Sepals of the pistillate flowers 2-3 mm long.
  6. Terminal panicle lobulate; sepals of the pistillate flowers obtuse, mucronulate; stamens 5; stem pilosulous, at least above; common weed in fields and waste ground. Aug.-Sept. Rough Pigweed ....*A. retroflexus* L.
  6. Panicle of few erect stiff spikes 5-25 cm long; sepals of the pistillate flowers acute or acuminate; stamens usually 3; stem glabrous or puberulent; waste ground; adv. from the western states. Aug.-Sept. ....*A. powellii* S.Wats.
3. Plants dioecious, the flowers all staminate or all pistillate; sepals of the pistillate flowers spatulate, clawed at base, 2.5-3 mm long; inflorescence of long slender, dense or interrupted terminal spikes; waste places, occasional; adv. from the western states ....*A. arenicola* I.M.Johnston
1. Flowers in small axillary clusters; plants diffusely branched or prostrate.
  7. Stems prostrate; seeds 1.5 mm in diameter; fields and roadsides, common. June-Oct. Prostrate Amaranth. [*A. blitoides* Wats.] ....*A. graecizans* L.
  7. Stems erect or ascending; seeds 1 mm in diameter; waste ground and fields, common. July-Sept. Tumbleweed ....*A. albus* L.

2. Acnida L. — Water-hemp

1. Utricle circumscissile; stem erect; fields, roadsides, and waste places, local; probably adv. from the West. July-Sept. ....*A. tamariscina* (Nutt.) Wood
1. Utricle indehiscent or bursting irregularly.
  2. Stem tall (0.5-2 m), erect; banks of streams, muddy shores, dried sloughs, sand bars, moist ground in woods, locally throughout Ill. July-Oct. Tall Water-hemp ....*A. altissima* Riddell
  2. Stem decumbent or ascending, 15-60 cm long; banks of streams, and mud flats, local. Aug.-Oct. ......*A. subnuda* (Wats.) Standl.

3. Tidestromia Standl.

T. lanuginosa (Nutt.) Standl. Adv. from the western states. Cook Co., *Moffatt* in 1893.

4. Froelichia Moench

1. Stem 60-100 cm tall, sparingly branched; wings of the fruiting calyx continuous, dentate; sandy soil; chiefly in the northern half of Ill.; also Kankakee Co. June-Oct. [*F. floridana* sensu auth., non (Nutt.) Moq.] ....*F. campestris* Small

1. Stem 30-60 cm tall, branched near the base; wings of the fruiting
calyx interrupted, forming 6 or 7 spine-like teeth; waste ground,
usually along railroads; adv. from w. of the Mississippi R.
June-Oct. ....*F. gracilis* (Hook.) Moq.

5. Iresine P.Br. — Blood-leaf

I. rhizomatosa Standl. Wet ground in woods, rare; Pulaski and
Wabash counties. Aug.-Oct. [*I. celosioides* sensu auth., non (L.)
Michx.].

29. Illecebraceae Lindl. — Whitlow-wort Family

1. Leaves oval ....1. *Paronychia*
1. Leaves linear-subulate ....2. *Scleranthus*

1. Paronychia Adans. — Forked-chickweed

1. Stem glabrous; sepals oval; utricle longer than the calyx; sandy
soil, locally throughout Ill. June-Aug. ....*P. canadensis* (L.) Wood
1. Stem puberulent; sepals ovate; utricle about as long as the calyx;
sandy soil, mostly in the southern part of the state. June-Sept.
[*Anychia polygonoides* Raf.] ....*P. fastigiata* (Raf.) Fern.

2. Scleranthus L.

S. annuus L. Waste ground, occasional; nat. from Eur. Apr.-Oct.

30. Phytolaccaceae Lindl. — Pokeweed Family

1. Phytolacca L. — Pokeweed

P. americana L. Woods and fields, common. June-Sept. [*P.
decandra* L.].

31. Nyctaginaceae Lindl. — Four-o'clock Family

1. Mirabilis L.
(*Allionia* Loefl.; *Oxybaphus* L'Her.)

1. Leaves ovate or ovate-lanceolate, all except the uppermost petiolate; gravelly or sandy soil, particularly along railroad embankments, common throughout Ill. May-Aug. Umbrella-wort ....
....*M. nyctaginea* (Michx.) MacM.
1. Leaves linear to lanceolate, sessile.
  2. Leaves lanceolate.
    3. Stem more or less glandular-pubescent; fruit with broad
smooth angles; sandy meadows or along railroads; known
from Cook, Jo Daviess, and Tazewell counties; adv. from
the western states. July-Aug. ....*M. hirsuta* (Pursh) MacM.
    3. Stem glabrous or nearly so; fruit with tuberculate angles;
pastures and borders of fields; known from Cook, Grundy,
and Logan counties; adv. from the southern states. July-
Aug. ....*M. albida* (Walt.) Heimerl

2. Leaves linear; stem glabrous; fruit with smooth angles; roadsides and waste places, occasional; adv. from the western states ....*M. linearis* (Pursh) Heimerl

32. Polygonaceae Lindl. — Buckwheat Family

1. Plants not climbing by tendrils; calyx-tube not enlarged in fruit; leaves with sheathing stipules.
    2. Sepals 6, the three inner ones becoming enlarged (valves) in fruit (except in the first species); stigmas tufted ....1. *Rumex*
    2. Sepals 5, sometimes 4, nearly equal; stigmas capitate.
        3. Leaves not hastate-deltoid, or if so, the stems climbing by prickles or reclining.
            4. Branches not at all adnate to the stem; flowers clustered (or if solitary not pink and the leaves not linear) ....2. *Polygonum*
            4. Branches more or less adnate to the internodes of the stem; stipular sheaths oblique or truncate, glabrous; flowers solitary in the axils of the bracts in slender panicled racemes; calyx pink; stamens 8; slender annual with linear leaves ....3. *Polygonella*
        3. Leaves hastate-deltoid; stem erect, smooth; flowers white; mature achenes much exserted from the calyx ....4. *Fagopyrum*
1. Plants climbing by tendrils; calyx-tube conspicuously enlarged in fruit, enclosing the achene; stipules obsolete; flowers in slender axillary and terminal racemes ....5. *Brunnichia*

1. Rumex L. — Dock

1. Leaves hastate, sometimes linear or lanceolate; plants with acid juice, dioecious or polygamous; rhizomes horizontal.
    2. Calyx essentially unchanged in fruit; achenes glandular, dull, much longer than the sepals; fields, roadsides, waste ground, common; nat. from Eur. May-July. Field Sorrel or Sour Dock ....*R. acetosella* L.
    2. Inner sepals winged in fruit, thin, reticulate, cordate, 3-4 mm wide, enclosing the smooth, glossy achene; sandy soil; Madison Co., *McDonald;* St. Clair Co., *Eggert* ....
    ....*R. hastatulus* Baldw.
1. Leaves not hastate or markedly acid; flowers perfect; roots stout.
    3. Inner sepals (valves) entire or merely denticulate.
        4. Leaves flat, not crisped, pale green or glaucescent, acute at each end; native species.
            5. Pedicels about equalling or shorter than the valves, curved.
                6. Only one valve (rarely two or three) bearing a tubercle; valves 4-5 mm long; leaves lanceolate; roadsides and alluvial soil, common. June. Pale Dock ....
                ....*R. altissimus* Wood
                6. Usually all three (rarely only 2) valves bearing a tubercle; valves 2.5-3 mm long; leaves linear-lanceolate; sandy soil, not common; throughout the state. June. [*R. mexicanus* sensu auth., non Meisn.] ....
                ....*R. triangulivalvis* (Danser) Rech.f.

5. Pedicels several times longer than the valves, deflexed, nearly straight, jointed close to the base; wet ground, common. June-July. Swamp Dock ....*R. verticillatus* L.

4. Leaves wavy-margined or crisped, dark green.

7. Only one of the valves bearing a small or rudimentary tubercle; valves cordate, nearly or quite entire, 5-6 mm broad; pedicels with a conspicuous joint; waste ground, occasional; nat. from Eur. May-July. Patience Dock ......
....*R. patientia* L.

7. Usually all three valves bearing well-developed tubercles.

8. Pedicels obscurely jointed; leaves 5-10 cm wide, the lower ones narrowed at the base; stem 1-2 m tall; wet ground, not common, chiefly in the northern half of the state. Aug.-Sept. Water Dock. [*R. britannica* sensu auth., non L.] ....*R. orbiculatus* A.Gray

8. Pedicels conspicuously jointed; leaves narrower, the lower ones truncate or cordate at the base; stem 30-90 cm tall; cultivated and waste ground, or roadsides, common; nat. from Eur. May-June. Curly Dock
....*R. crispus* L.

3. Valves with spinulose teeth.

9. Valves 3-4 mm long, deltoid, reticulate, only one-tubercled; pedicels jointed below the middle; lowest leaves broadly ovate, cordate at the base; plants perennial; fields and roadsides, common; nat. from Eur. June-Aug. Bitter Dock
....*R. obtusifolius* L.

9. Valves 2 mm long, with slender teeth, all three valves tubercled; pedicels jointed at base; leaves linear-lanceolate, narrowed at base, undulate or crisped; plants annual; sandy shores, local. July-Sept. [*R. persicarioides* sensu auth., non L.; *R. maritimus* sensu auth., non L.] ....
....*R. fueginus* Phil.

2. Polygonum L.

1. Flowers in small axillary clusters (or 1 or 2 in the upper axils); leaves jointed at base; stipules silvery; stems somewhat wiry, not twining.

2. Stems and branches terete or nearly so, striate, prostrate or ascending to erect.

3. Stems prostrate or spreading; sepals with white or pink margins; achenes dull, dark brown; waste ground, roadsides, along streets, very common and variable in appearance; nat. from Eur. June-Oct. [*P. neglectum* Besser; *P. buxiforme* Small]. Common Knotweed ....*P. aviculare* L.

3. Stems erect or ascending, branched; sepals with yellowish green margins; native species.

4. Leaves oval to obovate, 1-2.5 cm wide; achenes brown, dull or glossy; waste ground and disturbed soil. Aug.-Oct. [*P. achoreum* Blake]. Erect Knotweed ....*P. erectum* L.
4. Leaves linear-oblanceolate to narrowly elliptical, 2-5 mm wide; achenes black, glossy; in sandy or alluvial soil. July-Oct. [*P. exsertum* Small]. Bushy Knotweed ....
....*P. ramosissimum* Michx.
2. Stem and branches erect, sharply 4-angled; inflorescence slender; leaves plicate; sandy soil. July-Sept. Slender Knotweed ....*P. tenue* Michx.
1. Flowers in terminal or axillary spikes or racemes.
 5. Outer sepals not keeled or winged.
  6. Style short; sepals usually 5.
   7. Stem glabrous or pubescent, not retrorsely bristly.
    8. Panicle terminal, usually solitary; perennial marsh or aquatic or more or less amphibious herbs with long rhizomes.
     9. Panicle ovoid or ellipsoid, 1-3 cm long; leaves elliptical, glabrous, glossy above, obtuse or acute; shallow water. June-Aug. [*P. natans* (Michx.) Eaton, non Gueldenst.; *P. amphibium* of Am. auth., not L.]. The terrestrial pubescent form with lanceolate, acuminate leaves is f. *hartwrightii* (A.Gray) G.N.Jones. Water Smartweed ......*P. fluitans* Eaton
     9. Panicle linear-cylindrical, 3-9 cm long, the peduncle glandular-hispidulous or strigose; leaves lanceolate, acuminate; wet ground, common, except in the southern counties. July-Oct. [*P. emersum* (Michx.) Britt.; *P. muhlenbergii* (Meisn.) Wats.] ....
....*P. coccineum* Muhl.
    8. Panicles usually several, axillary as well as terminal; plants of moist rich soil.
     10. Stipular sheaths fringed with bristles.
      11. Calyx glandular-punctate.
       12. Panicles erect; stamens 8; achenes glossy; wet ground, common. July-Aug. Dotted Smartweed ....*P. punctatum* Ell.
       12. Panicles nodding in fruit; stamens 4 or 6; achenes dull; along ditches, common; nat. from Eur. Aug.-Oct. Water-pepper ....
....*P. hydropiper* L.
      11. Calyx not evidently punctate.
       13. Stems and peduncle glandular-hispidulous or pubescent; panicles nodding; flowers rose-color; achenes lenticular; plants annual.
        14. Leaves lanceolate; peduncles stipitate-glandular; achenes 1.8-2.5 mm long; sandy soil, local; Kankakee Co. July-Aug. ....*P. careyi* Olney

14. Leaves ovate; peduncles pubescent; a-
chenes about 3 mm long; stem 1-2 m
tall; waste places, roadsides, occasionally spread from cult. June-Oct. Native of Eurasia. Prince's Feather.
Kiss-me-over-the-garden-gate ....
....*P. orientale* L.
13. Stems and peduncles not glandular-hispidu-
lous or pubescent.
15. Panicles compact, ellipsoid, 7-10 mm
thick; leaves often with a more or less
evident dark blotch; flowers pink; cult.
ground, waste places, roadsides, fields,
common; nat. from Eur. May-Sept.
Lady's Thumb ....*P. persicaria* L.
15. Panicles slender, lax or interrupted;
achenes trigonal.
16. Sheaths strigose; calyx white or greenish; plants perennial; wet ground
or in shallow water, common. July-
Sept. [*P. opelousanum* Riddell; *P.
setaceum* Baldw.]. Mild Water-
pepper ......*P. hydropiperoides* Michx.
16. Sheaths glabrous; calyx rose; ·plants
annual; moist waste ground about
towns; native of trop. eastern Asia.
June-Oct. [*P. caespitosum* Blume]
..........................*P. longisetum* De Bruyn
10. Stipular sheaths not ciliate (except rarely some of the
uppermost); calyx not punctate; achenes glossy,
lenticular; plants annual.
17. Peduncles with short-stipitate glands; achenes
about 3 mm wide; panicles erect; cult. ground,
roadsides, fields, or along ditches, abundant
probably in every county. Aug.-Oct. [*P. longi-
stylum* Small] ....*P. pensylvanicum* L.
17. Peduncles with sessile glands, or glabrous; achenes
1.8-2 mm wide; panicles drooping or erect;
moist soil, common; probably nat. from Eur.
July-Sept. [*P. tomentosum* Schrank; *P. incarnatum* Ell.]. Pale Smartweed ....
....*P. lapathifolium* L.
7. Stem retrorsely bristly; leaves sagittate or hastate.
18. Leaves sagittate; stems 4-angled; stamens 8; style 3-
parted; achenes trigonal; wet ground, not common.
July-Oct. Arrow-vine ....*P. sagittatum* L.
18. Leaves hastate; stem ridged; stamens 6; style 2-parted;
achenes lenticular; swampy ground, apparently not
recently collected in Ill. ....*P. arifolium* L.

6. Style long, exserted, persistent, reflexed in fruit; calyx curved, 4-parted; racemes slender, rigid, greenish; leaves ovate, acuminate; woods, common. July-Sept. [*Tovara virginiana* (L.) Raf.] Jump-seed. Virginia Knotweed ....*P. virginianum* L.
5. Outer sepals keeled or winged at maturity.
  19. Stems twining or trailing.
    20. Outer sepals becoming conspicuously winged; achenes smooth, glossy; plants perennial.
      21. Mature fruiting calyx 8-10 mm long, the wings undulate or crisped; achenes 3.5-4.5 mm long; along fences, or borders of woods and thickets, common. July-Oct. Climbing False Buckwheat ....*P. scandens* L.
      21. Mature fruiting calyx 5-9 mm long, the wings flat; achenes 2-3 mm long; open woods, occasional. Aug.-Sept. [*P. dumetorum* of auth., not L.] ....*P. cristatum* Engelm. & Gray
    20. Outer sepals merely keeled at maturity; plants annual; achenes minutely roughened, dull, black, 3-4 mm long; fields and waste places, common throughout Ill.; nat. from Eur. June-Sept. Black Bindweed ....*P. convolvulus* L.
  19. Stems tall, stout, erect.
    22. Leaves 5-15 cm long, truncate or rounded at base; stems 1-2.5 cm tall; inflorescence lax, some of the axillary racemes much longer than the petioles; occasionally in waste ground about towns, spread from cult. and often forming vigorous colonies; native of Japan. July-Oct. [*P. sieboldii* de Vriese; *P. zuccarinii* Small]. Japanese Knotweed. Mexican-bamboo ....*P. cuspidatum* Sieb. & Zucc.
    22. Leaves 30-40 cm long, shallowly cordate at base; stems 2.5-4 m tall; inflorescence dense, the axillary racemes shorter than or equalling the petioles; native of Sakhalin I.; sometimes cultivated and occasionally established in Ill. Sacaline ....*P. sachalinense* F.Schmidt

3. Polygonella Michx. — Jointweed

P. articulata (L.) Meisn. Sandy soil, locally in n. Ill., extending southward to Peoria and Kankakee counties. July-Oct.

4. Fagopyrum Mill. — Buckwheat

F. esculentum Moench. Fields or roadsides, occasionally escaped from cult.; introd. from Eur. July-Sept.

5. Brunnichia Banks

B. cirrhosa Banks. River banks, thickets, or along fences, not common; known from Alexander, Franklin, Johnson, Massac, Pope, and Pulaski counties. Aug.-Oct.

33. Saururaceae Lindl. — Lizard-tail Family

1. Saururus L. — Lizard-tail

S. cernuus L. Wet ground in woods, or on muddy shores, locally abundant; extending northward to Henderson, Peoria, and Vermilion counties. June-Sept.

34. Rutaceae Juss. — Rue Family

1. Leaves pinnate; branches often prickly; fruit of 1-5 two-valved follicles ....1. *Zanthoxylum*
1. Leaves trifoliate; branches not prickly; fruit a 2-seeded, suborbicular samara ....2. *Ptelea*

1. Zanthoxylum L. — Prickly-ash

Z. americanum Mill. Woods and thickets, common in the northern half of Ill. Apr.-May.

2. Ptelea L. — Wafer-ash. Hop-tree

P. trifoliata L. Along streams and at the edges of woods, not uncommon. May-July.

35. Simarubaceae Lindl. — Quassia Family

1. Ailanthus Desf. — Tree of Heaven

A. altissima (Mill.) Swingle. Waste ground and edges of woods, common; native of China. June-July. [*A. glandulosa* Desf.].

36. Geraniaceae J.St.Hil. — Geranium Family

1. Leaves palmately veined and lobed or divided; antheriferous stamens 10, rarely 5 ....1. *Geranium*
1. Leaves pinnately veined and dissected; antheriferous stamens only 5 ....2. *Erodium*

1. Geranium L. — Cranesbill. Wild Geranium

1. Plants perennial with a stout caudex.
  2. Petals 14-22 mm long, purple, sometimes white, the flowers 2.5-3.5 cm in diameter; stem-leaves 2; style column 2.5-3.5 cm long; moist woods, and along roads, common throughout Ill. May-June ....*G. maculatum* L.
  2. Petals less than 1 cm long, whitish or pink, the flowers 6-8 mm in diameter; stem-leaves several; stems weak, diffusely branched; waste places, occasional; adv. from Asia; Ogle Co., *Bebb;* Champaign Co., *Gleason* in 1898; Winnebago Co., *E. W. & G. B. Fell* in 1947. Siberian Cranesbill ....*G. sibiricum* L.
1. Plants annual or biennial; petals 2-10 mm long.

3. Leaves palmately lobed; carpels attached to the styles; petals 2-7 mm long.
  4. Sepals awn-tipped (the tips 1-3 mm long) ; seeds reticulate.
    5. Fruiting pedicels much longer than the calyx; beak of mature style-column 4-6 mm long; fields and open woods, occasional; Cook and Lake counties. June-Aug. ....*G. bicknellii* Britt.
    5. Fruiting pedicels shorter than, or slightly longer than, the calyx; beak of mature style-column 1-2 mm long; roadsides, fields, and open woods. May-July ....*G. carolinianum* L.
  4. Sepals merely callus-tipped; seeds smooth or nearly so; carpels pubescent, not rugose; style-column beakless; waste places; nat. from Eur. May-Aug. ....*G. pusillum* Burm.f.
3. Leaves 3-divided; carpels deciduous from the styles; petals 8-10 mm long; moist ground, occasional; adv. from Eur. June-Sept. ....*G. robertianum* L.

2. **Erodium** L'Her. — Storksbill
E. cicutarium (L.) L'Her. Waste places; nat. from Eur. May-Aug.

37. **Linaceae** Dumort. — Flax Family
1. **Linum** L. — Flax
1. Petals blue (or white), 1-1.5 cm long; capsules 8-12 mm in diameter.
  2. Perennial; flowers 2-3 cm in diameter; sepals obtusish, ciliate; occasionally found as an escape from cult.; introd. from Eur. June-Aug. Perennial Flax ....*L. perenne* L.
  2. Annual; flowers 10-15 mm in diameter; sepals acute, the inner often ciliate; roadsides and waste places, occasional; introd. from Eur. June-Aug. Cultivated Flax ....*L. usitatissimum* L.
1. Petals yellow, 4-8 mm long; capsules 3-6 mm in diameter.
  3. Styles distinct; leaves without dark stipular glands; false septa of the capsule nearly complete, not ciliate; plants perennial.
    4. Inner sepals minutely glandular-ciliolate; sandy soil, local. July-Aug. [*L. medium* var. *texanum* (Planch.) Fern.] ....*L. medium* (Planch.) Britt.
    4. Sepals entire.
      5. Outer sepals 3-3.5 mm long at maturity; dry open woods, local; chiefly s. Ill.; also Cook and Lake counties. June-Aug. ....*L. virginianum* L.
      5. Outer sepals 2-2.5 mm long at maturity; damp ground, rare; Jackson, Johnson, and Pope counties. July-Aug. ....*L. striatum* Walt.
  3. Styles united below; outer sepals 4-6 mm long, lanceolate, acuminate, strongly glandular-ciliolate; leaves with dark stipular glands; false septa of the capsule incomplete, con-

spicuously ciliate; plants annual; dry soil, local. July-Sept.
....*L. sulcatum* Riddell

38. Oxalidaceae Lindl. — Wood-sorrel Family

1. Oxalis L.

1. Flowers purple (rarely white), 14-20 mm long; plants scapose, with a thick bulb-like or scaly rhizome; woods, common. Apr.-June. Violet Wood-sorrel ....*O. violacea* L.
1. Flowers yellow; stems leafy; rhizomes slender.
  2. Stems creeping, rooting at the nodes, the pubescence of spreading hairs; pedicels strigillose; a weed in greenhouses and gardens; native of Eur. Creeping Wood-sorrel. [*O. repens* Thunb.] ....*O. corniculata* L.
  2. Stems erect, or decumbent at the base.
    3. Pedicels and stems strigillose; capsules finely grayish-pubescent, abruptly pointed, the styles 1-2 mm long; fruiting pedicels becoming deflexed but the capsules erect; common in fields, along roads, or in open woods. May-Sept. Common Yellow Wood-sorrel [*O. stricta* of auth., not L.] ....*O. dillenii* Jacq.
    3. Pedicels and stems with spreading hairs, or the latter nearly glabrous; capsules sparsely glandular-pilose to nearly glabrous, gradually pointed, the styles 2-3 mm long; fruiting pedicels ascending or divergent.
      4. Petals 3-10 mm long; seeds about 1.5 mm long, with nearly continuous ridges; occasional plants have red foliage; roadsides and open woods, common. June-Nov. Upright Wood-sorrel. [*O. cymosa* Small; *O. europaea* Jord.] ....*O. stricta* L.
      4. Petals 12-16 mm long; capsules 6-10 mm long; seeds 2 mm long, the ridges discontinuous; woods, rare; near the Wabash R., Mt. Carmel, *Schneck* ......*O. grandis* Small

39. Limnanthaceae Lindl. — Limnanthes Family

1. Floerkea Willd. — False Mermaid

F. proserpinacoides Willd. Moist ground in woods, locally abundant; extending southward to Edwards and Crawford counties. Apr.-June.

40. Zygophyllaceae Lindl. — Caltrop Family

1. Flowers (in our species) 1-1.5 cm in diameter; carpels five, several-ovuled, at maturity bearing 2-4 prickles ....1. *Tribulus*
1. Flowers (in our species) 2-2.5 cm in diameter; carpels ten, 1-ovuled, tuberculate, not spiny ....2. *Kallstroemia*

1. Tribulus L. — Caltrop. Puncture-weed

T. terrestris L. Waste places and sandy soil, occasional; nat. from southern Eur. June-Sept.

2. Kallstroemia Scop.

K. intermedia Rydb. Railroad yards, occasional; adv. from southern U.S.; Blue Island, near Chicago, Cook Co., *Babcock; H. Eggert* in St. Clair Co. [*K. maxima* sensu auth., non (L.) T. & G.].

41. Balsaminaceae Lindl. — Jewel-weed Family

1. Impatiens L. — Jewel-weed

1. Flowers orange, thickly red-dotted; spur strongly incurved; moist woods, common. June-Sept. Spotted Touch-me-not ......
....*I. biflora* Walt.
1. Flowers pale yellow, sparingly red-dotted; spur bent at a right angle to the sac; moist woods, common. July-Sept. Pale Touch-me-not ....*I. pallida* Nutt.

42. Polygalaceae Reichenb. — Milkwort Family

1. Polygala L. — Milkwort

1. Plants perennial or biennial, usually several-stemmed (except *P. paucifolia*); leaves alternate.
   2. Flowers 1-3, terminal, rose-purple to white, 1.5-2 cm long; leaves oval, near the summit of the stem, the lower scale-like; rhizomes slender, bearing inconspicuous cleistogamous flowers; moist woods, rare; Cook Co. May-June. Fringed Polygala ....*P. paucifolia* Willd.
   2. Flowers several or many, 3-6 mm long, in terminal racemes.
      3. Leaves lanceolate to ovate, acuminate, 5-20 mm wide; flowers greenish-white; racemes compact; wings orbicular-ovate, 2-3 mm long; plants perennial; cleistogamous flowers absent; wooded banks, or roadsides, local; extending southward to Madison and Wabash counties. May-Sept. Seneca Snakeroot ....*P. senega* L.
      3. Leaves linear-oblanceolate, acutish, 2-6 mm wide; flowers rose-purple to pink; racemes loose; wings obovate, 4-6 mm long; plants biennial, with small cleistogamous flowers usually present at base; sandy soil in the northern half of Ill. June-Aug. ....*P. polygama* Walt.
1. Plants annual, single-stemmed; leaves linear or linear-oblanceolate.
   4. Racemes capitate, obtuse, more than 5 mm thick.
      5. Leaves alternate.
         6. Stem glaucous; leaves linear-subulate, distant; petals united into a tube about 5 mm long; wings linear, less than half the length of the keel; prairie soil, in the northern half of the state, rare. July-Sept. ....*P. incarnata* L.
         6. Stem leafy, not glaucous; petals not united into a long tube; wings oval, equalling or exceeding the keel; fields, meadows, and open woods. July-Sept. [*P. viridescens* L.] ....*P. sanguinea* L.

5. Leaves in whorls of four, linear-oblanceolate; wings acuminate; sandy soil in the northern half of the state. July-Sept. ....*P. cruciata* L

4. Racemes slender, cylindrical or linear, tapering, less than 5 mm thick.

7. Branches mostly opposite or whorled; racemes short-peduncled; flowers green or greenish; dry soil, locally throughout Ill. July-Sept. ....*P. verticillata* L.

7. Branches mostly alternate; racemes long-peduncled; flowers purplish or greenish-purple; woods and fields; extending northward to Cass and Cumberland counties. June-Aug. ....*P. ambigua* Nutt

43. Euphorbiaceae J. St. Hil. — Spurge Family

1. Flowers not in an involucre; calyx of 3-5 sepals; sap watery.
2. Pubescence of stellate hairs.
3. Flowers in spikes or glomerules; ovary 3- (2-4-) loculed ....1. *Croton*
3. Flowers scattered on the branchlets; ovary 1-loculed ....2. *Crotonopsis*
2. Pubescence, if any, of simple hairs.
4. Leaves entire; stamens usually 3; styles simple; bracts of the pistillate flowers not cleft ....3. *Phyllanthus*
4. Leaves serrate.
5. Bracts of the pistillate flowers cleft; styles many-cleft; stamens usually 8; stems not twining ....4. *Acalypha*
5. Bracts not cleft; styles 3; stamens 1-5; stem (in our species) twining, and the leaves ovate-cordate, dentate ....5. *Tragia*
1. Flowers in a cup-shaped calyx-like involucre; sepals rudimentary; sap milky.
6. Leaves opposite, oblique at base ....6. *Chamaesyce*
6. Leaves not oblique at base, alternate or opposite.
7. Inflorescences in a several-rayed umbel; stipules none ....7. *Euphorbia*
7. Inflorescences cymose; stipules gland-like ....8. *Poinsettia*

1. Croton L.

1. Leaves serrate; staminate flowers with a 4-parted calyx, 4 petals, a 4-rayed disk, and 8 stamens; pistillate flowers with a 5-parted calyx; styles 3, bifid; sandy soil; adv. from southern U.S. Aug.-Oct. Sand Croton ....*C. glandulosus* L.
1. Leaves entire.
2. Capsules clustered, erect, depressed-globose, 7-9 mm in diameter; styles 3, bifid or trifid; stamens 10-14; sandy soil; absent from the extreme northern counties. Aug.-Sept. ....*C. capitatus* Michx.
2. Capsules mostly solitary, pendent, ovoid, 3-4 mm long; style none, the stigmas 2, bifid; stamens 3-8; roadsides and fields; chiefly in the southern half of Ill.; also Cook Co. July-Oct. ....*C. monanthogynus* Michx.

2. **Crotonopsis** Michx.

1. Leaves lanceolate; fruit ovoid; fields and open woods, southern Ill. July-Sept. ....*C. elliptica* Willd
1. Leaves linear-lanceolate; fruit ellipsoid; dry sandy soil, not common; west-central Ill. July-Sept. ....*C. linearis* Michx.

3. **Phyllanthus** L.

P. caroliniensis Walt. Sandy soil, locally in the southern two-thirds of the state. May-Oct.

4. **Acalypha** L. — Three-seeded Mercury

1. Leaves slender-petioled.
    2. Leaves cordate at base, ovate; capsules echinate; staminate and pistillate flowers in separate spikes; roadsides, fields, bluffs, southern Illinois. July-Oct. [*A. caroliniana* sensu auth., non Walt.] ....*A. ostryaefolia* Riddell
    2. Leaves cuneate at base, rhombic-ovate to oval; capsules smooth; staminate and pistillate flowers in the same spike.
        3. Stem with short, curved hairs, or nearly glabrous; bracts of the pistillate flowers 5- to 7-lobed, bearing a few whitish stipitate glands (at least when young), or nearly glabrous.
            4. Leaves lance- to rhombic-ovate, 2-9 cm long; seeds 1.6-1.8 mm long; woods, fields, and roadsides, common. July-Oct. [*A. virginica* sensu auth., ex p.] ....*A. rhomboidea* Raf.
            4. Leaves broadly ovate, 7.5-10.5 cm long; seeds 2.5-3 mm long; river bottoms, rare; Vermilion Co., *H. E. Ahles 6989* in 1952 ....*A. deamii* (Weatherby) Ahles
        3. Stem with straight spreading hairs, in addition to the short curved ones; bracts with 9-15 lobes, hispid-pubescent on the veins and margins, not glandular; fields, roadsides, and wooded slopes, local. July-Oct. [*A. digyneia* Raf.] ....*A. virginica* L.
1. Leaves short-petioled (petiole ⅛ - ¼ the length of the blade), elliptic-lanceolate to lanceolate, or linear; bracts with 9-11 ovate to deltoid teeth; stem with short, curved hairs; woods, fields, and roadsides; chiefly in the southern half of the state. June-Sept. [*A. gracilens* var. *fraseri* (Muell.-Arg.) Weatherby] ....*A. gracilens* A.Gray

5. **Tragia** L.

T. cordata Michx. Banks of the Ohio R. at Golconda, Pope Co., *S. A. Forbes; E. J. Palmer.* [*T. macrocarpa* Willd.].

6. **Chamaesyce** S.F.Gray
(*Euphorbia* ex p.)

1. Leaves entire; stems prostrate; whole plant glabrous.
    2. Leaves roundish-oval, 1-3 mm long; sandy soil, local. July-Sept. ....*C. serpens* (HBK.) Small

2. Leaves oblong, longer than broad, 4-20 mm in length.
   3. Capsules 3-3.5 mm long; seeds 2-2.5 mm long; sandy soil,
      rare; Cook, Lake, and Peoria counties. July-Sept. ....
      ....*C. polygonifolia* (L.) Small
   3. Capsules 2-2.5 mm long; seeds 1.5 mm long; sandy soil, local.
      June-Sept. ....*C. geyeri* (Engelm.) Small
1. Leaves toothed, at least at the apex.
   4. Capsules glabrous; seeds wrinkled.
     5. Leaves toothed on both margins; styles 0.6-1 mm long.
       6. Stems usually ascending, glabrous or pilose in lines below;
         capsules 1.9-2.3 mm long; fields and roadsides, common
         throughout Ill. July-Sept. Nodding Spurge. [*E. preslii*
         Guss.; *E. hypericifolia* sensu auth., non L.] ....
         ....*C. maculata* (L.) Small
       6. Stems usually prostrate; stems pilose; capsules 1.6-1.9 mm
         long; fields and roadsides, rare; Jackson and Lake
         counties ....*C. vermiculata* (Raf.) House
     5. Leaves toothed only near tip; styles 0.3-0.5 mm long.
       7. Leaves linear-oblong; seeds with 5-6 sharp ridges; sandy
         or gravelly soil, not common; known from Cook, Henry,
         Lee, Peoria, and St. Clair counties. June-Sept. ....
         ....*C. glyptosperma* (Engelm.) Small
       7. Leaves ovate to oblong; seeds without sharp ridges; adv.
         from the western states; Cook Co. ....:........
         ....*C. serpyllifolia* (Pers.) Small
   4. Capsules pubescent; stems prostrate, villous.
     8. Leaves usually somewhat pubescent beneath; seeds 0.8-0.9
       mm long, minutely pitted and inconspicuously transverse-
       ly rugose; cultivated ground and roadsides, common. July-
       Oct. Milk Spurge. [*E. maculata* sensu auth., non L.] ....
       ....*C. supina* (Raf.) Moldenke
     8. Leaves glabrous beneath; seeds 1 mm long, papillose, ob-
       scurely wrinkled; sandy soil, local. July-Sept. ....
       ....*C. humistrata* (Engelm.) Small

7. **Euphorbia** L. — Spurge

1. Glands of the involucres with petal-like appendages.
   2. Leaves not conspicuously white-margined; plants perennial with
      a deep root; roadsides, fields, and open woods, common
      throughout Ill. June-Sept. Flowering Spurge. [*Tithymalop-
      sis corollata* (L.) Small] ....*E. corollata* L.
   2. Upper leaves conspicuously white-margined; plants annual;
      waste ground, escaped from cult.; native westward. July-
      Sept. Snow-on-the-mountain. [*Lepadena marginata* (Pursh)
      Nieuwl.] ....*E. marginata* Pursh
1. Glands of the involucres without petal-like appendages.
   3. Leaves entire.

4. Plants perennial, with a rhizome; stems clustered; capsules granular; seeds smooth.
   5. Leaves lanceolate to linear, 3-15 mm wide; a weed in fields and waste places in some of the northern counties; apparently migrating southward, and now known to occur as far south as Champaign and Vermilion counties; nat. from Eur. June-Sept. Leafy Spurge ....*E. esula* L.
   5. Leaves linear, 1-3 mm wide; roadsides and cemeteries; nat. from Eur. May-Sept. Cypress Spurge ......*E. cyparissias* L.
4. Plants annual or biennial; capsules smooth; seeds pitted.
   6. Seeds finely pitted, 1-1.5 mm long; lobes of the capsules 2-crested; waste places; nat. from Eur.; Menard Co. June-Sept. ....*E. peplus* L.
   6. Seeds coarsely pitted, 2 mm long; lobes of the capsules rounded; wooded slopes and gravelly soil, local. May-June ....*E. commutata* Engelm.
3. Leaves serrulate.
   7. Leaves pubescent beneath; an occasional weed in waste places; nat. from Eur. June-Aug. ....*E. platyphylla* L.
   7. Leaves glabrous or nearly so.
      8. Leaves spatulate; capsules warty; seeds smooth; moist ground, local. May-June ....*E. obtusata* Pursh
      8. Leaves obovate; capsules smooth; seeds reticulate; waste places; nat. from Eur. June-Oct. Wart Spurge ....
         ....*E. helioscopia* L.

8. Poinsettia Graham

1. Leaves chiefly opposite, dentate, strigillose, glands of the involucres stipitate; roadsides and fields, probably adv. from w. U.S. July-Sept. ....*P. dentata* (Michx.) Small
1. Leaves alternate, oval to linear, glabrous or nearly so, often lobed and red-based; glands sessile; roadsides and waste places. June-Aug. [*P. heterophylla* of auth.] ....*P. cyathophora* (Murr.) Small

44. Celastraceae Lindl. — Staff-tree Family

1. Leaves opposite; flowers axillary, cymose, or solitary; capsules 4- to 5-loculed, usually lobed ....1. *Euonymus*
1. Leaves alternate; flowers in terminal racemes; capsules 3-loculed, subglobose ....2. *Celastrus*

1. Euonymus L.

1. Erect shrubs.
   2. Leaves petioled; flower-parts commonly in fours; capsules smooth; woods near streams; throughout Ill. May-July. Wahoo ....*E. atropurpureus* Jacq.
   2. Leaves nearly sessile; flower-parts commonly in fives; capsules rough-warty; woods, rare and local; Pulaski and Wabash counties. May ....*E. americanus* L.

1. Decumbent shrubs, rooting at the nodes; woods, local. Trailing
   Strawberry-bush ....*E. obovatus* Nutt.

2. Celastrus L.

1. Leaves ovate-oblong, serrulate, pointed; rich soil, common. May-
   June. Climbing Bittersweet ....*C. scandens* L.
1. Leaves suborbicular, crenate, obtuse; introd. from Asia; occasional at edge of woods, or along roads. White Bittersweet ....
   ....*C. orbiculatus* Thunb.

45. Sapindaceae Juss. — Soapberry Family

1. Cardiospermum L. — Balloon-vine

C. halicacabum L. Native of the tropics, sometimes cultivated for
ornament; occasionally escaping, but seldom persisting; Jackson, Randolph, and St. Clair counties.

46. Staphyleaceae (DC.) Lindl. — Bladdernut Family

1. Staphylea L. — American Bladdernut

S. trifolia L. Moist woods and thickets, common. Apr.-May.

47. Hippocastanaceae T. & G. — Horse-chestnut Family

1. Aesculus L. — Horse-chestnut

1. Winter-buds sticky; leaflets usually 7; petals 5, white, blotched
   with red and yellow; stamens exserted; calyx 6-9 mm long,
   puberulent; fruit echinate; large tree, frequent in cult., but
   rarely wild and not established; native of Greece. May-June.
   Horse-chestnut ....*A. hippocastanum* L.
1. Winter-buds not sticky; leaflets usually 5; small trees, native.
   2. Flowers yellowish, 12-18 mm long; petals villous at the margin;
      stamens conspicuously exserted; calyx campanulate, 5-6 mm
      long; fruit echinate; woods, locally throughout Ill. except the
      northern counties. Apr.-May. Ohio Buckeye ....*A. glabra* L.
   2. Flowers 3-4 cm long, mostly red but some red and yellow;
      margin of petals glandular; stamens only slightly exserted;
      calyx tubular, 12-16 mm long; fruit smooth; woods, s. Ill.
      Apr. Red Buckeye. [*A. octandra* of auth., not Marsh.; *A.
      pavia* of auth., not L.] ....*A. discolor* Pursh

48. Aquifoliaceae Lindl. — Holly Family

1. Ilex L. — Holly

1. Leaves obovate, rounded at the apex, crenate; calyx-lobes not
   ciliate; nutlets ribbed; woods, bluffs, edges of ponds and
   swamps; in the counties bordering the Mississippi, Wabash,
   and Ohio rivers. April-May. Possumhaw. Swamp Holly ....
   ....*I. decidua* Walt.

1. Leaves elliptical, acuminate, serrate; calyx-lobes ciliate; nutlets smooth; woods and swamps; more frequent in the northern counties. Winterberry ....*I. verticillata* (L.) A.Gray

49. Anacardiaceae Lindl. — Sumac Family

1. Rhus L.

(*Toxicodendron* Mill.; *Schmaltzia* Desv.)

1. Leaves with 7-31 leaflets.
    2. Leaflets decurrent on the rachis, which is therefore conspicuously winged; fruit red, pubescent; roadsides, fields, and open woods, often in sandy soil, locally throughout Ill., except the central counties. July-Aug. Shining Sumac. Dwarf Sumac. [*R. copallina* var. *latifolia* Engler] ....*R. copallina* L.
    2. Leaflets not decurrent; rachis not winged.
        3. Leaflets serrate; fruit red, in terminal clusters.
            4. Twigs and leaves glabrous; along roads and fences, and in open woods, common throughout Ill. June-July. Smooth Sumac. [*R. media* Greene; *R. valida* Greene] ....*R. glabra* L.
            4. Twigs and petioles villous-hirsute; woods in the northern half of Ill.; occasionally introd. elsewhere. June-July. Staghorn Sumac. [*R. hirta* (L.) Sudw.] ....*R. typhina* L.
        3. Leaflets entire or nearly so; fruit glabrous, whitish or pale greenish, in axillary panicles; plants poisonous to the touch; tamarack bogs and swampy ground; Coles, Cook, Kankakee, Lake, McHenry, and Woodford counties. June-July. Poison Sumac. [*R. venenata* DC.] ....*R. vernix* L.
1. Leaves with 3 leaflets.
    5. Flowers in loose axillary panicles, appearing after the leaves; fruit glabrous, greenish-white; plants erect, trailing, or climbing, poisonous to the touch; along fences and in woods, or on sand dunes, common. May-July. Poison-ivy. [*R. toxicodendron* sensu auth., non L.] ....*R. radicans* L.
    5. Flowers in short dense panicled spikes, catkin-like before opening, appearing before or with the leaves; fruit red, pubescent; foliage not poisonous, fragrant when bruised.
        6. Flowers nearly sessile, appearing before the leaves; leaflets 2-6 cm long, rhombic-obovate to ovate, acute; petioles villosulous to nearly glabrous; gravelly or rocky banks, locally throughout Ill., except the northern counties; more frequent southward. Apr.-May. Fragrant Sumac. [*R. canadensis* Marsh., non Mill.; *R. crenata* sensu Rydb., non Thunb.; *Schmaltzia formosa* Greene; *S. illinoensis* Greene] ....*R. aromatica* Ait.
        6. Flowers on pedicels 2-3 mm long, on leafy twigs; leaflets 1-2.5 cm long, obtusish, crenately few-lobed or -toothed above the middle; petioles puberulent or tomentulose;

sandy banks and dunes in the western and northwestern
counties. May. [*Schmaltzia arenaria* Greene] ....
....*R. arenaria* (Greene) G.N.Jones

50. Aceraceae J.St.Hil. — Maple Family

1. Acer L. — Maple

1. Leaves simple, palmately-lobed; floral disk present; anthers ellipsoid, not apiculate.
   2. Leaves silvery-whitish or glaucous on the lower surface; flowers in dense sessile clusters, appearing before the leaves.
      3. Leaves 5-lobed, the lobes serrate or cleft or parted; petals none; ovary tomentose; samaras divergent, pubescent; chiefly in alluvial soil, common. Mar.-Apr. Silver Maple
      ....*A. saccharinum* L.
      3. Leaves 3- to 5-lobed, the lobes unequally crenate-serrate; petals 5; ovary glabrous; samaras incurved, glabrous at maturity.
         4. Leaves glabrous or nearly so on the lower surface at maturity; mature twigs glabrous; samaras 18-25 mm long, the wing 6-8 mm wide; woods, local; chiefly in southern Ill., but also in Cook, Lake, and McHenry counties. Mar.-Apr. Red Maple ....*A. rubrum* L.
         4. Leaves permanently tomentose beneath; twigs more or less pubescent at maturity; samaras 3.5-6 cm long, the wing 1-2 cm broad at the middle; swamps, rare, southern Ill.
         ....*A. drummondii* H.&A.
   2. Leaves not silvery-white beneath; flowers corymbose, appearing with the leaves.
      6. Leaves flat, 3- to 5-lobed, the lobes coarsely dentate, more or less glabrous; stipules absent; woods, common. Apr.-May. Sugar Maple ....*A. saccharum* Marsh.
      6. Leaves with drooping sides, usually with 3 main lobes, the lobes acuminate, entire or undulate or obtusely toothed; lower surface yellowish-green and softly pubescent, at least along the veins, varying to nearly glabrous in age; stipules often present, large, enclosing the bud; woods, local; May. Black Maple ....*A. nigrum* Michx.f.
1. Leaves 3- to 7-foliolate; trees dioecious; flowers greenish, drooping on slender pedicels, slightly before the leaves; anthers linear, apiculate; disk none; petals none; alluvial soil, common. Apr.-May. Box-elder ....*A. negundo* L.

51. Rhamnaceae R.Br. — Buckthorn Family

1. Leaves pinnately-veined; flowers greenish-yellowish; fruit a drupe ....
   ....1.   *Rhamnus*
1. Leaves triple-veined; flowers (in our species) white, fragrant; fruit a capsule ....2.   *Ceanothus*

1. **Rhamnus** L. — Buckthorn

1. Winter buds scaly.
　2. Leaves opposite or subopposite, ovate, abruptly acute; twigs rigid, often spine-like; flowers usually 4-merous; petals present; drupe with 3 or 4 nutlets; roadsides and edges of woods, occasional, in the northern half of Ill.; nat. from Eurasia. May-June. Common Buckthorn ....*R. cathartica* L.
　2. Leaves alternate; native shrubs 1-2 m tall; twigs not at all spine-like.
　　3. Leaves elliptical, serrulate, pubescent beneath; twigs puberulent; flowers 4-merous; petals present, small; drupe with 2 nutlets; alluvial soil, bluffs, river banks, the common species in Ill.; absent from the southern counties. May ....*R. lanceolata* Pursh
　　3. Leaves oval or obovate, strongly veined, crenate-serrate; twigs glabrous; flowers 5-merous; petals none; drupe with 3 nutlets; wooded swamps, chiefly in n. Ill. Alder Buckthorn ....*R. alnifolia* L'Her.
1. Winter buds naked; leaves alternate; flowers 5-merous; shrubs or small trees 3-10 m tall.
　4. Leaves obscurely serrulate; flowers in peduncled cymes, the pedicels pubescent; calyx-lobes lanceolate, acuminate; drupe 8-10 mm in diameter, with 3 nutlets; wooded slopes, rare; known from Gallatin, Jackson, Monroe, Pope, and Randolph counties. May-June. Carolina Buckthorn ....*R. caroliniana* Walt.
　4. Leaves entire or undulate; flowers fascicled; pedicels glabrous; calyx-lobes ovate, acute; drupe 6-8 mm in diameter, with 2 nutlets; woods and roadsides, occasional; nat. from Eurasia. May-June. Glossy Buckthorn ....*R. frangula* L.

2. **Ceanothus** L.

1. Leaves ovate, acute; seeds smooth; thickets and open woods, common. June-July. New Jersey Tea ....*C. americanus* L.
1. Leaves elliptic-lanceolate; seeds pitted; sandy soil in the northern counties of Ill., not common. [*C. ovalis* Bigel.] ......*C. ovatus* Desf.

52. **Vitaceae** Lindl. — Grape Family

1. Leaves simple, or pinnately compound.
　2. Inflorescence longer than broad; petals united in a cap, falling away without separating; pith interrupted at the nodes; fruit edible; leaves simple, palmately-lobed or dentate ....1. *Vitis*
　2. Inflorescence broader than long; petals separate, spreading; pith not interrupted at the nodes; fruit not edible ....2. *Ampelopsis*
1. Leaves palmately compound with usually 5 leaflets ....3. *Parthenocissus*

1. **Vitis** L. — Grape

1. Mature leaves grayish or rusty arachnoid-pubescent beneath.
　2. Pubescence of lower leaf surface a thin web; grapes 1-2.5 cm in

diameter; dry woods, rare; Randolph Co., *Weber* in 1958
....*V. lincecumii* Buckl.
2. Pubescence of lower leaf surface denser, deciduous; grapes 4-
    12 mm in diameter.
    3. Twigs terete or nearly so, glabrate; fruit glaucous, about 1 cm
        in diameter; woods, thickets, and river banks; in the north-
        ern two-thirds of the state. June-July. Summer Grape.
        [*V. bicolor* sensu Bailey, non LeConte; *V. argentifolia*
        Munson] ....*V. aestivalis* Michx.
    3. Twigs distinctly angular, permanently pubescent; fruit black,
        6-8 mm in diameter; woods and stream banks. June-July.
        Winter Grape ....*V. cinerea* Engelm.
1. Mature leaves green beneath, short-pubescent along the veins, or
    nearly glabrous.
    4. Leaves coarsely dentate or slightly 3-lobed; fruit black, glossy,
        not glaucous; in woods and along fences, common. May-
        June. Frost Grape. [*V. cordifolia* Lam.] ....*V. vulpina* L.
    4. Leaves sharply 3- to 5-lobed.
        5. Lobes acuminate, the sinuses rounded; fruit black, not
            glaucous; alluvial soil in the southern part of the state;
            Alexander, Jackson, Johnson, Massac, Pope, and Pulaski
            counties. May-July. Catbird Grape. [*V. rubra* Michx.;
            V. monosperma Michx.] ....*V. palmata* Vahl
        5. Lobes and sinuses acute; fruit glaucous; alluvial soil; through-
            out Ill. May-June. Riverbank Grape. [*V. vulpina* sensu
            auth., non L.] ....*V. riparia* Michx.

2. Ampelopsis Michx.

1. Leaves simple, ovate, serrate or slightly 3-lobed; woods, thickets,
    and along fences; s. Ill., extending northward along the river
    valleys to Hancock and Mason counties. June-July. Raccoon-
    grape. [*Cissus ampelopsis* Pers.; *Vitis indivisa* Willd] ....
    ....*A. cordata* Michx.
1. Leaves bipinnate, the leaflets ovate, toothed; moist woods;
    known from Alexander, Jackson, Pulaski, Randolph, and Union
    counties. July-Aug. Pepper-vine. [*A. bipinnata* Michx.; *Vitis
    arborea* L.; *Cissus stans* Pers.] ....*A. arborea* (L.) Koehne

3. Parthenocissus Planch.

1. Leaflets dull above, pale beneath; tendrils with 5-8 branches end-
    ing in adhesive tips; cymes usually crowded into terminal
    panicles; fruit 5-7 mm in diameter, 1- to 3-seeded; plants high-
    climbing; woods, and along fences, common. June-July. Vir-
    ginia Creeper. [*Parthenocissus inserta* (Kerner) K.Fritsch] ....
    ....*P. quinquefolia* (L.) Planch.
1. Leaflets somewhat glossy above, scarcely paler beneath; tendrils
    with 3-5 branches, usually without adhesive disks; cymes soli-

tary; fruit 8-10 mm in diameter, 3- to 4-seeded; plants usually low and trailing; thickets and along fences, local; Cook, Du Page, Kane, Lake, McHenry, Stephenson, and Winnebago counties. June-July. Woodbine ....*P. vitacea* (Knerr) Hitchc.

53. Rosaceae Juss. — Rose Family
(*Malaceae* Small; *Drupaceae* DC.)

1. Trees and shrubs.
  2. Pistils several to many, simple, or pistil apparently one, compound.
    3. Pistils 2-many, simple, superior; fruits achenes, drupelets, or follicles.
      4. Pistils 2-5, each becoming a 2- to 4-seeded follicle; shrubs with simple, serrate to entire, or slightly lobed leaves.
        5. Leaves palmately shallowly lobed; carpels 2-5, somewhat inflated at maturity; pubescence of stellate hairs ....1. *Physocarpus*
        5. Leaves serrate to entire; carpels 5-8, not inflated; pubescence of simple hairs, or plant glabrous ....2. *Spiraea*
      4. Pistils numerous, or rarely few, each becoming a 1-seeded achene or drupelet.
        6. Leaflets or leaves serrate.
          7. Flowers white or purple (in our species); leaves palmately compound (simple in one species), the stipules not adnate to the petiole; fruit an aggregate of 1-seeded drupelets forming a blackberry or raspberry ....11. *Rubus*
          7. Flowers rose (in our species); leaves pinnate (rarely 3-foliolate), the stipules adnate to the petiole; fruit of seed-like achenes enclosed in the hypanthium (calyx-tube) ......12. *Rosa*
        6. Leaflets entire, silky-pubescent; flowers yellow (species of) .... 6. *Potentilla*
    3. Pistil apparently 1, compound, inferior, enclosed by the calyx-tube; styles 2-5; fruit a pome.
      8. Leaves simple.
        9. Flowers in racemes; petals narrow; fruit small, berry-like, sweet, with thin pulp, its locules twice as many as the styles; branches not spiny ....13. *Amelanchier*
        9. Flowers in cymes or corymbs; petals roundish; locules of the fruit (carpels) the same number as the styles.
          10. Leaves entire ....14. *Cydonia*
          10. Leaves serrate, crenate, or lobed.
            11. Midvein of the leaves with small dark-colored glands on the upper surface; margins glandular-crenulate; flowers in compound cymes; anthers purple; styles united below; fruit small, berry-like; endocarp of the ripe carpels leathery ....16. *Aronia*
            11. Midvein not glandular; margins not glandular-crenulate.
              12. Inflorescence cymose; endocarp of the ripe carpels cartilaginous.
                13. Styles free; orifice of the receptacle closed by the disk; anthers pink or red; fruit containing numerous stone-cells ....17. *Pyrus*
                13. Styles united below the middle; orifice of the receptacle open; anthers white or yellow; fruit without stone-cells ....19. *Malus*

      12. Inflorescence corymbose; endocarp of the ripe carpels
          hard and bony; branches usually with spines ....
          .... 19. *Crataegus*
   8. Leaves pinnate; flowers in terminal compound cymes; petals
      roundish; styles 3, free; anthers white; pome small, berry-like,
      red, acid, 3-loculed; branches not spiny ....15. *Sorbus*
2. Pistil 1, simple, superior, 2-ovuled; style 1; fruit a 1-seeded drupe;
   leaves simple ....20. *Prunus*
1. Herbs; pistils several to many, simple, superior; fruit achenes, drupelets, or
   follicles.
   14. Pistils 2-5, becoming 2- to 4-seeded follicles. ·
      15. Leaves trifoliolate or 3-parted, nearly sessile; stipules large; flowers
         white or pinkish, in loose terminal panicles ....4. *Gillenia*
      15. Leaves pinnately compound.
         16. Leaves 2- to 3-pinnate; stipules minute or none; flowers numer-
            ous, unisexual, in a large panicle; petals white, about 1 mm
            long; follicles reflexed, usually 2-seeded ....3. *Aruncus*
         16. Leaves pinnately 3- to 9-lobed or -foliolate; flowers perfect,
            pink or purple, in dense cymose panicles ....7. *Filipendula*
   14. Pistils one to many, becoming 1-seeded achenes or drupelets.
      17. Pistils ripening into pulpy drupelets, forming a red raspberry; style
         terminal or nearly so; leaves 3-5-foliolate; petals white or pink
         .... 11. *Rubus*
      17. Pistils ripening into achenes.
         18. Calyx not bristly.
            19. Pistils several to many; petals present; calyx usually with 5
               sepal-like bractlets alternating with the sepals.
            20. Style deciduous from the mature achene.
                21. Receptacle becoming succulent, red (or white), and
                 edible in fruit (a strawberry); petals white (or
                 pink), obtuse; leaves trifoliolate ....5. *Fragaria*
               21. Plants not as above ....6. *Potentilla*
            20. Style persistent on the achene, jointed or plumose ....
              .... 8. *Geum*
           19. Pistils 1-3; sepals 4, petaloid; petals none; achene usually
             solitary, enclosed in the 4-angled calyx-tube; flowers (in
             our species) white, in a dense cylindrical spike ....
             .... 9. *Sanguisorba*
         18. Calyx-tube with hooked bristles; flowers yellow, in spike-like
           racemes; achenes 2 ....10. *Agrimonia*

1. **Physocarpus** Maxim. — Ninebark
(*Opulaster* Medic.; *Physocarpa* Raf.)

P. opulifolius (L.) Maxim. River banks, local. May-June. [*P. intermedius* (Rydb.) Schneid.].

2. **Spiraea** L.
1. Leaves glabrous or nearly so; follicles glabrous.
   2. Sepals acute; inflorescence glabrous or nearly so; rarely found
      as an escape from cult. ....*S. latifolia* (Ait.) Borkh.
   2. Sepals obtuse; inflorescence puberulent; moist ground. July-
      Aug. Meadowsweet ....*S. alba* DuRoi

1. Leaves tomentose beneath; follicles pubescent; wet ground; Cook, Iroquois, Kankakee, and Lake counties. Hardhack ....
....*S. tomentosa* L.

3. **Aruncus** Adans. — Goat's-beard

A. dioicus (Walt.) Fern. Wooded ravines, May-June. Of local occurrence throughout most of Ill., but apparently absent from the northeastern counties. [*A. sylvester* sensu auth., non Kostel.; *A. pubescens* Rydb.; *A. allegheniensis* Rydb.].

4. **Gillenia** Moench — Indian Physic. American Ipecac

G. stipulata (Muhl.) Trel. Rich woods; extending northward to La Salle Co.; more frequent southward. June-July.

5. **Fragaria** L. — Strawberry

1. Robust, thick-leaved garden plants, often 20-40 cm tall, sometimes escaped from cult. to roadsides and waste places; petals 9-12 mm long; fruit ovoid-globose, 2-3 cm in diameter; achenes set in shallow pits. May. Cultivated Strawberry ....
....*F. chiloensis* × *virginiana* Duch.
1. Native wild plants; fruit 6-15 mm in diameter; plants usually smaller.
   2. Leaflets firm, dull green above, petiolulate; flowers in corymbs; petals 5-10 mm long; fruit ovoid or subglobose, 1-1.5 cm in diameter at maturity, the achenes set in pits; calyx-lobes not reflexed; grassy banks and roadsides, or in open woods, very common. Apr.-June. Wild Strawberry. [*F. grayana* Vilm.]
   ....*F. virginiana* Duch.
   2. Leaflets thin, light green, subsessile; inflorescence irregular, the branches unequal; petals 3-6 mm long; fruit ovoid or conical, 6-9 mm in diameter, 1-1.5 cm long, the calyx-lobes spreading or reflexed; achenes superficial; rocky banks and open woods, in the n. half of Ill. May-June ......*F. americana* (Porter) Britt.

6. **Potentilla** L. — Cinquefoil

1. Shrubs 30-100 cm tall, the bark shreddy; leaflets 5-7, elliptical, 1-2 cm long, silky-pubescent, the margins entire, revolute; flowers 1.5-3 cm broad, yellow; in swamp, sandy, or limy soil, Cook, Jo Daviess, Kane, and Lake counties. June-Aug. Shrubby Cinquefoil ....*P. fruticosa* L.
1. Herbs; leaflets not entire.
   2. Petals maroon-purple, acute, shorter than the sepals; leaves pinnate, 5- to 7-foliolate, the leaflets oblanceolate, serrate, 3-8 cm long, glaucous beneath; receptacle becoming spongy; bogs and swamps; Cook, Lake, and McHenry counties. June-July. Purple Cinquefoil ....*P. palustris* (L.) Scop.

2. Petals yellow, white, or cream, obtuse or retuse; receptacle not
   becoming enlarged and spongy.
   3. Leaves (except the uppermost in *P. arguta*) pinnate.
      4. Flowers solitary on small pedicels; petals yellow; plants
         stoloniferous; leaflets 7-21, with smaller intermediate
         ones, sharply serrate, whitish silky-pubescent beneath;
         wet ground, Lake and Cook counties. May-Aug.
         [*Argentina anserina* (L.) Rydb.]. Silverweed ....
         ....*P. anserina* L.
      4. Flowers cymose; leaflets not whitish pubescent beneath; ·
         plants not stoloniferous.
         5. Petals white or cream; flowers 12-20 mm in diameter;
            stamens 30; style nearly basal; stem stout, 0.5-1 m tall,
            glandular-pubescent; gravelly soil in the northern
            half of Ill., not common. June-July. [*Drymocallis
            agrimonioides* (Pursh) Rydb.]. Tall Cinquefoil ....
            ....*P. arguta* Pursh
         5. Petals yellow; flowers 6-10 mm in diameter; stamens 20;
            style terminal; stem decumbent at base, 20-40 cm tall;
            wet ground, rare. St. Clair Co., *Brendel* ....
            ....*P. paradoxa* Nutt.
   3. Leaves palmate.
      6. Flowers cymose.
         7. Leaflets silvery-pubescent beneath; petals 4-5 mm long;
            sandy or gravelly soil in the northern half of the state;
            nat. from Eur. May-Sept. Silvery Cinquefoil ....
            ....*P. argentea* L.
         7. Leaflets green on both sides.
            8. Leaflets 5-9; petals pale yellow, about 1 cm long,
               longer than the sepals; stamens about 30; mature
               achenes reticulate; waste places and along roads,
               common; native of Eur. May-July. [*P. sulphurea*
               Lam.] ....*P. recta* L.
            8. Leaflets 3 or 5; petals yellow, equalling or shorter than
               the sepals.
               9. Leaves 3-foliolate; plants annual or biennial; style
                  fusiform, glandular at the base.
                  10. Petals obovate; stamens 15-20; achenes striate
                      when ripe, about 1 mm long; moist ground,
                      common throughout Ill. May-Oct. Rough
                      Cinquefoil. [*P. norvegica* L.] ....
                      ....*P. monspeliensis* L.
                  10. Petals cuneate; stamens about 10; achenes
                      smooth, 0.5-0.7 mm long; moist ground, s.w.
                      Ill., rare. June-July ....*P. millegrana* Engelm.
               9. Leaves usually 5-foliolate; plants perennial; style

filiform, not glandular; stamens about 20; roadsides and waste places, occasional; adv. from Eur.
June-Aug. ....*P. intermedia* L.

6. Flowers solitary, axillary, long-peduncled, 10-15 mm in
diameter; leaflets 5, oblanceolate, serrate; stem slender,
ascending or trailing; roadsides, gravelly soil, etc., common. May-June. [*P. canadensis* of auth. ex p.; *P.
simplex* var. *argyrisma* Fern.] Common Cinquefoil
....*P. simplex* Michx.

7. **Filipendula** Mill.

F. rubra (Hill) B.L.Robins. Queen-of-the-Prairie. Moist ground,
not common; n. Ill. June-July.

8. **Geum** L. — Avens

1. Petals yellow or white.
  2. Receptacle stalked in the calyx; petals yellow, 2 mm long;
  fruiting heads at maturity about 1 cm in diameter; achenes
  puberulent; woods, common. Apr.-May. Spring Avens ....
  ....*G. verum* (Raf.) T. & G.
  2. Receptacle sessile; calyx with 5 bractlets alternating with the
  sepals.
    3. Petals white or pale yellow, shorter than or equalling the
    calyx.
      4. Peduncles slender, softly puberulent, sometimes with a few
      longer, scattered hairs; receptacle villous or hirsute.
        5. Stem sparingly pubescent to glabrous; petals white, 3-5
        mm wide, 5-10 mm long, equalling or shorter than
        the calyx-lobes; woods, thickets, and roadsides, com-
        mon. June-Aug. White Avens ....*G. canadense* Jacq.
        5. Stem at least near base (and petioles) more or less
        densely pubescent with spreading or retrorse hairs
        about 2 mm long; petals pale yellow, 1-2 mm wide,
        2-4 mm long, much shorter than the calyx-lobes; dry
        woods, s. Ill., apparently not common. June-July ....
        ....*G. virginianum* L.
      4. Peduncles stouter, hirsute with spreading hairs 1-2 mm
      long; petals white, 3-5 mm long, much shorter than the
      calyx-lobes; receptacle glabrous or nearly so; stem hir-
      sute; wet ground in woods and thickets. June-July.
      [*G. virginianum* sensu auth., non L.] ....*G. laciniatum* Murr.
    3. Petals golden yellow, 5-10 mm long, exceeding the sepals;
    receptacle pubescent; moist thickets and roadsides in the
    northern counties. June-July. Yellow Avens ....
    ....*G. strictum* Ait.
1. Petals purplish.

6. Styles not jointed; dry ground, n. Ill. May-June ....
....*G. triflorum* Pursh
6. Styles jointed; wet meadows; Kane, McHenry, and Winnebago
    counties. May-Aug. Purple Avens ....*G. rivale* L.

9. Sanguisorba L.

S. canadensis L. Moist ground, rare; Ottawa, Sept. 28, 1882,
Seymour; Joliet, Sept. 25, 1907, *Hill;* Cass Co., *Geyer.*

10. Agrimonia L. — Agrimony

1. Principal leaflets 5-9, oval to obovate.
  2. Leaflets minutely gland-dotted beneath, merely sparsely hirsute
     along the veins, or nearly glabrous.
    3. Axis of raceme finely glandular and with a few long spreading
       hairs; fruiting calyx turbinate, 4-5 mm long; roots not
       tuberous; woods and thickets, centr. and n. Ill. June-Aug.
       [*A. hirsuta* (Muhl.) Bickn.] ....*A. gryposepala* Wallr.
    3. Axis of raceme glandular and puberulent but not hirsute;
       fruiting calyx hemispherical, 2-3 mm long; roots tuberous-
       thickened; woods; chiefly in the southern half of the state.
       July-Sept. [*A. striata* sensu auth., non Michx.] ....
       ....*A. rostellata* Wallr.
  2. Leaflets softly pubescent beneath, especially on the veins; axis
     of raceme softly appressed-pubescent, not glandular, and
     without longer spreading hairs; fruiting calyx turbinate, 2.5-3
     mm long, with few ascending or erect bristles; roots tuberous-
     thickened; open woods. July-Sept. [*A. mollis* (T. & G.)
     Britt.] ....*A. pubescens* Wallr.
1. Principal leaflets 11-17, lanceolate, pubescent and glandular-
    granuliferous beneath; fruiting calyx 3 mm long; moist ground
    throughout Ill. July-Sept. ....*A. parviflora* Ait.

11. Rubus L. — Bramble

1. Leaves simple, palmately 3- to 5-lobed, serrate, pubescent; stems
    erect, glandular-pubescent or bristly, not prickly; flowers purple;
    fruit red; woods and thickets, rare; Carroll, Cook, Kane, and
    La Salle counties. May-June. Flowering Raspberry ....
    ....*R. odoratus* L.
1. Leaves compound; flowers white.
  2. Stems herbaceous, not all prickly; leaflets 3, rarely 5; fruit red,
     globose; bogs in Cook, De Kalb, Lake, and Winnebago coun-
     ties. May-June. Dwarf Raspberry. [*R. triflorus* Richards.]
     ....*R. pubescens* Raf.
  2. Stems more or less woody, biennial or perennial, usually prickly
     or bristly.
    3. Leaves whitish-tomentulose beneath; petals 5-6 mm long, not
       longer than the sepals; fruit red or purplish, easily separat-
      ing from the receptacle. (Raspberries.)

4. Stems glaucous, recurved, rooting at the tips, not stoloniferous, with stout hooked prickles; inflorescence corymbiform, the pedicels prickly; fruit purplish-black; moist
ground, common. May-June. Black Raspberry ....
....*R. occidentalis* L.
4. Stems not glaucous, bristly-prickly, stoloniferous; inflores-
cence racemose; fruit red.
  5. Stems with dense, shaggy purple hairs; roadsides, occasional; introd from e. Asia. May-July. Wineberry
  ....*R. phoenicolasius* Maxim.
  5. Stems without dense, shaggy purple hairs.
    6. Pedicels and calyx glandular-setose; wet ground and
    thickets, n. Ill. May-June. Wild Red Raspberry.
    [*R. idaeus* L. var. *aculeatissimus* sensu auth., non
    Regel & Tiling] ....*R. strigosus* Michx.
    6. Pedicels and calyx tomentulose and often with small
    recurved prickles, not glandular; roadsides and near
    dwellings; occasionally persisting; nat. from Eur.
    May-June. Cultivated Raspberry ....*R. idaeus* L.
3. Leaves variously pubescent or glabrous, but not whitish-
tomentose beneath; fruit black when ripe, adhering to the
cone-like receptacle.
  7. Stems erect or arching, mostly 1-2 m tall; petals 1-1.5 cm
  long. (Blackberries.)
    8. Stems more or less prickly, not bristly, the prickles not
    numerous, confined to the angles of the stem.
      9. Leaflets laciniate; panicle 5- to 30-flowered, prickly
      and pubescent. Of European origin; cultivated, and
      sometimes escaped to roadsides and waste places.
      June-July. Evergreen Blackberry ....
      ....*R. laciniatus* Willd.
      9. Leaflets serrate or lobed, not laciniate.
        10. Peduncles and pedicels with stalked glands, also
        usually pubescent, and sometimes bearing small
        prickles; inflorescence racemose, not leafy, usual-
        ly standing well beyond the foliage, each pedicel
        subtended by a bract; open woods, pastures,
        roadsides, and along fences, common. May-
        June. [*R. villosus* sensu auth., non Thunb., *R.
        nigrobaccus* Bailey] ....*R. alleghemensis* Porter
        10. Peduncles and pedicels pubescent and sometimes
        prickly, but without stalked glands.
          11. Inflorescence elongate, racemose, leafy-bracted
          only at the base; young stems (primocanes)
          angled and grooved; thickets. May-June.
          Tall Blackberry. [*R. argutus* of auth., non
          Link; *R. schneckii* Bailey] ....
          ....*R. ostryifolius* Rydb.

11. Inflorescence short-corymbiform, conspicuously leafy-bracted throughout; primocanes
nearly terete; thickets. May-June. [*R. re-
curvans* Blanch.; *R. frondosus* Bigel.] ....
....*R. pennsylvanicus* Poir.

8. Stems setose or hispid, not or only weakly prickly, some-
times nearly unarmed; swales, rare, Kankakee Co.,
R. A. Schneider. [*R. offectus* Bailey; *R. schneideri*
Bailey] ....*R. setosus* Bigel.

7. Stems trailing or decumbent, slender, only the floral
branches erect. (Dewberries.)

12. Stems retrorsely bristly (or nearly unarmed), not prickly; leaflets firm, oblanceolate, glabrous on both sides,
glossy above, paler and dull beneath; petals 5-8 mm
long; meadows or low woods, n. Ill. June-July.
Swamp Dewberry ....*R. hispidus* L.

12. Stems usually with weak curved prickles.

13. Stems bearing glandular bristles among the prickles;
leaves coriaceous, often persistent; dry soil, s. Ill.
Apr.-May. Southern Dewberry ....
....*R. trivialis* Michx.

13. Stems with few, firm, flat-based prickles along the
angles; leaves deciduous; fields, roadsides, and
woods, common. April-June. Dewberry. [*R. villosus* Ait., non Thunb.; *R. procumbens* Muhl.,
nom. nud.; *R. canadensis* sensu auth., non L.]
....*R. flagellaris* Willd.

12. Rosa L. — Rose

1. Styles united in a protruding column about as long as the stamens;
sepals reflexed, deciduous from the fruit; stems recurving,
climbing or trailing; prickles curved.

2. Leaflets 5-9 (usually 9); flowers numerous, small, white, fragrant, 1.5-2 cm in diameter, paniculate; sepals ovate, often
with narrow appendages; stipules deeply fringed or pectinate;
fruits 5-8 mm in diameter; often planted and more or less
persistent; native of Japan. May-June. Japanese Rose
....*R. multiflora* Thunb.

2. Leaflets 3 (or 5); stipules entire or denticulate; flowers 3-8 cm
in diameter; borders of woods, moist thickets, pastures, and
hedgerows, common throughout Ill. June-July. Climbing
Rose. Var. *tomentosa* T. & G. (*R. rubifolia* R.Br.) has the
leaflets pubescent beneath ....*R. setigera* Michx.

1. Styles distinct, not exserted; leaflets 5-11; stems erect or arching.

3. Achenes lining the inner wall as well as the base of the
receptacle.

4. Stems with bristles and slender prickles; leaflets usually 3 or

5, pubescent beneath; flowers usually solitary, "double"; shrubs persisting after cult. or occasionally apparently spontaneous, but not established in Ill.; native of Eur. June. ....*R. gallica* L.

4. Stems with stout prickles; leaflets 5-9; flowers usually corymbose.

   5. Leaflets doubly serrate with gland-tipped teeth, pubescent or more or less glandular beneath; sepals glandular-hispid on the back; pedicels usually glandular-hispid.

      6. Leaflets suborbicular to broadly oval, obtuse or acutish, pubescent and glandular beneath, fragrant; styles pubescent; sepals tardily deciduous from the mature fruit, or sometimes long-persistent; roadsides and fields, nat. from Eur. June. [*R. rubiginosa* L.] Sweetbriar ....*R. eglanteria* L.

      6. Leaflets ovate or oval, acute or short-acuminate, more or less pubescent on both sides, more or less glandular beneath; styles glabrous or nearly so; sepals soon deciduous from the mature fruit; roadsides and pastures, occasional; native of Eur. June ....*R. micrantha* Sm.

   5. Leaflets simply and sharply serrate, glabrous on both sides, glossy above, rarely slightly glandular on the midrib beneath, oval or ovate, acute; styles pubescent; sepals glabrous on the back, in fruit reflexed and tardily deciduous, two or more of them usually pinnately lobed; roadsides and fields, occasional; nat. from Eur. June. Dog Rose ....*R. canina* L.

3. Achenes confined to the bottom of the receptacle.

   7. Sepals reflexed after flowering and deciduous from the mature fruit.

      8. Tall shrubs 1-2 m high; leaflets beneath (and rachis) softly pubescent, closely serrulate, acute at each end; stipules linear, more or less involute; prickles usually more or less curved, flattened at the base; moist thickets or swampy ground, local. June-July. Swamp Rose. [*R. carolina* of auth., non L.] ....*R. palustris* Marsh.

      8. Low shrubs 20-75 cm tall; leaflets rather coarsely serrate, glabrous, or pubescent only on the veins beneath; infrastipular prickles usually present, straight; stipules oblanceolate; dry soil along roads or edges of woods, the common species throughout Ill. May-Aug. Pasture Rose. [*R. humilis* Marsh.; *R. virginiana* of auth., non Mill.] ....*R. carolina* L.

   7. Sepals erect and connivent or spreading after flowering, persistent on the mature fruit.

      9. Flowers mostly corymbose; native species.

         10. Tall shrubs 1-2 m high, the branches usually without prickles; hypanthium usually smooth, but the sepals

glandular; stipules flat; leaflets 5 or 7, rarely 9, sharply serrate; thickets and open woods, local; chiefly in
the northern half of the state; also Union Co. May-
June. Meadow Rose ....*R. blanda* Ait.
10. Low shrubs 20-50 cm tall; prickles numerous.
　11. Leaves puberulent or pubescent; leaflets usually 9,
　　　sometimes 7 or 11, mostly 1.5-4 cm long; stems
　　　semi-herbaceous, weak and bristly, dying back to
　　　near the ground; infrastipular prickles lacking;
　　　roadsides and hedgerows, chiefly in northern and
　　　central Ill., s. to Tazewell Co. June-July. [*R.
　　　pratincola* Greene, non A.Br.; *R. heliophila*
　　　Greene; *R. relicta* Erlanson] ....*R. suffulta* Greene
　11. Leaves glabrous; hypanthium and pedicels without
　　　glands; leaflets 7 or 9, obtuse, 1-2 cm long;
　　　flowers small; along railroad, apparently native,
　　　Hanover, Jo Daviess Co., June 7, 1945, *G. N.
　　　Jones 17273* ....*R. lunellii* Greene
9. Flowers usually solitary; cultivated species.
　12. Leaves and stems glabrous or nearly so, the stems very
　　　spiny; cultivated, rarely persisting in Ill.; native of
　　　Eurasia. May-June. Scotch Rose. [*R. pimpinelli-
　　　folia* L.; *R. illinoensis* E.G.Baker] ......*R. spinosissima* L.
　12. Leaves and stems tomentose, the stems spiny; roadsides,
　　　escaped from cult. ....*R. rugosa* Thunb.

13. **Amelanchier** Medic. — Shadbush. Serviceberry

1. Top of the ovary glabrous; petals 12-18 mm long; trees or tall
　shrubs with short-acuminate, ovate or obovate leaves cordate or
　rounded at base.
　2. Young leaves and racemes densely white-tomentose, soon gla-
　　brous; sepals triangular, acute; fruit somewhat dry and mealy,
　　insipid and falling early; lowest fruiting pedicels 1-2.5 cm
　　long; wooded hillsides and banks, not uncommon throughout
　　Ill. Apr.-May. [*A. canadensis* sensu auth., non L.] ....
　　..*A. arborea* (Michx.f) Fern.
　2. Young leaves and racemes nearly or quite glabrous from the
　　first; sepals lanceolate, acuminate; fruit sweet and juicy;
　　lowest fruiting pedicels mostly 2.5-5 cm long; wooded hill-
　　sides in the n. part of Ill. Apr.-May ....*A. laevis* Wieg.
1. Top of the ovary tomentose; petals 4-12 mm long; dwarf shrubs
　or small trees; leaves commonly oval, acutish or obtuse.
　3. Young leaves green and glabrous or nearly so from the first,
　　unfolded and more than half grown at flowering time; strag-
　　gling shrubs or small trees up to 8 m tall; Lake and Winne-
　　bago counties ....*A. interior* Nielsen

3. Young leaves densely white-tomentose; dwarf colonial shrubs 0.5-1.5 m tall; rocky or sandy soil; in the northern and western counties, s. to Mercer and Will counties. May. Low Shadbush. [*A. humilis* Wieg.; *A. stolonifera* Wieg.] ....*A. spicata* (Lam.) K.Koch

14. **Cydonia** Mill. — Quince
C. oblonga Mill. Fully established on Atwood Ridge, Union Co.; native of Asia. May.

15. **Sorbus** L. — Mountain-ash
1. Winter-buds densely whitish-villous, 5-10 mm long; leaflets elliptical, acute, 3-5 cm long; flowers 8-9 mm broad; fruits 9-11 mm in diameter; native of Eur.; cultivated, and occasionally escaping to woods or roadsides. European Mountain-ash. Often mistaken for the following species ....*S. aucuparia* L.
1. Winter-buds glabrous, glutinous, 1-2 cm long; leaflets lanceolate, acuminate, finely serrate, 5-9 cm long; flowers 5-6 mm broad; fruits 4-6 mm in diameter; rocky woods, rare, near Oregon, Ogle Co., June 2, 1888, *M. B. Waite;* now probably extinct in Ill. American Mountain-ash ....*S. americana* Marsh.

16. **Aronia** Medic. — Chokeberry
1. Inflorescence and lower surface of leaves nearly or quite glabrous; fruit black, soon falling; moist sandy woods, and edges of bogs in northern Ill.; also on exposed sandstone cliffs in southern Ill., Saline Co., *Mohlenbrock & Voigt* in 1958. May-June. Black Chokeberry ....*A. melanocarpa* (Michx.) Ell.
1. Inflorescence and lower surface of leaves tomentose; fruit purplish-black, long-persistent; Cook, Kankakee, and Winnebago counties. Purple Chokeberry ....*A. prunifolia* (Marsh.) Rehd.

17. **Pyrus** L. — Pear
P. communis L. Cultivated and found occasionally as an escape in woods or along roads; native of Eur. May.

18. **Malus** Mill. — Apple
1. Calyx glabrous outside (rarely somewhat villous); leaves glabrous or nearly so; mature fruit 1-3 cm in diameter; woods in the southern half of Ill. Apr.-May. Wild Sweet Crabapple. [*Pyrus coronaria* L.; *M. angustifolia* (Ait.) Michx.; *M. lancifolia* Rehd.] ....*M. coronaria* (L.) Mill.
1. Calyx tomentose; leaves pubescent beneath, at least along the veins.

2. Leaves irregularly toothed, notched, or lobed, narrowed at the base; calyx-lobes erect or spreading; fruit 3-5 cm in diameter; woods, common. May. Iowa Crabapple. [*Pyrus ioensis* (Wood) Bailey] ....*M. ioensis* (Wood) Britt.
2. Leaves crenate-serrate, rounded or cordate at base; calyx-lobes usually reflexed at anthesis; fruit larger; cultivated, and not infrequently wild; native of Eurasia. Apr.-May. Apple. [*Pyrus malus* L.; *M. sylvestris* of auth., not Mill.] ....
....*M. pumila* Mill.

19. **Crataegus** L. — Hawthorn

1. Leaves widest near the middle or toward the apex, cuneate at the base.
    2. Blades usually widest above the middle, mostly obovate or spatulate, the margins merely serrate or only obscurely lobed; calyx-lobes entire.
        3. Veins of leaves running to sinuses as well as lobes; cultivated, but rarely spontaneous in Ill.; Cook Co., *V. H. Chase*. English Hawthorn ....*C. monogyna* Jacq.
        3. Veins of leaves running only to lobes.
            4. Leaves firm, glossy above, not deeply impressed-veined.
                5. Pedicels and leaves glabrous; pastures and open woods, especially near streams, common. May-June. Cockspur Thorn. [*C. attenuata* Ashe; *C. arduennae, barrettiana, calophylla, effulgens, farwellii* Sarg.] ....
                ....*C. crusgalli* L.
                5. Pedicels and leaves pubescent; wooded hillsides and bluffs in s. Ill. May-June. [*C. pilifera* Sarg.] ....
                ....*C. engelmanni* Sarg.
            4. Leaves thinner, dull, impressed-veined above.
                6. Pedicels and leaves glabrous; open woods, usually along streams; in the northern half of the state, Fulton, Peoria, Stark, and Will counties. May-June. [*C. disperma, grandis* Ashe; *C. peoriensis* Sarg.; *C. hannibalensis* Palmer] ....*C. cuneiformis* (Marsh.) Egglest.
                6. Pedicels and leaves pubescent, at least when young.
                    7. Terminal leaves obovate, deeply lobed; pastures and open woods throughout Ill. May-June. [*C. pratensis* Sarg.]. A form with yellow fruits, f. *aurea* (Ait.) Rehd., occurs in Ill. ....*C. punctata* Jacq.
                    7. Terminal leaves elliptical, not lobed or only slightly lobed; swampy woods, rare; Jackson Co. ....
                    ....*C. collina* Chapm.
    2. Blades prevailingly widest near the middle; calyx-lobes usually glandular-serrulate.
        8. Blades more or less pubescent beneath, at least in the axils of the veins; pedicels pubescent.

9. Lower surface of mature leaves sparsely pubescent along the sides of the veins with short, somewhat stiff hairs; corymbs sparingly pubescent; stamens 10 or 20, the filaments short; thorns usually numerous, stout, 5-9 cm long; fruit subglobose, nodding; banks of streams; chiefly in the northern half of Ill. May. [*C. macracantha* Lodd.; *C. illinoiensis* Ashe; *C. corporea, divida, gaultii, gemmosa, laxiflora, longispina, rutila, vegeta* Sarg.] ....*C. succulenta* Schrad.

9. Lower surface of leaves softly pubescent, especially on the veins; petioles wing-margined; corymbs tomentose; stamens mostly 20, the filaments slender; thorns few, slender, or none; fruit ellipsoid, erect; thickets and open woods, generally distributed in Ill., flowering in the latter part of May and early part of June. [*C. tomentosa* sensu auth., non L.; *C. chapmani* (Beadle) Ashe; *C. structilis* Ashe; *C. hispidula, mollicula, whittakeri* Sarg.] ....*C. calpodendron* (Ehrh.) Medic.

8. Blades glabrous or essentially so; calyx-lobes entire.

10. Leaves oval or rhombic, acute or acutish, the base cuneate; lower surface with tufts of tomentum in the axils of the veins; styles and nutlets usually 5; alluvial soil; w. and s. Ill. [*C. arborescens* Ell.; *C. atrorubens, durifolia, schneckii* Ashe; *C. acutifolia, dawsoniana, erecta, insignis, larga, mitis, ovata, pechiana* Sarg.; *C. nitida* (Engelm.) Sarg.] ....*C. viridis* L.

10. Leaves short-obovate to suborbicular, usually incised with shallow lobes, glabrous at maturity; styles and nutlets 2 or 3; thickets and open woods, not uncommon, from Jersey, Macoupin, and Shelby counties northward. May-June ....*C. margaretta* Ashe

1. Leaves prevailingly widest below the middle or toward the subcordate, truncate, rounded, or broadly cuneate base.

11. Leaves glabrous or nearly so at maturity, or only slightly pubescent beneath.

12. Leaves deltoid-cordate (often conspicuously 3- to 5-lobed); calyx-lobes deltoid, entire; fruit 5-7 mm in diameter, the calyx deciduous; chiefly s. Ill., but extending northward to Fayette Co. [*C. cordata* Ait.] ....*C. phaenopyrum* (L.f.) Medic.

12. Leaves otherwise; calyx-lobes lanceolate; fruiting calyx usually persistent.

13. Calyx-lobes entire or nearly so; inflorescence glabrous.

14. Leaves thin, scabrellous on the upper surface when young, soon glabrous; stamens 10 or fewer; fruiting calyx sessile; thickets, pastures, or open woods, usually near streams, n.e. Ill. May. [*C. egani, ferrissii* Ashe; *C. apiomorpha, cyanophylla, demissa,*

depilis, lucorum, paucispina, sextilis, taetrica, tarda; C. macrosperma var. *demissa* (Sarg.) Egglest.] ....*C. macrosperma* Ashe

14. Leaves glabrous on both surfaces, firm to subcoriaceous at maturity; stamens 15-20; fruiting calyx with a distinct neck; common throughout Ill. May. [*C. conjuncta, dissona* Sarg.] ....
...........................*C. pruinosa* (Wendl.) K.Koch

13. Calyx-lobes glandular-serrate throughout.

15. Inflorescence glabrous; Richland, Vermilion, and Wabash counties ....*C. coccinioides* Ashe

15. Inflorescence with pubescent pedicels; thickets and borders of woods, usually near streams in the n. half of Ill. [*C. albicans, amicta* Ashe; *C. assurgens, corusca, delecta, elongata, hillii, magniflora, pedicellata, sertata, trachyphylla* Sarg.] ....
...........................*C. coccinea* L.

11. Leaves persistently softly pubescent beneath; pedicels villous; anthers yellow; fruit usually more or less pubescent, at least toward the base, 12-20 mm in diameter; open woods, usually near streams, apparently the commonest species in Ill. Apr.-May. Red Haw. [*C. coccinea* var. *mollis* T. & G.; *C. subvillosa* Schrad.; *C tomentosa* var. *mollis* (T. & G.) A.Gray; *C. lanigera, ridgwayi, sera, umbrosa* Sarg.; *C. altrix, valens, venosa, verna* Ashe; *C. mollis* var. *sera* (Sarg.) Egglest.] ....*C. mollis* (T. & G.) Scheele

20. **Prunus** L. — Plum. Cherry

1. Flowers nearly sessile; ovary and fruit densely tomentose.
   2. Flowers pink; leaves lanceolate; cultivated, and sometimes spontaneous; native of Asia. Apr.-May. Peach. [*Amygdalus persica* L.] ....*P. persica* (L.) Batsch.
   2. Flowers white; leaves ovate; introd. from Eur. and sometimes escaped from cult. Apricot ....*P. armeniaca* L.
1. Flowers pedicelled, white; ovary and fruit glabrous.
   3. Flowers in small umbels or corymbs, usually 2-5 or solitary (occasionally 6- to 10-flowered in *P. mahaleb*).
      4. Flowers small, the petals only 3-6 mm long.
         5. Small trees or tall shrubs with relatively broad lanceolate to oval or obovate leaves toothed to the base, usually appearing after the flowers.
            6. Leaves lanceolate to ovate-lanceolate, acuminate.
               7. Pedicels 3-6 mm long, puberulent; fruit globose, 12-15 mm in diameter; forming thickets in sandy soil, chiefly s. Ill.; native southward. May. Chickasaw Plum ....*P. angustifolia* Marsh.

7. Pedicels 8-14 mm long, glabrous; fruit 6-7 mm in diameter; wet woods or in bogs, n. Ill. Apr. Wild Red Cherry ....*P. pennsylvanica* L.f.
6. Leaves ovate to suborbicular, apiculate, crenate, glandular between the teeth; fruit ovoid, black or nearly so, 7-10 mm long; roadsides, occasionally escaped from cult.; introd. from Eur. May. Mahaleb Cherry ....*P. mahaleb* L.
5. Dwarf shrubs; leaves oblanceolate, acute, serrate except toward the cuneate base; fruit nearly globose, black, acid, 1-1.5 cm in diameter at maturity; sandy soil, n. Ill. Apr.-May. Sand Cherry ....*P. pumila* L.
4. Flowers larger, the petals 6-16 mm long.
8. Leaves serrate, the sharp teeth not ending in a gland; petals 7-10 mm long; calyx-lobes not glandular-serrate.
9. Petioles glabrous beneath; lower surface of mature blades glabrous except along the veins; young twigs glabrous; borders of woods, common. Apr.-May. Wild Plum ....*P. americana* Marsh.
9. Petioles pubescent all around; blades usually more or less softly pubescent beneath; young twigs puberulent; woods and roadsides, common. Apr.-May. [*P. americana* var. *mollis* T. & G.] ....
..............................*P. lanata* (Sudw.) Mack. & Bush
8. Leaves crenate-serrate, the teeth ending in a gland; calyx-lobes more or less glandular-serrulate; petioles glabrous beneath; twigs glabrous.
10. Petals 12-15 mm long; leaves broadly obovate or oval; river banks, woods, and thickets, not common; extending southward to Pike Co. May. Canada Plum ....*P. nigra* Ait.
10. Petals 6-8 mm long.
11. Leaves thickish at maturity, narrowly obovate to elliptical, acuminate, irregularly serrate, glossy above, conspicuously veiny beneath; flowers opening when the leaves are half grown; roadsides and edges of woods, common. Apr.-May. Hortulan Plum ....*P. hortulana* Bailey
11. Leaves thinner, elliptic-lanceolate, acute, finely and evenly glandular-serrate, the veins not conspicuous beneath; flowers opening before the leaves have expanded; borders of woods, s. Ill., extending northward to St. Clair and Crawford counties. Apr.-May. Wild Goose Plum ....
..............................*P. munsoniana* Wight & Hedr.
3. Flowers several to many, in elongate racemes.
12. Leaves thin, obovate, sharply serrate with erect or spreading teeth; sepals nearly orbicular, glandular-serrate, decidu-

ous; woods and thickets, extending southward to Christian
and Madison counties. May. Common Chokecherry. The
form with the lower surface of the leaves, young twigs,
and rachis of inflorescence pubescent is f. *deamii* G. N.
Jones ....*P. virginiana* L.
12. Leaves firm, oval or lanceolate, crenulate-serrate with in-
curved teeth; sepals obscurely glandular, persistent; woods
and along fences, common throughout Ill. May. Wild
Black Cherry ....*P. serotina* Ehrh.

54. Leguminosae P.F.Gmel. — Pea Family

1. Trees or shrubs.
    2. Leaves simple, entire, suborbicular to reniform; flowers pink, perfect, in
    sessile umbels, appearing before the leaves; pods 6-8 cm long, pointed
    at each end ....3. *Cercis*
    2. Leaves compound.
        3. Erect shrubs or trees.
            4. Shrubs; flowers in racemes.
                5. Twigs and petioles hispid; petals 5; pods linear, hispid, several-
                seeded ....21. *Robinia*
                5. Twigs and petioles not hispid; corolla of one purple petal; pods
                short, 1- to 2-seeded ....17. *Amorpha*
            4. Trees; petals 5.
                6. Leaves odd-pinnate, with 5-17 leaflets; flowers white, 1-2.5 cm
                long.
                    7. Stipules spiny, woody; stipels setaceous; bark rough; stamens
                    diadelphous; racemes 7-15 cm long ....21. *Robinia*
                    7. Stipules and stipels none; bark smooth; wood yellow; stamens
                    distinct; inflorescence 15-50 cm long ....7. *Cladrastis*
                6. Leaves 1- to 2-pinnate.
                    8. Leaflets ovate, entire, acute or acuminate; flowers pinkish-
                    white, 1.5 cm long, in many-flowered racemes; pods woody;
                    trees without spines ....4. *Gymnocladus*
                    8. Leaflets oval or lanceolate, remotely denticulate, obtuse; flowers
                    small, greenish-yellow, in axillary spikes; pods leathery;
                    trees usually with spines on the trunk and branches ....
                    ....5. *Gleditsia*
        3. Twining shrubs, not prickly; flowers purple, showy, racemose; petals
        5; leaflets 9-13; pods many-seeded ....22. *Wisteria*
1. Herbs.
    9. Leaves simple; petals yellow ....9. *Crotalaria*
    9. Leaves compound (rarely 1-foliolate).
        10. Leaves even-pinnate (or bipinnate), or leaflets only 2.
            11. Leaves ending in a tendril; flowers papilionaceous.
                12. Style terete, pubescent near the apex ....30. *Vicia*
                12. Style flattened, pubescent along the inner side ....31. *Lathyrus*
            11. Leaves not ending in a tendril; leaflets numerous, small; flowers
            not at all papilionaceous, in globose heads.
                13. Leaves bipinnate.
                    14. Plants glabrous or nearly so; flowers greenish-white; petals
                    distinct or nearly so; pods flat, smooth ....1. *Desmanthus*

14. Plants with recurved prickles; flowers rose colored; corolla funnel-form; pods prickly, 4-angled, or nearly terete ....2. *Schrankia*
13. Leaves pinnate; flowers yellow ....6. *Cassia*
10. Leaves not even-pinnate.
  15. Leaves trifoliolate, or digitate with usually not more than 5 leaflets (rarely unifoliolate).
    16. Leaves (and other parts of the plant) more or less glandular-punctate; leaflets 3-5, entire ....16. *Psoralea*
    16. Leaves not at all glandular-punctate.
      17. Leaflets toothed.
        18. Flowers capitate.
          19. Pods straight; stamens adherent to the corolla ....
          ....12. *Trifolium*
          19. Pods curved or coiled; stamens free from the corolla ....14. *Medicago*
        18. Flowers reflexed in long slender racemes, white or yellow; pods small, straight, reflexed ....13. *Melilotus*
      17. Leaflets entire.
        20. Fruit a loment, i.e., breaking transversely into 1-seeded, indehiscent segments, or consisting of a single segment.
          21. Pods 1- to several-jointed and -seeded; leaflets usually stipellate; flowers purple or white ....
          ....27. *Desmodium*
          21. Pods of a single 1-seeded joint (the lower joint when present empty and stalk-like); leaflets without stipels, usually prominently veined.
            22. Flowers purplish or yellowish-white; stamens diadelphous (9 + 1); anthers all alike; pods not longitudinally ribbed 28 *Lespedeza*
            22. Flowers yellow; stamens monadelphous; anthers in 2 series; pods longitudinally ribbed ....
            ....29. *Stylosanthes*
        20. Fruit a legume.
          23. Leaflets not stipellate.
            24. Flowers in heads; pods small, often included in the calyx, 1- to 6-seeded, not stipitate; stamens diadelphous ....12. *Trifolium*
            24. Flowers in racemes, or solitary.
               25. Flowers whitish (or yellow) in racemes; stamens distinct; pods stipitate, turgid or inflated; plants tending to turn black in drying ....8. *Baptisia*
               25. Flowers pink, solitary; stamens diadelphous; pods linear, somewhat compressed, not stipitate ....15. *Hosackia*
          23. Leaflets stipellate.
            26. Style glabrous; plants twining; flowers purplish or white.
              27. High-climbing vines; leaflets usually lobed; flowers with the odor of grapes ....
              .... 38. *Pueraria*

27. Erect or weak twining herbs; leaflets seldom
   lobed; flowers without the odor of grapes.
   28. Calyx usually 5-toothed, not bracteolate;
      leaflets ovate ....39. *Amphicarpa*
   28. Calyx deeply 4-cleft, subtended by a
      pair of bractlets; leaflets oval ....
      ....40. *Galactia*
26. Style pubescent on the upper surface.
   29. Flowers yellow; stems twining; leaflets
      ovate; pods 10-20 cm long ....35. *Vigna*
   29. Flowers bluish or nearly white.
      30. Flowers 4-5 cm long, solitary or in pairs
         in the axils, pale blue and lilac, deli-
         cately veined; stem ascending or
         twining ....37. *Clitoria*
      30. Flowers smaller, racemose or umbellate.
         31. Flowers in short sessile axillary
            racemes; stem erect; pods straight
            or nearly so, almost sessile, some-
            what flattened ....34. *Glycine*
         31. Flowers in racemes or umbels on
            long axillary perduncles; stems
            twining or trailing.
            32. Flowers in long loose racemes;
               keel of the corolla spirally
               coiled; pods falcate ....
               ....33. *Phaseolus*
            32. Flowers few, in umbel-like
               clusters; keel of the corolla
               strongly incurved but not
               spirally coiled; pods straight
               or nearly so ......36. *Strophostyles*
15. Leaves with 5 or more leaflets.
   33. Leaves punctate.
      34. Pods covered with hooked prickles; flowers whitish;
         stamens 10 ....25. *Glycyrrhiza*
      34. Pods without hooked prickles.
         35. Corolla of 1 petal; stamens 10 ....17. *Amorpha*
         35. Corolla of 5 petals.
            36. Stamens 10 or rarely 9; leaflets (in our species)
               4-6 mm long ....18. *Dalea*
            36. Stamens 5; leaflets (in our species) 6-35 mm long
               ....19. *Petalostemum*
   33. Leaves not punctate; corolla papilionaceous; pods several-
      seeded.
      37. Leaflets 5-11.
         38. Flowers yellow, borne in umbels ....11. *Lotus*
         38. Flowers not yellow, borne in axillary or terminal
            racemes.
            39. Stems twining or climbing; leaflets 5-7 (rarely 3),
               ovate or ovate-lanceolate; flowers in axillary
               racemes ....32. *Apios*

39. Stems erect; leaflets 7-11, oblanceolate; flowers
   blue (or pink or white), in terminal racemes
   ....10. *Lupinus*
37. Leaflets 11-31.
   40. Plants hoary-pubescent; flowers in terminal racemes
      ....20. *Tephrosia*
   40. Plants strigose to glabrous; flowers in axillary racemes
      or headlike umbels.
      41. Flowers racemose; pods not 4-angled or -jointed.
         42. Leaves even-pinnate ....24. *Sesbania*
         42. Leaves odd-pinnate ....23. *Astragalus*
      41. Flowers umbellate; pods linear, 4-angled, jointed
         ....26. *Coronilla*

1. Desmanthus Willd. — Illinois Mimosa

D. illinoensis (Michx.) MacM. River banks or along railroads,
local; July-Aug. [*Acuan illinoensis* (Michx.) Ktze.]

2. Schrankia Willd. — Sensitive-brier
(*Leptoglottis* DC.; *Morongia* Britt.)

S. uncinata Willd. Dry sandy soil, rare; Peoria, Aug. 1901, and
June 1903, *McDonald*. [*L. nuttallii* DC.; *M. uncinata* (Willd.) Britt.;
S. nuttallii (DC.) Standl.].

3. Cercis L. — Redbud

C. canadensis L. Woods, common throughout Ill., except the
northern counties. Apr.-May.

4. Gymnocladus Lam. — Kentucky Coffee-tree

G. dioicus (L.) K.Koch. Woods, common throughout Ill. May-
June.

5. Gleditsia L.

1. Pods 10-50 cm long, many-seeded, indehiscent; spines stout, often
   compound, rarely absent; woods, common throughout Ill.
   May-June. Honey Locust. The spineless form is *f. inermis* (L.)
   Zabel ....*G. triacanthos* L.
1. Pods obliquely oval, 2-4 cm long, 1-seeded, at length dehiscent;
   spines slender, mostly simple; borders of swamps, s. and w. Ill.,
   not common. Water Locust ....*G. aquatica* Marsh.

6. Cassia L.
(*Chamaecrista* Moench; *Ditremexa* Raf.)

1. Leaflets 2-6 cm long, 1-3 cm wide; corolla regular, the petals nearly equal; leaves not sensitive to the touch; stipules deciduous;
   calyx-lobes obtuse; stamens 10, the upper 3 imperfect.
   2. Leaflets 8-20; petiole with a gland near the base; pods 6-13
      cm long, 5-10 mm wide.

3. Leaflets lanceolate, acuminate; stipules lanceolate; petiolar gland globose; petals 1.5-2 cm long; plants annual; waste ground, occasional; native of the tropics; Chicago, *Moffatt* in 1897. Coffee-weed ....*C. occidentalis* L.
3. Leaflets elliptical, mucronate; stipules setaceous; petals 10-12 mm long; plants perennial, native.
   4. Ovary villous; petiolar gland clavate; pods loosely villous, the segments about as long as broad; seeds flat, suborbicular; alluvial soil, roadsides, or in open woods. July-Aug. ....*C. hebecarpa* Fern.
   4. Ovary strigose; petiolar gland ovoid; pods glabrous or sparsely hirtellous, the segments much shorter than broad; seeds plump, ellipsoid or obovoid; roadsides and alluvial soil. July-Aug. [*C. medsgeri* Shafer] ....
   ....*C. marilandica* L.
2. Leaflets 4-6, obtuse; gland between the lowest pair of leaflets; pods 10-15 cm long, 2-5 mm wide; waste ground, occasional; native of the tropics. July-Sept. ....*C. tora* L.
1. Leaflets 5-20 mm long, 2-5 mm wide; corolla irregular, the petals unequal; calyx-lobes acuminate; anthers all perfect; stipules persistent; leaflets 12-28, somewhat sensitive to the touch.
   5. Flowers 2-4 cm broad, slender-pedicelled; anthers 10, unequal; pods 4-6 cm long; fields and meadows; common. July-Oct. Partridge-pea. [*C. chamaecrista* sensu auth., non L.; *C. robusta* Pollard] ....*C. fasciculata* Michx.
   5. Flowers 5-10 mm broad, short-pedicelled; anthers 5, nearly equal; pods 2.5-4 cm long; woods and fields; Cook, Henderson, and Kankakee counties, and southward. July-Sept. ....
   ....*C. nictitans* L.

7. Cladrastis Raf. — Yellow-wood

C. lutea (Michx.f.) K.Koch. Rich woods, rare; Alexander and Gallatin counties.

8. Baptisia Vent. — Wild Indigo

1. Leaves glabrous; racemes bractless or the bracts minute; calyx 6-8 mm long; pods ellipsoid, 2-3 cm long; prairie soil and open woods throughout Ill. June-July. ....*B. leucantha* T. & G.
1. Leaves pubescent; racemes conspicuously bracted; calyx 6-10 mm long; pods ovoid, 4-5 cm long at maturity; prairie soil and open woods throughout Ill. May-June. [*B. bracteata* of auth., not Muhl.] ....*B. leucophaea* Nutt.

9. Crotolaria L — Rattle-box

1. Stem slender, 10-50 cm tall; leaves elliptical, 3-8 cm long; calyx villous; racemes 2-4-flowered; seeds 2-3 mm in diameter; dry soil, nearly throughout Ill. June-Sept. ....*C. sagittalis* L.

1. Stem 0.5-2 m tall; leaves obovate, obtuse, 6-20 cm long; calyx glabrous; racemes many-flowered; seeds 4-5 mm in diameter; roadsides and fields, s. Ill. Sept.-Oct. Introd. from the tropics. Alexander Co., *H. M. Franklin* in 1949 ....*C. spectabilis* Roth

10. **Lupinus** L. — Lupine
L. perennis L. Sandy soil, locally in n. Ill. May-June.

11. **Lotus** L. — Bird's-foot Trefoil
L. corniculatus L. Widespread, perhaps in grass seed, becoming fairly common in some places during the last twenty years; introd. from Eur. June-Aug.

12. **Trifolium** L. — Clover
1. Flowers white, purple, or pink.
  2. Flowers short-pedicelled, becoming reflexed in age.
    3. Heads 2.5-3 cm broad; plants annual or biennial; woods and fields, local. May-June. Buffalo Clover ....*T. reflexum* L.
    3. Heads less than 2.5 cm broad.
      4. Flowers white; stems creeping and rooting, the peduncles arising from near the ground; fields, roadsides, waste places, lawns, open woods, common; nat. from Eur. May-June. White Clover ....*T. repens* L.
      4. Flowers pink or purple-tinged; stems erect or ascending not rooting from the nodes; fields, roadsides, and waste places; nat. from Eur. June-Sept. Alsike Clover ....*T. hybridum* L.
  2. Flowers sessile or nearly so.
    5. Heads cylindrical; calyx-teeth plumose-pubescent.
      6. Corolla white, shorter than the calyx; gravelly soil, roadsides, fields, or open woods; nat. from Eur. June-Sept. Rabbit-foot Clover ....*T. arvense* L.
      6. Corolla crimson, longer than the calyx; cultivated and occasionally spontaneous in fields and waste places; introd. from Eur. June- July. Crimson Clover ....*T. incarnatum* L.
    5. Heads subglobose to ovoid.
      7. Heads 2-3 cm in diameter; corolla magenta (or white), 12-15 mm long; leaflets usually with a pale mark; plants perennial; roadsides, fields, and waste places, common; nat. from Eur. May-Aug. Red Clover ....*T. pratense* L.
      7. Heads smaller; corolla rose; calyx becoming inflated after fruiting.
        8. Corolla resupinate, so that the standard lies below; plants annual with ascending branches; waste ground, occasional; introd. from Eur. May-Sept. Resupinate or Persian Clover .... *T. resupinatum* L.

8. Corolla not resupinate; plants perennial, the stems creeping and rooting at the nodes; waste ground, occasional,
introd. from Eur. May-Aug. Strawberry Clover ....
....*T. fragiferum* L.
1. Flowers yellow, shortly pedicellate, becoming reflexed in age.
  9. Leaflets sessile; stipules linear; heads 1-2 cm in diameter; roadsides, fields, and open woods; nat. from Eur. June-July.
  Yellow Hop-clover ....*T. agrarium* L.
  9. Terminal leaflet petiolulate; stipules ovate-lanceolate; heads 4-
  12 mm in diameter.
    10. Heads 20- to 40-flowered; standard distinctly striate; road-
    sides, fields, and waste places; nat. from Eur. June-Aug.
    Low Hop-clover ....*T. procumbens* L.
    10. Heads 3- to 15-flowered; standard faintly striate; road-
    sides and waste places; nat. from Eur. June-July. Little
    Hop-clover ....*T. dubium* Sibth.

13. **Melilotus** Mill. — Sweet Clover

1. Flowers yellow, 5-6 mm long; seeds oval.
  2. Pods (and ovary) glabrous, 2.5-3.5 mm long, strongly reticulate
  and transversely ridged, the upper suture not carinate; seeds
  not emarginate or punctate; wing-petals shorter than the
  standard but longer than the keel; waste places, fields, and
  roadsides; nat. from Eur. May-Sept. Yellow Sweet Clover
  ....*M. officinalis* (L.) Lam.
  2. Pods (and ovary) strigose, 4.5-5.5 mm long, weakly reticulate,
  not transversely ridged, the upper suture carinate; seeds
  punctate, emarginate; wing-petals and standard often longer
  than the keel; roadside; Lake Co. ....*M. altissima* Thuill.
1. Flowers white, 3-4.5 mm long; pods glabrous, 2.5-3.5 mm long;
  seeds orbicular; wing-petals shorter than the standard but equalling the keel; waste places, fields, and roadsides; nat. from Eur.
  May-Sept. White Sweet Clover ....*M. alba* Desr.

14. **Medicago** L.

1. Flowers bluish-purple; fields and roadsides, common; nat. from
  Eur. May-Sept. Alfalfa ....*M. sativa* L.
1. Flowers yellow.
  2. Pods straight, pubescent; fields and waste places, common; nat.
  from Eurasia. May-July. Black Medic ....*M. lupulina* L.
  2. Pods spirally coiled, smooth or spiny.
    3. Pods smooth; flowers about 3 mm long; waste ground; introd.
    from Eur. Jackson Co. ....*M. orbicularis* (L.) All.
    3. Pods spiny; flowers about 6 mm long; introd. from Eur.
    Jackson Co. ....*M. arabica* (L.) Huds.

15. Hosackia Dougl.

H. americana (Nutt.) Piper. Dry soil, rare; adv. from the West; Cook Co., *W. S. Moffatt* in 1893; Greene Co., *F. E. McDonald* in 1904. June-Aug.

16. Psoralea L. — Scurf-pea

1. Leaves pinnately 1- to 3-foliolate; pods rugose-reticulate.
   2. Leaflets ovate, acuminate; pods 1 cm long; stem 1-1.5 m tall; river banks, not common. June-July. [*Orbexilum onobrychis* (Nutt.) Rydb.] ....*P. onobrychis* Nutt.
   2. Leaflets elliptical; pods 4 mm long; stem 30-60 cm tall; wooded ridges and slopes, not common, s. Ill. June-July. [*Orbexilum pedunculatum* (Mill.) Rydb.] ....*P. psoralioides* (Walt.) Cory
1. Leaves digitately 3- to 5-foliolate; leaflets oblanceolate; pods about 8 mm long, not rugose-reticulate; dry soil, locally in northern Ill., extending southward to Madison and Monroe counties. June-Oct. [*P. floribunda* Nutt.] ....*P. tenuiflora* Pursh

17. Amorpha L.

1. Leaflets 2-5 cm long; shrubs 1.5-6 m tall; pods usually 2-seeded, 6-8 mm long.
   2. Leaves dull above; petiolules pubescent; river banks and alluvial soil, locally throughout Ill. May-June. Indigo Bush ....*A. fruticosa* L.
   2. Leaves glossy above; petiolules glabrous; along rivers, rare; Pope Co. May-June ....*A. nitens* Boynton
1. Leaflets 9-18 mm long; densely canescent shrubs less than 1 m tall; pods 1-seeded, 3-4 mm long; prairie soil and hillsides, locally nearly throughout Ill. June-July. Lead-plant ....*A. canescens* Pursh

18. Dalea Juss.

D. alopecuroides Willd. Fields and roadsides, occasional. Aug.-Sept. [*Parosela dalea* (L.) Britt.].

19. Petalostemum Michx. — Prairie-clover

1. Calyx-tube densely silky-velutinous; leaflets 3-9; corolla rose-purple, rarely white; in sandy or gravelly soil along roads or in open woods, local. July-Aug. Purple Prairie-clover ....*P. purpureum* (Vent.) Rydb.
1. Calyx-tube glabrous.
   2. Leaflets 5-9; flowers white; in habitats similar to the preceding species, but of less frequent occurrence. June-Aug. White Prairie-clover ....*P. candidum* (Willd.) Michx.
   2. Leaflets 13-31; flowers rose-purple; river banks and gravelly soil, rare, or probably now extinct in Ill. July-Sept. ....*P. foliosum* A.Gray

20. **Tephrosia** Pers. — Goat's-rue

T. virginiana (L.) Pers. Dry sandy soil. June-July. [*T. virginiana* var. *holosericea* (Nutt.) T. & G.].

21. **Robinia** L. — Locust

1. Tree to 25 m tall; twigs and petioles glabrous; flowers white, in pendulous racemes; commonly cultivated and abundantly naturalized in Ill.; native along the Ohio R., in southeastern Ill., and eastward. May-June. Black Locust ....*R. pseudoacacia* L.
1. Shrubs to 9 feet tall; stem viscid or bristly; flowers pink or rose.
    2. Stems bristly with stiff hairs; planted and sometimes persisting or spontaneous; native of southeastern U.S. May-June. Bristly Locust. Rose Acacia ....*R. hispida* L.
    2. Stems viscid, never bristly; escaped from cult.; Jo Daviess and Lee counties. Clammy Locust ....*R. viscosa* Vent.

22. **Wisteria** Nutt.

1. Inflorescence glandular; leaflets 9-15; swampy woods, rare, s. Ill.; also Washington and Peoria counties, where it is probably escaped from cult. June-July. Kentucky Wisteria. [*W. frutescens* sensu auth., non (L.) Poir.] ....*W. macrostachya* Nutt.
1. Inflorescence not glandular; leaflets 15-19; escaped from cult.; nat. from Japan. [*W. sinensis* sensu auth., non (Sims) Sweet] ....
....*W. floribunda* (Willd.) DC.

23. **Astragalus** L. — Milk-vetch

1. Flowers purplish.
    2. Calyx puberulent; flowers 8-10 mm long; pods glabrous; dry soil, local; w. Ill.; [*Holophacos distortus* (T. & G.) Rydb.] ....*A. distortus* T. & G.
    2. Calyx hirsute; flowers 15-20 mm long; pods hirsute; Boone Co., May 23, 1918, *H. C. Benke* 2456 (as *A. hypoglottis*); adv. from w. U.S. [*A. agrestis* sensu auth., non Dougl.] ....
....*A. goniatus* Nutt.
1. Corolla whitish or cream or greenish-yellow.
    3. Calyx-teeth subulate.
        4. Leaflets 1.5-4 cm long; pods ellipsoid, glabrous; river banks and hillsides throughout Ill. June-Aug. ....*A. canadensis* L.
        4. Leaflets 5-15 mm long; pods ovoid, pubescent; dry slopes, or on prairie soil; Grundy, Lake, La Salle, Lee, and Ogle counties. May-June ....*A. tennesseensis* A.Gray
    3. Calyx-teeth deltoid; leaflets 5-15 mm long; pods glabrous, sub-globose; prairies, rare; Macoupin, Madison, St. Clair, and Will counties. [*Geoprumnon trichocalyx* (Nutt.) Rydb.] ....
....*A. trichocalyx* Nutt.

24. **Sesbania** Scop.

S. exaltata (Raf.) Cory. Adv. from southern U.S.; Pulaski Co.

25. **Glycyrrhiza** L. — Wild Licorice
G. lepidota Pursh. Waste ground, occasional; adv. from west of the Mississippi R.

26. **Coronilla** L. — Crown-vetch
C. varia L. Roadsides and waste places, occasional; adv. from Eur. June-Aug.

27. **Desmodium** Desv. — Tick-clover
(*Meibomia* Heist.)

1. Pods conspicuously long-stipitate, the stipe 2-3 times the length of the calyx; stipules small, inconspicuous, setaceous, deciduous.
   2. Panicle on a leafy stem; fruiting pedicels 5-8 mm long.
      3. Leaves scattered along the stem; corolla white, 5-6 mm long; woods, chiefly in the s. part of the state, but extending northward to St. Clair and Wabash counties. July-Sept. ....*D. pauciflorum* (Nutt.) DC.
      3. Leaves clustered at the base of the peduncle; corolla rose-purple, 6-7 mm long; rich woods, common. June-Aug. [*D. acuminatum* DC.; *D. grandiflorum* sensu Robins. & Fern., non DC.; *M. grandiflora* sensu auth., non Ktze.] ....
         ....*D. glutinosum* (Muhl.) Wood
   2. Panicle on a long leafless peduncle; fruiting pedicels 1-2 cm long; corolla rose-purple, 6-11 mm long; leaflets oval or ovate, acute, glabrous or sparingly pubescent; woods, common. July-Aug. ....*D. nudiflorum* (L.) DC.
1. Pods short-stipitate or sessile.
   4. Stipules conspicuous, persistent, lanceolate to ovate, acuminate.
      5. Stems trailing, pilose; leaflets nearly orbicular, obtuse; stipules ovate-lanceolate, ciliate; woods, s. Ill., extending northward to Vermilion and St. Clair counties. Aug.-Sept. [*M. michauxii* Vail] ....*D. rotundifolium* DC.
      5. Stems erect or ascending.
         6. Joints of the pods rhombic, longer than broad.
            7. Leaflets obtusish, ovate or oval, somewhat rough-pubescent on both surfaces, pale and reticulate beneath, about the same length as the petiole; stem pubescent; open woods; absent from the northern counties. July-Aug. ....*D. canescens* (L.) DC.
            7. Leaflets acuminate, longer than the petiole.
               8. Leaves glabrous; bracts of the inflorescence not ciliate; woods throughout Ill. July-Sept. ....
                  ....*D. cuspidatum* (Muhl.) Loud.
               8. Leaves pubescent beneath; bracts of the inflorescence ciliate; open woods. July-Aug. ....
                  ....*D. longifolium* (T. & G.) Smyth
         6. Joints of the pods oval; leaflets lanceolate or ovate-lanceolate, reticulate beneath, pilosulous; stem uncinate-

pubescent; in woods and along roads throughout Ill., except the northern counties. July-Aug. ....
....*D. illinoense* A. Gray
4. Stipules small, inconspicuous, setaceous, usually soon deciduous.
  9. Leaves sessile or nearly so, the leaflets linear or lanceolate, obtusish, thickish, reticulate, pubescent beneath; stem puberulent; pods 1- to 3-jointed; open woods. July-Sept.
....*D. sessilifolium* (Torr.) T. & G.
  9. Leaves petioled.
    10. Pods distinctly stipitate, the stipe exceeding the calyx.
      11. Stem and leaves glabrous or nearly so.
        12. Leaflets ovate or broadly oval, pale beneath; flowers pink, 9-14 mm long; woods, chiefly in s. Ill. Aug.-Sept. ....*D. laevigatum* Nutt.
        12. Leaflets elliptic-lanceolate; flowers violet-purple, 5-8 mm long; open woods, common. July-Sept. ....
....*D. paniculatum* (L.) DC.
      11. Stem and leaves pubescent; flowers purple, 6-9 mm long.
        13. Leaflets ovate, thick, coriaceous, velutinous beneath; wooded slopes and ridges, s. Ill. Aug.-Sept. [*D. viridiflorum* sensu auth., non (L.) DC.] ....
....*D. nuttallii* (Schindl.) Schubert
        13. Leaflets elliptical or oval, appressed-pubescent beneath; dry soil, usually in open woods. Aug.-Sept. [*D. dillenii* sensu auth., non Darl.] ....
....*D. glabellum* (Michx.) DC.
    10. Pods short-stipitate or sessile, the stipe not exceeding the calyx-lobes.
      14. Flowers showy, 8-12 mm long, in dense panicled racemes; joints of the pods 3-5; prairie soil. July-Sept.
....*D. canadense* (L.) DC.
      14. Flowers small, 2-6 mm long, in loose panicled racemes; joints of the pods 1-3.
        15. Leaflets scabrous, softly pubescent, pale green and reticulate beneath, 2.5-5 cm long; stem puberulent; corolla 5-6 mm long; sandy soil in open woods, chiefly w. and s. Ill. Aug.-Sept. ....
....*D. rigidum* (Ell.) DC.
        15. Leaflets not scabrous, 1-2.5 cm long, glaucous beneath; corolla 2-4 mm long.
          16. Stem and leaves glabrous; wooded slopes and ridges, locally in central Ill. July-Sept. ....
....*D. marilandicum* (L.) DC.
          16. Stem pubescent; leaves more or less pubescent; open woods in s. Ill. July-Sept. [*D. obtusum* (Muhl.) DC.; *M. obtusa* (Muhl.) Vail] ....
....*D. ciliare* (Muhl.) DC.

28. **Lespedeza** Michx. — Bush-clover

1. Plants entirely herbaceous, erect, prostrate, or ascending.
   2. Perennials with subulate stipules, minute bracts, and narrow calyx-lobes. .
      3. Corolla purple; flowers of two kinds, some without petals.
         4. Flower-clusters on slender peduncles that are conspicuously longer than the subtending leaves.
            5. Stems trailing; inflorescence capitate or spicate.
               6. Stems glabrous or finely appressed-pubescent; sandy soil in woods, s. Ill. June-Sept. Creeping Bush-clover ....*L. repens* (L.) Bart.
               6. Stems softly pubescent with spreading hairs; wooded slopes and ridges, s. Ill., extending northward to Sangamon and Macon counties. July-Sept. Trailing Bush-clover ....*L. procumbens* Michx.
            5. Stems erect, sparsely appressed-pubescent; inflorescence loosely paniculate; in oak woods throughout the state. July-Sept. ....*L. violacea* (L.) Pers.
         4. Flower-clusters sessile or nearly so.
            7. Leaflets densely velutinous beneath; woods, local; chiefly in the s. half of Ill. Aug.-Sept. ....
            ....*L. stuvei* Nutt.
            7. Leaflets glabrous, or strigose beneath.
               8. Leaflets oval; sandy soil in woods in the s. half of the state. Aug.-Sept. ....*L. intermedia* (Wats.) Britt.
               8. Leaflets linear; sandy soil in woods nearly throughout Ill. Aug.-Sept. Slender Bush-clover ....
               ....*L. virginica* (L.) Britt.
      3. Corolla white or yellowish white, with a purple spot on the standard; flowers all alike.
         9. Leaflets elliptical to suborbicular.
            10. Peduncles equalling the cylindrical dense spikes; leaves from orbicular to oval; sandy soil on wooded slopes and ridges, local. Aug.-Sept. ....*L. hirta* (L.) Hornem.
            10. Peduncles usually shorter than the dense subglobose heads; leaves elliptical; sandy soil along roads and in open woods throughout Ill. Aug.-Sept. What may be a hybrid between this species and *L. virginica* (*L. simulata* Mack. & Bush) has been collected in Crawford Co. [*L. longifolia* DC.] ....*L. capitata* Michx.
         9. Leaflets linear; spikes slender, loose; prairie soil, rare; known in Ill. from Cook, McHenry, and Winnebago counties. Aug.-Sept. ....*L. leptostachya* Engelm.
   2. Annuals with scarious ovate-lanceolate stipules and bracts; calyx-lobes as broad as long; flowers solitary or 2 or 3 in the axils.

11. Stem retrorsely strigose; leaflets elliptical; petioles 1-2 mm long; pods not glandular; fields and roadsides; introd. from Asia. Aug.-Oct. Japan Bush-clover. Common Lespedeza ....*L. striata* (Thunb.) H. & A.

11. Stem antrorsely strigose to nearly glabrous; leaflets obovate, ciliate, often emarginate; petioles 4-10 mm long; pods glandular; fields and roadsides; recently introd. from Asia. Sept.-Oct. Korean Lespedeza ....*L. stipulacea* Maxim.

1. Plants suffruticose or somewhat shrubby, 1-3 m tall.

12. Leaflets elliptical, acute, 2-6 cm long; flowers rose-purple, 10-12 mm long, in racemes forming terminal panicles 30-60 cm long; fields and roadsides, occasional, native of Japan. Aug.-Sept. ....*L. thunbergii* (DC.) Nakai

12. Leaflets linear-oblanceolate, cuneate, 1-2 cm long; flowers 7-9 mm long, whitish with purple spots, 1-4 in the leaf-axils; plants virgate; fields and roadsides; extensively planted as a forage crop and soil-binder, now tending to spread from cult.; introd. from China and Japan. Aug.-Oct. Chinese Bush-clover ....*L. cuneata* (Dum.-Cours.) G. Don

29. **Stylosanthes** Sw. — Pencil-flower

S. biflora (L.) BSP. Dry soil in woods and on bluffs, chiefly in the s. half of Ill. June-Aug.

30. **Vicia** L. — Vetch

1. Flowers solitary or in pairs, axillary, nearly sessile; annuals.

2. Flowers 2-2.5 cm long; leaflets oblanceolate to oval; pods brown; fields and waste places; escaped from cult.; introd. from Eur. July-Aug. Spring Vetch ....*V. sativa* L.

2. Flowers 10-18 mm long; leaflets linear to linear-oblong; pods black when mature; fields and waste places; escaped from cult.; introd. from Eur. July-Aug. Common Vetch ....*V. angustifolia* Reich.

1. Flowers in 3-40-flowered racemes on axillary peduncles.

3. Racemes one-sided, densely 10-30-flowered.

4. Flowers 9-12 mm long, bluish purple (rarely white); calyx rounded or only slightly gibbous at base, the pedicel basal; pods 1.5-2 cm long; seeds 2.5 mm in diameter, black; roadsides and fields, occasional; introd. from Eur. June-Aug. Tufted Vetch ....*V. cracca* L.

4. Flowers 13-18 mm long, crimson, fading blue, rarely white; calyx strongly gibbous at base, the pedicel appearing lateral; pods 2.5-3.5 cm long; seeds 3-4 mm in diameter, dark brown.

5. Plants conspicuously pilose; lower calyx teeth about 3 mm long; roadsides and fields, common; nat. from Eur. June-Sept. Winter Vetch ....*V. villosa* Roth

5. Plants sparsely pilosulous or glabrate; lower calyx teeth about 2 mm long; waste places, becoming common; nat. from Eur. May-July ....*V. dasycarpa* Ten.

3. Racemes loosely 3-12 (-20)-flowered.

  6. Corolla 8-12 mm long, white, the keel tipped with blue; racemes longer than or equalling the subtending leaves; stipules entire; woods in the northeastern counties. May-June. Carolina Vetch ....*V. caroliniana* Walt.

  6. Corolla 15-18 mm long, bluish purple; racemes shorter than the subtending leaves; stipules sharply toothed; meadows and thickets in the northern third of the state. June-July. American Vetch ....*V. americana* Muhl.

31. Lathyrus L. — Wild Pea

1. Flowers purple, or purplish to pink or white.

  2. Leaflets 4-14.

    3. Stipules much smaller than the leaflets; corolla 1-1.5 cm long.

      4. Racemes 2- to 8-flowered; leaflets 4-8.

        5. Stem distinctly winged; leaflets linear to elliptical; flowers 1.5-2.5 cm long; moist ground and open woods in the n. half of Ill. May-July. [*L. palustris* var. *linearifolius* Ser.] ....*L. palustris* L.

        5. Stem merely angled; leaflets elliptical to oval; flowers 10-15 mm long; moist ground and thickets, southw. to St. Clair and Wabash counties. June-July ....*L. myrtifolius* Muhl.

      4. Racemes 10- to 24-flowered; leaflets 8-14, oval; stem 4-angled, puberulent or glabrous; open woods and moist thickets, n. Ill. May-June. [*L. venosus* var. *intonsus* Butters & St.John] ....*L. venosus* Muhl.

    3. Stipules broad, foliaceous, nearly as large as the adjacent leaflets; stem glabrous; leaflets 6-10, thick, oval; racemes 6- to 10-flowered; flowers about 2 cm long; sandy soil, rare; near Lake Michigan. June-Aug. Beach Pea. [*L. japonicus* Willd. var. *glaber* (Ser.) Fern.] ....*L. maritimus* (L.) Bigel.

  2. Leaflets 2; stem and petioles winged.

    6. Perennial; peduncle with 4-10 flowers; frequently cultivated and sometimes spontaneous; waste places and along roads; introd. from Eur. Everlasting Pea ....*L. latifolius* L.

    6. Annual; peduncle with 1-2 flowers; escaped from cult. Sweet Pea ....*L. odoratus* L.

1. Flowers yellowish-white; stipules large; leaflets ovate or broadly oval; peduncles 2-5 cm long; stem terete; woods, n. Ill. May-July ....*L. ochroleucus* Hook.

32. Apios Medic. — Groundnut

1. Flowers brownish-purple, the standard rounded or retuse at apex, not appendaged rhizomes moniliform, with several or many globose or ellipsoid tubers; woods and thickets, throughout Ill. July-Aug. ....*A. americana* Medic.
1. Flowers greenish-white, tinged with rose, the standard with a spongy appendage; tuber solitary, 10-20 cm thick; Wolf Lake, Union Co., *G. D. Fuller* in 1941 ....*A. priceana* B.L.Robins.

33. Phaseolus L. — Kidney Bean

P. polystachyus (L.) BSP. Woods and thickets, in s. Ill. July-Sept.

34. Glycine L. — Soybean

G. max (L.) Merr. Extensively cultivated, and sometimes spontaneous; native of Asia. July-Sept. [*Soja max* (L.) Piper; *G. soja* (L.) Sieb. & Zucc.].

35. Vigna Savi — Cow Pea

V. sinensis (L.) Endl. Cultivated, and occasionally spontaneous; native of Asia. July-Sept.

36. Strophostyles Ell. — Wild Bean

1. Leaflets all entire; pods 2.5-5 cm long.
  2. Leaflets ovate to lanceolate; flowers pink, 10-12 mm long; pods sparingly pubsecent; seeds mealy-pubescent; plants perennial with elongate fruiting peduncles; sandy soil, infrequent, s. Ill. July-Sept. ....*S. umbellata* (Muhl.) Britt.
  2. Leaflets narrowly elliptical to linear; flowers 5-6 mm long, purplish; pods 2.5-3.5 cm long, pubescent; seeds becoming glossy; plants annual; river banks or open woods, local; nearly throughout Ill. July-Sept. [*S. pauciflora* (Benth.) Wats., non *Phaseolus pauciflorus* Don] ....*S. leiosperma* (T. & G.) Piper
1. Leaflets, at least some of them, usually shallowly lobed; flowers 7-10 mm long, greenish-purple; pods 5-9 cm long, glabrous or sparsely strigose; seeds 5-9 mm long; sandy soil along roads or in open woods. July-Sept. [*S. angulosa* Ell.; *S. diversifolius* Pers.; *S. missouriensis* (Wats.) Small] ....*S. helvola* (L.) Britt.

37. Clitoria L. — Butterfly Pea

C. mariana L. Dry woods, s. Ill., rare. June-Aug.

38. Pueraria DC. — Kudzu-vine

P. lobata (Willd.) Ohwi. Planted for forage and to retard erosion; tending to become weedy in s. Ill.; native of e. Asia. Aug.-Sept.

39. Amphicarpa Ell. — Hog-peanut

1. Stem with closely reflexed hairs or glabrate; leaflets thin; inflorescence simple, 1- to 8-flowered; pods pubescent on the margins; woods, common. Aug.-Sept. [*A. monoica* (L.) Ell.; *Falcata comosa* sensu Britt., non *Glycine comosa* L.] ....*A. bracteata* (L.) Fern.
1. Stem brownish hirsute-villous; leaflets firm; inflorescence branched, 7- to 17-flowered; pods pubescent throughout; woods, common. Aug.-Sept. [*A. bracteata* var. *comosa* (L.) Fern.; *Falcata pitcheri* (T. & G.) Ktze.] ....*A. comosa* (L.) G.Don

40. Galactia P.Br. — Milk Pea

G. volubilis (L.) Britt. Dry soil, s. Ill., extending northward to Jackson and Gallatin counties. July-Aug. [*G. mississippiensis* (Vail) Rydb.].

55. Hydrangeaceae Dumort. — Hydrangea Family

1. Flowers all fertile, solitary, or in cymes or racemes; stamens 15-60 ....1. *Philadelphus*
1. Flowers in terminal corymbs, of 2 kinds, the marginal ones usually enlarged and sterile; stamens usually 10 ....2. *Hydrangea*

1. Philadelphus L. — Mock-orange

1. Sepals glabrous outside.
2. Flowers usually solitary or 2 or 3 together, scentless; sepals 5-7 mm long, about equalling the calyx-tube; twigs glabrous; cultivated and occasionally escaped; native of s.e. U.S. May. Scentless Mock-orange ....*P. inodorus* L.
2. Flowers in 5-7-flowered cymes, very fragrant; sepals 12-15 mm long, exceeding the calyx-tube; twigs pubescent; native of Eur.; commonly cultivated and sometimes escaped. May-June. Sweet Mock-orange ....*P. coronarius* L.
1. Sepals pubescent outside; flowers scentless or slightly fragrant, in 5-7-flowered cymes; apparently indigenous on rocky bluffs of Ohio R., near Golconda, Pope Co., *E. J. Palmer*. [*P. verrucosus* Schrad.] ....*P. pubescens* Loisel.

2. Hydrangea L. — Wild Hydrangea

H. arborescens L. Ravines and wooded banks throughout Ill., except the northern counties.

56. Escalloniaceae Dumort. — Escallonia Family
(*Iteaceae* Agardh)

1. Itea L. — Virginia Willow

I. virginica L. Swamps, rare, s. Ill.; known from Alexander, Johnson, Pope, Pulaski, and Union counties. May-June.

57. Grossulariaceae Dumort. — Gooseberry Family

1. Ribes L. — Gooseberry. Currant
(*Grossularia* Mill.)

1. Branches usually with spines or prickles.
    2. Ovary and fruit setose; calyx-lobes shorter than the tube; woods and river banks, local. Apr-May. Pasture Gooseberry. [*R. gracile* Michx.] ....*R. cynosbati* L.
    2. Ovary and fruit smooth; calyx-lobes equalling or exceeding the tube.
        3. Stamens exserted; flowers greenish-white; spines 5-15 mm long; woods and river banks, nearly throughout Ill. Apr.-May. The common gooseberry in Ill. ....*R. missouriense* Nutt.
        3. Stamens included; flowers green or purplish; spines 3-8 mm long; swamps and bogs, n. Ill. May-June. Wild Gooseberry ....*R. hirtellum* Michx.
1. Branches not at all spiny or prickly.
    4. Leaves minutely resinous-dotted and more or less pubescent beneath.
        5. Flowers yellowish, glabrous, 8-10 mm long; bracts longer than the pedicels; thickets and moist woods, chiefly n. Ill., but extending southward to Coles, Christian, and Pike counties. May-June. American Black Currant. [*R. floridum* L'Her.] ....*R. americanum* Mill.
        5. Flowers greenish or purplish, 5-6 mm long; bracts shorter than the pedicels; occasionally cultivated, but rarely persisting; Lake Co., *H. E. Ahles* in 1952. Black Currant ....*R. nigrum* L.
    4. Leaves not resinous-dotted; shrubs escaped from cult.
        6. Flowers greenish; calyx saucer-shaped; fruit red; rarely persisting around old dwellings; native of Eur. Garden Currant. [*R. rubrum* sensu auth., non L.] ....*R. sativum* (Reichenb.) Syme
        6. Flowers yellow; calyx tubular; fruit black; cultivated ground and roadsides, occasional; native of central U.S. Buffalo Currant. [*R. aureum* sensu auth., non Pursh] ....*R. odoratum* Wendl.

58. Hamamelidaceae Lindl. — Witch-hazel Family

1. Leaves palmately veined and lobed; flowers apetalous ....1. *Liquidambar*
1. Leaves pinnately veined, wavy-toothed; petals linear, yellow ......2. *Hamamelis*

1. Liquidambar L. — Sweet-gum

L. styraciflua L. Swampy woods; s. Ill., extending northward to Jersey, Jasper, and Crawford counties. Apr.-May.

2. Hamamelis L. — Witch-hazel

H. virginiana L. Woods, local; n. Ill., extending southward to McDonough, Wabash, and White counties. Oct.

59. Platanaceae Lindl. — Plane-tree Family

1. Platanus L. — Sycamore

P. occidentalis L. In woods and along streams, common throughout Ill. May.

60. Crassulaceae DC. — Stonecrop Family

1. Sedum L. — Stonecrop

1. Leaves thick, terete or nearly so.
  2. Petals yellow; leaves obovoid, densely imbricated, about 3 mm long; follicles 3-4 mm long; plants perennial; rocky places and roadsides; occasionally escaped from cult.; native of Eur. June-Aug. Mossy Stonecrop ....*S. acre* L.
  2. Petals rose-purple, pink, or white; leaves linear, crowded, 5-25 mm long, about 2 mm wide; follicles 4-6 mm long; on rocks, s. Ill. May-July ....*S. pulchellum* Michx.
1. Leaves flat, broad.
  3. Petals white; leaves roundish-obovate, entire, chiefly in whorls of 3 or the upper alternate; rocky woods, and in moist soil in wooded ravines, local. May. Wild Stonecrop ....
    ....*S. ternatum* Michx.
  3. Petals pink or purple; leaves oval or obovate, dentate or entire, alternate, 2-5 cm long.
    4. Petals pink, 3-4 times the length of the sepals; follicles attenuate to the slender style; cliffs, not common; s. Ill. Aug.-Sept. American Orpine .... *S. telephioides* Michx.
    4. Petals purple, about twice the length of the sepals; follicles abruptly pointed with the short style; sometimes escaping to roadsides and waste places; native of Eurasia. Aug.-Sept. Live-forever. [*S. purpureum* Link; *S. telephium* sensu auth., non L.] ....*S. triphyllum* (Haw.) S.F.Gray

61. Penthoraceae Van Tieghem — Penthorum Family

1. Penthorum L. — Ditch Stonecrop

P. sedoides L. Wet ground, common throughout Ill. July-Sept.

62. Saxifragaceae DC. — Saxifrage Family

1. Ovary 1-loculed; placentae parietal or nearly basal.
  2. Petals entire; inflorescence paniculate; leaves all basal ....1. *Heuchera*
  2. Petals fringed; inflorescence racemose; stem with a pair of opposite, sessile leaves ....2. *Mitella*
1. Ovary 2-loculed; placentae axial.
  3. Stamens 5; seeds wing-margined ....3. *Sullivantia*
  3. Stamens 10; seeds wingless ....4. *Saxifraga*

1. Heuchera L. — Alumroot

1. Calyx 2-5 mm long.
   2. Calyx 2-2.5 mm long, nearly regular; petals white; shaded cliffs; s. Ill. July-Oct. [*H. rugelii* Shuttlw.] ....*H. parviflora* Bartl.
   2. Calyx 4-5 mm long, oblique; petals greenish or purplish; bluffs and rocky banks, in the s. half of the state, not common. May-June ....*H. hirsuticaulis* (Wheelock) Rydb.
1. Calyx 6-8 mm long, decidedly oblique; river banks, cliffs, or dry woods; s. to Madison, Marion, and Clay counties. May-June. [*H. hispida* sensu auth., non Pursh; *H. americana* sensu auth., non L.; *H. richardsonii* var. *grayana* Rosend., Butters & Lakela] ....*H. richardsonii* R.Br.

2. Mitella L. — Miterwort. Bishop's-cap

M. diphylla L. Wooded ravines, not common; chiefly in the n. half of the state, but also in Jackson, Pope, and Williamson counties. May.

3. Sullivantia T. & G.

S. renifolia Rosend. Cliffs, rare; Carroll, De Kalb, Jo Daviess, Stephenson, and Winnebago counties. June-July.

4. Saxifraga L. — Saxifrage

1. Sepals becoming reflexed; plants 30-90 cm tall; leaves 10-30 cm long, entire or nearly so.
   2. Leaves pilose beneath; petals white, longer than the elliptical sepals; filaments filiform; moist shaded sandstone cliffs, rare; Gallatin, Jackson, Jo Daviess, La Salle, Ogle, and Union counties. May ....*S. forbesii* Vasey
   2. Leaves glabrous or nearly so beneath; petals greenish, equalling the deltoid sepals; filaments subulate; meadows, local. May-June ....*S. pennsylvanica* L.
1. Sepals ascending; plants 8-30 cm tall; leaves 2-10 cm long, dentate or crenate; rocky bluffs, rare; Hardin Co. ....*S. virginiensis* Michx.

63. Parnassiaceae Dum. — Grass-of-Parnassus Family

1. Parnassia L. — Grass-of-Parnassus

P. glauca Raf. Wet ground in the n. half of Ill. July-Sept. [*P. caroliniana* sensu auth., non Michx.].

64. Adoxaceae Fritsch — Moschatel Family

1. Adoxa L. — Musk-root

A. moschatellina L. Apple River Canyon, Jo Daviess Co., May 8, 1937, *N. C. Fassett 18709;* June 18, 1937, *F. J. Hermann 8896.*

65. Fagaceae A.Br. — Beech Family

1. Staminate flowers in small pendent globose heads on slender peduncles; nuts sharply trigonal; winter-buds lanceoloid, acuminate ....1. *Fagus*
1. Staminate flowers in slender catkins.
  2. Staminate catkins erect or ascending, 15-30 cm long; involucre prickly, 2- to 7-flowered ....2. *Castanea*
  2. Staminate catkins pendent; fruit an acorn in a scaly involucre-cup; winter-buds ovoid, obtuse or acute ....3. *Quercus*

1. Fagus L. — Beech

F. grandifolia Ehrh. Woods, especially near streams, local; chiefly in the valleys of the Mississippi, Ohio, and Wabash rivers; absent from central and western Ill.

2. Castanea Mill. — Chestnut

C. dentata (Marsh.) Borkh. Rocky woods, very rare. Probably now extinct in Ill.

3. Quercus L. — Oak

1. Leaves entire, elliptical or oblanceolate, bristle-tipped.
  2. Leaves permanently stellate-tomentulose beneath; woods, common. Shingle Oak ....*Q. imbricaria* Michx.
  2. Leaves quite glabrous on both surfaces, or sometimes sparsely pubescent on the lower surface along the midvein; borders of streams and swamps, rare; Massac Co. Willow Oak ....
    --*Q. phellos* L.
1. Leaves not entire.
  3. Leaf-lobes with bristle-tips; acorns maturing the second season. (Red or Black Oaks.)
    4. Leaves obovate, the apex obscurely 3- or 5-lobed, abruptly contracted toward the base, brownish stellate-tomentulose beneath; buds conical-fusiform, 8-10 mm long; acorn-cups turbinate, 1.5-2 cm in diameter, enclosing half the acorn; upland woods, in the s. half of the state, extending northward to Mercer, Tazewell, and Coles counties. Blackjack Oak ....*Q. marilandica* Muench.
    4. Leaves pinnately 5- to 9-lobed or cleft.
      5. Leaves grayish-tomentulose beneath; lobes often falcate; acorn globose; cup saucer-shaped; woods, not common; s. Ill. Spanish Oak. [*Q. pagodaefolia* Ashe] ....
        --*Q. falcata* Michx.
      5. Leaves glabrous or nearly so, not grayish-tomentulose beneath, but often with tufts of hairs in the axils of the principal veins.
        6. Leaves lobed about halfway to the midvein; acorn-cup shallow, saucer-shaped; winter-buds nearly glabrous; inner bark gray or reddish; woods, common. Red

Oak. [*Q. borealis* Michx.f.; *Q. borealis* var. *maxima*
(Marsh.) Ashe] ....*Q. rubra* L.
6. Leaves usually cleft more than halfway to the midvein.
   7. Acorn-cup shallow, saucer-shaped, enclosing not more
      than one-third of the acorn; inner bark gray or
      reddish; winter-buds glabrous or sparsely pubescent.
      8. Acorn-cup 1-1.5 cm in diameter, the rim only 3-4
         mm high; acorn 1-1.5 cm long; woods along
         streams. Pin Oak ....*Q. palustris* Muench.
      8. Acorn-cup 16-22 mm in diameter, the rim 5 mm or
         more high; acorn 1.8-2.5 cm long; woods near
         streams, in the s. half of Ill. [*Q. schneckii* Britt.]
         ....*Q. shumardii* Buckl.
   7. Acorn-cup hemispherical or turbinate, enclosing about
      one-half of the mature acorn.
      9. Scales of the acorn-cup closely appressed; winter-
        buds conical, sparsely pubescent to glabrous.
        10. Acorn-cup 15-25 mm in diameter, the scales
           glabrate, glossy; acorn ovoid; inner bark
           reddish or gray; upland woods, s. Ill., rare;
           Jackson, Pulaski, Richland, Union, Wabash,
           and White counties. Scarlet Oak ....
           ....*Q. coccinea* Muench.
        10. Acorn-cup 10-15 mm in diameter, the scales
           puberulent; acorn ellipsoid; inner bark yel-
           lowish; upland woods; n. Ill., s. to La Salle
           and Iroquois counties. Northern Pin Oak.
           Hill's Oak ....*Q. ellipsoidalis* E.J.Hill
      9. Scales of the acorn-cup pubescent, loosely imbri-
        cated, the upper forming a fringed border; cup
        18-25 mm in diameter; winter-buds large, angu-
        lar, grayish-pubescent; inner bark yellowish or
        orange, upland woods, common. Black Oak ....
        ....*Q. velutina* Lam.
3. Leaf-lobes not bristle-tipped; acorns maturing in the autumn of
  the first year.
  11. Leaves irregularly deeply lobed, often somewhat lyrate.
    (White Oaks.)
    12. Mature leaves usually glabrous and glaucous beneath;
      winter-buds nearly or quite glabrous; acorns 1.5-2 cm
      long, 3-4 times the length of the shallow cup; upland
      woods, common. White Oak ....*Q. alba* L.
    12. Mature leaves pubescent beneath; acorn-cup one-half to
      one-third the length of the acorn; buds ovoid,
      pubescent.
      13. Young twigs pubescent; lower surface of leaves gray-
        ish or brownish stellate-pubescent; mature acorns

ovoid, 1-2 cm long, about 1 cm in diameter; cup one-third to one-half as long as the acorn, nearly sessile; upland woods, common in the s. part of the state, but extending northward to Hancock, McDonough, Mason, Coles, and Clark counties. Post Oak ....*Q. stellata* Wang.

13. Young twigs glabrous or nearly so; lower surface of leaves whitish-tomentulose; mature acorns 2-3.5 cm long, the cup 2-5 cm in diameter, short-peduncled.

14. Upper scales of acorn-cup caudate-acuminate, forming a fringe around the acorn, which is half immersed in the cup; leaf-buds acutish, the terminal 5-8 mm long; vigorous 1-year-old twigs sometimes with corky ridges; bottomland and upland woods, chiefly in calcareous or neutral soils, common. Bur Oak. State tree of Ill. ....*Q. macrocarpa* Michx.

14. Scales broad, not caudate-acuminate; acorn nearly or quite immersed in the cup; buds obtuse, the terminal 2-4 mm long; swamps and bottomland woods in the southern third of the state, n. to Jasper and Adams counties. Overcup Oak ....*Q. lyrata* Walt.

11. Leaves angularly dentate, coarsely toothed or merely undulate, but not at all or only slightly lobed. (Chestnut Oaks.)

15. Leaves elliptical or lanceolate, glossy dark green above, more or less whitish stellate-tomentulose beneath, with 8-13 pairs of lateral veins, each vein ending in an acutish, mucronate, often incurved tooth; acorns nearly sessile, or short-peduncled, 10-18 mm long; hillsides and wooded bluffs, common. Chinquapin Oak. [*Q. acuminata* (Michx.) Houba] ....*Q. muhlenbergii* Engelm.

15. Leaves obovate, cuneate toward the base, angularly shallowly coarsely dentate; acorns 2-3 cm long.

16. Leaves regularly obtusely dentate; lateral veins 9-12 pairs; fruit sessile or short-peduncled, the peduncles less than 1 cm long; bottomlands and borders of streams, s. Ill. Swamp Chestnut Oak. Cow Oak. Basket Oak. [*Q. prinus* sensu auth., non L.] ....*Q. michauxii* Nutt.

16. Leaves undulate-crenate or coarsely sinuate.

17. Lateral veins 10-16 pairs; fruit sessile or nearly so; hillsides and crests of ridges in Alexander and Union counties. Chestnut Oak. [*Q. montana* Willd.] ....*Q. prinus* L.

17. Lateral veins 4-8 pairs; fruit on peduncles 2-6 cm
long; alluvial soil nearly throughout Ill.
Swamp White Oak. [*Q. platanoides* (Lam.)
Sudw.] ....*Q. bicolor* Willd.

The following known or supposed hybrids have been reported growing spontaneously in Illinois: *Q. alba* × *bicolor* [× *Q. jackiana* Schneid.], Cook, Randolph. — *Q. alba* × *macrocarpa* [× *Q. bebbiana* Schneid.], Winnebago. — *Q. alba* × *muhlenbergii* [× *Q. deamii* Trelease], White. — *Q. alba* × *stellata* [× *Q. fernowi* Trelease], Winnebago. — *Q. bicolor* × *lyrata* [× *Q. humidicola* E. J. Palmer], Clay, Pulaski, Richland. — *Q. imbricaria* × *falcata* [× *Q. anceps* E. J. Palmer], Gallatin, Hardin. — *Q. imbricaria* × *marilandica* [× *Q. tridentata* (A. DC.) Engelm.], Richland. — *Q. imbricaria* × *palustris* [× *Q. exacta* Trelease], Richland, St. Clair, Vermilion, Wabash. — *Q. imbricaria* × *rubra* [× *Q. runcinata* (A. DC.) Engelm.], Champaign, Johnson, Richland, St. Clair, Wayne. — *Q. imbricaria* × *velutina* [× *Q. leana* Nutt.], Cook, Fulton, Hancock, Hardin, Johnson, Peoria, Richland, Sangamon, Wabash, Will, — *Q. macrocarpa* × *muhlenbergii* [× *Q. hillii* Trelease], Cook, Richland. — *Q. marilandica* × *velutina* [× *Q. bushii* Sarg.], Hancock, Henderson, Randolph, Richland, Union, Wabash, Woodford. — *Q. palustris* × *phellos* [× *Q. schochiana* Dieck], Alexander, Massac, Pulaski. — *Q. phellos* × *velutina* [× *Q. filialis* Little], "s. Ill."

66. Betulaceae Agardh — Birch Family

1. Nuts small, compressed and often winged, without an involucre, borne in catkins; staminate flowers consisting of 2-4 stamens and a 2- to 4-parted calyx.
  2. Scales of the pistillate catkins 3-lobed, deciduous (sometimes only tardily so); stamens 2, bifid; leaf-buds sessile, with 3 or more scales; bark often peeling horizontally ....1. *Betula*
  2. Scales of the pistillate catkins 5-lobed, woody, persistent; stamens 4; buds usually stalked and with 2 valvate scales ....2. *Alnus*
1. Nuts with a foliaceous involucre or subtended by or enclosed in a large bractlet, borne in clusters or catkins; stamens 3-10; calyx none; buds with several scales.
  3. Shrubs; leaves broadly cordate-ovate, doubly serrate, usually with 5-8 pairs of veins; leaf-buds obtuse; nuts in clusters, each enclosed in a foliaceous involucre ....3. *Corylus*
  3. Small trees; leaves oval or ovate, with 9 or more pairs of veins; leaf-buds acute; fruits in pendent catkins, the nut subtended by or enclosed in a large bractlet.
    4. Fruiting bracts foliaceous, 3-lobed; bark of the trunk and branches smooth; lower surface of leaves glossy green with small tufts of whitish hairs in the axils of the principal veins; lateral veins unbranched; anthers glabrous ....4. *Carpinus*
    4. Fruiting bracts becoming sac-like, inflated, enclosing the nut; bark rough, scaly; lower surface of leaves pale dull green, thinly short-pilose; lateral veins usually forked near the margin; anthers pilose at apex ....5. *Ostrya*

1. Betula L. — Birch

1. Trees up to 30 m tall, with acute or acuminate, serrate or double-

serrate leaves; bark of trunk and large branches peeling horizontally in thin strips.

2. Bark chalky- or silvery-white; fruiting catkins cylindrical, slender-peduncled, usually pendulous, the scales deciduous; wing of the fruit distinctly broader than nutlet; cold woods, local; Carroll, Cook, Jo Daviess, and Lake counties. May. Paper Birch. Canoe Birch ....*B. papyrifera* Marsh.

2. Bark of trunk gray or brown; fruiting catkins erect or suberect, the scales more or less persistent; wing of the fruit not broader than the nutlet.

   3. Fruiting catkins nearly sessile, ovoid or subglobose; bracts ciliate; leaves oval; bark of twigs with faint wintergreen flavor; wooded areas in the n. half of Ill.; known from Du Page, Lake, Lee, Ogle, and Winnebago counties. Yellow Birch. [*B. lutea* var. *macrolepis* Fern.] ....
....*B. lutea* Michx.f.

   3. Fruiting catkins short-peduncled, ellipsoid; bracts tomentose; leaves rhombic-ovate; bark bitter, not aromatic; river banks; the common birch in Ill.; chiefly in w. and s. Ill.; also Kankakee Co. May. River Birch ....*B. nigra* L.

1. Shrubs 0.5-6 m tall; bark brown, not exfoliating; twigs of the season pubescent or puberulent, sometimes glandular.

   4. Leaves ovate, acute, 3-6 cm long, serrate; boggy meadows; Volo and Waukegan, Lake Co., *G. N. Jones.* [*B. glandulifera* × *lutea* Rydb.; *B. lutea* × *pumila* var. *glandulifera* Rosend.]
....*B. purpusii* Schneid.

   4. Leaves obovate to suborbicular, obtuse, or acutish, mostly 1.5-3 cm long, crenate-dentate; twigs without glands; bogs, northeastern Ill., in Boone, Cook, Lake, McHenry, and Winnebago counties. May. Dwarf Birch. [*B. pumila* var. *glandulifera* Regel, with leaves glandular-resiniferous, usually on both sides, and the two-year-old twigs with scattered glands, has been collected in Lake Co. (*A. Chase, E. J. Hill, G. N. Jones*), and Winnebago Co. (*E. W. & G. B. Fell*)] ....
....*B. pumila* L.

2. Alnus B.Ehrh. — Alder

1. Leaves with 9-12 veins on each side of midrib; shrubs.

   2. Leaves oval to ovate, doubly or coarsely serrate, usually rounded at the base; stipules lanceolate; nut orbicular; wet ground, rare; Boone, Cook, Lake, McHenry, and Winnebago counties. June. Speckled Alder. [*A. incana* sensu auth.] ....
....*A. rugosa* (DuRoi) Spreng.

   2. Leaves obovate, finely serrate, tapering at the base; stipules oval; nut ovate; wet ground, s. Ill. Apr.-May. Smooth Alder. [*A. rugosa* sensu auth., non Spreng.] ....*A. serrulata* (Ait.) Willd.

1. Leaves with 4-7 veins on each side of midrib; small tree; nat. from Eur. in a few places in Cook, Du Page, Piatt, and Will counties. Black Alder. [*A. vulgaris* Hill] ....*A. glutinosa* (L.) Gaertn.

3. Corylus L. — Hazel

C. americana Walt. Thickets and borders of woods throughout Ill. Mar.-Apr.

4. Carpinus L. — Blue Beech

C. caroliniana Walt. Muscle Tree. Woods, common. Apr.-May.

5. Ostrya Scop. — Ironwood. Hop-hornbeam

O. virginiana (Mill.) K.Koch. Woods, common. Apr.-May.

67. Juglandaceae Lindl. — Walnut Family

1. Pith of twigs lamellate or chambered; staminate catkins sessile or nearly so; leaflets conduplicate in vernation; nut enclosed in an indehiscent husk .... 1. *Juglans*
1. Pith solid; staminate catkins slender, long-peduncled; leaflets involute in vernation; husk of nut splitting into 4 halves ....2. *Carya*

1. Juglans L. — Walnut

1. Fruit subglobose, obtuse, papillose, not viscid; leaf-scars without a tuft of hairs on upper margin; bark dark brown, the ridges rough; stamens 20-30; nut corrugated, 4-loculed at base; woods, common. May. Black Walnut ....*J. nigra* L.
1. Fruit ellipsoid, pointed, viscid; leaf-scars with a pubescent fringe along the upper margin; bark gray, the ridges smooth; stamens 8-12; nut 4-ribbed, deeply sculptured, 2-loculed at the base; woods, rare. May. Butternut ....*J. cinerea* L.

2. Carya Nutt. — Hickory
(*Hicoria* Raf.)

1. Leaflets 9-17 (usually 13), lanceolate, acuminate, the lateral ones somewhat falcate; bud-scales 4 or 6, valvate.
  2. Rachis and lower surface of leaflets pubescent; staminate catkins fascicled; nut smooth, ellipsoid; seed edible, not bitter; river-bottom woods, common; extending northward to Jo Daviess, Peoria, Woodford, Fayette, and Lawrence counties. Apr.-May. Pecan. [*C. pecan* (Marsh.) Engler & Graebn.] ....
...............................*C. illinoensis* (Wang.) K.Koch
  2. Leaves glabrous or nearly so; catkins in threes on a common peduncle; nut sharply angled; seed very bitter; bark of old trunks exfoliating in long strips; river-bottoms, rare, s. Ill.; known from Alexander, Gallatin, Massac, Pulaski, and Union counties. Mar.-Apr. Water Hickory. Bitter Pecan ....
...............................*C. aquatica* (Michx.f.) Nutt.
1. Leaflets 5-9 (rarely 11).

3. Bud-scales mustard-yellow, 4 or 6, valvate (in pairs) ; lateral leaflets somewhat falcate; fruit nearly globose, 2.5-3.5 cm in diameter, the husk thin, the nut angled, thin-shelled, the seed becoming very bitter; bark of trunk gray, close, scaly or fissured; woods, common throughout Ill. May-June. Yellow-bud Hickory. Bitternut Hickory. [*C. amara* Nutt.; *Hicoria minima* (Marsh.) Britt.] ....*C. cordiformis* (Wang.) K.Koch

3. Buds not yellow; bud-scales 6-10, imbricated.

  4. Buds large, pubescent, nearly or quite glandless, the terminal one 1-2.5 cm long; twigs stout, grayish; fruits globose or subglobose, 3-7 cm in diameter, the dry husk 4-10 mm thick; seed edible, of good flavor. (Hickories.)

    5. Leaflets usually 7; nut thick-shelled (2 mm).

      6. Leaf-rachis copiously stellate-pubescent; 1-year-old twigs pubescent; bark of old trunks tight, gray, with irregular shallow fissures; nut subglobose, 2.5-3.5 cm long, rounded at base, short-pointed at apex; upland woods nearly throughout Ill., except the n.w. counties. Mocker-nut. Bigbud Hickory. [*C. alba* (L.) K.Koch, non Nutt.] ....*C. tomentosa* (Poir.) Nutt.

      6. Rachis of mature leaves and 1-year-old twigs glabrous or puberulent; bark on old trees separating into long shaggy strips; nut generally somewhat compressed, 4-6 cm long, often ellipsoid, pointed at each end; moist rich woods and river-bottoms, local; extending northward to Henderson, Peoria, and Champaign counties. Apr.-May. Shellbark Hickory ....
....*C. laciniosa* (Michx.f) Loud.

    5. Leaflets usually 5; rachis pubescent to glabrous; bark shaggy on old trunks; nut 2-3 cm long, subglobose, compressed, angular, pointed, the shell thin (1 mm) ; woods, common. Apr.-June. Shagbark Hickory. [*C. alba* Nutt.]
....*C. ovata* (Mill.) K.Koch

  4. Buds small, 5-10 mm long; twigs slender, reddish-brown, glabrous; dry husk of fruit 1-3 mm thick; bark tight, brown or dark gray, scaly or fissured, not shaggy. (Pignuts.)

    7. Leaflets usually 7; fruits covered with minute yellowish glands, the husk freely splitting to the base.

      8. Bud-scales copiously glandular-dotted; leaf-rachis and lower surface of leaflets pubescent and glandular; fruits ellipsoid, 3.5-4 cm long; upland woods in the southern two-thirds of Ill. Black Hickory. [*C. buckleyi* Durand; *H. villosa* (Sarg.) Ashe; *C. arkansana* Sarg.] ....*C. texana* Buckl.

      8. Bud-scales puberulent, or the outer ones glabrous, not copiously glandular-dotted; mature leaves glabrous or nearly so; fruits subglobose, 2.5-3 cm in diameter; woods, central and southern Ill., extending northward

to Adams, Mason, Champaign, and Vermilion counties. Apr.-June. Small-fruited Hickory. False Shag-
bark. [*C. microcarpa* Nutt.] ......*C. ovalis* (Wang.) Sarg.
7. Leaflets usually 5, rarely 7 or 3, glabrous; outer bud-scales,
rachises, and twigs glabrous; fruits obovoid to subglobose,
2-4 cm long, the husk tardily splitting to near the middle; woods throughout Ill., not infrequent. Pignut
Hickory. [*C. megacarpa* Sarg.] ......*C. glabra* (Mill.) Sweet

68. Myricaceae Horan. — Bayberry Family

1. Comptonia L'Her. — Sweetfern

C. peregrina (L.) Coult. Open woods in Cook, Kankakee, Will,
and Winnebago counties. Apr.-May. [*Myrica asplenifolia* L.].

69. Salicaceae Lindl. — Willow Family

1. Catkin-scales fimbriate; leaves mostly broad, long-petioled; buds with
several scales ....1. *Populus*
1. Scales entire; leaves usually narrow and short-petioled; bud-scale one ....
.... 2. *Salix*

1. Populus L. — Poplar

1. Petioles terete or nearly so, not strongly flattened laterally.
  2. Buds small, pubescent or glabrous, not viscid.
    3. Leaves sinuate-dentate to lobed; capsules 2-4 mm long;
    catkin-scales fringed with silky hairs; stigmas linear; bark
    smooth, whitish-gray, rough only at the base of old trunks;
    introd. species.
      4. Leaves persistently densely white-tomentose beneath, 3- to
      5-lobed or irregularly dentate; buds copiously white-
      tomentose; stigmas yellow; roadsides and yards, often
      escaped from cult.; introd. from Eurasia. Apr. White
      Poplar ....*P. alba* L.
      4. Leaves glabrous at maturity, gray-canescent beneath when
      young, glabrate, the margins sinuate-dentate; bud-scales
      ciliate or finely pubescent; stigmas purple; introd. from
      Eur.; cultivated, and persisting in a few places. Gray
      Poplar ....*P. canescens* (Ait.) Sm.
    3. Leaves crenate-serrate, ovate, cordate at base, long-petioled,
    tomentose when young, becoming glabrous or remaining
    floccose beneath; bark furrowed; capsules 7-9 mm long;
    catkin-scales glabrous; stigmas broad; borders of swamps,
    s. Ill., local; Apr.-May. Swamp Cottonwood ....
    ....*P. heterophylla* L.
  2. Buds (at least the terminal) elongated, pointed, glabrous, glossy,
  resinous-aromatic; leaves ovate-lanceolate, pale beneath,
  crenulate-serrate; bark smooth; capsules on short stout ped-

icels; catkin-scales with silky hairs; stigmas broad; river banks and wet ground, Cook and Lake counties. Balsam Poplar. [*P. tacamahaca* Mill.] ....*P. balsamifera* L.

1. Petioles strongly flattened laterally, at least near the blade.
  5. Buds pubescent or glabrous, not glutinous; catkin-scales with silky hairs; stigmas linear; leaves dull or gray-green.
    6. Leaves coarsely dentate, the blades 6-10 cm long, white-tomentose beneath when young, glabrate in age, broadly ovate, the base truncate to broadly cuneate; bud-scales finely appressed-pubescent, glabrate; wooded bluffs in the n. two-thirds of the state. Apr.-May. Large-toothed Aspen ....*P. grandidentata* Michx.
    6. Leaves finely crenate, glabrous from the beginning, ovate to orbicular, the blades 3-6 cm long; buds glabrous (or merely ciliolate), glossy; thickets and margins of woods; in the central and northern parts of the state, southward to Macoupin and Coles counties. Apr. Quaking Aspen ....*P. tremuloides* Michx.
  5. Buds viscid, glossy, glabrous; catkin-scales glabrous; stigmas broad; leaves bright or yellow-green.
    7. Leaves rhombic-ovate, cuneate at base, crenate-serrate; petioles glandless; branches closely ascending or nearly erect, forming a narrow tree; native of Eur.; cultivated, and sometimes found wild. Lombardy Poplar ....*P. nigra* var. *italica* Muench.
    7. Leaves broadly deltoid, mostly truncate at base, coarsely dentate with incurved teeth; petioles usually with a pair of glands at the base of the blade; branches widely spreading, forming a broad-crowned tree; along streams and in low ground, common. Mar.-Apr. Eastern Cottonwood ....*P. deltoides* Marsh.

2. Salix L. — Willow

1. Scales of the catkins pale green or yellowish, caducous; catkins on short leafy lateral branchlets.
  2. Style not more than 0.5 mm long.
    3. Ovaries and capsules distinctly pedicelled.
      4. Ovaries and capsules glabrous; leaves lanceolate, petioled, finely serrate; stamens 3-9.
        5. Capsules 3-6 mm long at maturity.
          6. Mature capsules ovoid-conical, 3-4 mm long; petioles 2-6 mm long.
            7. Leaves linear-lanceolate, green on both sides; common along streams. May. Black Willow ....*S. nigra* Marsh
            7. Leaves lanceolate, conspicuously glaucous beneath; rare; Madison Co., *Eggert, Glatfelter;* St. Clair

Co., *Engelmann.* [*S. wardi* Bebb.; *S. longipes*
Shuttlw.] ....*S. caroliniana* Michx.
6. Mature capsules lanceoloid, 5-6 mm long; leaves
lanceolate, paler and somewhat glaucous beneath,
the petioles usually 5-15 mm long; along streams.
Apr.-May. Peach-leaved Willow ....
....*S. amygdaloides* Anders.
5. Capsules 7-11 mm long; shrubs or small trees, 2-4 m tall;
swamps and bogs; Lake Co. June. Autumn Willow
...............................*S. serissima* (Bailey) Fern.
4. Ovaries and capsules appressed-silky at first, soon glabrous;
leaves linear, subsessile, remotely denticulate; stamens 2;
shrub; common along streams. Apr.-June. Sandbar
Willow. [*S. longifolia* sensu Muhl., non Lam.] ....
....*S. interior* Rowlee
3. Ovaries and capsules nearly sessile, glabrous; stamens 2; tree;
commonly planted and often spontaneous; introd. from
Eur. May. The commoner form, var. *vitellina* (L.) Koch,
has glabrous leaves and yellowish twigs. White Willow
....*S. alba* L.
2. Style distinct, 0.5-1 mm long; ovaries and capsules glabrous.
8. Catkins slender, 4-7 mm in diameter at flowering time, 8-
18 mm thick in fruit; stamens 2; tree; native of Eur.; often
planted, and self-propagating from broken branchlets.
Apr.-May. Brittle Willow ....*S. fragilis* L.
8. Catkins stout, 8-14 mm in diameter at flowering time, 2-2.5
cm thick in fruit; stamens 5; style almost 1 mm long;
shrubs; swamps, and along streams and lake shores in the
northern third of Ill. Shining Willow ....*S. lucida* Muhl.
1. Scales of the catkins brown to black (except *S. bebbiana*), persistent; stamens 2.
9. Ovaries and capsules glabrous.
10. Style 0.5-1.5 mm long; scales densely silky-villous; young
twigs often more or less puberulent; leaves serrate or
serrulate.
11. Flowering catkins appearing before the leaves, sessile or
nearly so, subtended by a few bracts; leaves pale green
or more or less glaucous beneath, at least at maturity.
12. Style 0.5 mm long; capsules 4-7 mm long, on pedicels
1-2 mm long; leaves lanceolate, acuminate, becoming glabrous or nearly so; wet ground, rather common. Apr.-May. [*S. missouriensis* Bebb; *S. cordata* Muhl., non Michx.] ....*S. rigida* Muhl.
12. Style 1 mm long; capsules 7-10 mm long, on pedicels
2-4 mm long; leaves ovate-lanceolate, acute; sandy
ground, thickets, meadows, and swamps, in the
northern third of the state. May. Blue-leaf Willow

[*S. glaucophylla* sensu auth.] ....
....*S. glaucophylloides* Fern.
   11. Flowering catkins on short leafy peduncles 1-2 cm long;
       style 0.7-1.5 mm long; capsules 5-8 mm long, the
       pedicels less than 1 mm long; leaves ovate to oval,
       acute or abruptly acuminate, silky-pubescent, not
       glaucous; sandy shores, n.e. Ill. [*S. syrticola* Fern.;
       S. adenophylla Hook.] ....*S. cordata* Michx.
 10. Style 0.1-0.2 mm long, the stigmas therefore sessile or nearly
     so; scales glabrous on the back, pilose within; twigs gla-
     brous; leaves oblanceolate or elliptical, entire, glaucous
     beneath; catkins appearing with the leaves; bogs and
     wet meadows; Cook, Henry, Lake, McHenry, Peoria,
     and Woodford counties. Apr.-May ....*S. pedicellaris* Pursh
9. Ovaries and capsules pubescent.
   13. Catkins with some small leafy bracts at base, in flower as
       the leaf-buds are opening.
      14. Scales yellowish or pink-tipped, thinly villous, shorter
          than the pedicel; capsules 6-10 mm long; stigmas
          nearly sessile; leaves elliptical, entire, or nearly so,
          tomentose beneath; wet ground in n. Ill. May. Bebb
          Willow [*S. rostrata* sensu auth., non Thuill.] ....
          ....*S. bebbiana* Sarg.
      14. Scales dark brown or black.
         15. Style 1-1.5 mm long; capsules white-tomentose, 6-8
             mm long at maturity; leaves thick, elliptical-
             lanceolate, the revolute margins entire or repand;
             bogs in the n. half of Ill. May. Sage Willow ....
             ....*S. candida* Fluegge
         15. Style less than 0.5 mm long; ovaries and capsules
             appressed-pubescent.
            16. Leaves serrulate to serrate.
               17. Capsules acuminate, 6-8 mm long, the pedicel
                   2.5-5 mm long; catkins 10-15 mm long;
                   leaves linear-oblanceolate, glandular-ser-
                   rulate; wet ground in the n. third of the
                   state. Apr.-May ....*S. petiolaris* Sm.
               17. Capsules obtuse, 3-5 mm long, the pedicels 1-
                   1.5 mm long; catkins 18-30 mm long;
                   leaves lanceolate, acuminate, finely serrate;
                   wet ground, local. Apr. Silky Willow ....
                   ....*S. sericea* Marsh.
            16. Leaves entire or nearly so, narrowly oblanceolate;
                capsules 5-6 mm long; Kankakee, Kankakee
                Co., *Hill* in 1874; Chicago, Cook Co., *Hill* in
                1894 ....*S. subsericea* (Anders.) Schneid.
 13. Catkins sessile or nearly so, appearing before the leaves;
     young twigs glabrous or puberulent.

18. Cultivated shrubs; leaves oval 2-6 cm wide, the margins
    somewhat undulate, crenate to entire, glaucous, reticu-
    late, grayish pubescent; chiefly staminate; rarely per-
    sisting near old dwellings; native of Eur. Mar.-April.
    Goat Willow ....*S. caprea* L.
18. Native shrubs.
    19. Pistillate catkins 2-4 cm long, becoming 4-6 cm long
        in fruit; mature capsules 7-10 or 12 mm long;
        pedicel shorter than the scale; leaves elliptical to
        obovate, glabrous or nearly so at maturity, glaucous
        beneath; tall shrubs (2-7 m high); wet ground,
        local. Apr.-May. Pussy Willow [*S. eriocephala*
        Michx.; *S. prinoides* Pursh; *S. discolor* var. *lati-
        folia* Anders.] ....*S. discolor* Muhl.
    19. Pistillate catkins 1.5-2 cm long, becoming 2-4 cm
        long in fruit; mature capsule 6-9 mm long; pedicel
        equalling or slightly longer than the scale; leaves
        linear-oblanceolate, pubescent beneath; low shrubs
        of sandy or clayey soil, common. Apr.-May.
        Prairie Willow [*S. tristis* Ait.] ....*S. humilis* Marsh.

70. Ulmaceae Mirb. — Elm Family

1. Leaves with 1 principal vein from the base, the lateral veins straight,
   parallel, usually more than 10 pairs; flowers in clusters on twigs of the
   preceding season; twigs with solid pith.
   2. Flowers appearing before the leaves; fruit a 1-seeded, flat, thin-winged
      samara; leaves usually doubly serrate ....1. *Ulmus*
   2. Flowers appearing with the leaves; fruit nut-like, muricate; leaves simply
      serrate ....2. *Planera*
1. Leaves (at least when mature) with 3-5 veins from the base, the lateral
   veins curved, fewer than 10 pairs; flowers borne on the twigs of the
   season, appearing with the leaves; twigs with chambered pith; fruit a
   drupe; bark corky-ridged ....3. *Celtis*

1. Ulmus L. — Elm

1. Flowers drooping, on slender pedicels; calyx not ciliate; leaves
   glabrous or nearly so above; nut scabrous.
   2. Branches not corky-winged; buds glabrous or nearly so; fruit
      glabrous except the ciliate margins; woods, common. Apr.
      American or White Elm ....*U. americana* L.
   2. Branches (at least some of them) usually more or less corky-
      winged; fruit pubescent.
      3. Buds pubescent; leaves 5-13 cm long; flowers racemose;
         woods in the n. half of the state. Apr.-May. Rock Elm
         [*U. racemosa* Thomas, non Borkh.] ....*U. thomasi* Sarg.
      3. Buds glabrous or puberulent, not ciliate; leaves 2-8 cm long;
         flowers fascicled; hillsides, cliffs, ridges; s. Ill. Mar-Apr.
         Winged Elm ....*U. alata* Michx.

1. Flowers nearly sessile in erect dense clusters; branches not corky-winged.
   4. Buds reddish-pubescent; stamens 5-9; samaras pubescent in the center; mature leaves harshly scabrous-pubescent, 10-20 cm long, with characteristic slippery-elm odor; woods, common. Apr. [*U. fulva* Michx.] Slippery Elm ......*U. rubra* Muhl.
   4. Buds and twigs glabrous; stamens 4 or 5; samaras glabrous; leaves smooth, 2-7 cm long; small tree, frequently planted, occasionally found wild; native of Asia. Mar.-Apr. Siberian Elm ....*U. pumila* L.

2. Planera J.F.Gmel. — Water Elm

P. aquatica [Walt.] J. F. Gmel. Swamps, not common; known from Alexander, Johnson, Massac, and Pulaski counties. Apr.-May.

3. Celtis L. — Hackberry

1. Leaves sharply serrate; drupes 7-9 mm in diameter at maturity; fruiting pedicels longer than the petioles; nutlet brownish, 6-8 mm long, obovoid, pitted; tree, 10-20 m tall; woods, usually near streams, common. Apr.-May. Hackberry [*C. crassifolia* Lam.] ....*C. occidentalis* L.
1. Leaves entire or with a few teeth; nutlet 5-6 mm long, globose, pitted.
   2. Leaves lanceolate, long-acuminate, usually broadly cuneate at base; fruiting pedicels longer than the petioles; drupes 4-6 mm in diameter; tree, 10-30 m tall; woods and river banks, s. Ill., in the valley of the Wabash R., northward to Lawrence Co., and the Mississippi valley northward to Adams Co. Sugarberry [*C. mississippiensis* Bosc] ....*C. laevigata* Willd.
   2. Leaves ovate, short-acuminate, usually rounded or subcordate at base; fruiting pedicels about as long as the petioles; drupes 6-8 mm in diameter; shrub or small tree to 4 m tall; rocky banks of streams, rare and local; s. Ill., northward along the Mississippi R. to Henderson Co. Dwarf Hackberry ....
   ....*C. pumila* (Muhl.) Pursh

71. Moraceae Lindl. — Mulberry Family

1. Leaves serrate or lobed, more or less 3-veined from the base; branches never spiny.
   2. Twigs glabrous or pubescent; leaves alternate; bud-scales 3-6; fruit aggregate, ellipsoid, edible ....1. *Morus*
   2. Young twigs hirsute; leaves often opposite; buds with 2 or 3 scales; fruit in globose heads, not edible ....2. *Broussonetia*
1. Leaves entire, pinnately-veined; branches usually spiny, staminate flowers in loose racemes, the pistillate in globose heads; fruit large, globose, yellowish-green, 8-12 cm in diameter ....3. *Maclura*

1. Morus L. — Mulberry

1. Leaves becoming scabrous above, the lower surface pubescent, or hispidulous along the veins; lateral lobes, if present, caudate; buds somewhat divergent, acute; fruit reddish-purple, 2 cm or more in length; native tree; woods, common. May-June. Red Mulberry ....*M. rubra* L.
1. Leaves glabrous, somewhat glossy and nearly smooth above; lower surface glabrous or nearly so, except on the veins or in their axils; lateral lobes usually obtuse; native of Asia.
   2. Fruit whitish or pinkish, 1-1.5 cm long; cultivated, and rarely escaped. May. White Mulberry ....*M. alba* L.
   2. Fruit dark red, smaller; a small bushy tree; leaves commonly much lobed; along fences and in woods, common; absent from the southern counties. [*M. alba* var. *tatarica* (L.) Ser.] ....*M. tatarica* L.

2. Broussonetia L'Her. — Paper Mulberry

B. papyrifera (L.) Vent. Planted as a shade tree, and sometimes escaped from cult.; introd. from e. Asia; Hardin, Jackson, Pope, and Randolph counties.

3. Maclura Nutt. — Osage-orange. Hedge-apple

M. pomifera (Raf.) Schneid. Commonly planted for fences and windbreaks, sometimes spontaneous; native in Ark., e. Okla., and e. Tex. May-June.

72. Cannabinaceae Lindl. — Hemp Family

1. Erect herbs; pistillate flowers in spikes ....1. *Cannabis*
1. Stems twining; pistillate flowers in catkin-like drooping clusters (hops) ....2. *Humulus*

1. Cannabis L. — Hemp.   Marijuana

C. sativa L. Moist soil, edges of fields, along roads, waste ground, local; nat. from Asia. July-Sept.

2. Humulus L. — Hop

1. Leaves 3-lobed or unlobed, the petioles usually shorter than the blades; pistillate catkins much enlarging and becoming cone-like, the bracts obtuse or acutish, glandular at the base, not ciliate; native perennial along fences and in sandy soil at edges of woods, common. Aug.-Oct. American Hop [*H. lupulus* sensu auth., non L.] ....*H. americanus* Nutt.
1 Leaves deeply 5- to 7-lobed; pistillate catkins not greatly enlarging in fruit, the bracts acuminate, ciliate; annual, native of Asia; waste places, sparingly nat. in Ill. Japanese Hop. [? *Antidesma scandens* Lour.] ....*H. japonicus* Sieb. & Zucc.

73. **Urticaceae** Reichenb. — Nettle Family

1. Leaves mostly opposite.
    2. Plants often with some stinging hairs; stigma capitate-tufted ....1. *Urtica*
    2. Plants without stinging hairs.
        3. Plants perennial, more or less pubescent; stems opaque; stipules separate; stigma filiform ....2. *Boehmeria*
        3. Plants annual, chiefly glabrous; stems translucent; stipules united; stigma capitate-tufted ....3. *Pilea*
1. Leaves alternate.
    4. Plants with stinging hairs; leaves ovate, 5-12 cm broad; flowers in loose branched cymes ....4. *Laportea*
    4. Plants without stinging hairs; leaves lanceolate, less than 2.5 cm wide; flower-clusters sessile in the leaf-axils ....5. *Parietaria*

1. **Urtica** L. — Nettle

1. Plants perennial, 0.5-3 m tall; flower-clusters in branched paniculate spikes; alluvial soil in the n. half of the state. July-Aug. [*U. procera* Muhl.; *U. dioica* of auth., non L.] Common Nettle ....*U. gracilis* Ait.
1. Plants annual; flower-clusters shorter than the petioles.
    2. Leaves ovate, crenate-serrate, the upper ones much smaller; achenes oval, 1.2 mm long; alluvial soil, usually near base of cliffs; known from Alexander and Jackson counties. Apr.-July ....*U. chamaedryoides* Pursh
    2. Leaves oval to ovate, deeply laciniate-dentate; stem leafy to the tip; achenes ovate, 1.7 mm long, microscopically puncticulate; waste places, occasional; nat. from Eur. Burning Nettle. June-Sept. ....*U. urens* L.

2. **Boehmeria** Jacq. — False Nettle

1. Leaves thin, smooth or slightly scabrous above, the petioles about as long as the blades; moist woods. July-Sept. ....
....*B. cylindrica* (L.) Sw.
1. Leaves firm, strongly scabrous above, the petioles much shorter than the blades; marshy ground, rare ....*B. drummondiana* Wedd.

3. **Pilea** Lindl. — Clearweed

1. Mature achenes yellowish green, oval, 1-1.5 mm long, with brown or purple spots; moist shaded ground, common. July-Sept. ....
....*P. pumila* (L.) A.Gray
1. Mature achenes green or dark purple, ovate, 1.5-2 mm long, with a very narrow hyaline margin; moist ground, rare; July-Sept. [*P. opaca* (Lunell) Rydb.] ....*P. fontana* (Lunell) Rydb.

4. **Laportea** Gaud. — Wood Nettle

L. canadensis (L.) Gaud. Woods, common. July-Aug.

5. **Parietaria** L. — Pellitory

P. pennsylvanica Muhl. Woods, common. May-Sept.

74. **Lauraceae** Lindl. — Laurel Family

1. Flowers appearing with or before the leaves in corymbose racemes; anthers 4-loculed; leaves often lobed; fruit blue-black ....1. *Sassafras*
1. Flowers in small roundish nearly sessile umbel-like clusters on bare twigs; anthers 2-loculed; leaves always entire; fruit red ....2. *Lindera*

1. **Sassafras** Nees — Sassafras

S. albidum (Nutt.) Nees. Rich woods, common throughout Ill., except the extreme northern counties. May. [*S. variifolium* (Salisb.) Ktze; *S. officinale* Nees & Eberm.; *S. albidum* var. *molle* (Raf.) Fern.].

2. **Lindera** Thunb. — Spice-bush

L. benzoin (L.) Blume. In moist woods and along streams, common. Mar.-Apr. [*Benzoin aestivale* (L.) Nees]. Specimens with petioles and lower surface of blades more or less pubescent [*L. benzoin* var. *pubescens* (Palmer & Steyerm.) Rehd.], have been mistaken for *L. melissaefolium* (Walt.) Blume, a species of more southerly range which does not occur in our limits.

75. **Lythraceae** Lindl. — Loosestrife Family

1. Flowers regular; petals equal.
    2. Calyx campanulate or hemispherical.
        3. Flowers small, axillary, solitary or few.
            4. Petals 4; calyx with appendages in the sinuses.
                5. Flowers solitary; capsules 4-loculed, septicidal ....1. *Rotala*
                5. Flowers usually more than 1 in each axil; capsules 2- to 4-loculed, irregularly dehiscent ....2. *Ammannia*
            4. Petals absent; calyx without appendages; flowers solitary; capsules indehiscent ....3. *Peplis*
        3. Flowers large (2 cm in diameter), in axillary clusters, trimorphous; petals usually 5; plants semi-shrubby ....4. *Decodon*
    2. Calyx cylindrical, striate; petals 5-7, usually 6 ....5. *Lythrum*
1. Flowers irregular and unsymmetrical; petals ovate, purple, unequal; plants glandular-pubescent ....6. *Cuphea*

1. **Rotala** L.

R. ramosior (L.) Koehne. Wet ground throughout Ill. July-Sept.

2. **Ammannia** L.

A. coccinea Rottb. Muddy banks and shores, local; common throughout Ill., except the extreme northern counties. July-Aug.

3. **Peplis** L. — Water-purslane

P. diandra Nutt. Wet ground or shallow water, rare. June-Aug. [*Ammannia nuttallii* (T. & G.) A.Gray; *Didiplis diandra* (Nutt.) Wood].

4. **Decodon** J.F.Gmel. — Swamp Loosestrife

D. verticillatus (L.) Ell. Swamps, not common. July-Aug.

5. **Lythrum** L. — Loosestrife

1. Flowers large, 12-15 mm in diameter, whorled in terminal spicate panicles; leaves opposite or whorled; stamens twice as many as the petals; swamps and wet meadows, occasional; nat. from Eur. June-Aug. Purple Loosestrife ....*L. salicaria* L.
1. Flowers small, 6-10 mm in diameter, solitary, axillary; leaves mostly alternate; stamens and petals 5-7; meadows and road-sides, common throughout Ill. June-Aug. Common Loosestrife ....*L. alatum* Pursh

6. **Cuphea** P.Br. — Waxweed

C. petiolata (L.) Koehne. Dry soil throughout Ill., except the extreme northern counties. July-Oct. [*C. viscosissima* Jacq.; *Parsonsia petiolata* (L.) Rusby].

76. **Thymelaeaceae** C.F.Meiss. — Mezereum Family

1. **Dirca** L. — Leatherwood

D. palustris L. Woods and thickets, local. Apr.-May.

77. **Elaeagnaceae** Lindl. — Oleaster Family

1. Leaves opposite; stamens 8 ....1. *Shepherdia*
1. Leaves alternate; stamens 4 ....2. *Elaeagnus*

1. **Shepherdia** Nutt. — Canadian Buffalo-berry

S. canadensis (L.) Nutt. Dry bluffs and banks or ravines near L. Michigan; Lake Forest, Lake Co., *E. J. Hill* in 1904; Glencoe, Cook Co., *G. D. Fuller* in 1943.

2. **Elaeagnus** L. — Russian Olive

E. angustifolia L. Cultivated, and sometimes escaped; introd. from Eur.

78. **Passifloraceae** Dumort. — Passion-flower Family

1. **Passiflora** L. — Passion-flower

1. Leaves deeply 3- to 5-lobed, the lobes serrate; flowers subtended by a conspicuous involucre of 3 bracts; petals lavender or whitish; berry 5-7 cm long, yellow; dry soil, s. Ill. May-July ....*P. incarnata* L.
1. Leaves obtusely 3-lobed above the middle, the lobes entire; flowers without an involucre; petals greenish-yellow; berry about 1 cm long, purple; thickets, s. Ill., extending northward to Pike, and Vermilion counties. May-July. [*P. lutea* var. *glabriflora* Fern.] ....*P. lutea* L.

79. **Cactaceae** Lindl. — Cactus Family

1. **Opuntia** Mill. — Prickly-pear

O. rafinesquii Engelm. Sandy soil, locally abundant; chiefly in the valleys of the Illinois, Mississippi, and Ohio rivers; also near Lake Michigan. [(?) *O. humifusa* Raf.]

80. Loasaceae Reichenb. — Loasa Family

1. Mentzelia L.

M. oligosperma Nutt. Stick-leaf. Bluffs, rock ledges, and hill prairies, rare; western Ill. near the Mississippi River from Adams to Randolph counties. June-July.

81. Cucurbitaceae B.Juss. — Gourd Family

1. Corolla yellow, 6-15 cm long; fruit smooth; stem trailing ....1. *Cucurbita*
1. Corolla greenish-white, small.
  2. Fruit glabrous; seeds numerous; tendrils simple; stem glabrous ....
    .... 2. *Melothria*
  2. Fruit prickly, 1- or few-seeded; tendrils branched.
    3. Stem and leaves glabrous; fruit an inflated usually 4-seeded pod
      dehiscing at the apex and bursting irregularly ....3. *Echinocystis*
    3. Stem and leaves more or less pubescent; fruits indehiscent, 1-seeded,
      usually 3-10 together ....4. *Sicyos*

1. Cucurbita L.

C. foetidissima HBK. Missouri Gourd. Dry ground, occasional, usually along railroads; adv. from west of the Mississippi R. [*Pepo foetidissima* (HBK.) Britt.].

2. Melothria L.

M. pendula L. Creeping Cucumber. Bluffs and thickets, rare; Thebes, Alexander Co., *H. M. Franklin* in 1949; Belle Smith Springs, Pope Co., *R. Thorne* in 1958. June-Sept.

3. Echinocystis T. & G. — Wild Balsam-apple

E. lobata (Michx.) T. & G. Alluvial soil, and waste places, local. July-Sept. [*Micrampelis lobata* (Michx.) Greene].

4. Sicyos L. — Bur-cucumber

S. angulatus L. Alluvial soil, and in fields throughout Ill. July-Sept.

Three members of this family are occasional escapes from cult. These are *Cucumis sativus* L., Cucumber; *Lagenaria vulgaris* Seringe, Gourd; and *Citrullus vulgaris* Schrad., Watermelon.

82. Melastomaceae R.Br. — Melastoma Family

1. Rhexia L. — Meadow-beauty

1. Stem 4-angled; leaves sessile; hypanthium setose; moist sand-barrens, or in peaty soil, locally throughout Ill. July-Sept. ....
....*R. virginica* L.

1. Stem nearly terete; leaves short-petioled, narrow; hypanthium glabrous or nearly so; moist sandy soil, rare; Mason Co., *Brendel;* Massac Co., *Gleason.* June-Sept. [*R. mariana* var. *leiosperma* Fern. & Grisc.] ....*R. mariana* L.

83. Onagraceae Dumort. — Evening-primrose Family
(*Epilobiaceae* Vent.)

1. Flowers usually with 4 petals (rarely 5 or 0); sepals 4-6 (rarely apparently only 2); stamens 4-12.
  2. Fruit a many-seeded capsule opening by valves or by a pore.
    3. Seeds with a tuft of silky hairs; flowers (in our species) not yellow ....1. *Epilobium*
    3. Seeds without hairs.
      4. Hypanthium scarcely or not at all extended beyond the ovary.
        5. Stamens 8-12, in two series ....2. *Jussiaea*
        5. Stamens 4 ....3. *Ludwigia*
      4. Hypanthium conspicuously extended beyond the ovary into a tube ....4. *Oenothera*
  2. Fruit indehiscent, deciduous; flowers pink ....5. *Gaura*
1. Flowers with 2 notched white petals, 2 sepals, and 2 stamens; fruit indehiscent, obovoid, with hooked bristly hairs ....6. *Circaea*

1. Epilobium L. — Willow-herb

1. Petals 1-2 cm long; stigma 4-lobed; stem 0.5-2 m tall.
  2. Stem puberulent or glabrous; leaves alternate, entire or denticulate; petals entire; stamens and style declined; edges of woods and burned-over ground, local; known from Cook, Lake, La Salle, McHenry, and Winnebago counties. June-Aug. Fireweed [*Chamaenerion spicatum* (Lam.) S.F.Gray] ....*E. angustifolium* L.
  2. Stem hirsute; leaves mostly opposite, sharply serrulate; petals notched, stamens and styles erect; moist ground, occasional; adv. from Eur.; Chicago, Cook Co., *J. A. Steyermark* in 1948. June-Aug. ....*E. hirsutum* L.
1. Petals 3-8 mm long; stigma entire; stem 20-90 cm tall.
  3. Leaves lanceolate, denticulate; stems with decurrent lines from the bases of the leaves.
    4. Seeds 1-1.5 mm long; coma reddish-brown; moist ground, local. Aug.-Sept. ....*E. coloratum* Muhl.
    4. Seeds 0.5-1 mm long; coma white; moist ground, in the n. counties, not common. July-Sept. ......*E. adenocaulon* Haussk.
  3. Leaves linear, or linear-lanceolate, mostly entire; no decurrent lines on stem.
    5. Stem, leaves, and capsules copiously soft-pubescent with short straight hairs; leaves mostly 4-8 mm wide; petals 7-8 mm long; seeds 2 mm long; wet ground, rare; Lake, McHenry, Peoria, Winnebago, and Woodford counties. July-Sept. [*E. molle Torr.,* non Lam.; *E. densum* Raf.] ....*E. strictum* Muhl.

5. Stem, leaves, and capsules crisp-puberulent; leaves 1-4 mm
wide; petals 3-5 mm long; wet ground, rare; known from
Jo Daviess, Lake, Lee, Mason, Peoria, and Winnebago
counties. Aug.-Sept. [*E. lineare* Muhl., nom. illegit.; *E.
densum* sensu auth., non Raf.] ....*E. leptophyllum* Raf.

2. Jussiaea L. — Primrose-willow

1. Stems erect; petals 5-10, rarely 12 mm long.
2. Petals and calyx-lobes 4; stem winged; wet ground in the southernmost counties, rare. July-Sept. ......*J. decurrens* (Walt.) DC.
2. Petals and calyx-lobes 5; stem not winged; along river courses,
rare; known from Alexander, Jackson, and Randolph coun-
ties ....*J. leptocarpa* Nutt.
1. Stems creeping or floating; petals 10-15 mm long; muddy banks
or in water, not common; chiefly in s. Ill., but also Vermilion
and Mason counties. May-Sept. [*J. diffusa* Forsk.] ......*J. repens* L.

3. Ludwigia L. — False Loosestrife

1. Leaves opposite, oval; stems procumbent or floating; petals small,
pink, or absent; capsules 4-sided, 3-4 mm long; muddy shores
and ditches, local. July-Aug. [*Isnardia palustris* L.; *L. palustris*
var. *americana* Fern. & Grisc.] ....*L. palustris* (L.) Ell.
1. Leaves alternate, elliptical; stem erect.
2. Flowers short-stalked; petals yellow, conspicuous; capsules
cubical, 5-7 mm long, opening by a terminal pore; wet
ground, common. June-Sept. Seed-box [*L. alternifolia* var.
pubescens Palmer & Steyerm.] ....*L. alternifolia* L.
2. Flowers sessile, inconspicuous.
3. Capsules turbinate, the calyx-lobes 3 mm long; petals minute,
greenish; ditches, swamps, muddy shores, locally throughout Ill. July-Sept. ....*L. polycarpa* Short & Peter
3. Capsules cylindrical, the calyx-lobes about 1 mm long; petals
none; swamps, s. Ill., rare. July-Sept. [*L. cylindrica* Ell.]
....*L. glandulosa* Walt.

4. Oenothera L. — Evening-primrose

1. Leaves not linear-filiform; stigma 4-lobed (only slightly in *O.
serrulata*).
2. Calyx-lobes reflexed; stamens equal in length (except *O. serrulata*); flowers more or less nocturnal; petals yellow;
capsules terete or round-angled; plants biennial or annual.
3. Hypanthium above the ovary 6-8 mm long; adv. from the
west; Cook and Peoria counties ....*O. serrulata* Nutt.
3. Hypanthium above the ovary at least 15 mm long, usually
much longer.
4. Capsules lanceoloid-cylindrical, 4-7 mm thick at maturity
(at least at base).

5. Petals 1-3 mm wide; adv. from the northeast; Boone, Christian, and McHenry counties. June-July ....*O. cruciata* Nutt.
5. Petals more than 3 mm wide.
  6. Plants green; free tips of sepals 3 mm long; roadsides, fields, and waste places, very common. June-Oct. Common Evening-primrose [*O. cymbatilis* Bartlett] ....*O. biennis* L.
  6. Plants canescent; free tips of sepals 2 mm long; roadsides and fields, occasional; adv. from w. of the Mississippi R. Aug. [*O. biennis* var. *canescens* T. & G.; *O. canovirens* Steele] ....*O. strigosa* (Rydb.) Mack. & Bush
4. Capsules linear-cylindrical, 2-3 mm thick.
  7. Upper and median leaves remotely denticulate to entire; flowers many, in a terminal raceme; petals 12-25 mm long, rhombic-ovate; capsules 1-2 mm long, strigose; sandy soil, local; chiefly in the n. half of Ill., but extending southward near the Mississippi R. to Pulaski Co. June-Sept. ....*O. rhombipetala* Nutt.
  7. Upper and median leaves sinuately dentate or pinnatifid; flowers few, axillary; petals 5-12 mm long, obovate; capsules 2-3 cm long, pilose; sandy soil, locally throughout Ill. [*Raimannia laciniata* (Hill) Rose; *O. sinuata* L.] ....*O. laciniata* Hill
2. Calyx-lobes erect or ascending, cohering in pairs; stamens unequal in length, the alternate ones somewhat longer; flowers diurnal; capsules 4-angled; plants perennial.
  8. Petals yellow; capsules 4-winged; leaves entire or denticulate.
  9. Stem erect; petals 1-3 cm long; capsules 1.5-2 cm long.
    10. Petals 1-3 cm long; buds and inflorescence erect, not nodding.
      11. Stem pilose; capsules sparsely pilose, the hairs glandless; leaves elliptical-lanceolate, hirsute on both surfaces; roadsides and fields, not infrequent. June-Oct. Common Sundrops [*O. pratensis* (Small) B.L.Robins.] ....*O. pilosella* Raf.
      11. Stem short-pubescent; capsules with a few glandtipped hairs; leaves linear-oblanceolate, strigose; dry soil, rare; Johnson, Pulaski, and Saline counties. [*O. fruticosa* sensu auth., non L.] ....*O. tetragona* Roth
    10. Petals 5-10 mm long; buds and tip of inflorescence nodding; stem strigose; dry soil, not common; Cook and Winnebago counties. June-Aug. Small Sundrops [*O. pumila* L.] ....*O. perennis* L.
  9. Stem decumbent, strigillose; petals 5-7 cm long; hypanthium 5-15 cm long; capsules 5-8 cm long, 4-6 cm wide;

sandy or rocky soil, rare; St. Clair Co., *Mulford* in 1895.
[*Megapterium missouriense* (Sims) Spach] ....
....*O. missouriensis* Sims
8. Petals white or pink, 2.5-4 cm long; buds nodding; capsules
4-angled and ribbed, canescent-strigose, stipitate; leaves
dentate to pinnatifid, puberulent; roadsides, occasional;
native w. of the Mississippi R. June-July. White Evening-
primrose [*Hartmannia speciosa* (Nutt.) Small] ....
....*O. speciosa* Nutt.
1. Stem-leaves linear-filiform; stigma shallowly lobed; petals 3-4 mm
long; capsules ellipsoid, sessile, 4-angled, 4-6 mm long; sandy
soil, usually on bluffs, locally in s. Ill. May-June. [*Kneiffia linifolia* (Nutt.) Spach; *Peniophyllum linifolium* (Nutt.) Pennell;
Stenosiphon linifolium (Nutt.) Britt.] ....*O. linifolia* Nutt.

5. Gaura L. — Butterfly-weed

1. Ovary and fruit on pedicels 1-3 mm long; dry hillsides, rare;
Hardin Co. ....*G. filipes* Spach
1. Ovary and fruit sessile.
  2. Petals 7-9 mm long; anthers linear, attached near the base;
  fruit 4-angled, pubescent, 5-6 mm long; roadsides, fields, and
  open woods. July-Sept. ....*G. biennis* L.
  2. Petals 2-3 mm long; anthers oval, attached near the middle;
  fruit fusiform, 4-nerved, glabrous, 6-8 mm long; roadsides,
  rare; adv. from w. U.S. June-July ....*G. parviflora* Dougl.

6. Circaea L. — Enchanter's-nightshade

1. Stem 30-60 cm tall; leaves shallowly undulate-dentate, usually
rounded at the base; fruit 2-loculed, 4 mm long at maturity;
woods, common. June-July. [*C. lutetiana* sensu auth., non L.]
....*C. latifolia* Hill
1. Stem 10-30 cm tall; leaves sharply dentate, mostly cordate; fruit
1-loculed, 2 mm long; moist banks and ravines in deep woods;
Lake Bluff, Lake Co., *E. J. Hill;* Elgin, Kane Co., *Vasey;*
Jo Daviess Co., *Pepoon & Moffatt.* June-July ....*C. alpina* L.

84. Haloragaceae Horan. — Water-milfoil Family

1. Leaves whorled (rarely subopposite or alternate), at least the immersed
ones pinnately dissected; stamens 4-8; fruit 4-lobed ....1. *Myriophyllum*
1. Leaves alternate, dentate or pectinate-pinnatifid; stamens 3-4; fruit 3-
angled ....2. *Proserpinaca*

1. Myriophyllum L. — Water-milfoil

1. Carpels rounded and smooth on the back.
  2. Floral leaves (bracts) entire or denticulate.
    3. Leaves verticillate in fours or fives; lakes and slow streams,

in Boone, Cook, Du Page, Lake, and McHenry counties.
[*M. exalbescens* Fern.] ....*M. spicatum* L.
3. Leaves chiefly scattered, or absent from the flowering stems;
muddy shores and shallow water, rare ....
....*M. humile* (Raf.) Morong
2. Floral leaves pinnatifid or pectinate; leaves verticillate in threes
and fours; lakes and slow streams, local ....*M. verticillatum* L.
1. Carpels 2-keeled and roughened on the back; stamens 4.
4. Floral leaves (bracts) ovate or lanceolate, serrate; ponds and
  - slow streams, local ....*M. heterophyllum* Michx.
4. Floral leaves linear, pectinate; ditches and muddy shores,
chiefly in w. Ill. [*M. scabratum* Michx.] ....
....*M. pinnatum* (Walt.) BSP.

2. Proserpinaca L. — Mermaid-weed

P. palustris L. Ponds and slow streams, locally throughout Ill. July-
Sept. [*P. palustris* var. *amblygona* Fern.; *P. palustris* var. *crebra* Fern.
& Grisc.]

85. Callitrichaceae Lindl.

1. Callitriche L. — Water-starwort

1. Fruit short-peduncled; bracts absent; plants terrestrial, growing on
moist soil, local; known from Champaign, Coles, Jackson, Macoupin, St. Clair, and Wabash counties. [*C. austini* Engelm.]
....*C. terrestris* Raf.
1. Fruit sessile; plants aquatic or amphibious.
2. Fruit oval, flat, longer than the styles; in ponds and slow
streams, very local ....*C. palustris* L.
2. Fruit obovate, convex, shorter than the styles; locally throughout Ill. [*C. hermaphroditica* sensu auth., non L.] ....
....*C. heterophylla* Pursh

86. Hippuridaceae Sagor. & G. Schneid.

1. Hippuris L. — Mare's-tail

H. vulgaris L. Ponds and streams, rare; known from Kane, Lake,
and McHenry counties. June-Aug.

87. Aristolochiaceae Blume — Birthwort Family

1. Stem prostrate, rooting at the nodes; flowers regular, 3-lobed; calyx persistent; stamens 12 ....1. *Asarum*
1. Stem erect or twining; flowers very irregular, the calyx deciduous; stamens
6 ....2. *Aristolochia*

1. Asarum L. — Wild Ginger

1. Calyx-lobes deltoid-ovate, shortly acuminate, scarcely longer than
the calyx-tube, spreading or reflexed at flowering time; woods,
common. Apr.-May ....*A. reflexum* Bickn.

1. Calyx-lobes lanceolate, caudate-acuminate, much longer than the tube, erect or spreading at flowering time; wooded hillsides, local; extending southward to Knox, Tazewell, and Coles counties. May-June ....*A. acuminatum* (Ashe) Bickn.

2. **Aristolochia** L. — Birthwort

1. Low herb; flowers purple, 1-1.5 cm long, solitary on slender basal scaly peduncles; calyx-tube curved like the letter S; capsule subglobose, ridged, about 1 cm in diameter.
    2. Leaves ovate-lanceolate, cordate; rich woods; locally northward to La Salle Co. Virginia Snakeroot ....*A. serpentaria* L.
    2. Leaves narrowly sagittate or hastate; swamps, rare; Pulaski Co., *H. E. Ahles* in 1952 ....*A. nashii* Kearney
1. Twining shrub; flowers on axillary solitary pubescent bractless peduncles; calyx tomentose, the tube abruptly bent, yellowish-green, about 3 cm long, dark purple within; leaves suborbicular or broadly ovate, tomentose; capsule ellipsoid, 4-6 cm long; rich woods, rare; extending northward to Wabash and Macoupin counties. May-June. Dutchman's Pipe ....*A. tomentosa* Sims

88. **Santalaceae** R.Br. — Sandalwood Family

1. **Comandra** Nutt. — False Toadflax

C. umbellata (L.) Nutt. Sandy soil or grassy roadsides, locally nearly throughout Ill. May-June. [*C. richardsiana* Fern.].

89. **Loranthaceae** D.Don — Mistletoe Family

1. **Phoradendron** Nutt. — American Mistletoe

P. flavescens (Pursh) Nutt. Parasitic on American elm, black gum, oak, and other deciduous trees in s. Ill., extending northward to Randolph, Saline, and Crawford counties.

90. **Cornaceae** Link — Dogwood Family
(*Nyssaceae* Endl.; *Alangiaceae* Lindl.)

1. Flowers 4-merous, perfect; leaves opposite (except *Cornus alternifolia*) ......
    .... 1. *Cornus*
1. Flowers 5-merous, polygamous; leaves alternate ....2. *Nyssa*

1. **Cornus** L. — Dogwood
(*Chamaepericlymenum* Hill; *Cynoxylon* Raf.; *Svida* Opix ex Small)
1. Flowers cymose or paniculate, without an involucre; fruit white or blue.
    2. Leaves chiefly alternate and clustered toward the ends of the branchlets; pith white; fruit bluish black, glaucous; woods, usually near streams, chiefly in the northern two-thirds of the state. May-June. Alternate-leaved Dogwood ....
    ....*C. alternifolia* L.f.

2. Leaves opposite.
   3. Lower surface of blades with appressed hairs, or none.
      4. Leaves green beneath, not at all farinose; pith white; fruit turning bluish; low woods, or in swamps, s. Ill. June. [*C. stricta* Lam.] ....*C. foemina* Mill.
      4. Leaves pale and microscopically farinose or pulverulent beneath.
         5. Young twigs tomentulose; pith brown; fruit blue; moist ground, common throughout Ill. May-June. [*C. purpusi* Koehne; *C. amomum* of auth., not Mill.] Pale Dogwood ....*C. obliqua* Raf.
         5. Young twigs strigillose to glabrous; fruit white.
            6. Mature twigs gray or brown; cymes loosely-flowered, convex; stone of the fruit not compressed; erect shrubs chiefly along fences, roadsides, and in clearings, common. May-June. [*C. paniculata* L'Her.] Gray Dogwood ....*C. racemosa* Lam.
            6. Mature twigs bright red; pith white; cymes dense, flat-topped; stone compressed; stoloniferous spreading shrubs of swampy ground, in the n. part of the state, extending southward in the valley of Illinois R. to Tazewell Co. June-July. Red-osier Dogwood ....
                ....*C. stolonifera* Michx.
   3. Lower surface of blades with loose, partly spreading pubescence, at least on the veins.
      7. Leaves ovate-lanceolate to elliptical; veins 3 or 4 pairs; fruit white.
         8. Leaves finely pubescent on the upper surface; pith white, large; branches red; lake shores, Cook and Lake counties. Bailey's Dogwood ....*C. baileyi* Coult. & Evans
         8. Leaves scabrous above; pith brown, small; branches gray or brown; moist ground on roadsides or along streams, common. May-June. [*C. asperifolia* of auth., not Michx.] Rough-leaved Dogwood ....
           ....*C. drummondi* C.A.Mey.
      7. Leaves roundish-ovate, woolly pubescent beneath at maturity; veins usually 6-9 pairs; branches gray or brown, pith white; fruit light blue; dry woods, n. Ill., extending southward to Kankakee and La Salle counties. May. [*C. circinata* L'Her.] Round-leaved Dogwood ....
           ....*C. rugosa* Lam.
1. Flowers capitate, with an involucre; fruit red.
   9. Tree; fruit ellipsoid; dry woods, local; chiefly in the s. half of the state, extending northward to Vermilion and Schuyler counties. April-May. Flowering Dogwood ....*C. florida* L.
   9. Herb or subshrub 10-20 cm tall; fruit globose; woods, known from Lake, Cook, Ogle, and La Salle counties. May-June. Bunchberry ....*C. canadensis* L.

2. Nyssa L. — Tupelo

1. Leaves entire; pistillate flowers 2-several together; fruit ovoid,
   8-12 mm long; rich soil, s. Ill., also in Cook and Kankakee
   counties. May. Sour Gum. Black Gum [*N. multiflora* Wang.;
   N. sylvatica var. *caroliniana* (Poir.) Fern.] ......*N. sylvatica* Marsh.
1. Leaves more or less dentate with 1 or more large angular teeth, or
   entire; pistillate flower solitary; fruit ellipsoid, 1.5-3 cm long;
   swamps and low woods, s. Ill., extending northward to Crawford Co. in the valley of the Wabash R. Tupelo Gum [*N. uni-
   flora* Wang.] ....*N. aquatica* L.

91. Araliaceae Vent. — Ginseng Family

1. Leaves alternate; carpels 5; fruit black ....1. *Aralia*
1. Leaves usually three in a whorl; carpels 2 or 3; fruit red or yellowish ....
   .... 2. Panax

1. Aralia L.

1. Shrub or small tree, prickly; woods in southern Ill. July-Aug.
   Hercules'-club ....*A. spinosa* L.
1. Herbs.
   2. Umbels numerous; woods, local. July-Aug. American Spike-
      nard ....*A. racemosa* L.
   2. Umbels 2-7.
      3. Plant leafy-stemmed, prickly or bristly; woods, rare; Cook
         and Lake counties. June-July. Bristly Aralia ....
         ....*A. hispida* Vent.
      3. Plant acaulescent, not bristly; moist ground in woods; chiefly
         in the northern half of the state; also Macoupin Co. May-
         June. Wild Sarsaparilla ....*A. nudicaulis* L.

2. Panax L. — Ginseng

P. quinquefolius L. Rich woods, becoming rather rare. July-Aug.

92. Umbelliferae Scop. — Parsley Family

1. Leaves simple, rigid, parallel-veined, remotely bristly on the margins; inflorescence capitate ....1. *Eryngium*
1. Leaves compound; inflorescence umbellate.
   2. Ovary and fruit with straight or curved bristles or prickles.
      3. Ovary and fruit with straight bristles; fruit much longer than wide;
         leaves ternately decompound with lanceolate or ovate, toothed
         leaflets; flowers (in our species) white; roots aromatic ....5. *Osmorhiza*
      3. Ovary and fruit with hooked or barbed bristles.
         4. Plants glabrous; leaves palmately 3- to 7-foliolate; ovary and fruit
            with hooked bristles ....4. *Sanicula*
         4. Plants pubescent; leaves pinnately decompound.
            5. Ovary and fruit with hooked bristles; rays of the umbel short
               ....3. *Torilis*
            5. Ovary and fruit with barbed bristles ....2. *Daucus*
   2. Ovary and fruit not at all bristly or prickly (rarely tuberculate).

6. Fruit 2-4 times longer than wide; flowers white.
  7. Leaves trifoliolate with ovate leaflets; involucels none ....
  ....6. *Cryptotaenia*
  7. Leaves ternately compound, the leaflets pinnatifid, or leaves tri-
    foliolate with narrow leaflets; involucels present.
    8. Leaves ternately compound, the leaflets never falcate ....
    ....11. *Chaerophyllum*
    8. Leaves with 3 principal divisions, the leaflets falcate ......12. *Falcaria*
6. Fruit less than twice as long as wide.
  9. Leaves palmately or ternately divided.
    10. Leaves copiously soft-pubescent; umbels 15-30 cm broad; outer
      petals larger, 2-cleft ....25. *Heracleum*
    10. Leaves usually glabrous; none of the petals enlarged.
      11. Plants annual; leaves divided into filiform segments; flowers
        white; fruit ovoid, tuberculate, 1 mm long ....13. *Spermolepis*
      11. Plants perennial; leaf-segments broader; fruit not tuber-
        culate.
        12. Central flower and fruit of the umbellet sessile; flowers
          yellow; fruit flattened laterally, the ribs filiform ....
          ....14. *Zizia*
        12. Central flower and fruit not sessile.
          13. Plants tall, with elongated roots; involucre absent or
            inconspicuous.
            14. Leaflets not entire.
              15.Flowers yellow (rarely purple) calyx-teeth
                evident; fruit slightly flattened dorsally, the
                ribs strongly winged ....20. *Thaspium*
              15. Flowers white; calyx-teeth small or obsolete.
                16. Leaves finely divided; plants of wet
                  ground ....26. *Conioselinum*
                16. Leaves not finely divided ....23. *Angelica*
            14. Leaflets entire; plants glaucous and glabrous ....
            ....15. *Taenidia*
          13. Plants small, with a tuber, flowering early in spring;
            anthers purple; petals not inflexed at the tip; in-
            volucre present ....7. *Erigenia*
  9. Leaves pinnately divided.
    17. Involucre present, conspicuous; flowers white.
      18. Stem mottled with purple; leaflets ovate or lanceolate, in-
        cised or serrate; ribs of the fruit prominent; oil-tubes none
        ....16. *Conium*
      18. Stem not purple-marked.
        19. Leaves with filiform divisions.
          20. Fruits flattened-ellipsoid, 4 mm long, the ribs filiform,
            all alike; plants perennial ....10. *Carum*
          20. Fruits ovoid, 1-3 mm long, the ribs unlike, the lateral
            prominent, corky; annuals ....17. *Ptilimnium*
        19. Leaflets linear to lanceolate or ovate.
          21. Leaflets regularly and sharply serrate to the base.
            22. Fruit with slender inconspicuous filiform ribs;
              stylopodium conical; oil-tubes numerous and
              contiguous ....9. *Berula*

22. Fruit with equal, prominently corky ribs; stylopodium depressed; oil-tubes 1-3 in each interval
....18. *Sium*
21. Leaves remotely and irregularly dentate usually only
above the middle, or entire ....27. *Oxypolis*
17. Involucral bracts none, or few and soon deciduous.
23. Flowers white; fruit somewhat flattened laterally.
24. Leaflets serrate ....19. *Cicuta*
24. Leaflets not serrate ....8. *Perideridia*
23. Flowers yellow; fruit flattened dorsally.
25. Leaf-segments filiform; slender annuals ....21. *Anethum*
25. Leaf-segments broader.
26. Stem terete; fruit with thick corky margin, obscure
ribs and numerous oil-tubes; plants perennial ....
....22. *Polytaenia*
26. Stem grooved; fruit with filiform dorsal ribs, thin
wings, and solitary oil-tubes; stout biennial ....
.... 24. *Pastinaca*

1. **Eryngium** L. — Rattlesnake-master

E. yuccifolium Michx. Meadows, roadsides, and prairie soil; probably in every county, but not particularly abundant. July-Aug.

2. **Daucus** L. — Carrot

1. Biennial, 30-90 cm tall, with a taproot; umbel 5-12 cm broad, the
outer rays 2.5-8 cm long; central flower purple or rose; ultimate
segments of leaves lanceolate; fields, roadsides, waste places,
very common; nat. from Eur. July-Nov. Carrot ....*D. carota* L.
1. Annual, 10-30 cm tall; umbel 2-5 cm broad, the rays 4-12 mm
long; all flowers white; ultimate segments of leaves linear; Perry
Co., *R. A. Evers* in 1949; Jackson Co., *R. H. Mohlenbrock* in
1954 ....*D. pusillus* Michx.

3. **Torilis** Adans. — Hedge Parsley

T. japonica (Houtt.) DC. Waste ground and edges of woods,
occasional; nat. from Eur. [*T. anthriscus* (L.) Gmel.].

4. **Sanicula** L. — Sanicle. Snakeroot

1. Styles longer than the bristles of the fruit, recurved.
2. Petals greenish-white; sepals subulate; fruit sessile, 6 mm long;
woods, local; chiefly in the n. half of Ill. May-June. Black
Snakeroot ....*S. marilandica* L.
2. Petals yellowish-green; sepals oval or lanceolate; fruit pedicel-
late, 3 mm long; woods, common. May-June. Common
Snakeroot ....*S. gregaria* Bickn.
1. Styles shorter than the bristles.
3. Mature fruit globose, 4-5 mm long; staminate flowers short-
pedicelled; woods, local. June-Sept. Short-styled Snakeroot
....*S. canadensis* L.

3. Mature fruit ellipsoid, 6-7 mm long; pedicels of the staminate
flowers slender, 4 mm long, tipped with the conspicuous persistent beak-like calyx; woods in the n. part of the state.
June-July. Large-fruited Snakeroot ....*S. trifoliata* Bickn.

5. Osmorhiza Raf. — Sweet Cicely
(*Washingtonia* Raf.)

1. Styles and stylopodium 1-1.5 mm in length, not longer than the
   petals; stems and petioles villous; woods, common. Apr.-June.
   [*O. brevistylis* DC.] ....*O. claytonii* (Michx.) Clarke
1. Styles and stylopodium 2-4 mm long, exceeding the petals; stem
   and petioles glabrous or pubescent; woods, common. Apr.-June.
   [*O. longistylis* var. *villicaulis* Fern.; *O. longistylis* var. *brachy-
   coma* Blake] ....*O. longistylis* (Torr.) DC.

6. Cryptotaenia DC. — Honewort
C. canadensis (L.) DC. Woods, common throughout Ill. June-
July.

7. Erigenia Nutt. — Harbinger-of-spring
E. bulbosa (Michx.) Nutt. Woods, locally throughout Ill., except
the northwestern counties. Mar.-May.

8. Perideridia Reichenb.
(*Eulophus* Nutt., non R.Br.)
P. americana (Nutt.) Reichenb. Thickets and edges of woods,
local; rare in the southern counties. July.

9. Berula Hoffm. — Water Parsnip
B. incisa (Torr.) G.N.Jones. Swamps, not common; Kane,
Mason, Peoria, Tazewell, and Woodford counties. July-Sept. [*B.
erecta* sensu Cov., non *Sium erectum* Huds.; *B. pusilla* (Nutt.) Fern.].

10. Carum L. — Caraway
C. carvi L. Waste ground, and roadsides; escaped from cult.; nat.
from Eur. July-Sept.

11. Chaerophyllum L. — Chervil
1. Fruits broadest near the middle; plants usually glabrous or sparsely pubescent; moist ground, common. Apr.-May ....
   ....*C. procumbens* (L.) Crantz
1. Fruits broadest below the middle; plants densely pubescent; moist
   or dry sandy soil, rare; s. Ill. Mar.-May ....*C. tainturieri* Hook.

12. Falcaria Host.
F. sioides (Wibel) Aschers. Schuyler Co., *R. T. Rexroat* in 1955.
Native of Eurasia.

13. Spermolepis Raf.

S. inermis (Nutt.) Math. & Const. Sandy soil, local; southward to Macoupin Co. June.

14. Zizia Koch — Golden-alexanders

1. Basal leaves ternately divided; fruit ellipsoid, 3.5-4 mm long at maturity; roadsides, fields, meadows, open woods, common; rare in the southern counties. May-June ....*Z. aurea* (L.) Koch
1. Basal leaves ovate or suborbicular, deeply cordate, crenate; fruit oval, 3 mm long; Boone, Cook, De Kalb, Lee, McHenry, and Winnebago counties. [*Thaspium trifoliatum* var. *apterum* A. Gray; *Z. cordata* sensu auth., non (Walt.) Koch] ....
....*Z. aptera* (A. Gray) Fern.

15. Taenidia (Torr. & Gray) Drude

T. integerrima (L.) Drude. Woods and thickets, often on eroding clay banks, common throughout Ill. May-June.

16. Conium L. — Poison-hemlock

C. maculatum L. Waste places; nat. from Eur. June-July.

17. Ptilimnium Raf. — Bishop's-weed

1. Fruit 2-4 mm long and broad; leaves petioled, the segments 5-10 mm long, crowded, appearing verticillate; swampy ground, s. Ill., rare. June-Oct. [*P. capillaceum* sensu auth., non (Michx.) Raf.] ....*P. costatum* (Ell.) Raf.
1. Fruit about 1.5 mm long and 1 mm wide; leaves sessile or very short-petioled, the segments 1-6 cm long, alternate or opposite; swamps, s. Ill., rare. May-Sept. ....*P. nuttallii* (DC.) Britt.

18. Sium L. — Water Parsnip

S. suave Walt. Wet ground or occasionally in water, locally throughout Ill. June-Aug. [*S. cicutaefolium* Schrank].

19. Cicuta L. — Cowbane

1. Leaflets narrowly linear; axils of the upper leaves bearing bulblets; swamps in the northern half of the state. July-Sept. ....
....*C. bulbifera* L.
1. Leaflets lanceolate; axils of the leaves never bearing bulblets; swamps and wet meadows, locally throughout Ill. June-Aug. Water Hemlock ....*C. maculata* L.

20. Thaspium Nutt.

1. Flowers deep yellow or sometimes purple; stem glabrous; basal leaves either cordate or ternate; woods and river banks, common. May-June. [*T. trifoliatum* var. *flavum* Blake; *Zizia sylvatica* Benke; *T. aureum* sensu auth., non (L.) Nutt.] ....
....*T. trifoliatum* (L.) A.Gray

1. Flowers pale yellow or cream; stem puberulent at the nodes; leaves 1- to 3-ternate; woods near streams, local. May-June ....
....*T. barbinode* (Michx.) Nutt.

21. Anethum L. — Dill

A. graveolens L. Waste ground; escaped from cult.; native of Eur. July-Sept.

22. Polytaenia DC. — Prairie Parsley

P. nuttallii DC. Dry soil, locally throughout Ill. May-June.

23. Angelica L. — Angelica

1. Stem pubescent; fruit roundish, pubescent, 4 mm broad; oil-tubes several, distinct; dry soil in southern Illinois. July. [*A. villosa* (Walt.) BSP., non Lag.] ....*A. venenosa* (Greenw.) Fern.
1. Stem glabrous; fruit ellipsoid, 6 mm long, glabrous; oil-tubes continuous; river banks, locally in the n. half of the state. June ....*A. atropurpurea* L.

24. Pastinaca L. — Parsnip

P. sativa L. Roadsides, fields, and waste places, very common; nat. from Eur. June-Aug.

25. Heracleum L. — Cow Parsnip

H. lanatum Michx. Wet ground, locally in the n. two-thirds of the state. June-Aug. [*H. maximum* Bartr., *nom. illegit.*].

26. Conioselinum Hoffm. — Hemlock Parsley

C. chinense (L.) BSP. Wet ground, rare; Cook and Kane counties. Aug.-Sept. [*C. canadense* (Michx.) T. & G.].

27. Oxypolis Raf. — Cowbane

O. rigidior (L.) Raf. Swamps, locally throughout Ill. Aug.- Sept.

93. Ericaceae DC. — Heath Family

1. Ovary superior.
  2. Plants saprophytic, without chlorophyll, white, pink, or tawny, often turning blackish in drying ....3. *Monotropa*
  2. Plants with ordinary green foliage.
    3. Corolla polypetalous.
      4. Leaves alternate or somewhat whorled; filaments dilated ....
      ....1. *Chimaphila*
      4. Leaves all basal; filaments subulate ....2. *Pyrola*
    3. Corolla sympetalous.
      5. Leaves entire.
        6. Erect shrubs; fruit a capsule.

7. Leaves short-petioled, deciduous, not revolute-margined; flowers
   large, showy, somewhat irregular; anthers awnless ....
   ....4. *Rhododendron*
7. Leaves sessile or nearly so, revolute-margined, evergreen, pale
   beneath; flowers small, white, nodding; anthers awned ....
   ....5. *Andromeda*
6. Trailing shrubs; leaves petioled.
   8. Blades cordate at the base; corolla salverform; fruit a capsule
      ....7. *Epigaea*
   8. Blades cuneate at the base; corolla urceolate; fruit a drupe
      ....9. *Arctostaphylos*
5. Leaves denticulate or serrate.
   9. Leaves resinous-dotted beneath; flowers in terminal leafy-bracted
      racemes; fruit a capsule ....6. *Chamaedaphne*
   9. Leaves not resinous-dotted; flowers axillary; berries red ....
      ....8. *Gaultheria*
1. Ovary inferior; fruit a berry; shrubs.
   10. Corolla sympetalous, urceolate or ovoid; erect shrubs; fruit black or
       bluish.
       11. Leaves resinous-dotted; ovary 10-loculed; drupe with 10 nutlets ......
           ....10. *Gaylussacia*
       11. Leaves not resinous-dotted; ovary 4- to 5-loculed; fruit a many-
           seeded berry ....11. *Vaccinium*
   10. Corolla deeply 4-cleft, the lobes reflexed; flowers nodding on slender
       pedicels; trailing shrubs with small evergreen leaves; berries red, acid
       ....12. *Oxycoccus*

1. **Chimaphila** Pursh — Pipsissewa

C. corymbosa Pursh. Dry woods, rare. Lake, McHenry, and Winnebago counties. June-Aug. [*C. umbellata* of auth., not *Pyrola
umbellata* L.; *C. umbellata* var. *cisatlantica* Blake]. *C. maculata* (L.)
Pursh, with lanceolate, whitish-variegated leaves, has been erroneously
attributed to Ill.

2. **Pyrola** L. — Wintergreen

1. Style curved downward.
   2. Sepals lanceolate, 2.5-3 mm long, much longer than broad;
      leaf-blades suborbicular, glossy, about as long as the petioles;
      shaded mossy sandstone slope near Oregon, Ogle Co. ....
      ....*P. americana* Sweet
   2. Sepals ovate, acute, 2 mm long, about as broad as long; leaf-
      blades oval, dull, longer than the petioles; woods, northern
      Ill., rare. June-Aug. Shinleaf ....*P. elliptica* Nutt.
1. Style straight; raceme 1-sided; leaves oval; woods, rare; Cook Co.,
   Babcock; Winnebago Co., *E. W. Fell* in 1946. June-Aug. ....
   ....*P. secunda* L.

3. **Monotropa** L.

1. Flower solitary; plants glabrous, waxy-white or pink (drying
   black); style shorter than the ovary, glabrous; rich woods, rare
   or local throughout Ill. June-Sept. Indian Pipe ......*M. uniflora* L.

1. Flowers several; plants pubescent, tawny or reddish; style longer than the ovary, pubescent; saprophytic on humus in woods, rare; Coles, Cook, Cumberland, Jackson, Kankakee, and Piatt counties. June-Aug. [*M. hypopitys* sensu A.Gray, non L.]. Pinesap ....*M. lanuginosa* Michx.

4. Rhododendron L.

(*Azalea* L.)

R. roseum (Loisel.) Rehd. Rocky woods, rare; Alexander and Union counties. May. [*A. nudiflora* sensu auth., non L.; *R. canescens* sensu auth., non Sweet; *A. prionophylla* Small].

5. Andromeda L.

A. glaucophylla Link. Bog-rosemary. Bogs, rare; Lake and McHenry counties. May-June.

6. Chamaedaphne Moench — Leatherleaf

C. calyculata (L.) Moench. Swamps and bogs; Cook and Lake counties. May.

7. Epigaea L. — Trailing Arbutus

E. repens L. "Illinois," without definite locality, *Vasey*. Now extinct in Illinois.

8. Gaultheria L. — Creeping Wintergreen

G. procumbens L. Checkerberry. Woods, rare; Cook, Lake, La Salle, and Ogle counties. June-Aug.

9. Arctostaphylos Adans.

A. uva-ursi (L.) Spreng. Kinnikinnick. Woods and dunes, local; known from Cook, Lake, Ogle, Peoria, and Winnebago counties. May-June.

10. Gaylussacia HBK.

G. baccata (Wang.) K.Koch. Black Huckleberry. Rocky woods and hillsides in northern Ill. May-June.

11. Vaccinium L.

1. Shrubs mostly 2-10 m tall.
    2. Leaves glossy above, coriaceous at maturity, the margins entire, usually bearing a few small glands toward the base; anthers 2-awned; berries black, inedible; open woods in southern Ill. May-June. Farkleberry ....*V. arboreum* Marsh.
    2. Leaves not glossy, entire or ciliolate-serrulate, acute; anthers awnless; berries glaucous; swamps and bogs; known from Cook, McHenry, and Winnebago counties. May-June. Highbush Blueberry ....*V. corymbosum* L.
1. Low shrubs usually less than 1 m tall.

3. Twigs densely pubescent; leaves entire, elliptical, softly pubescent; shrubs 20-60 cm tall; moist ground, rare, in Lake,
   La Salle, Ogle, and Winnebago counties. May-June. Canada Blueberry [*V. canadense* Kalm] ....*V. myrtilloides* Michx.
3. Twigs glabrous, or more or less puberulent in lines, rugulose;
   leaves mostly serrulate with bristle-tipped teeth, glabrous or
   finely pubescent.
   4. Leaves narrowly elliptical, 7-13 mm wide, bright green on
      both sides; shrubs 5-35 cm tall; sandy soil or in open
      woods, northern Ill. May-June. Low-bush Blueberry [*V.*
      pensylvanicum Lam., non Mill.; *V. nigrum* (Wood) Britt.]
      ....*V. angustifolium* Ait.
   4. Leaves oval, 1-3 cm wide, paler beneath or glaucous; shrubs
      30-90 cm tall; chiefly in the southern counties, but also in
      Cook, Kankakee, Lee, Peoria, and Menard counties. May-
      June. Hill Blueberry ....*V. vacillans* Torr.

12. Oxycoccus Hill — Cranberry

O. macrocarpus (Ait.) Pursh. Bogs; known from Cook, McHenry,
and Will counties. June-Aug. [*Vaccinium macrocarpon* Ait.].

94. Ebenaceae Vent. — Ebony Family

1. Diospyros L. — Persimmon

D. virginiana L. Woods, chiefly in the southern part of the state,
but extending northw. to Peoria Co. May-June.

95. Styracaceae A.DC. — Storax Family

1. Ovary superior; fruit subglobose, drupaceous ....1. *Styrax*
1. Ovary inferior; fruit nut-like, elongate, winged ....2. *Halesia*

1. Styrax L. — Storax

S. americana Lam. Swamps and banks of streams, rare, s. Ill.,
extending northward to Lawrence Co. Apr.-May.

2. Halesia Ellis — Silverbell Tree

H. carolina L. Woods, and along streams, rare; Massac Co. Apr.-
May.

96. Sapotaceae Dumort. — Sapodilla Family

1. Bumelia Sw.

1. Leaves, pedicels, and calyces glabrous or nearly so; clusters many-
   flowered; moist thickets and bluffs in southern Ill. June-Aug.
   Southern Buckthorn ....*B. lycioides* (L.) Pers.
1. Leaves (beneath), pedicels, and calyces tomentose; clusters 6- to
   12-flowered; woods and bluffs, southern Ill., rare. June-July.
   Woolly Buckthorn ....*B. lanuginosa* (Michx.) Pers.

97. Primulaceae Vent. — Primrose Family

1. Lobes of the calyx and corolla erect or spreading, not reflexed.
2. Plants small, scapose, acaulescent, terrestrial.
   3. Corolla-tube equalling or exceeding the calyx; plants perennial ....
      ....1. *Primula*
   3. Corolla-tube shorter than the calyx; annuals ....2. *Androsace*
2. Plants with leafy stems.
   4. Plants aquatic; immersed leaves pectinate ....3. *Hottonia*
   4. Plants not aquatic; leaves entire.
      5. Leaves alternate.
         6. Flowers solitary, axillary, sessile; capsule circumscissile ....
            ....4. *Centunculus*
         6. Flowers in axillary racemes; capsules opening by 5 valves ....
            ....5. *Samolus*
      5. Leaves mostly opposite or whorled.
         7. Flowers white; leaves mostly near apex of stem ....6. *Trientalis*
         7. Flowers yellow or scarlet; stems leafy.
            8. Flowers scarlet (rarely white); capsules circumscissile; plants
               annual ....7. *Anagallis*
            8. Flowers yellow; capsules dehiscent by valves; plants perennial
               ....8. *Lysimachia*
1. Corolla-lobes reflexed; stamens exserted, connivent, forming a cone; leaves
   all basal ....9. *Dodecatheon*

1. Primula L. — Primrose

P. mistassinica Michx. Limestone cliffs in Apple River Canyon, Jo Daviess Co. May-June. [*P. mistassinica* var. *noveboracensis* Fern.].

2. Androsace L.

A. occidentalis Pursh. Sandy soil, local. April.

3. Hottonia L. — American Featherfoil

H. inflata Ell. In shallow water, rare; Jackson and Union counties. June-Aug.

4. Centunculus L. — Chaffweed

C. minimus L. Moist ground, chiefly in the w. and s. counties. May-Sept.

5. Samolus L. — Brookweed

S. parviflorus Raf. Wet soil nearly throughout Ill., except the northeastern counties. June-Aug. [*S. floribundus* HBK.; *S. "pauciflorus"* Deam]

6. Trientalis L. — Star-flower

T. borealis Raf. Woods and thickets, known from Cook, Lake, La Salle, Ogle, and Winnebago counties. June-July. [*T. americana* Pursh].

7. Anagallis L. — Pimpernel

A. arvensis L. Waste places, occasional; nat. from Eur. June-Aug.

8. Lysimachia L. — Loosestrife
(*Steironema* Raf.)

1. Leaves gland-dotted (sometimes obscurely so).
  2. Plants more or less pubescent; corolla not dark-streaked.
    3. Calyx 4-5 mm long, often dark-margined; flowers in terminal leafy panicles; roadsides and waste places, occasional; adv. from Eur. July-Sept. ....*L. vulgaris* L.
    3. Calyx 7-10 mm long, not dark-margined; flowers in axillary whorls; roadsides and waste places, occasional; adv. from Eur. June-July ....*L. punctata* L.
  2. Plants glabrous or nearly so.
    4. Stem erect; leaves lanceolate or elliptical; corolla usually with purple streaks or dots.
      5. Leaves usually whorled; flowers axillary; fields and open woods in the northern counties. June-July. Whorled Loosestrife ....*L. quadrifolia* L.
      5. Leaves mostly opposite.
        6. Flowers in terminal racemes; corolla-lobes lanceolate; wet soil in the n. half of the state. June-July. Swamp-candle ....*L. terrestris* (L.) BSP.
        6. Flowers in small head-like axillary spikes; corolla-lobes linear; wet ground or shallow water in the northern third of the state; also Wabash Co., *Schneck* in 1881. May-June. Tufted Loosestrife [*Naumburgia thyrsiflora* (L.) Duby] ....*L. thyrsiflora* L.
    4. Stem trailing; leaves opposite, roundish; flowers axillary; corolla not purple-marked; capsules rarely produced; moist ground, common; nat. from Eur. May-July. Moneywort ....*L. nummularia* L.
1. Leaves not gland-dotted; stem erect; flowers nodding, on slender axillary pedicels.
  7. Leaves firm, linear, 2-8 mm wide, 1-veined, the lateral veins obscure; moist ground, locally throughout Ill. June-Aug. ....*L. quadriflora* Sims
  7. Leaves pinnately veined.
    8. Leaves elliptical-lanceolate, 1-2 cm wide, short-petioled, sparsely ciliate at base.
      9. Leaves paler beneath, with scarcely any distinction of petiole and blade; calyx-lobes not evidently nerved; plants with slender rhizomes; woods and thickets, common throughout Ill. June-Aug. ....*L. lanceolata* Walt.
      9. Leaves equally green on both sides, gradually tapering into the narrowly winged petiole; calyx-lobes evidently 3-nerved; plants not stoloniferous; moist ground, local. July-Aug. ....*L. hybrida* Michx.
    8. Leaves ovate or ovate-lanceolate.
      10. Petioles conspicuously ciliate; median and lower blades 6-15 cm long; corolla-lobes 10-13 mm long; stem erect,

60-90 cm tall; capsules 5-6 mm long; moist ground, common throughout Ill. June-Aug. ...._L. ciliata_ L.
10. Petioles glabrous or nearly so; blades 2-6 cm long; corolla-lobes 3-5 mm long; stems becoming decumbent and often rooting at the nodes; capsules about 3 mm long; swampy woods, s. Ill. Aug. ...._L. radicans_ Hook.

9. **Dodecatheon** L. — Shooting-star

1. Leaf-blades oblanceolate, tapering into the petiole.
  2. Mature capsules ellipsoid, thick-walled, reddish-brown; anthers 7-10 mm long; corolla lilac to white; leaves often reddish at base; meadows, hillsides, or along railroads throughout Ill. May-June ...._D. meadia_ L.
  2. Mature capsules cylindrical, thin-walled, light brown; anthers 5-7 mm long; corolla rose-purple; leaves pale bluish-green, not reddish at base; bluffs of the Mississippi River in Carroll and Jo Daviess counties ...._D. amethystinum_ Fassett
1. Leaf-blades broadly ovate, abruptly contracted at the base; corolla dark purple or rarely white; rich woods and rocky ledges, southern Ill., rare ...._D. frenchii_ (Vasey) Rydb.

98. **Oleaceae** Lindl. — Olive Family

1. Leaves compound; fruit a samara ....1. _Fraxinus_
1. Leaves simple; fruit a capsule, drupe, or berry.
  2. Leaves finely serrulate ....2. _Forestiera_
  2. Leaves entire; introd. shrubs.
    3. Leaves elliptical- to ovate-lanceolate; fruit a black berry-like drupe
    ....3. _Ligustrum_
    3. Leaves ovate; fruit a capsule ....4. _Syringa_

1. **Fraxinus** L. — Ash

1. Petioles velvety-pubescent; calyx evident on the fruit; wing of the samara extending down the sides; twigs terete, pubescent when young.
  2. Samara 2.5-5 cm long, 5-7 mm wide, the body terete; calyx 1-2 mm long; leaflets serrate or entire, acute at the base; leaf-scars nearly straight at the top; moist ground, local. Red Ash ...._F. pennsylvanica_ Marsh.
  2. Samara 5-7 cm long, about 1 cm wide, the body flattened; calyx 3-6 mm long; leaflets usually entire, the lower surface light green; leaf-scars deeply notched at the top; wet ground, local-ly in the s. part of the state. Pumpkin Ash ...._F. tomentosa_ Michx.f.
1. Petioles glabrous or nearly so; twigs glabrous.
  3. Calyx evident on the fruit; body of the samara terete or nearly so; leaflets 5-9, commonly 7, usually more or less petiolulate; twigs terete.

4. Wing of the samara almost entirely terminal; leaflets ovate-lanceolate or oval, entire or nearly so, glabrous beneath or pubescent; leaf-scars deeply notched at the top; woods, common throughout Ill. White Ash. [*F. biltmoreana* Beadle] ....*F. americana* L.
4. Wing extending down the sides of the samara; leaflets elliptic-lanceolate, usually serrate, acuminate at each end, glabrous except along the midvein beneath; leaf-scars nearly straight at the top; low woods and along roads, common. Green Ash ....*F. lanceolata* Borkh.
3. Calyx none or minute; body of the samara flattened, the wing decurrent; leaflets 7-11.
5. Twigs terete; lateral leaflets sessile; flowers polygamous; wet ground, local; chiefly in the n. part of the state, but extending southward along river valleys to Rock Island, Peoria, and Wabash counties. Black Ash ....*F. nigra* Marsh.
5. Twigs usually prominently quadrangular; lateral leaflets shortly petiolulate; flowers perfect; woods, locally nearly throughout Ill. Blue Ash ....*F. quadrangulata* Michx.

2. **Forestiera** Poir. — Swamp-privet

F. acuminata (Michx.) Poir. River banks and swamps, extending northward to Wabash and Lawrence counties, and in the w. part of Ill. to Fulton Co. Apr.-May.

3. **Ligustrum** L. — Privet

L. vulgare L. Commonly cult. and occasionally persisting about abandoned dwellings; sometimes spontaneous in woods and along roads; native of Europe. June.

4. **Syringa** L. — Lilac

S. vulgaris L. Occasionally persisting about abandoned dwellings; native of s.e. Eur. May.

99. **Apocynaceae** Lindl. — Dogbane Family

1. Leaves alternate; flowers in terminal corymbiform cymes; corolla salverform, purple ....1. *Amsonia*
1. Leaves opposite.
 2. Leaves not evergreen; flowers not solitary or blue.
  3. Climbing plants; corolla funnelform, yellowish; flowers fragrant ....
   ....2. *Trachelospermum*
  3. Erect plants; corolla campanulate or cylindrical, pink or whitish ....
   ....3. *Apocynum*
 2. Leaves evergreen; stems trailing; flowers solitary, axillary, blue ......4. *Vinca*

1. **Amsonia** Walt.

A. tabernaemontana Walt. Moist ground, locally throughout Ill., except the northern counties. May-June.

2. Trachelospermum Lemaire

T. difforme (Walt.) A.Gray. Moist woods and along streams, southern Ill., rare. June-July.

3. Apocynum L. — Dogbane

1. Corolla 2-3 times as long as the calyx, pink or pink-striped.
    2. Corolla 6-9 mm long, pink, its lobes soon recurved; leaves drooping or spreading; roadsides and open woods, common. June-Aug. Spreading Dogbane ....*A. androsaemifolium* L.
    2. Corolla 4-7 mm long, its lobes not recurved; leaves ascending; open woods, occasional; Peoria, *McDonald; Chase*. Probably hybrids of *A. androsaemifolium* and *A. cannabinum* ....
    ....*A. medium* Greene
1. Corolla 2.5-4 mm long, less than twice the length of the calyx, its lobes shorter than the tube; leaves ascending, glabrous or pubescent.
    3. Leaves of main stem short-petioled, elliptical, acute at apex, narrowed at base; corolla nearly white; follicles 12-20 cm long, curved; coma of seed 2-3 cm long; roadsides, fields, open woods, common. June-Aug. [*A. pubescens* R.Br.] ....
    ....*A. cannabinum* L.
    3. Leaves of main stem subsessile or sessile, oval or ovate, obtuse or acutish, the lower rounded, truncate or subcordate and often clasping at base; corolla greenish white; follicles 4-10 cm long, nearly straight; coma 8-18 mm long; roadsides and fields, common throughout Ill. June-Aug. [*A. hypericifolium* Ait.] ....*A. sibiricum* Jacq.

4. Vinca L. - Periwinkle

V. minor L. Running-myrtle. Roadsides, woods, cemeteries; nat. from Eur. May-June.

100. Asclepiadaceae Lindl. — Milkweed Family

1. Stem erect or decumbent, not twining.
    2. Corolla-lobes reflexed ....1. *Asclepias*
    2. Corolla-lobes erect-spreading; hoods prominently crested within ....
    ....2. *Asclepiodora*
1. Stem twining.
    3. Leaves cordate; corolla-lobes erect.
        4. Corolla-lobes 5-6 mm long; pollinia pendulous; corona of 5 lanceolate erect segments ....3. *Ampelamus*
        4. Corolla-lobes 8-12 mm long; pollinia horizontal; corona a disk or cup ....4. *Gonolobus*
    3. Leaves not cordate; corolla rotate, the lobes triangular-ovate, about 1 mm long; pollinia pendulous ....5. *Cynanchum*

1. Asclepias L. — Milkweed

1. Hoods of the crown each with a small incurved horn within.
    2. Flowers orange or yellow; plants hirsute; sap watery; umbels

cymose, terminal, many-flowered; leaves lanceolate, acute, alternate, or a few opposite; follicles tomentulose, 7-15 cm long, 1-1.5 cm thick; roadsides or open woods, common. June-Aug. Butterfly-weed [*A. decumbens* L.]......*A. tuberosa* L.

2. Flowers not orange or yellow; plants not hirsute; sap milky.
   3. Leaves narrowly linear, mostly in whorls of 4-6; flowers white; follicles erect, glabrous, narrowly lanceoloid, 6-10 cm long, on erect pedicels; roadsides, or sandy soil in fields and open woods, common. June-Aug. Horsetail Milkweed ....*A. verticillata* L.
   3. Leaves not narrowly linear.
      4. Leaves sessile or clasping, opposite (rarely some whorled); plants glabrous, pale green, somewhat glaucous.
         5. Follicles smooth; umbel solitary, terminal.
            6. Leaves elliptical, cordate-clasping, wavy-margined, obtuse, mucronulate, 7-15 cm long; corolla pale greenish-purple, 8-9 mm long; sandy soil along roads and in open woods, extending southward to St. Clair and Wabash counties. June-July ....*A. amplexicaulis* Sm.
            6. Leaves lanceolate to ovate-lanceolate, sessile, flat, acute or obtusish, 3-7 cm long, the margins minutely roughened; flowers greenish-white; dry ground, rare; Fulton, Gallatin, Hancock, Henderson, and Peoria counties ....*A. meadii* Torr.
         5. Follicles somewhat echinate toward the apex with a few short blunt processes, glabrous, 8-13 cm long, ovoid or lanceoloid; umbels terminal and lateral; leaves obtuse, mucronulate, elliptical, the margins flat; prairie soil, or along roads, extending southward to Coles, Bond, and Monroe counties. June-Aug. Smooth Milkweed ....*A. sullivantii* Engelm.
      4. Leaves manifestly petioled.
         7. Leaves pubescent beneath; fruiting pedicels deflexed.
            8. Follicles tomentose, 2-3 cm thick, warty with soft-spinulose subulate processes; flowers lavender and green; roadsides, fields, and woods, common throughout Ill. June-Aug. Common Milkweed ....*A. syriaca* L.
            8. Follicles smooth, less than 2 cm thick.
               9. Corolla-lobes dark purple, 8-10 mm long; hoods red or purple; follicles 9-12 cm long; leaves 10-20 cm long; sandy soil, along roads, and in open woods, local. June-July. Purple Milkweed ....*A. purpurascens* L.
               9. Corolla-lobes greenish-white tinged with purple, 4-5 mm long; hoods yellowish; follicles 6-8 cm long; leaves 5-8 cm long; open woods, rare;

Cook, Kankakee, and McHenry counties..............
....*A. ovalifolia* Dec.
7. Leaves glabrous or nearly so.
  10. Fruiting pedicels erect or recurved; leaves lanceolate, acuminate; corolla-lobes 3-5 mm long.
    11. Flowers rose-purple, rarely whitish; leaves all opposite; moist ground, roadside ditches, river banks, or in swamps, common. July-Aug. Swamp Milkweed ....*A. incarnata* L.
    11. Flowers pink or white; leaves thin.
      12. Flowers pink; median leaves usually whorled; seeds with a coma; dry woods, chiefly in w. and s. Ill. May-June ....*A. quadrifolia* Jacq.
      12. Flowers white; leaves all opposite; seeds usually without a coma; wet ground in woods, s. Ill., rare. June-Aug. ....
....*A. perennis* Walt.
  10. Fruiting pedicels deflexed; corolla-lobes 6-8 mm long.
    13. Umbel loose, the pedicels drooping, 2.5-5 cm long; leaves thin, elliptic-lanceolate, acuminate; corolla-lobes obtusish, greenish, the hoods white or pink; stem 1-1.5 m tall; woods. June-July. Poke Milkweed [*A. phytolaccoides* Pursh]..........
....*A. exaltata* (L.) Muhl.
    13. Umbel compact, the pedicels erect or ascending, 1-2 cm long; leaves oval, firm, obtuse and mucronate, or acute; corolla-lobes white, acute, the hoods purplish; stem 30-90 cm tall; sandy soil, not common; s. Ill., extending northward to Wabash and St. Clair counties. June-July. White Milkweed ....*A. variegata* L.
1. Hoods without a horn; flowers greenish.
  14. Umbel solitary, terminal; plants hirsute; leaves lanceolate, acutish; stem 10-30 cm tall; dry ground, in the n. part of the state. June-Aug. ....*A. lanuginosa* Nutt.
  14. Umbels several; plants puberulent or glabrate; stem 30-90 cm tall.
    15. Umbels peduncled; leaves alternate, linear-lanceolate, acuminate; hoods entire; roadsides and fields. July-Aug.
....*A. hirtella* (Pennell) Woodson
    15. Umbels sessile; leaves chiefly opposite.
      16. Leaves lanceolate; umbels many-flowered; pedicels pubescent; hoods entire; roadsides and fields, local. June-Aug. ....*A. viridiflora* Raf.
      16. Leaves linear; umbels 10- to 15-flowered; pedicels puberulent; hoods 3-toothed; dry upland woods; Quincy, Adams Co., *R. Brinker 3495*. [*Asclepias stenophylla* A.Gray] ....*A. angustifolia* Nutt.

2. **Asclepiodora** A.Gray — Spider Milkweed

A viridis (Walt.) A.Gray. Dry soil, not common; s. Ill., northward to Bond and Fayette counties. June-July.

3. **Ampelamus** Raf. — Bluevine

A. albidus (Nutt.) Britt. River banks and thickets, or along fences; chiefly in the southern half of the state, but extending northward to Vermilion, Champaign, Putnam, and Henry counties. July-Aug. [*Gonolobus laevis* sensu auth., non Michx.].

4. **Gonolobus** Michx. — Climbing Milkweed

1. Flowers greenish-yellow; pedicels glabrous; follicles angular, smooth, glabrous; along fences and in open woods; Alexander, Hardin, Pulaski, and Union counties. June-July. [*Vincetoxicum gonocarpos* Walt.] ....*G. gonocarpos* (Walt.) Perry
1. Flowers reddish-purple; pedicels pubescent; follicles pubescent, muricate; woods; Pope Co., *G. H. Boewe.* July-Aug. [*Vincetoxicum obliquum* (Jacq.) Britt.; *Matelea obliqua* (Jacq.) Woodson] ....*G. obliquus* (Jacq.) R.Br.

5. **Cynanchum** L.

C. nigrum (L.) Pers. Waste places; escaped from gardens; introd. from Eur.

101. **Loganiaceae** Dumort. — Logania Family

1. **Spigelia** L. — Indian Pink

S. marilandica L. Woods and thickets in s. Ill., extending northward to Jefferson Co. May-June.

102. **Gentianaceae** Dumort. — Gentian Family

1. Leaves not scale-like.
  2. Leaves opposite.
    3. Style filiform, mostly deciduous; anthers becoming twisted or revolute at maturity.
      4. Corolla salverform; stigmas roundish ....1. *Centaurium*
      4. Corolla rotate; stigmas linear ....2. *Sabatia*
    3. Style short or none; anthers straight; corolla funnelform or salverform, without glands ....3. *Gentiana*
  2. Leaves whorled; stem 1-3 m tall; anthers straight; corolla rotate, with 4 lobes and 1 or 2 nectariferous glands for each lobe ....4. *Frasera*
1. Leaves (at least the lower) reduced to scales; stem slender or filiform.
  5. Calyx-lobes 4; corolla 3-4 mm long; leaves all reduced to scales ....
  ....5. *Bartonia*
  5. Calyx-lobes 2; corolla about 1 cm long; upper leaves normal ....6. *Obolaria*

1. **Centaurium** Hill — Centaury

C. pulchellum (Sw.) Druce. Wet ground, nat. from Eur.; Cook Co. June-Sept.

2. **Sabatia** Adans. — Rose-gentian

1. Branches opposite; stem 60-90 cm tall; calyx about half the length of the corolla, the calyx-tube about 2 mm long; moist ground, locally throughout Ill., except the n.w. counties. July-Aug. ....
....*S. angularis* (L.) Pursh
1. Branches chiefly alternate; stems 15-40 cm tall; calyx about as long as the corolla, the calyx-tube 5-ribbed, 5-6 mm long; prairie soil, rare; Peoria Co., *McDonald;* Washington Co., *Eggert* ....*S. campestris* Nutt.

3. **Gentiana** L. — Gentian

1. Annuals; corolla without plaits or teeth in the sinuses.
   2. Corolla-lobes fringed or dentate; flowers 3-5 cm long.
      3. Leaves lanceolate or ovate-lanceolate, with rounded or sub-cordate bases; corolla-lobes conspicuously fringed all around the summit, scarcely fringed on the sides; low ground, n. Ill., rare. Sept.-Oct. Fringed Gentian ....
....*G. crinita* Froel.
      3. Leaves linear or linear-lanceolate; corolla-lobes shortly fringed or merely dentate at the summit, fringed on the sides; meadows, n. Ill., rare. Aug.-Oct. Small Fringed Gentian ....*G. procera* Holm
   2. Corolla-lobes with entire or rarely denticulate margins; flowers 1-2.5 cm long; dry soil, southward to Macoupin and Clark counties. Aug.-Oct. Stiff Gentian ....*G. quinquefolia* L.
1. Perennials; corolla with membranous toothed or lobed plaits in the sinuses.
   4. Margins of leaves and calyx-lobes microscopically scabrous or ciliate; corolla usually blue.
      5. Anthers separate or merely connivent; dry ground, chiefly in the northern half of the state, but extending southward to Washington and Marion counties. Sept.-Oct. Downy Gentian ....*G. puberula* Michx.
      5. Anthers cohering in a ring or short tube.
         6. Corolla-lobes distinct, longer than or equalling the plaits; wet ground, rare; n.e. Ill.; also Pope Co. Aug.-Oct. Soapwort Gentian ....*G. saponaria* L.
         6. Corolla-lobes none or minute, the plaits very broad; moist ground, rare. Aug.-Oct. Closed Gentian ....
....*G. andrewsii* Griseb.
   4. Margins of leaves and calyx-lobes smooth or nearly so; corolla yellowish-white; moist soil, rare, extending southward to St. Clair and Wabash counties. Aug.-Oct. Yellowish Gentian
....*G. flavida* A.Gray

4. **Frasera** Walt. — American Columbo

F. caroliniensis Walt. Dry ground, in the southern half of the state. June-Aug. [*Swertia caroliniensis* (Walt.) Kuntze]

5. **Bartonia** Muhl.

B. virginica (L.) BSP. Yellow Bartonia. Moist ground, rare; Clark, Cook, Kankakee, Ogle, Will, and Winnebago counties.

6. **Obolaria** L. — Pennywort

O. virginica L. Woods and thickets, southern Ill., rare.

103. **Menyanthaceae** G. Don — Buckbean Family

1. **Menyanthes** L. — Buckbean

M. trifoliata L. In bogs and shallow water; Cook, Kane, Kankakee, Lake, McHenry, and Peoria counties. May-June.

104. **Polemoniaceae** Juss. — Phlox Family

1. Leaves opposite, simple, entire; corolla salverform ....1. *Phlox*
1. Leaves alternate.
  2. Leaves simple, entire (our species); corolla pink, salverform; plants
    annual ....2. *Collomia*
  2. Leaves pinnate or pinnately parted; plants perennial (our species).
    3. Leaves pinnately parted into filiform divisions and the corolla scarlet,
      pink or white, 2.5-3.5 cm long (our species) ....3. *Gilia*
    3. Leaves odd-pinnate; corolla blue ....4. *Polemonium*

1. **Phlox** L. — Phlox

1. Stem erect or ascending, 30-120 cm tall; corolla-lobes entire or
  emarginate.
  2. Lobes of the calyx not longer than its tube.
    3. Calyx-lobes subulate; panicle pyramidal; leaves often 3 cm
      broad; alluvial soil; extending northward to Knox and
      Kankakee counties. July-Sept. Garden Phlox ....
      ....*P. paniculata* L.
    3. Calyx-lobes lanceolate; leaves usually less than 2 cm broad.
      4. Flowers in an elongated panicle usually more than twice as
        long as wide; stem often purple-streaked; moist ground,
        locally in the northern half of the state. June-Aug.
        Sweet-William Phlox ....*P. maculata* L.
      4. Flowers in corymbiform cymes; stem green; roadsides and
        and open woods, common. May-July. Smooth Phlox.
        A hybrid between *P. glaberrima* and *P. pilosa* has been
        collected in Champaign Co. ....*P. glaberrima* L.
  2. Lobes of the calyx longer than its tube.
    5. Upper leaves linear or linear-lanceolate; stem erect or nearly
      so, without decumbent sterile leafy shoots; sandy soil in

open woods and along roads, common. May-Aug. Downy
Phlox [*P. argillacea* Clute & Ferris] ....*P. pilosa* L.
5. Upper leaves lanceolate or elliptical; stem decumbent at base,
bearing sterile leafy shoots; moist woods, common. Apr.-
June. Woodland Phlox ....*P. divaricata* L.
1. Stem diffuse, much-branched, 10-20 cm long; corolla-lobes bifid;
calyx-lobes somewhat longer than the tube; plants puberulent;
sandy soil, not uncommon. Apr.-June. Sand Phlox [*P. stellaria*
sensu auth., non A.Gray] ....*P. bifida* Beck

2. Collomia Nutt.

C. linearis Nutt. Dry sandy soil, locally in the northern half of Ill.;
adv. from the West. May-Aug.

3. Gilia Ruiz & Pavon

G. rubra (L.) Heller. Standing Cypress. Escaped from gardens in
a few places; native of southern U.S. June-Aug.

4. Polemonium L.

P. reptans L. Thickets and open woods, locally throughout Ill.
May-June.

105. Convolvulaceae Vent. — Morning-glory Family

1. Plants with chlorophyll and normal leaves, not parasitic.
2. Styles 2-cleft ....1. *Stylisma*
2. Style undivided.
  3. Corolla funnelform to campanulate; stamens and style included.
    4. Stigmas 2, linear to fusiform; calyx with a pair of subtending sepal-
    like bracts (these in one species some distance below the calyx)
    ....2. *Convolvulus*
    4. Stigma 1, capitate; calyx not subtended by a pair of sepal-like bracts
    ....3. *Ipomoea*
  3. Corolla salverform, scarlet; stamens and styles exserted ....4. *Quamoclit*
1. Plants leafless, parasitic, twining; corolla small ....5. *Cuscuta*

1. Stylisma Raf.

S. pattersoni (Fern. & Schubert) G.N.Jones. Sandy prairie, rare;
Oquawka, Henderson Co., Aug. 10, 1873, *H. N. Patterson; V. H.
Chase* in 1934. [*Breweria pickeringii* of auth., not (Torr.) A.Gray;
Bonamia pickeringii of auth., not (Torr.) A.Gray].

2. Convolvulus L. — Bindweed

1. Corolla 3-5 cm long; calyx closely subtended and enclosed by two
large bracts.
2. Plants erect, ascending, or decumbent, finely pubescent; petioles
  about one-quarter the length of the blades; dry sandy or
  rocky soil, local; s. to St. Clair and Wabash counties. June-
  Aug. Dwarf Bindweed ....*C. spithamaeus* L.
2. Plants twining or trailing; petioles longer.

3. Leaves triangular-hastate or sagittate; flowers single.
    4. Leaves hastate, the basal lobes angled; plants glabrous or sparsely pubescent; roadsides, and along fences, common. June-Aug. American Bindweed [*C. sepium* sensu auth., non L.; *C. fraterniflorus* Mack. & Bush] ....
    ....*C. americanus* (Sims) Greene
    4. Leaves sagittate, the basal lobes rounded; plants copiously soft-pubescent; peduncles usually not exceeding the leaves; waste places, occasional; native of e. and s.e. U.S.; on railroad ballast, Diamond L., Lake Co., *Gates* in 1907. Trailing Bindweed ....*C. repens* L.
3. Leaves narrowly hastate; flowers double, pink; plants pubescent; waste places, occasional; native of Asia. Japanese Bindweed ....*C. japonicus* Thunb.
1. Corolla about 2 cm long; bracts small, attached some distance below the flowers; fields and waste places, common; nat. from Eur. June-Sept. Field Bindweed ....*C. arvensis* L.

3. Ipomoea L. — Morning-glory

1. Calyx-lobes obtuse, glabrous, elliptical, 1.5-2 cm long; corolla 5-8 cm long, white, the tube purple within; leaves ovate, cordate; stem glabrous; capsules ovoid, 2- to 4-seeded; seeds hairy; root perennial, often large; fields, thickets, and waste places throughout Ill. June-Sept. Wild Sweet-potato ....
    ....*I. pandurata* (L.) G.F.W.Mey.
1. Calyx-lobes acute or attenuate, pubescent; stem pubescent; capsules globose; seeds glabrous; plants annual.
    2. Calyx-lobes elliptical or lanceolate, acute or acuminate.
        3. Corolla 1.5-2.5 cm long, white; calyx 10-12 mm long, the lobes ciliate, acuminate; leaves entire to 3-angled; fields and along streams, s. Ill., extending northward to Peoria, Woodford, and Hancock counties. July-Oct. Small-flowered Morning-glory ....*I. lacunosa* L.
        3. Corolla 5-7 cm long, purple, pink, variegated, or white; calyx 12-16 mm long, hirsute toward the base; leaves ovate, cordate, rarely 3-lobed; fields and waste places; native of trop. Am. Aug.-Oct. Common Morning-glory ....
    ....*I. purpurea* (L.) Roth
    2. Calyx-lobes linear-lanceolate, attenuate, copiously hirsute below, 1.5-2.5 cm long; corolla 2.5-4 cm long, purple; leaves 3-lobed; fields and waste ground; native of trop. Am. July-Oct. Ivy-leaved Morning-glory ....*I. hederacea* Jacq.

4. Quamoclit Moench — Red Morning-glory

Q. coccinea (L.) Moench. Fields and roadsides, occasional; native of trop. Am. July-Oct.

5. Cuscuta L. — Dodder

1. Sepals nearly or quite separate.
   2. Flowers cymose, pedicelled; scales short; bracts entire; on various herbs. Aug.-Sept. ....*C. cuspidata* Engelm.
   2. Flowers sessile in dense clusters; bracts serrulate.
      3. Styles as long as the ovary; bracts few, broad, appressed; parasitic on various shrubs and herbs. July-Oct. ....
      ....*C. compacta* Juss.
      3. Styles longer than the ovary; bracts numerous, narrow, their tips recurved; chiefly on Solidago, Aster, Helianthus, and other genera of Compositae ....*C. glomerata* Choisy
1. Sepals united below into a synsepalous calyx.
   4. Flowers nearly sessile.
      5. Corolla-scales fimbriate.
         6. Flowers 1.5 mm long; calyx-lobes overlapping, forming angles at the sinuses; seeds depressed-globose, 1 mm long; on various herbs and shrubs. June-Oct. [*C. arvensis* Beyr.] ....*C. pentagona* Engelm.
         6. Flowers 2-3 mm long; calyx-lobes not overlapping; seeds ovoid, 1.5 mm long; parasitic on various herbs. June-Oct. ....*C. campestris* Yuncker
      5. Corolla-scales obsolete; calyx-lobes acutish; on Polygonum and other herbs. Aug.-Oct. ....*C. polygonorum* Engelm.
   4. Flowers distinctly short-pedicelled.
      7. Corolla-lobes with inflexed tips.
         8. Scales ovate, fimbriate; capsule enclosed by the corolla; on herbs and low shrubs, chiefly Compositae and Leguminosae; known from St. Clair and Wabash counties ....
         ....*C. indecora* Choisy
         8. Scales obsolete; withered corolla remaining at the base of the capsule; parasitic on hazel (Corylus) and other shrubs, and on various herbs. Aug.-Oct. ....
         ....*C. coryli* Engelm.
      7. Corolla-lobes not inflexed.
         9. Flowers usually 4-merous; styles about as long as the ovary; scales small, irregularly fimbriate; capsule depressed globose; on various herbs and shrubs. Aug.-Oct. ....
         ....*C. cephalanthi* Engelm.
         9. Flowers 5-merous; styles shorter than the ovary; scales long, fimbriate toward the apex; capsule ovoid; parasitic on a number of different species of herbs and shrubs. July-Oct. ....*C. gronovii* Willd.

106. Hydrophyllaceae Lindl. — Waterleaf Family

1. Leaves not entire.
   2. Flowers solitary on short pedicels; stamens included ....1. *Ellisia*

2. Flowers in scorpioid cymes or loose racemes.
   3. Corolla-lobes convolute in the bud; placentae dilated, enclosing the
    , ovules and seeds; plants perennial or biennial, with long-petioled
    basal leaves ....2. *Hydrophyllum*
   3. Corolla-lobes imbricated in the bud; placentae not dilated, merely
    forming ridges on the wall of the ovary; plants (in our species)
    annual (or biennial) with leafy stems, but no conspicuous basal
    leaves ....3. *Phacelia*
1. Leaves entire ....4. *Hydrolea*

1. Ellisia L. — Waterpod

E. nyctelea L. Woods, thickets, cult. ground, and waste places,
common throughout Ill., except the extreme southern counties. Apr.-
May.

2. Hydrophyllum L. — Waterleaf

1. Leaves pinnately divided; calyx without appendages between the
   lobes; plants perennial.
   2. Stem glabrous or sparsely pubescent; leaf-segments 5-7, acu-
    minate; calyx-lobes linear, strigillose on the back, ciliate;
    corolla pale lavender; moist woods, common. May-June........
    ....*H. virginianum* L.
   2. Stem retrorsely hirsute; leaf-segments 9-13, obtusish; calyx-lobes
    lanceolate, short-pubescent, and hispidulous; corolla white;
    woods, in s.e. Ill. May-June ....*H. macrophyllum* Nutt.
1. Leaves (at least the upper ones) palmately 5- to 9-lobed.
   3. Pedicels glabrous or nearly so; calyx-appendages minute or
    none; corolla whitish; plants perennial; woods, local. June-
    July ....*H. canadense* L.
   3. Pedicels rather copiously pilose-hispid; calyx with reflexed
    appendages (1-2 mm long) between the lobes; corolla laven-
    der; plants biennial; woods, common. May-June. [*Decemium
    appendiculatum* (Michx.) Brand] ....*H. appendiculatum* Michx.

3. Phacelia Juss.

1. Stamens longer than the corolla, the filaments pilose; corolla blue,
   about 1 cm long, appendaged within, the lobes entire; inflorescence glandular, loosely many-flowered; plants biennial; moist
   thickets and along streams. Apr.-June ......*P. bipinnatifida* Michx.
1. Stamens not longer than the corolla, the filaments glabrous;
   corolla without appendages; inflorescence not glandular; plants
   annual.
   2. Corolla about 4 mm long, the lobes entire; calyx-lobes pubes-
    cent on the back; racemes 2- to 5-flowered; woods, local;
    Adams, Jackson, Johnson, Union, and Washington counties.
    [*P. covillei* Wats.] ....*P. ranunculacea* (Nutt.) Constance
   2. Corolla 6-7 mm long, the lobes fringed; calyx-lobes glabrous on
    the back, the margins ciliate; racemes 10- to 20-flowered,
    strongly 1-sided; moist woods and thickets, usually in allu-
    vial soil in the s. half of Ill. May-June ....*P. purshii* Buckl.

4. Hydrolea L.

H. affinis A.Gray. Wet ground in woods, or in shallow ponds, s. Ill., rare; Alexander, Jackson, Massac, Pulaski, and Union counties. [(?) *H. uniflora* Raf.].

107. Solanaceae Pers. — Nightshade Family

1. Trailing or climbing shrubs; leaves entire; fruit a red berry ....1. *Lycium*
1. Herbs, usually erect, rarely climbing.
  2. Fruit enclosed in the inflated calyx.
    3. Flowers purple or blue; calyx split to the base ....2. *Nicandra*
    3. Flowers yellowish, usually with a purplish center; calyx toothed, not split ....3. *Physalis*
  2. Fruit not enclosed in an inflated calyx.
    4. Corolla rotate; anthers connivent.
      5. Anthers mostly opening by apical pores or clefts; seeds glabrous ....4. *Solanum*
      5. Anthers tapering to a sharp or narrow sterile tip, dehiscing from apex to base; seeds pubescent ....5. *Lycopersicum*
    4. Corolla not rotate; anthers separate.
      6. Corolla campanulate, purplish, veiny, the lobes slightly unequal; calyx campanulate, persistent, reticulate-veined in fruit; inflorescence large and spike-like ....6. *Hyoscyamus*
      6. Corolla funnelform; flowers solitary.
        7. Calyx tubular, soon circumscissile above the base; flowers 6-20 cm long; capsules usually spiny ....7. *Datura*
        7. Calyx deeply 5-cleft, persistent; flowers somewhat smaller; capsules not spiny ....8. *Petunia*

1. Lycium L. — Matrimony-vine

1. Leaves lanceolate; corolla-tube longer than the limb; calyx-lobes obtuse; occasional about old dwellings and along roads; escaped from cult.; native of Eurasia. May-Sept. Common Matrimony-vine ....*L. halimifolium* Mill.
1. Leaves rhombic-ovate to ovate-lanceolate; corolla-tube shorter than the limb; calyx-lobes acute; sometimes cult. and occasionally spont.; native of China. June-Oct. Chinese Matrimony-vine ....*L. chinense* Mill.

2. Nicandra Adans. — Apple-of-Peru

N. physalodes (L.) Gaertn. Fields and waste places, occasional; native of Peru. July-Sept.

3. Physalis L. — Ground-cherry

1. Stems and leaves sparsely pubescent or glabrous.
  2. Plants perennial with a horizontal rhizome, the stem often breaking off when pulled out of the ground.
    3. Pedicels glabrous.
      4. Leaves ovate, sharply dentate; flowers white; fruiting calyx red, 4-5 cm long; waste places, occasional, rarely spreading from cult.; native of Eur. Chinese Lantern Plant ....*P. alkekengi* L.

4. Leaves elliptical-lanceolate, entire or nearly so; flowers yellow with a brownish center; fruiting calyx green, 3-3.5 cm long; an occasional railroad migrant from the western states. July-Sept. ....*P. longifolia* Nutt.
3. Pedicels pubescent.
  5. Pedicels strigillose to hispidulous, the hairs pointing forward; fruiting calyx scarcely sunken at the base.
    6. Pedicels antrorsely strigillose; stem and leaves nearly glabrous, the latter ovate-lanceolate; anthers 3 mm long, shorter than the strongly flattened filaments; roadsides and cult. ground, common. June-Sept. Smooth Ground-cherry ......*P. subglabrata* Mack. & Bush
    6. Pedicels antrorsely hispidulous; stem and leaves short-hirtellous, the latter elliptical-lanceolate; anthers 2 mm long, longer than the filaments; dry ground, occasional; adv. from western U.S. May-July ....*P. lanceolata* Michx.
  5. Pedicels retrorsely or spreading-hispidulous; anthers 2 mm long, not longer than the slender filaments; fruiting calyx pyramidal-ovoid, obtusely 5-angled, deeply impressed at the base; roadsides and cult. ground, common. May-July. [*P. lanceolata* of auth., not Michx.]. Virginia Ground-cherry ....*P. virginiana* Mill.
2. Plants annual with fibrous roots, easily pulled out of the ground.
  7. Pedicels much shorter than the flowers, puberulent or glabrous; calyx-lobes deltoid-ovate; corolla with a brownish-purple center; waste places and cultivated ground, occasional; native of Mexico and southwestern U.S. Tomatillo ....*P. ixocarpa* Brot.
  7. Pedicels longer than the flowers; corolla wholly yellow; calyx-lobes lanceolate.
    8. Pedicels much longer than the fruiting calyx; corolla 5-8 mm broad; alluvial soil, occasional. July-Sept. ....*P. pendula* Rydb.
    8. Pedicels scarcely longer than the fruiting calyx; corolla 8-10 mm broad; waste places, occasional ....*P. angulata* L.
1. Stem and leaves more or less glandular-pubescent or villous; pedicels spreading-pubescent.
  9. Plants perennial with a rhizome.
    10. Pubescence of forked hairs; leaves elliptical, entire or somewhat sinuate, tapering at the oblique base; waste ground, roadsides, along railroads, occasional; native west of the Mississippi R. Cook Co., *Pepoon;* Peoria, *V. H. Chase* in 1921 ....*P. pumila* Nutt.
    10. Pubescence of simple hairs; leaves ovate, rounded to obliquely subcordate at base, sinuate, copiously grayish villosulous, the pubescence usually glandular and viscid; sandy or alluvial soil, in fields and open woods, or in waste

ground and along roads, common. June-Sept. ....
....*P. heterophylla* Nees
9. Plants annual; anthers purple, 1-2 mm long.
 11. Stems slender, spreading, diffusely branched, sharply angled;
  leaves thin, undulate or entire; corolla 10-12 mm in diameter; anthers 1.5-2 mm long; fields, waste places, roadsides, local. June-Oct. ....*P. pubescens* L.
 11. Stem stout, erect, obtusely angled; leaves thick, cordate,
  sinuate-dentate to the base; corolla 4-8 mm in diameter;
  anthers 1-1.5 mm long; alluvial soil, fields, roadsides,
  waste ground, chiefly in western Ill. July-Sept. ....
  ....*P. pruinosa* L.

4. **Solanum** L. — Nightshade

1. Plants more or less prickly; pubescence of stellate hairs.
 2. Leaves toothed or entire; flowers lavender, purple, or white;
  berry not enclosed in the calyx; plants perennial.
  3. Leaves green, coarsely dentate; the pubescence hirsute; berry
   1.5-2 cm in diameter; fields, roadsides, waste places, or in
   open woods, common. June-Sept. Horse-nettle ....
   ....*S. carolinense* L.
  3. Leaves silvery stellate-canescent, elliptic-lanceolate, repand-
   dentate to entire; berry 8-12 mm in diameter; roadsides,
   railroads, and waste places, occasionally adv. from the
   Great Plains; Adams Co., *R. Brinker* in 1944. May-Sept.
   Silver-leaved Nightshade ....*S. elaeagnifolium* Cav.
 2. Leaves irregularly pinnately obtusely 5- to 7-lobed; flowers
  yellow, 2-2.5 cm in diameter; berry enclosed by the prickly
  calyx; plants annual; cultivated ground and roadsides, common; native of the Great Plains; adv. in Ill. Buffalo-bur
  [*Androcera rostrata* (Dunal) Rydb.] ....*S. rostratum* Dunal
1. Plants not prickly or stellate-pubescent.
 4. Plants perennial, climbing or twining; flowers purple, or sometimes white; berries scarlet, poisonous; moist ground, common; nat. from Eur. June-Oct. Deadly Nightshade ....
  ....*S. dulcamara* L.
 4. Plants annual, erect or spreading; flowers white.
  5. Leaves pinnatifid; berries 1-1.5 cm in diameter, green when
   ripe; an occasional weed in cultivated ground or waste
   places; Cook Co., *Moffatt;* Carroll Co., *Clinton.* June-
   Sept. ....*S. triflorum* Nutt.
  5. Leaves entire or sinuate; berries 5-8 mm in diameter, black
   when ripe; roadsides, river banks, and cultivated ground;
   nat. from Eur. June-Oct. Black Nightshade ......*S. nigrum* L.

5. **Lycopersicum** Hill

 L. esculentum Mill. Tomato. Occasionally escaped from cult.,
but not persistent; native of S.Am. July-Oct.

6. Hyoscyamus L. — Henbane

H. niger L. Waste places, occasional; native of Eur. June-Sept.

7. Datura L.

1. Corolla 6-10 cm long; leaves angle-toothed; waste places and cultivated ground, not uncommon; nat. from the tropics. June-Oct. Jimson-weed ....*D. stramonium* L.
1. Corolla 10-20 cm long; leaves entire or undulate; waste places, not common; nat. from trop. Asia. July-Sept. [*D. metel* sensu auth. non L.]...*D. innoxia* Mill.

8. Petunia Juss.

P. axillaris BSP., with white flowers, the cylindrical corolla-tube 3-4 times the length of the calyx; *P. violacea* Lindl., and *P. hybrida* Vilm., with flowers red or violet, the former with corolla 3-4 cm long, the latter 5-9 cm long; all native to S.Am., frequently cultivated and occasionally apparently spontaneous, but not established in Ill.

108. Scrophulariaceae Lindl. — Figwort Family

1. Anther-bearing stamens 5; corolla rotate; leaves alternate ....1. *Verbascum*
1. Anther-bearing stamens 4 or 2.
    2. Corolla spurred at base; capsules opening by one or more slits or pores near the apex.
        3. Leaves pinnately veined.
            4. Leaves linear to narrowly lanceolate.
                5. Flowers in racemes ....6. *Linaria*
                5. Flowers solitary in the leaf axils ....7. *Chaenorrhinum*
            4. Leaves ovate to orbicular ....8. *Kickxia*
        3. Leaves palmately veined and lobed ....9. *Cymbalaria*
    2. Corolla not spurred; capsules 2- to 4-valved.
        6. Fifth sterile stamen present, either elongated, or represented by a scale or small gland on the upper side of the corolla-tube.
            7. Sterile stamen elongated.
                8. Flowers in a dense spike; seeds winged; anthers woolly; leaves serrate, petioled; plants glabrous ....2. *Chelone*
                8. Flowers in a terminal panicle or raceme; seeds wingless ....
                ....3. *Penstemon*
            7. Sterile stamen represented by a small gland or scale on the upper inner side of the corolla.
                9. Corolla maroon or purplish-green; leaves petioled, sharply serrate or dentate; perennials ....4. *Scrophularia*
                9. Corolla blue and white; upper leaves sessile; annuals ......5. *Collinsia*
        6. Fifth sterile stamen absent.
            10. Fertile stamens 2.
                11. Calyx 5-parted; two stamens anther-bearing, and two sterile, or the latter sometimes absent.
                    12. Corolla purplish; calyx without bracts; sterile filaments 2-forked, slightly exserted ....10. *Lindernia*

12. Corolla whitish or yellow; calyx (in our species) subtended by a pair of sepal-like bracts; sterile filaments simple, included or lacking ....11. *Gratiola*
11. Calyx usually 4-parted; stamens 2, both fertile.
  13. Leaves mostly in whorls of 3-6, rarely opposite; corolla tubular-funnelform ....17. *Veronicastrum*
  13. Leaves opposite or alternate.
    14. Leaves, at least the lower, opposite; corolla rotate, 4-lobed, blue or white ....15. *Veronica*
    14. Leaves alternate, mostly basal; in our species the corolla 2-lipped, and the greenish-yellow flowers in a terminal spike; basal leaves ovate ....19. *Synthyris*
10. Stamens 4, all fertile.
  15. Stamens not enclosed in the upper lip of the corolla.
    16. Corolla distinctly bilabiate.
      17. Calyx 5-angled, 5-toothed; leaves serrate ....12. *Mimulus*
      17. Calyx 5-parted, not angled.
        18. Leaves entire (in our species) ....13. *Bacopa*
        18. Leaves not entire.
          19. Leaves pinnatifid; sepals distinct or nearly so, linear ....14. *Leucospora*
          19. Leaves toothed or incised.
            20. Flowers 7 mm long, blue ....15. *Mazus*
            20. Flowers 10 mm long, white with purple lines ....16. *Mecardonia*
    16. Corolla with a spreading, slightly unequally 5-lobed limb.
      21. Corolla somewhat campanulate or rotate; anthers 2-loculed.
        22. Anthers pubescent; style slender.
          23. Corolla yellow; capsule acute or acuminate; leaves petioled, pinnatifid (in our species); plants parasitic on the roots of oak trees ....20. *Aureolaria*
          23. Corolla purple, pink, or white; capsule obtuse, mucronate; leaves sessile, linear to filiform or lanceolate ....21. *Gerardia*
        22. Anthers glabrous; style short; corolla yellow; leaves mostly pinnatifid, the upper alternate, lanceolate ....22. *Dasistoma*
      21. Corolla salverform; anthers 1-loculed; flowers in an elongated spike ....23. *Buchnera*
  15. Stamens included in the upper lip of the corolla.
    24. Anther-sacs dissimilar, unequal; leaves alternate, cleft or lobed (in our species) ....24. *Castilleja*
    24. Anther-sacs alike, parallel.
      25. Leaves pinnately lobed and crenate ....25. *Pedicularis*
      25. Leaves entire; floral bracts toothed ....26. *Melampyrum*

1. Verbascum L. — Mullein

1. Plants densely tomentose with stellate hairs; flowers yellow, in a dense spike; leaves decurrent.
  2. Flowers 1.5-2 cm in diameter; leaves strongly decurrent; stem

usually simple; fields, roadsides, waste places, common; nat.
from Eur. June-Aug. Common Mullein ....V. thapsus L.
2. Flowers 2.5-4 cm in diameter; leaves only slightly decurrent;
stem usually branched; waste places, occasional; adv. from
Eur. July-Aug. Chicago, E. E. Sherff in 1945 ....
....V. phlomoides L.
1. Plants glabrous below, glandular above; flowers racemose; corolla
white or yellow.
  3. Pedicels much longer than the calyx; roadsides and pastures,
  common; nat. from Eur. June-Aug. Moth Mullein ....
  ....V. blattaria L.
  3. Pedicels shorter than the calyx; reported from Pulaski Co.;
  native of Eur. ....V. virgatum Stokes

2. Chelone L. —Turtlehead

1. Corolla white or tinged with pink; sepals obscurely ciliolate; sterile
filament green; wet ground in woods, local; chiefly in the northern two-thirds of the state. July-Oct. [C. linifolia (Coleman)
Pennell ex Rydb.; C. glabra var. elongata Pennell & Wherry]
....C. glabra L.
1. Corolla rose-purple; sepals ciliolate; sterile filament whitish; low
woods in the southern and western counties. Aug.-Oct. . [C.
obliqua var. speciosa Pennell & Wherry] ....C. obliqua L.

3. Penstemon Mitch. — Penstemon

1. Plants more or less glandular or pubescent, at least on the calyces
and pedicels; corolla 1.5-3 cm long; leaves denticulate or entire.
  2. Stem pubescent or puberulent.
    3. Sepals at anthesis 3-6 mm long.
      4. Corolla 23-28 mm long, the throat purple, the lobes white;
      anther-locules about as wide as long, saucer-like at
      maturity; leaves glabrous or glabrescent throughout, or
      pubescent with long trichomes only along the midrib on
      the lower surface; bluffs, dry woods, thickets, local, n.e.
      Ill. ....P. hirsutus (L.) Willd.
      4. Corolla 17-22 mm long, white, merely lined with purple;
      anther-locules longer than broad, cup-like at maturity;
      leaves more or less softly puberulent-pubescent over the
      lower surface; roadsides and dry open woods, common
      throughout Ill. May-June ....P. pallidus Small
    3. Sepals in anthesis 2-3 mm long, acute; corolla 1.5-2 cm long,
    the throat inflated, only slightly ridged within, the anterior
    lobes scarcely exceeding the posterior ones; dry woods, rare;
    Pope and Wabash counties. May-June ......P. deamii Pennell
  2. Stem glabrous (often puberulent in P. calycosus) below the inflorescence.

5. Inflorescence strict; corolla white, nearly funnelform, the lobes widely spreading; calyx-lobes ovate-lanceolate, 3-5 mm long; sandy soil in open woods. May-July..................
....*P. tubaeflorus* Nutt.
5. Inflorescence open, paniculate; corolla gradually enlarged upward, the lobes erect or ascending.
 6. Calyx-lobes ovate-lanceolate, acuminate, evidently scarious-margined; anthers hirtellous; corolla white or purple-tinged; stem glabrous, glossy; sandy soil in fields and thickets, and open woods. May-July. [*P. alluviorum* Pennell] Foxglove Penstemon ....*P. digitalis* Nutt.
 6. Calyx-lobes linear-attenuate; corolla more or less violet-purple; anthers glabrous; stem finely puberulent to nearly glabrous, dull; alluvial soil and wooded slopes. May-July ....*P. calycosus* Small
1. Plants glabrous throughout and somewhat glaucous; leaves entire, obtuse, the upper nearly orbicular; corolla 4-5 cm long, lavender; sandy soil. May-June. Henderson Co., *Patterson* in 1873; apparently the only Ill. collection ....*P. grandiflorus* Nutt.

4. Scrophularia L. — Figwort

1. Corolla dull; sterile stamen brownish-purple; capsules ovoid, glossy, 4-7 mm long; woods throughout Ill. July-Sept. ....
....*S. marilandica* L.
1. Corolla glossy; sterile stamen greenish-yellow; capsules subglobose, dull, 7-9 mm long; open woods in the northern half of Ill.; extending southward to Cumberland Co. June. [*S. leporella* Bickn.] ....,,, ...*S. lanceolata* Pursh

5. Collinsia Nutt.

1. Pedicels mostly longer than the corollas; corolla-lobes retuse, the upper lip white; seeds 2.5-3 mm long; moist woods, locally throughout Ill. Apr.-May. Blue-eyed Mary ....*C. verna* Nutt.
1. Pedicels about as long as the corollas; corolla-lobes deeply notched, the upper lip pale lilac or whitish; seeds 1-1.5 mm long; sandy soil on hillsides in open woods near Shelbyville in 1947, *U. L. Evans, G. D. Fuller, & G. N. Jones.* Violet Collinsia ....
....*C. violacea* Nutt.

6. Linaria Mill. — Toadflax

1. Flowers yellow.
 2. Leaves linear, narrowed at base; roadsides and fields; nat. from Eur. May-Sept. Butter-and-Eggs ....*L. vulgaris* Hill
 2. Leaves ovate to ovate-lanceolate, clasping; a garden escape, sometimes persisting; native of Eur. ......*L. dalmatica* (L.) Mill.
1. Flowers blue (or white).
 3. Corolla 5-10 mm long, the spur 2-4 mm long; seeds smooth;

sandy soil in the northern half of Ill. May-June. Blue Toad-
flax ....L. canadensis (L.) Dum.-Cours.
3. Corolla 10-12 mm long, the spur 5-9 mm long; seeds rugulose;
sandy soil, rare; Alexander Co. ....L. texana Scheele

7. Chaenorrhinum Reichenb.

C. minus (L.) Lange. Dwarf Snapdragon. Roadsides and waste
places, especially along cindery railroad embankments; nat. from Eur.
May-Aug. [L. minor (L.) Desf.].

8. Kickxia Dumort.

K. elatine (L.) Dumort. Waste ground; nat. from Eur. June-Sept.
[Linaria elatine (L.) Mill.].

9. Cymbalaria Hill — Kenilworth Ivy

C. muralis Gaertn., Mey. & Scherb. In waste places, greenhouses,
old gardens or woodlands, rarely escaped from cult.; introd. from Eur.
May-Oct.

10. Lindernia All.

1. Lower pedicels about as long as the subtending leaves; calyx-lobes
   about equalling or slightly longer than the capsules; seeds pale
   yellow; moist ground, often along streams, ditches, and ponds,
   locally abundant throughout Ill. July-Sept. ....
   ....L. dubia (L.) Pennell
1. Pedicels much longer than the subtending leaves; calyx-lobes
   usually slightly shorter than the capsule; seeds brownish yellow;
   river banks, muddy shores, borders of ponds. July-Oct. ....
   ....L. anagallidea (Michx.) Pennell

11. Gratiola L.

1. Corolla golden-yellow, 10-15 mm long; sterile filaments 2, slender;
   capsule 3 mm long; seeds brown; leaves entire or remotely denticulate; plants perennial, with rhizomes; wet ground, rare;
   Forest Park, Cook Co., Seymour. [G. lutea Raf.] ....
   ....G. aurea Muhl.
1. Corolla light yellow or white, 6-12 mm long; sterile filaments
   minute or none; capsules 3-7 mm long; seeds yellow; leaves
   repand to serrate; annuals with fibrous roots.
   2. Pedicels slender, 1-2.5 cm long in fruit, equalling or exceeding
      the leaves; plants glandular-puberulent; capsules ovoid; wet
      ground and borders of ponds, not uncommon. May-Aug.
      [G. virginiana sensu auth., non L.] ....G. neglecta Torr.
   2. Pedicels stouter, usually shorter than the leaves, less than 1 cm
      long; plants glabrous; capsules globose; shores and ditches,
      less common than the preceding. May-June. [G. sphaero-
      carpa Ell.] ....G. virginiana L.

12. **Mimulus** L. — Monkey Flower

1. Corolla violet; stem erect; leaves lanceolate to oval.
   2. Leaves sessile, clasping; pedicels longer than the calyx; along streams, not uncommon. July-Sept. A putative hybrid between this and the following species has been collected once in Cass Co. ....*M. ringens* L.
   2. Leaves short-petioled; pedicels shorter than the calyx; wet ground throughout Ill., except the northern counties. July-Sept. ....*M. alatus* Ait.
1. Corolla yellow; stems slender, creeping; leaves suborbicular; wet ground in the northern half of the state, rare. June-Sept. [*M. glabratus* var. *fremontii* (Benth.) Grant; *M. jamesii* T. & G.]
   ....*M. geyeri* Torr.

13. **Bacopa** Aubl. — Water Hyssop

B. rotundifolia (Michx.) Wettst. Margins of ponds, local. July-Sept. [*Bramia rotundifolia* (Michx.) Britt.].

14. **Leucospora** Nutt.

L. multifida (Michx.) Nutt. Sandy soil near streams throughout Ill., except the extreme northern counties. July-Oct. [*Capraria multifida* Michx.; *Conobea multifida* (Michx.) Benth.].

15. **Mazus** Lour.

M. japonicus (Thunb.) Ktze. Waste ground, or in lawns; adv. from e. Asia; Chicago, *G. D. Fuller* in 1943. [*M. rugosus* Lour.].

16. **Mecardonia** Ruiz & Pavon

M. acuminata (Walt.) Small. Wet ground, rare; Wabash Co.

17. **Veronicastrum** Fabr. — Culver-root
(*Leptandra* Nutt.)

V. virginicum (L.) Farw. Meadows and thickets, common. July-Aug. [*Veronica virginica* L.].

18. **Veronica** L. — Speedwell

1. Flowers in racemes; perennials with rhizomes.
   2. Racemes in the axils of the leaves.
      3. Capsules pubescent; stems and leaves pubescent.
         4. Leaves incised-dentate, sessile; stem pubescent in two lines; racemes loosely flowered; pedicels as long as the calyx; waste places, occasional; adv. from Eur. May-July. Germander Speedwell ....*V. chamaedrys* L.
         4. Leaves serrate, short-petioled; stem pubescent all over; racemes compact; pedicels shorter than the calyx; waste ground; nat. from Eur. May-Sept. ....*V. officinalis* L.

3. Capsules glabrous (or with a few gland-tipped hairs); stems and leaves glabrous or sparsely glandular-puberulent; plants of wet soil.

    5. Leaves linear or linear-lanceolate, entire or remotely denticulate; capsules much broader than long, notched at both ends, much shorter than the pedicels; along ditches and ponds. June-Aug. ....*V. scutellata* L.

    5. Leaves lanceolate to ovate, serrate or crenate; capsules nearly orbicular.

        6. Leaves short-petioled; plants glabrous throughout; swampy ground in the northern half of the state, rare. June-Aug. ....*V. americana* (Raf.) Schw.

        6. Leaves sessile, clasping; plants minutely glandular, at least in the inflorescence; ditches and sloughs in the northern half of Ill., not common. June-Sept. [*V. connata* Raf.] ....*V. catenata* Pennell

2. Racemes terminal; leaves ovate or oval, entire or obscurely crenate, glabrous; capsules puberulent, orbicular, obcordate, 3-4 mm broad; roadsides, fields, or lawns; nat. from Eurasia. Apr.-June ....*V. serpyllifolia* L.

1. Flowers solitary in the axils of the upper leaves; plants annual.

    7. Leaves oblanceolate or spatulate to linear, entire or shallowly toothed, glabrous; corolla whitish, 3 mm in diameter; capsules emarginate, 3-4 mm broad, the style not more than 0.5 mm long; stem glabrous or with gland-tipped trichomes; fields, gardens, and roadsides, common. May-June. [*V. xalapensis* HBK.] ....*V. peregrina* L.

    7. Leaves ovate or oval, serrate or dentate, pubescent; corolla blue; capsules obcordate.

        8. Pedicels 1-2 mm long; corolla 2-3 mm broad; capsules 3-4 mm broad; lawns, fields, and waste places, common; nat. from Eur. Apr.-June ....*V. arvensis* L.

        8. Pedicels longer.

            9. Pedicels equalling or shorter than the leaves; corolla 4-5 mm in diameter; capsules 4-5 mm broad, the sepals ovate or oval, 4-5 mm long; waste places, or in lawns, occasional; nat. from Eur. Mar.-May. [*V. polita* Fries] ....*V. didyma* Tenore

            9. Pedicels as long as the leaves or longer; corolla about 1 cm in diameter; capsules 7-8 mm broad; an occasional weed in lawns and waste ground; nat. from Eur. Apr.-Aug. [*V. tournefortii* sensu C.C.Gmel., non Schmidt; *V. buxbaumii* Tenore; *V. byzantina* (Sm.) BSP.] ....*V. persica* Poir.

19. Synthyris Benth.
(*Besseya* Rydb.)

S. bullii (Eaton) Heller. Sandy or gravelly soil, locally in n.w. Ill., extending southward to Henderson Co.; also in Cass and Menard counties. May-June. [*S. houghtoniana* Benth.]

20. Aureolaria Raf. — False Foxglove
(*Dasystoma* Benth.)

1. Plants perennial, not glandular; corolla 3-5 cm long; seeds winged.
  2. Plants glabrous or nearly so; stem glaucous; sandy soil in open woods; said to be parasitic on roots of *Quercus* spp. Aug.-Sept. [*D. virginica* ex p. sensu Britt.; *D. quercifolia* (Pursh) Benth.; *Gerardia virginica* sensu auth., non *Rhinanthus virginicus* L.] ....*A. flava* (L.) Farw.
  2. Plants grayish-puberulent; open woods, local. July-Oct. [*A. grandiflora pulchra* Pennell] ....*A. grandiflora* (Benth.) Pennell
1. Plants annual, more or less glandular; corolla 2-3 cm long; capsules ellipsoid, 1-1.5 cm long; seeds wingless; dry open woods; known from Cook, Kankakee, Will, and Winnebago counties. Aug.-Sept. [*A. pedicularia intercedens* Pennell] ....
....*A. pedicularia* (L.) Raf.

21. Gerardia L.
(*Agalinis* Raf.)

1. Leaves auriculate at base, lanceolate; flowers 1.5-2 cm long, nearly sessile; anthers of the shorter filaments smaller; fields and open woods. Aug.-Sept [*Tomanthera auriculata* (Michx.) Raf.; *Otophylla auriculata* (Michx.) Small] ....*G. auriculata* Michx.
1. Leaves linear, entire, not auriculate; anthers uniform.
  2. Pedicels of the flowers less than twice the length of the calyx.
    3. Capsules ellipsoid, 8-10 mm long; calyx-teeth triangular-lanceolate; corolla 18-25 mm long; leaves scabrous; gravelly or sandy soil, local. Aug.-Sept. ....*G. aspera* Dougl.
    3. Capsules subglobose, 3-6 mm long; calyx-teeth subulate, short.
      4. Flowers 2-3 cm long; moist sandy soil. Aug.- Oct. ....
....*G. purpurea* L.
      4. Flowers 14-18 mm long; moist ground, not common. Aug.-Sept. ....*G. paupercula* A.Gray
  2. Pedicels of the flowers more than twice the length of the calyx.
    5. Leaves linear to linear-lanceolate, flat; moist ground, and on wooded slopes, local. Aug.-Oct. ....*G. tenuifolia* Vahl
    5. Leaves filiform-linear, the margins revolute.
      6. Stem strict, simple or few-branched, striate-angled, the angles minutely scabrellous; dry sandy soil, local. Aug.-Sept. ....*G. skinneriana* Wood
      6. Stem usually much-branched, nearly terete (at least

below), smooth or nearly so; wooded slopes and ridges, local. Aug.-Oct. ....*G. gattingeri* Small

22. Dasistoma Raf. — Mullein Foxglove

D. macrophylla (Nutt.) Raf. Dry soil in woods near streams; locally nearly throughout Ill. July-Aug. [*Seymeria macrophylla* Nutt.].

23. Buchnera L. — Blue Hearts

B. americana L. Sandy soil, rare; Calhoun, Cook, Menard, and St. Clair counties. July-Sept.

24. Castilleja Mutis — Indian Paint Brush

1. Plants perennial, 10-30 cm tall; bracts green; corolla yellowish-white, 4-5 cm long; gravelly or sandy soil in n. Ill. June-Aug.
   ....*C. sessiliflora* Pursh
1. Plants annual or biennial, 30-60 cm tall; bracts scarlet or yellowish; corolla green, 2-2.5 cm long; moist ground nearly throughout Ill., except the southern counties. May-June ....
   ....*C. coccinea* (L.) Spreng.

25. Pedicularis L. — Lousewort

1. Stem 60-90 cm tall; leaves opposite, nearly sessile, shallowly lobed; spikes 5-10 cm long; lower lip of the corolla 10-12 mm long, nearly as long as the upper; capsules ovoid, scarcely longer than the calyx; swampy ground, southward to Macoupin and Wabash counties. Aug.-Oct. ....*P. lanceolata* Michx.
1. Stem 10-30 cm tall; leaves alternate, petioled, deeply lobed; spikes 10-20 cm long; lower lip of the corolla about 8 mm long, much shorter than the upper; capsules lanceoloid, about three times as long as the calyx; sandy soil in open woods. May ....
   ....*P. canadensis* L.

26. Melampyrum L. — Cow-wheat

M. lineare Desr. Moist ground, rare; Cook Co. June-Aug. [*M. americanum* Michx.].

109. Bignoniaceae Pers. — Trumpet-creeper Family

1. Trees; leaves simple, ovate.
   2. Leaves opposite; stamens 4; capsules ovoid; pith chambered or hollow
      ....1. *Paulownia*
   2. Leaves usually in whorls of 3; stamens 2; capsules long-cylindrical; pith continuous ....2. *Catalpa*
1. Climbing or trailing shrubs; leaves compound; anther-bearing stamens 4.
   3. Leaflets 2, entire; leaves with a tendril; pods flat ....3. *Bignonia*
   3. Leaflets 7-11, serrate; leaves without a tendril; pods cylindrical ....
      ....4. *Campsis*

1. **Paulownia** Sieb. & Zucc. — Princess Tree

P. tomentosa (Thunb.) Steud. Cultivated; native of China; sometimes spontaneous in s. Ill. [*P. imperialis* Sieb. & Zucc.]. Apr.-May.

2. **Catalpa** Scop.

1. Flowers in many-flowered crowded panicles 20-25 cm long; calyx glabrous; corolla 3-4 cm in diameter, thickly spotted on the inner surface, the lower lobe entire or nearly so; capsules thinwalled, 5-8 mm in diameter; leaves short-acuminate, with an unpleasant odor when bruised; commonly planted; native of southeastern U.S. ....*C. bignonioides* Walt.
1. Flowers in few-flowered open panicles about 15 cm long; calyx often sparsely pubescent; corolla about 6 cm in diameter, inconspicuously spotted within, the lower lobe emarginate; capsules thick-walled, about 1.5 cm in diameter; leaves caudate-acuminate, inodorous; woods, s. Ill., often planted elsewhere. June-July. [*C. cordifolia* Duham.] ....*C. speciosa* Warder

3. **Bignonia** L.

B. capreolata L. Cross-vine. Alluvial soil, s. Ill., northw. to Richland Co. Apr.-May. [*Anisostichus capreolata* (L.) Bureau].

4. **Campsis** Lour. — Trumpet-creeper

C. radicans (L.) Seem. Open woods and fields throughout Ill., except the northern counties. June-Aug. Native in s. Ill., but in e. Ill. probably adv.; reported by Patterson in 1876 as occurring in "Peoria and Henderson counties, southward."

110. **Acanthaceae** J.St.Hil. — Acanthus Family

1. Corolla irregular; stamens 2.
  2. Flowers without bracts, in long-peduncled axillary spikes or heads ....
  ....1. *Dianthera*
  2. Flowers with broad bracts, in nearly sessile axillary or terminal panicles
  ....2. *Dicliptera*
1. Corolla nearly regular; stamens 4 ....3. *Ruellia*

1. **Dianthera** L. — Water-willow

1. Flowers in capitate spikes 1-3 cm long; stem 30-90 cm tall; leaves linear-lanceolate; common along muddy shores and in shallow water throughout Ill. June-Aug. ....*D. americana* L.
1. Flowers scattered along one side of the slender peduncles; stem 10-30 cm tall; leaves elliptical; wet woods and borders of swamps, rare; Alexander and Pulaski counties ....
  ....*D. lanceolata* (Chapm.) Small

2. **Dicliptera** Juss.

D. brachiata (Pursh) Spreng. Low rich woods, rare; Massac Co., *R. A. Evers* in 1951.

3. Ruellia L.

1. Stem hirsute; calyx-lobes linear-filiform, 0.5-1 mm wide, exceeding the capsule; leaves nearly sessile; roadsides and open woods, common throughout Ill. June-Aug. [*R. ciliosa* of auth., not Pursh; *R. caroliniensis* of auth., not (Walt.) Steud.] ....
....*R. humilis* Nutt.
1. Stem glabrous or puberulent; leaves short-petioled.
   2. Calyx-lobes linear-lanceolate, 2-4 mm wide, about equalling the capsule; flowers sessile or nearly so, or the peduncle 5-15 mm long; alluvial soil throughout the state except the northern counties. June-Aug. Smooth Ruellia ....*R. strepens* L.
   2. Calyx-lobes subulate-filiform, shorter than the capsule; flowers on slender peduncles 2-10 cm long, bearing a pair of leaf-like bracts at the apex; dry open woods, s. Ill. June-Aug. Stalked Ruellia ....*R. pedunculata* Torr.

111. Plantaginaceae Lindl. — Plantain Family

1. Plantago L. — Plantain

1. Leaves basal; plant scapose.
   2. Leaves ovate, oval, lanceolate or spatulate, not linear.
      3. Leaves narrowed at the base; veins free to the base; scapes solid.
         4. Spikes cylindrical.
            5. Capsules 4- to 15-seeded; corolla-lobes spreading or reflexed in fruit; leaves ovate or oval; plants perennial.
               6. Capsules 4-5 mm long; sepals elliptic, acutish, 2.5-3 mm long; seeds 1.5-2 mm long; leaves often glossy green, the petioles usually purplish at base; waste places, roadsides, lawns, fields, and open woods, very common. June-Sept. Common Plantain ....
               ....*P. rugelii* Dec.
               6. Capsules about 3 mm long; sepals oval, obtuse, 1.5-2 mm long; seeds 0.6-1.2 mm long; leaves dull green; waste places and lawns in cities, not common in Ill.; nat. from Eur. Broad-leaved Plantain ....
               ....*P. major* L.
            5. Capsules 2- to 4-seeded, ellipsoid, 2-3 mm long; leaves spatulate, obovate, or narrowly ovate.
               7. Corolla-lobes erect and closed over the tip of the capsule; flowers not fragrant; plants annual or biennial; common in fields and on roadsides throughout Ill. May-July ....*P. virginica* L.
               7. Corolla-lobes spreading or reflexed; flowers fragrant; plants perennial; adv. from Eurasia. Cook Co., *G. D. Fuller & O. M. Shantz* in 1940. Apr.-June
               ....*P. media* L.

4. Spikes ellipsoid; leaves lanceolate; seeds 2, hollowed on the inner surface; waste places, roadsides, fields, lawns, very common; nat. from Eur. May-Sept. Buckhorn Plantain .... *P. lanceolata* L.

3. Leaves, or .some of them, cordate at base; veins branching from the midrib; spikes cylindrical; scapes hollow; capsules 2- to 4-seeded, 4-5 mm long; along ditches, rare. May-July. Heart-leaved Plantain ....*P. cordata* Lam.

2. Leaves linear.

   8. Bracts conspicuously longer than the flowers, linear; leaves 3-8 mm wide; capsules 2-seeded; fields, roadsides, and open woods, common throughout Ill. June-Aug. Bracted Plantain ....*P. aristata* Michx.

   8. Bracts inconspicuous; leaves 1-4 mm wide.

      9. Spikes densely tomentose, cylindrical, obtuse, 3-12 cm long, 5-8 mm thick; capsules 2-seeded; sandy soil in fields and along roads in the northern half of the state. May-Aug. ....*P. purshii* R. & S.

      9. Spikes glabrous, linear, 2-8 cm long, 3-4 mm thick; leaves linear-filiform.

         10. Capsules 4-seeded, less than twice as long as the calyx; leaves mostly entire; fields, roadsides, and open woods; chiefly in the southern part of the state, northward to Hancock and Champaign counties. Apr.-May ....
.... *P. pusilla* Nutt.

         10. Capsules 7- to 30-seeded, about twice the length of the calyx; leaves often with several small teeth or linear lobes; sandy soil; Union Co. May ....
.... *P. heterophylla* Nutt.

1. Leaves opposite or whorled, linear, sessile, pubescent, the leafy stem 15-45 cm tall; flowers in capitate spikes; capsules 2-seeded; waste ground, occasional; adv. from Eurasia; known from Champaign, Cook, Lake, McHenry, and Winnebago counties. July-Sept. [*P. arenaria* Waldst. & Kit.] ....
.... *P. indica* L.

112. Lentibulariaceae Lindl. — Bladderwort Family

1. Utricularia L. — Bladderwort

1. Pedicels recurved in fruit.

   2. Flowers 1-2 cm long, the spur conspicuous, slightly curved upward; ponds and slow streams, chiefly in the northern half of the state. July-Aug. [*U. vulgaris* var. *americana* A. Gray; *U. macrorhiza* LeConte] .... *U. vulgaris* L.

   2. Flowers 4-6 mm long; spur short, blunt, almost obsolete; lake shores or stagnant water; Lake Co., *Hill;* Ringwood, McHenry Co., *Vasey.* .... *U. minor* L.

1. Pedicels erect or ascending in fruit; spur evident.
   3. Stems slender, elongated, creeping in shallow water.
      4. Leaf-segments capillary; upper lip of the corolla equalling
        the lower; lake shores or shallow water, local. Aug.-Oct.
        .... *U. gibba* L.
      4. Leaf-segments linear, flat, often minutely serrulate; upper
        lip of the corolla about half the length of the lower;
        shallow water; Lake, Ogle, and Tazewell counties. July-
        Aug. .... *U. intermedia* Hayne
   3. Stems short, submerged in the mud; leaves rarely seen; corolla
      1.5-2 cm broad, the subulate spur 7-12 mm long, pointing
      downward; lake shores and peat bogs, rare; Lake Co., *Hill;*
      Cook Co., *Pearsall* in 1943. July-Aug. Horned Bladderwort
      [*Stomoisia cornuta* (Michx.) Raf.] .... *U. cornuta* Michx.

113. **Orobanchaceae** Lindl. — Broomrape Family

1. Flowers of 2 kinds, the lower cleistogamous and fertile, the upper complete
  but usually sterile; stamens included; branches slender, ascending, simple
  ....1. *Epifagus*
1. Flowers all perfect and complete.
  2. Flowers in a thick scaly spike; stamens exserted; plants glabrous ....
    ....2. *Conopholis*
  2. Flowers solitary or racemose; stamens included; plants glandular-
    puberulent ....3. *Orobanche*

1. **Epifagus** Nutt. — Beech-drops

E. virginiana (L.) Bart. Under beech trees, parasitic; locally in
the s. half of Ill., extending northw. in the valley of the Wabash R.
to Clark Co. Sept.-Oct.

2. **Conopholis** Wallr. — Squaw-root

C. americana (L.f.) Wallr. In wooded ravines, parasitic on roots
of oak trees; locally in the n. half of Ill., as far s. as Clark Co.
May-July.

3. **Orobanche** L. — Broomrape

1. Flowers numerous, sessile or short-stalked, spicate or racemose.
  2. Calyx 4-lobed, the lobes triangular-ovate, about as long as
    the tube; flowers subtended by 1 large and 2 small bracts;
    raceme loosely flowered; stem branched; parasitic on roots
    of herbaceous plants, rare; adv. from Eur.; Rantoul, Cham-
    paign Co., Aug. 28, 1895, *G. P. Clinton* ....*O. ramosa* L.
  2. Calyx 5-cleft, the lobes linear-lanceolate, 7-8 mm long, longer
    than the tube; flowers subtended by 1 or 2 bracts; spikes
    terminal, dense; stem simple; parasitic on various plants,
    particularly *Ambrosia, Artemisia,* and other *Compositae* in
    sandy soil, not common; known from Lee, Menard, Wabash,
    and White counties. Aug.-Sept. [*Myzorrhiza ludoviciana*
    (Nutt.) Rydb.] .... *O. ludoviciana* Nutt.

1. Flowers few or solitary on bractless scapes; calyx 5-cleft.
   3. Flowers 3-15; calyx-lobes triangular-lanceolate, shorter than
      the tube; parasitic on *Artemisia* and other *Compositae;* in
      sandy soil, locally in the northern counties. ....
      ....*O. fasciculata* Nutt.
   3. Flower solitary; calyx-lobes subulate, longer than the tube;
      parasitic on various plants, not common. May-July.
      [*Anoplanthus uniflorus* (L.) Endl.] .... *O. uniflora* L.

114. Martyniaceae Link — Martynia Family

1. Proboscidea Keller — Unicorn Plant

P. louisianica (Mill.) Thell. River banks and waste ground, local.
July-Sept. [*Martynia louisianica* Mill.; *M. proboscidea* Glox.; *P.
jussieui* Keller].

115. Boraginaceae Lindl. — Borage Family

1. Ovary undivided, the style terminal; corolla regular, blue or white, the
   stamens included ....1. *Heliotropium*
1. Ovary 4-lobed, the style arising between the lobes.
   2. Corolla regular; stamens included, equal.
      3. Nutlets bearing barbed prickles; flowers blue, reddish, or white; plants
         pubescent.
         4. Nutlets divergent, covered with short prickles ....2. *Cynoglossum*
         4. Nutlets erect, prickly on the margin, rarely also on the back.
            5. Fruiting pedicels recurved or reflexed; style shorter than the
               nutlets; plants biennial or perennial ....3. *Hackelia*
            5. Fruiting pedicels erect; style longer than the nutlets; plants
               annual ....4. *Lappula*
      3. Nutlets not prickly.
         6. Receptacle conical; corolla yellow; pubescent weedy annuals ....
            ....5. *Amsinckia*
         6. Receptacle flat or convex.
            7. Plants glabrous, perennial; corolla blue (rarely whitish), tubular-
               funnelform; nutlets wrinkled when dry ....6. *Mertensia*
            7. Plants pubescent.
               8. Anthers connivent around the style; corolla blue, rotate ....
                  ....12. *Borago*
               8. Anthers not connivent around the style.
                  9. Scar of nutlets small, flat; nutlets smooth, glossy (except
                     Lithospermum arvense).
                     10. Corolla salverform, the lobes obtuse, spreading.
                        11. Racemes bractless.
                           12. Corolla white with yellow throat ....7. *Allocarya*
                           12. Corolla blue or white ....8. *Myosotis*
                        11. Racemes bracteate, each flower borne in the axil of a
                           bract; corolla yellow, or white, the tube cylindrical,
                           often elongate ....9. *Lithospermum*
                     10. Corolla tubular or funnelform.

      13. Corolla greenish-white ....10. *Onosmodium*
      13. Corolla blue ....13. *Anchusa*
  9. Scar of nutlets large, concave; throat of the corolla with 5
      lanceolate, acute, denticulate-margined appendages; coarse
      pubescent perennials with wide leaves ....14. *Symphytum*
2. Corolla irregular, blue; stamens unequal, exserted; nutlets wrinkled;
    plants hispid-pubescent ....11. *Echium*

1. **Heliotropium** L. — Heliotrope

1. Leaves spatulate to linear.
  2. Plant glabrous, glaucous, succulent; leaves spatulate; in sandy
    or saline soil, w. Ill., in Menard and St. Clair counties;
    adv. from s. U.S. June-Sept. ....*H. curassavicum* L.
  2. Plant strigose-canescent; leaves linear; rocky ledges, southwest-
    ern Ill. ....*H. tenellum* (Nutt.) Torr.
1. Leaves ovate or oval, long-petioled; plants pubescent; corolla blue,
    4-6 mm in diameter; fruit strongly ribbed, deeply 2-lobed;
    waste ground in the southern half of Ill.; nat. from Asia.
    July-Nov. ....*H. indicum* L.

2. **Cynoglossum** L. — Hound's-tongue

1. Stem pilose; corolla reddish or white; lower leaves spatulate;
    inflorescence many-flowered, leafy; plant biennial; pastures
    and waste places, common; nat. from Eur. June. Common
    Hound's-tongue. .... *C. officinale* L.
1. Stem hispidulous; corolla blue; lower leaves oval; inflorescence
    few-flowered, leafless; plant perennial; woods in s. Ill. May.
    Wild Comfrey ....*C. virginianum* L.

3. **Hackelia** Opiz

1. Nutlets of the globose fruit equally short-prickly over the whole
    back; woods and thickets throughout Ill. July-Sept. [*Lappula
    virginiana* (L.) Greene] .... *H. virginiana* (L.) I. M. Johnst.
1. Nutlets of the pyramidal fruit only marginally prickly, the backs
    merely muriculate; Apple River, Jo Daviess Co., *Pepoon &
    Moffatt* in 1896; *F. J. Hermann* in 1937. ....
    .... *H. americana* (A. Gray) Fern.

4. **Lappula** Moench — Stickseed

1. Nutlets with a double row of prickles; waste places, pastures,
    roadsides, common throughout Ill.; nat. from Eur. June-Oct.
    European Stickseed [*Echinospermum lappula* (L.) Lehm.;
    L. echinata Gilib., nomen invalidum] ....*L. myosotis* Moench
1. Nutlets with a single row of prickles; adv. from western U.S.; Rock
    Island Co. [*L. redowskii* var. *occidentalis* (S. Wats.) Rydb.]
    .... *L. occidentalis* (S. Wats.) Greene

5. Amsinckia Lehm.

A. spectabilis Fisch. & Mey. Waste ground, occasionally adv. from western U.S.; Rantoul, Champaign Co., *W. N. Clute* in 1908; Sycamore, De Kalb Co., *G. N. Jones* in 1945. June-July.

6. Mertensia Roth — Bluebells

M. virginica (L.) Pers. Woods, common throughout Ill. Apr.-May.

7. Allocarya Greene

A. figurata Piper. Moist ground, St. Clair Co., *J. Neill* in 1947. Rarely adv. from northwestern U.S.

8. Myosotis L. — Forget-me-not

1. Corolla 5-10 mm in diameter, bright blue, with a yellow eye.
  2. Calyx strigose, the triangular lobes shorter than the tube; perennials with decumbent stems; wet ground, particularly along streams; cult. and occasionally established; nat. from Eur. May-Oct. True Forget-me-not ....*M. scorpioides* L.
  2. Calyx with uncinate or glandular pubescence, at least toward the base, the lanceolate lobes longer than the tube; erect annual or biennial; waste ground, occasionally persisting near gardens; native of Europe; Jackson Co., *J. Biggs* in 1958. Garden Forget-me-not ....*M. sylvatica* Hoffm.
1. Corolla white, 1-2 mm in diameter; plants native, annual or biennial.
  3. Fruiting calyx 4-5 mm long, bearing few hooked hairs; nutlets 1-1.3 mm broad; stem 5-30 cm tall; sandy soil in open woods and fields, common. May-July. [*M. verna* Nutt.] ....
....*M. virginica* (L.) BSP.
  3. Fruiting calyx 5-7 mm long, with many hooked hairs; nutlets 2-2.5 mm broad; stem 30-50 cm tall; rich soil in woods, not common, s. Ill. May-June ....*M. macrosperma* Engelm.

9. Lithospermum L. — Gromwell. Puccoon

1. Perennials; corolla yellow; nutlets white, smooth, glossy.
  2. Corolla greenish-yellow, 4-5 mm long.
    3. Leaves lanceolate, acute, 6-12 mm broad; nutlets ovoid, 3 mm long; corolla longer than the calyx; waste ground, occasional; nat. from Eur. May-Aug. .... *L. officinale* L.
    3. Leaves elliptic-lanceolate to ovate, acuminate, 1-4.5 cm broad; nutlets globose-ovoid, 4 mm long; corolla shorter than the calyx; dry soil. May-June ....
.... *L. latifolium* Michx.
  2. Corolla bright yellow or orange, 1-3 cm long.
    4. Corolla-lobes erose-denticulate, the tube 1.5-3 cm long; later flowers cleistogamous, smaller; leaves linear; sandy soil,

chiefly in n. Ill., but extending southward along the valley
of the Illinois R. May-July. Narrow-leaved Puccoon [*L.
linearifolium* Goldie; *L. angustifolium* Michx., non Forsk.]
.... *L. incisum* Lehm.
4. Corolla-lobes entire, the tube less than 1.5 cm long; flowers
all complete; leaves lanceolate.
    5. Stems and leaves hispid-pubescent; corolla light-yellow,
      pubescent within at the base; sandy soil. May-July.
      [*L. gmelini* of auth.; *L. croceum* Fern.] ....
      .... *L. caroliniense* (Walt.) MacM.
    5. Stems and leaves soft-pubescent; corolla orange-yellow,
      glabrous within; nutlets 2.5-3 mm long; sandy or prairie
      soil. Apr.-June. Hoary Gromwell ....
      .... *L. canescens* (Michx.) Lehm.
1. Annual; corolla white; nutlets gray, wrinkled and pitted; roadsides, waste places and fields, common; nat. from Eur. Apr.-
June. Field Gromwell ....*L. arvense* L.

10. Onosmodium Michx. — Marbleseed

1. Leaves and stems shaggy-pubescent; stem 90-120 cm tall; nutlets
with a slight constriction or rim at base; dry banks and fields,
local. June-July. .... *O. hispidissimum* Mack.
1. Leaves and stems grayish-pubescent with mostly appressed hairs;
stem 40-60 cm tall; nutlets rounded at base, not at all constricted; hillsides, bluffs, and thickets, w. Ill., local. June-July
.... *O. occidentale* Mack.

11. Echium L.

E. vulgare L. Blueweed. Waste places, roadsides, and fields; nat.
from Eur. June-Aug.

12. Borago L. — Borage

B. officinalis L. Occasionally adv. in waste ground, or escaped from
cult.; native of Eur. July-Sept.

13. Anchusa L. — Alkanet

A. officinalis L. Roadsides and waste places, occasional; adv. from
Eur. May-Oct.

14. Symphytum L. — Comfrey

S. officinale L. Roadsides and waste places, occasional; adv. from
Eur.; Champaign Co., *Waite;* McHenry Co., *Nason.*

116. Verbenaceae J.St.Hil. — Verbena Family

1. Corolla 5-lobed, nearly regular; calyx tubular; fruit splitting into 4 nutlets
....1. *Verbena*
1. Corolla 4-lobed and 2-lipped; calyx short, 2-cleft; fruit splitting into 2
nutlets ....2. *Phyla*

1. Verbena L. — Vervain

1. Flowers 1.5-2.5 cm long; bracts shorter than the calyx; leaves incisely lobed or toothed; open woods, occasional. May-Aug. .... *V. canadensis* (L.) Britt.
1. Flowers 4-10 mm long.
  2. Bracts longer than the flowers; stems decumbent, hirsute; roadsides and waste places. June-Sept. [*V. bracteosa* Michx.] .... *V. bracteata* Lag. & Rodr.
  2. Bracts shorter than the flowers; stem erect; spikes slender or filiform.
    3. Corolla white; spikes filiform; calyx in fruit 2 mm or less in length; leaves serrate; roadsides and open woods, common. July-Sept. Hybridizes with *V. bracteata* and *V. stricta*. White Vervain. .... *V. urticifolia* L.
    3. Corolla lavender-purple to blue (rarely pink); spikes slender; fruiting calyx more than 2 mm long.
      4. Plants soft-pubescent; leaves oval, serrate; calyx 4-5 mm long; nutlets ellipsoid, 2.5 mm long; roadsides and fields, common. June-Sept. Hoary Vervain. ....
      .... *V. stricta* Vent.
      4. Plants glabrous, or sparsely rough-pubescent.
        5. Leaves lanceolate, acuminate, the petioles 1-2 cm long; calyx 2-3 mm long; nutlets smooth, 1.5-2 mm long; roadsides and open woods, common. July-Sept. Blue Vervain. .... *V. hastata* L.
        5. Leaves linear to oblanceolate, obtuse, sessile or nearly so; calyx 3-4 mm long; nutlets reticulate, 3 mm long; roadsides and fields. June-Aug. Narrow-leaved Vervain [*V. angustifolia* Michx.]. Hybridizes with *V. stricta, V. hastata,* and *V. bracteata.* ....
        .... *V. simplex* Lehm.

2. Phyla Lour. — Frog-fruit
(*Lippia* [Houst.] L.)

P. lanceolata (Michx.) Greene. River banks, shores, along ditches, and in wet meadows, common. June-Sept. [*L. lanceolata* var. *recognita* Fern. & Grisc.].

117. Phrymaceae Schauer — Lopseed Family
1. Phryma L. — Lopseed

P. leptostachya L. Alluvial soil in woods, common throughout Ill. June-Aug.

118. Labiatae Juss. — Mint Family
(*Lamiaceae* Lindl.; *Menthaceae* L.F.Ward ex Safford)

1. Corolla nearly regular, almost equally 5- (or 4-) lobed.
  2. Leaves entire or essentially so; plants glandular-puberulent.
    3. Stamens included or only slightly exserted; calyx nearly equally 5-toothed ....3. *Isanthus*

3. Stamens long-exserted and strongly upcurved; calyx with 3 long and
2 short teeth ....4. *Trichostema*
2. Leaves serrate, crenate, or pinnatifid.
4. Fertile stamens 2; plants inodorous ....28. *Lycopus*
4. Fertile stamens 4; plants strongly aromatic ....29. *Mentha*
1. Corolla very irregular (strongly zygomorphic).
5. Calyx with a small crest or callosity on the upper side, 2-lipped; stamens
4 ....5. *Scutellaria*
5. Calyx not crested.
6. Flowers in compact axillary whorls, or in terminal heads or capitate
clusters.
7. Bracts broad, conspicuous; corolla 2-5 cm long; flowers in dense
head-like clusters; calyx tubular, equally 5-toothed, 15-nerved;
stamens 2 ....21. *Monarda*
7. Bracts smaller or absent; corolla shorter.
8. Stem corymbosely branched, stiffly erect; flower-heads clustered;
leaves linear, lanceolate, or ovate; calyx nearly regular, 5-
toothed, 10- to 13-nerved ....26. *Pycnanthemum*
8. Stem simple or with few branches.
9. Calyx with 10 recurved teeth; corolla white, 5-6 mm long;
leaves ovate, petioled, crenate, rugose; stem canescent ....
.... 6. *Marrubium*
9. Calyx with fewer than 10 teeth.
10. Anther-bearing stamens 4.
11. Corolla blue, apparently unilabiate, the upper lip short,
truncate; calyx 10- to many-nerved; ovary not deeply
lobed ....2. *Ajuga*
11. Corolla bilabiate; ovary deeply 4-lobed.
12. Calyx not 2-lipped, the 5 teeth equal.
13. Stamens conspicuously exserted beyond the
corolla ....7. *Agastache*
13. Stamens not conspicuously exserted.
14. Calyx-teeth rigid, spine-tipped.
15. Leaves lobed ....14. *Leonurus*
15. Leaves not lobed ....15. *Galeopsis*
14. Calyx-teeth not spine-tipped.
16. Calyx 15-nerved; corolla 8-10 mm long,
white with purple dots ....8. *Nepeta*
16. Calyx about 5-nerved; corolla purple, 12-
24 mm long ....16. *Lamium*
12. Calyx 2-lipped, the teeth conspicuously unequal.
17. Stem erect or ascending.
18. Leaves entire or sparingly crenate; floral
bracts ciliate; calyx reticulate-veiny, somewhat 10-nerved ....13. *Prunella*
18. Leaves coarsely sharply serrate; floral bracts
pectinate; calyx 13- to 15-nerved ....
....11. *Dracocephalum*
17. Stems prostrate, the flowering branches erect or
ascending, pubescent; leaves oval, obtuse,
entire, short-petioled, 6-15 mm long; corolla
purplish ....25. *Thymus*

10. Anther-bearing stamens 2; calyx pubescent, 13-nerved, the
teeth subulate ....20. *Blephilia*
6. Flowers in racemes, spikes, cymes, or solitary or few in the axils of
the leaves.
19. Flowers cymose; leaves linear ....18. *Satureja*
19. Flowers not cymose.
20. Calyx deeply 4-cleft; corolla greenish-yellow, 3-4 cm long;
flowers solitary, axillary; leaves thin, cordate, palmately
veined, the blade shorter than the petiole ....12. *Synandra*
20. Calyx 5-toothed, or 2-lipped.
21. Leaves reniform, crenate, petioled; stems trailing; flowers
bluish-purple, axillary ....9. *Glecoma*
21. Leaves not reniform.
22. Flowers 4-6 mm long.
23. Leaves linear or lanceolate, entire or sparingly
serrate; flowers bluish-purple; stamens 2 ....
....22. *Hedeoma*
23. Leaves ovate, purplish-green, coarsely dentate;
flowers whitish; stamens 4 ....31. *Perilla*
22. Flowers more than 6 mm long.
24. Corolla with the upper lip apparently obsolete;
stamens erect, exserted; flowers in long racemes
....1. *Teucrium*
24. Corolla conspicuously bilabiate.
25. Leaves toothed.
26. Flowers in loose terminal panicles; corolla
light yellow; fertile stamens usually only 2;
calyx 2-lipped ....30. *Collinsonia*
26. Flowers not in loose terminal panicles.
27. Calyx nearly equally 5-toothed.
28. Flowers 1.5-3.5 cm long; spikes continuous, loosely flowered; fertile
stamens 4 ....10. *Physostegia*
28. Flowers smaller.
29. Stamens 2, long-exserted; calyx
densely villous in the throat;
corolla purplish-pink, 5 mm
long; stem slender, stiff, corymbosely branched; leaves ovate,
subsessile, sharply serrate, acuminate; plant very aromatic
..................................27. *Cunila*
29. Stamens 4, not long-exserted;
spikes composed of interrupted
whorls of flowers ....17. *Stachys*
27. Calyx 2-lipped.
30. Fertile stamens 2; corolla purplish
..................................19. *Salvia*
30. Fertile stamens 4; corolla white ....
..................................23. *Melissa*
25. Leaves (in our species) entire, linear, sessile or
nearly so; flowers 1-5 in the axils; plants
often with short basal sterile stolons bear-

ing oval leaves purplish beneath; corolla
purple, 8-9 mm long, puberulent; stamens 4
....24. *Clinopodium*

1. Teucrium L. — Wood-sage

1. Calyces and upper part of stem pannose, with short, somewhat
   curved, glandless hairs; corolla about 1.5 cm long; moist
   ground, common. June-Aug. .... *T. canadense* L.
1. Calyces and upper part of stem short-villous with straight, often
   somewhat glandular hairs; corolla 8-12 mm long; moist
   ground, locally in the northern two-thirds of the state. July-
   Sept. [*T. boreale* Bickn.] .... *T. occidentale* A. Gray

2. Ajuga L. — Bugleweed

A. genevensis L. Waste ground, fields, roadsides, occasional; escaped from cult.; native of Eur.; Cook, Du Page, and McHenry counties. May-July.

3. Isanthus Michx. — False Pennyroyal

I. brachiatus (L.) BSP. Gravelly or sandy soil along roads or in
fields or open woods, local. Aug.-Sept.

4. Trichostema L. — Bluecurls

T. dichotomum L. Sandy soil in open woods, rare.

5. Scutellaria L. — Skullcap

1. Flowers in axillary or terminal racemes.
   2. Flowers 6-7 mm long; plants glabrous throughout or puberu-
      lent above; moist ground, common. July-Sept. ....
      ....*S. lateriflora* L.
   2. Flowers 12-25 mm long.
      3. Leaves cordate; stem and inflorescence softly glandular-
         pubescent; corolla 2-2.5 cm long; woods, locally through-
         out Ill. June-July. Heart-leaved Skullcap [*S. cordifolia*
         Muhl.; *S. versicolor* Nutt.] .... *S. ovata* Hill
      3. Leaves narrowed at the base.
         4. Stem pilose; calyces glandular-pilose; corolla 12-16 mm
            long; wooded slopes, s. Ill., rare. June-July. Hairy
            Skullcap [*S. ovalifolia* Pers.; *S. pilosa* sensu Michx., non
            Hill] .... *S. elliptica* Muhl.
         4. Stem puberulent; calyces canescent, not glandular; corolla
            18-20 mm long, puberulent; woods, extending north-
            ward to Vermilion and Peoria counties. June-Aug.
            Downy Skullcap [*S. canescens* Nutt.; *S. serrata* sensu
            auth., non Andr.] .... *S. incana* Biehler
1. Flowers solitary in the axils of the leaves.
   5. Flowers 16-22 mm long; wet ground, chiefly in the northern
      half of the state. June-Sept. [*S. epilobiifolia* A. Hamilt.] ....
      .... *S. galericulata* L.

5. Flowers 5-10 mm long.
6. Stem glabrous or puberulent.
7. Stem glabrous or nearly so; median and lower leaves noticeably crenate; nutlets slender-stalked, conspicuously winged; rhizomes filiform; moist ground in woods in the southern two-thirds of Ill. May-June. [*S. ambigua* Nutt.; *S. nervosa* var. *calvifolia* Fern.] .... *S. nervosa* Pursh
7. Stem puberulent on the angles with minute upwardly appressed or curved non-glandular trichomes; nutlets wingless; rhizomes moniliform; roadsides and wooded slopes and ridges, common. May-June. [*S. ambigua* sensu auth., non Nutt.; *S. parvula* var. *ambigua* sensu Fern.] .... *S. leonardi* Epling
6. Stem and leaves more or less glandular-pubescent; rhizomes moniliform.
8. Lower leaf-surface with sessile glands; stem evenly pilose; rocky woods or ledges, gravelly or sandy slopes, banks, or hills, and in sandy barrens throughout Ill. May-June. [*S. parvula* var. *mollis* A. Gray; *S. campestris* Britt.] .... *S. parvula* Michx.
8. Lower leaf-surface with glandular hairs; stem pilose on the angles; sandy soil, rare, southern Ill. .... *S. australis* (Fassett) Epling

6. Marrubium L. — Common Horehound

M. vulgare L. Waste places, roadsides, fields, and open woods, common; nat. from Eur. June-Oct.

7. Agastache Clayton — Giant Hyssop

1. Stem and branches glabrous or puberulent; corolla cream or yellowish; bracts ovate, green; calyx-lobes ovate, 1-1.5 mm long, acutish; roadsides, fields, and open woods, common. July-Oct. .... *A. nepetoides* (L.) Ktze.
1. Stem and branches pilosulous; corolla whitish to pale purplish; bracts roundish, abruptly apiculate; calyx-lobes lanceolate, acuminate, 2-2.5 mm long; sandy soil in open woods and along roads, infrequent. Aug.-Sept. .... *A. scrophulariaefolia* (Willd.) Ktze.

8. Nepeta L. — Catnip

N. cataria L. Pastures, roadsides, waste places, and open woods, common; nat. from Eur. June-Sept.

9. Glecoma L. — Ground-ivy

G. hederacea L. Frequent in waste places, lawns, along roads, and in moist open woods; nat. from Eur. Apr.-June. Two forms are represented in Ill.; the usual form has the corolla 10-15 mm long; plants with corollas 16-22 mm long are rarely found.

10. **Physostegia** Benth. — Obedient Plant

1. Corollas 18-22 mm long; leaves oblanceolate or lanceolate, thin, the upper nearly as large as the median ones; anthers 1-1.5 mm long; calyx campanulate; alluvial soil, local. Aug.-Oct. .... *P. speciosa* Sweet
1. Corollas 2.5-3.5 cm long; leaves mostly linear-lanceolate, firm, the uppermost much reduced; anthers 1.6-2 mm long; calyx tubular-campanulate; prairie soil, often along railroads, local, July-Oct. [*P. angustifolia* Fern.] .... *P. virginiana* (L.) Benth.

11. **Dracocephalum** L. — Dragonhead

(*Moldavica* Adans.)

D. parviflorum Nutt. Dry soil, rare; Kane, Lee, Menard, Stark, Vermilion, and Winnebago counties. May-Aug.

12. **Synandra** Nutt.

S. hispidula (Michx.) Britt. Wooded ravines, rare; known to occur in Jackson Co. May-June.

13. **Prunella** L. — Selfheal

P. vulgaris L. Carpenter-weed. Roadsides, waste places, fields, and open woods, common; nat. from Eur. June-Oct.

14. **Leonurus** L. — Motherwort

1. Calyx much shorter than the corolla; lower leaves palmately 3- to 5-lobed; corolla pale lilac, 8-10 mm long; waste places, fields, roadsides, and open woods, common; nat. from Eur. May-Aug. ....*L. cardiaca* L.
1. Calyx nearly as long as the corolla; lower leaves coarsely toothed; corolla pink, 5 mm long; waste places, occasional; nat. from Eur. June-Sept. Lion's tail ....*L. marrubiastrum* L.

15. **Galeopsis** L.

1. Stems bristly-hairy; nat. from Eur.; Boone, Cook, and Henderson counties. Hemp-nettle ....*G. tetrahit* L.
1. Stems with soft appressed hairs; adv. from Eur.; Cook Co. ....*G. ladanum* L.

16. **Lamium** L. — Dead-nettle

1. Corolla 2-2.5 cm long; leaves usually white-marked, ovate, petioled; calyx sparingly pubescent or nearly glabrous; nutlets 3 mm long; plants perennial; waste places, occasional; adv. from Eurasia; scarcely established in Ill. May-July. Spotted Dead-nettle ....*L. maculatum* L.
1. Corolla less than 2 cm long; leaves not white-marked; nutlets 2 mm long; annuals or biennials.

2. All the leaves petioled, ovate; calyx thinly pubescent; waste places, occasional; adv. from Eur. Apr.-May. Purple Dead-nettle ....*L. purpureum* L.
2. Upper leaves sessile or clasping, orbicular or reniform; calyx densely pubescent; early flowers cleistogamous; cultivated ground and waste places; nat. from Eur. Mar.-May. Henbit Dead-nettle ....*L. amplexicaule* L.

17. Stachys L. — Hedge-nettle

1. Stem hispidulous or hirsute only on the angles or glabrous throughout.
   2. Leaves short-petioled or nearly sessile.
      3. Calyx glabrous, or with a few trichomes toward the base; leaves nearly glabrous, lance-linear, narrowed at the base; moist ground, local. July-Aug. [*S. ambigua* (A.Gray) Britt., non Sm.] ....*S. aspera* Michx.
      3. Calyx pilose; leaves lanceolate, pubescent; moist ground, chiefly in the northern counties, not common. July-Aug. [*S. aspera* of auth., not Michx.; *S. tenuifolia* var. *aspera* Fern.; *S. tenuifolia* var. *platyphylla* Fern.; *S. tenuifolia* var. *hispida* (Pursh) Fern.] ....*S. hispida* Pursh
   2. Leaves longer petioled, the petioles of the median leaves 3 cm long.
      4. Calyx smooth or sometimes setulose; leaves usually linear-lanceolate; moist ground, common. July-Sept. [*S. glabra* Riddell; *S. palustris* var. *glabra* (Riddell) A. Gray] ....
      .... *S. tenuifolia* Willd.
      4. Calyx puberulent, leaves usually ovate; low wet ground, rare; Alexander, Hardin, and Massac counties ....
      ....*S. clingmanii* Small
1. Stem retrorsely pubescent on the sides as well as the angles; leaves lanceolate, sessile or nearly so; calyx hirsute; moist ground, common. May-Sept. [*S. homotricha* (Fern.) Rydb.; *S. ambigua* sensu Epling, non Sm.] ....*S. arenicola* Britt.

18. Satureja L. — Summer Savory

S. hortensis L. Waste places; introd. from Eur.; an occasional garden escape.

19. Salvia L. — Sage

1. Leaves chiefly basal; corolla 1.5-2.5 cm long; plants perennial.
   2. Leaves lyrate-lobed or pinnatifid; calyx pilose on the lower half; rocky woods and thickets, locally in s. Ill. May-June. Cancer-weed ....*S. lyrata* L.
   2. Leaves crenate, often red-spotted; calyx hirsute, and with some stipitate glands; escaped from cult., native of Eur.; has been collected in Lake and Piatt counties......*S. pratensis* L.

1. Stem more or less leafy; leaves elliptical-lanceolate.
  3. Corolla-tube exserted from the calyx.
    4. Corolla 15-30 mm long; occasionally adv. from the Great
      Plains ....*S. pitcheri* Torr.
    4. Corolla 10-14 mm long; dry gravelly soil, occasional; adv.
      from Eur. ....*S. sylvestris* L.
  3. Corolla-tube included in the calyx; adv. from w. U.S. July-
    Sept. Rocky Mountain Sage [*S. lanceaefolia* Poir.] ....
    ....*S. reflexa* Hornem.

20. **Blephilia** Raf. — Wood Mint

1. Leaves elliptic-lanceolate, nearly odorless, the petioles 2-10 mm
long; stem usually simple, the pubescence of short, curved
hairs; calyx 8-11 mm long; woods, locally throughout Ill. May-
June ....*B. ciliata* (L.) Benth.
1. Leaves ovate-lanceolate, with strong peppermint odor, the petioles
1-3 cm long; stem often branched, the pubescence pilose; calyx
6-8 mm long; woods, common throughout Ill. May-Sept. ....
....*B. hirsuta* (Pursh) Benth.

21. **Monarda** L. — Bergamot Mint

1. Heads (flower-clusters) solitary and terminal on the stem or
branches; stamens longer than the upper lip of the corolla.
  2. Corolla scarlet, 3-5 cm long, puberulent; bracts red; leaves
    petioled; occasionally escaped from cult.; Wabash Co.,
    Schneck in 1874; Chicago, Cook Co., fide *Higley & Raddin;*
    Barrington, Lake Co., *J. A. Steyermark* in 1946. July-
    Sept. ....*M. didyma* L.
  2. Corolla purple, pink, or white.
    3. Leaves sessile or nearly so; calyx-teeth 2.5-4 mm long; corolla
      pale purplish or white, the lower lip spotted; roadsides,
      pastures and open woods in the southern half of Ill. May-
      June ....*M. bradburiana* Beck
    3. Leaves distinctly petioled; calyx-teeth 1-2 mm long.
      4. Corolla lilac-purple (rarely white) 2-3.5 cm long; stem
        often branched; fields, open woods, and roadsides,
        common. June-Aug. Wild Bergamot [*M. fistulosa* var.
        mollis (L.) Benth.] .... *M. fistulosa* L.
      4. Corolla white or yellowish-white, 2-2.5 cm long; stem
        usually simple; woods, local; chiefly in the centr.
        counties. June-Aug. ....*M. clinopodia* L.
1. Heads in several verticillate glomerules; corolla yellowish-white
or pink.
  5. Calyx-lobes triangular, short; corolla yellowish, the upper lip
    purple-spotted; stamens included; bracts yellowish and
    purple; sandy soil, local. Aug.-Sept. Our plants belong to
    subsp. *villicaulis* Pennell. Spotted Horsemint ......*M. punctata* L.

5. Calyx-lobes subulate-aristate; corolla pink or white, not spotted; dry ground, occasionally adv. from the west; Cook Co. Lemon Mint [*M. pectinata* sensu auth., non Nutt.] ....
....*M. citriodora* Cerv.

22. Hedeoma Pers.

1. Leaves elliptical, sparingly serrate, petioled; calyx with the upper teeth triangular-lanceolate, the lower subulate; dry soil in fields, along roads, and in open woods, common. July-Oct. American Pennyroyal ....*H. pulegioides* (L.) Pers.
1. Leaves linear, entire, sessile, ciliate; calyx-teeth all subulate; sandy soil in open woods, chiefly in the n. half of the state, but extending southw. along the Mississippi R. June-July. Rough Pennyroyal ....*H. hispida* Pursh

23. Melissa L. — Balm

M. officinalis L. Waste places, occasional; introd. from Eur. June-Aug.

24. Clinopodium L. — Basil

C. arkansanum (Nutt.) House. Rocky woods or sandy ground, local; chiefly in n.e. Ill. June-Aug. [*C. glabrum* (Nutt.) Kuntze; *Satureja arkansana* (Nutt.) Briq.; *S. glabella* var. *angustifolia* (Torr.) Svens.]

25. Thymus L. — Thyme

T. serpyllum L. Roadsides and old fields and gardens, rarely collected; introd. from Eur. July-Aug.

26. Pycnanthemum Michx. — Mountain Mint

1. Leaves ovate to ovate-lanceolate.
   2. Upper leaves whitish; calyx-teeth and bracts pubescent and usually with long bristles; roadsides, fields, and open woods, s. Ill. July-Sept. ....*P. pycnanthemoides* (Leavenw.) Fern.
   2. Upper leaves not whitish; calyces and bracts canescent; woods, s. Ill. Aug.-Sept. ....*P. incanum* (L.) Michx.
1. Leaves lanceolate to linear-lanceolate or linear.
   3. Stem glabrous throughout (or rarely with a few minute curved hairs); leaves linear; calyx-lobes subulate-lanceolate; dry soil in open woods, along roads, and in fields, common. June-Sept. ....*P. flexuosum* (Walt.) BSP.
   3. Stem pubescent.
      4. Stem short-pubescent on the angles; leaves linear-lanceolate, glabrous or nearly so; moist ground in woods and along roads. July-Sept. ....*P. virginianum* (L.) Dur. & Jacks.
      4. Stem copiously short-pilose throughout, or at least above the middle; leaves elliptic-lanceolate, finely pubescent on veins beneath; sandy soil along roads and in open woods; chiefly n. and central Ill. July-Sept. ....*P. pilosum* Nutt.

27. **Cunila** L. — Stone Mint

C. origanoides (L.) Britt. Wooded ridges in southern Ill. Aug.-Oct.

28. **Lycopus** L. — Water Horehound
1. Calyx-teeth lanceolate, shorter than or equalling the mature nutlets; leaves serrate, not incised.
    2. Base of plant and stolons lacking tubers; nutlets sharply muricate on top, 1.7-2 mm long at maturity; wet ground, not infrequent. July-Oct. .... *L. virginicus* L.
    2. Base of rhizome and tips of stolons often bearing a tuber; nutlets smooth or merely rugulose on top, 1-1.5 mm long when mature; moist ground in the northern part of the state, extending southward to Tazewell and Champaign counties. Aug.-Sept. ....*L. uniflorus* Michx.
1. Calyx-teeth subulate, much longer than the nutlets.
    3. Lower leaves petiolate.
        4. Leaves dentate or coarsely serrate; corolla 2-3 mm long, twice the length of the calyx; wet ground, locally throughout Ill., except the northern counties. Aug.-Sept. ....
        ....*L. rubellus* Moench
        4. Leaves (at least the lower) more or less incised or sinuately pinnatifid; corolla slightly longer than the calyx; wet ground, the common species throughout Ill. July-Sept. [*L. sinuatus* Ell.] ....*L. americanus* Muhl.
    3. Lower leaves sessile; waste ground, not common; known from Bureau, Whiteside, Cook, Henry, and Lake counties. July-Aug. ....*L. asper* Greene

29. **Mentha** L. — Mint
1. Whorls of flowers mostly in terminal spikes.
    2. Stem glabrous or nearly so.
        3. Leaves sessile or subsessile; calyx 1-1.5 mm long; moist ground, occasional; nat. from Eur. July-Sept. Spearmint
        ....*M. spicata* L.
        3. Leaves all distinctly short-petioled; calyx 2-3 mm long; waste places and along roads; nat. from Eur. July-Sept. Peppermint ....*M. piperita* L.
    2. Stem pubescent, at least at the nodes.
        4. Spikes slender, less than 1 cm thick, often interrupted; leaves rugose, roundish-ovate, finely pubescent and reticulate beneath; waste ground, rarely escaped from cult.; nat. from Eur. Round-leaved Mint ....*M. rotundifolia* (L.) Huds.
        4. Spikes 1 cm thick, dense.
            5. Leaves sessile, not crisped; stem and calyx finely pubescent; roadsides and waste places, occasional; introd. from Eur. Woolly Mint ....*M. alopecuroides* Hull
            5. Leaves crisped, wavy, short-petioled; calyx nearly glabrous; roadsides and waste places, escaped from cult.; native of Eur. July-Sept. Crisp Mint ....*M. crispa* L.

1. Whorls of flowers all axillary.
  6. Upper leaves much smaller than the others; moist shaded ground, or in waste places, occasional; introd. from Eur. July-Oct. Small-leaved Mint ......*M. cardiaca* Gerarde ex Baker
  6. Upper leaves little, if at all, reduced.
    7. Stem glabrous; moist ground, not common; nat. from Eur. Aug.-Oct. ....*M. gentilis* L.
    7. Stem pubescent or puberulent, at least on the angles; moist ground, common throughout Illinois. July-Sept. [*M. arvensis* var. *canadensis* (L.) Briq.; *M. arvensis* var. *glabrata* (Benth.) Fern.] Wild Mint. ....*M. canadensis* L.

30. Collinsonia L. — Richweed

C. canadensis L. Woods, chiefly in southern Ill., but extending northward to Clark and Champaign counties. July-Sept.

31. Perilla L. — Beefsteak-plant

P. frutescens (L.) Britt. Roadsides, waste places and in woods; native of Asia; becoming a common weed in southern Ill.; also Peoria Co., *V. H. Chase.* July-Oct.

119. Rubiaceae B.Juss. — Madder Family

1. Shrubs; leaves opposite or whorled; flowers in dense globose heads ....2. *Cephalanthus*
1. Herbs.
  2. Leaves opposite.
    3. Flowers axillary, sessile or nearly so.
      4. Plants pubescent; fruit separating into 2 or 3 indehiscent carpels ....4. *Diodia*
      4. Plants glabrous; fruit a capsule of 2 carpels, one dehiscent, the other indehiscent ....5. *Spermacoce*
    3. Flowers pedicellate, cymose or solitary.
      5. Plants trailing; fruit a pair of united red drupes ....3. *Mitchella*
      5. Plants erect; fruit a capsule ....1. *Houstonia*
  2. Leaves apparently in whorls of 4-8 ....6. *Galium*

1. Houstonia L. — Bluets

1. Flowers cymose; stems 10-30 cm tall; plants perennial.
  2. Sepals at anthesis longer than the calyx-tube, and in fruit longer than the capsule; capsule as broad as long.
    3. Leaves lanceolate; calyx nearly as long as the corolla-tube; the linear sepals much longer than the capsule and about twice the length of the calyx-tube; prairie soil or in open woods in the s. half of the state, extending northw. to Menard and Champaign counties. May-July. [*H. purpurea* of auth. not L.] ....*H. lanceolata* (Poir.) Britt.
    3. Leaves linear-oblanceolate to linear; calyx shorter than the corolla-tube.

4. Leaves linear-oblanceolate, 2-6 mm wide; cymes compact,
the pedicels 2-4 mm long; corolla-lobes puberulent
within; sepals much longer than the capsule; thin soil on
wooded ridges and slopes, locally in the n. counties.
May-July ....*H. longifolia* Gaertn.
4. Leaves linear, 1-3 mm wide; cymes loose, the filiform pedicels mostly 4-12 mm long; corolla-lobes short-villosulous
within; sepals only slightly longer than the capsule; rocky
woods, s. Ill. May-July ....*H. tenuifolia* Nutt.
2. Sepals subulate, shorter than the calyx-tube and the capsule;
leaves narrowly linear, many of them fascicled; capsules
slightly longer than broad; bluffs and ledges in the s. and s.w.
counties, not common. [*H. angustifolia* Michx.] ....
....*H. nigricans* (Lam.) Fern.
1. Flowers solitary; stems very slender, 1-5 (-15) cm tall.
5. Pedicels mostly 2-5 cm long; flowers 8-15 mm long, with a
yellow center, the corolla-tube more than twice the length of
the calyx; plants perennial with a filiform rhizome; fields and
open woods, locally in the e. and s. counties. Apr.-June ....
....*H. caerulea* L.
5. Pedicels mostly 0.5-2 cm long; flowers 6-9 mm long, the corolla-
tube not more than twice the length of the calyx; plants
annual.
6. Calyx about half the length of the corolla-tube; hillsides and
bluffs, s. Ill. Apr.-May. [*H. patens* Ell.] ....*H. pusilla* Schoepf
6. Calyx nearly as long as the corolla-tube; dry ground in the w.
and s. counties. Apr.-May ....*H. minima* Beck

2. Cephalanthus L. — Buttonbush

C. occidentalis L. Along streams and lake shores, and in swamps,
common throughout Ill. June-Aug. Var. *pubescens* Raf., with twigs
and lower surface of leaves softly pubescent, is found occasionally in
s. Ill.

3. Mitchella L. — Partridge-berry

M. repens L. In rocky woods or on sandstone ledges, local. May-
July.

4. Diodia L. — Buttonweed

1. Leaves elliptic-lanceolate, 6-16 mm wide; corolla about 1 cm
long; style 2-parted; fruit ellipsoid, 7-9 mm long, strongly fur-
rowed, tipped with 2 slender calyx-teeth; wet ground in woods,
s. Ill. June-Aug. ....*D. virginiana* L.
1. Leaves linear-lanceolate, rigid, rough, 3-6 mm wide; corolla 4-6
mm long; style undivided; fruit turbinate, 4-5 mm long,
tipped with 4 short calyx-teeth; fields, roadsides, and open
woods nearly throughout Ill. July-Aug. Rough Buttonwood
....*D. teres* Walt.

5. Spermacoce L.

S. glabra Michx. Smooth Buttonweed. Muddy shores, river banks, and wet ground in woods in the southern and western counties, extending northw. to Peoria Co. July-Aug.

6. Galium L. — Bedstraw

1. Ovary and fruit uncinate-hispid, or at least puberulent.
2. Leaves cuspidate, 1-veined, 6-8 in each whorl.
3. Leaves narrowly oblanceolate to linear; stems long, weak, reclining, retrorsely hispidulous; plants annual.
4. Leaves 2-8 mm long; fruits 4-5 mm in diameter, the hairs pustulate at base; peduncles subtended by a whorl of leaf-like bracts, or cymes 1-3 flowered in the upper axils; corolla white, 2 mm in diameter; woods and thickets, very common. Apr.-June. Goose-grass ....*G. aparine* L.
4. Leaves 0.5-2 cm long, narrower and more hispidulous; fruits 1.5-3 mm in diameter, the hairs not pustulate; corolla green, 1 mm in diameter; peduncles with only 2 leaf-like bracts; cymes 2-9-flowered; waste places, occasional; adv. from Eur. May-June ....*G. vaillantii* DC.
3. Leaves narrowly oval; corolla greenish-white; plants perennial; damp woods. June-Aug. Sweet-scented Bedstraw ....*G. triflorum* Michx.
2. Leaves not cuspidate, 4 in each whorl.
5. Flowers solitary, sessile, axillary, white, subtended by a pair of foliaceous bracts; leaves elliptical, ciliate, 5-10 mm long, 1-2 mm wide, 1-veined; rocky ledges in s.w. Ill. May-June ....*G. virgatum* Nutt.
5. Flowers in cymes or panicles.
6. Leaves narrowly lanceolate or linear, glabrous or nearly so, or the margins and midveins scabrous; flowers white, numerous in a terminal panicle; in sandy or rocky soil along roads or in woods and thickets, or occasionally in bogs. May-July. Northern Bedstraw ....
....*G. boreale* L.
6. Leaves oval, more or less pubescent.
7. Leaves 1-veined, or obscurely 3-veined at base, oval; flowers greenish-purple, pedicelled, paniculate; fruit 3-4 mm in diameter; woods, local. June-Aug. ....
....*G. pilosum* Ait.
7. Leaves 3-veined, oval-lanceolate; flowers greenish-yellow, puberulent, sessile or nearly so, in few-flowered cymes; fruit 2-3 mm in diameter; woods. May-July. Wild Licorice [*G. circaezans* var. *hypomalacum* Fern.] ....*G. circaezans* Michx.
1. Ovary and fruit glabrous.

8. Flowers yellow, numerous, paniculate; leaves linear, revolute-margined, cuspidate, 6-8 in each whorl, becoming deflexed; stem puberulent; waste places and fields, occasional; adv. from Eur. June-July. Yellow Bedstraw ....*G. verum* L.
8. Flowers white.
  9. Leaves cuspidate, 5-7 (usually 6) in each whorl.
    10. Stems puberulent or glabrous; plants more or less erect.
      11. Leaves linear; plants usually 15-30 cm tall; dry woods, common. June-July......*G. concinnum* T. & G.
      11. Leaves oblanceolate; plants usually over 30 cm tall; introd. from Eur.; Champaign and Henry counties ....*G. mollugo* L.
    10. Leaves narrowly elliptical-oblanceolate, 2.5-4 mm wide, the margins retrorsely scabrellous; stems reclining or trailing, retrorsely scabrous on the angles, 0.5-2 m long; swamps and thickets in n. Ill. July-Aug. Rough Bedstraw ....*G. asprellum* Michx.
  9. Leaves blunt, linear or linear-spatulate.
    12. Corolla 4-lobed, the lobes acute; leaves mostly in fours; stem erect.
      13. Leaves spreading or ascending; fruit 3 mm in diameter; moist ground, common. May-June. [*G. tinctorium* sensu auth., non L.] ....*G. obtusum* Bigel.
      13. Leaves mostly reflexed; fruit 1-1.5 mm in diameter; swampy ground, rare; Boone, Lake, and McHenry counties. June-July ....*G. labradoricum* (Wieg.) Wieg.
    12. Corolla 3-lobed, the lobes obtuse; leaves of the main stem mostly in sixes and fives; stems diffuse, slender.
      14. Pedicels smooth, straight, 2-6 mm long; flowers in twos and threes; wet ground, n.e. Ill., rare. May-Sept. [*G. claytoni* Michx.] ....*G. tinctorium* L.
      14. Pedicels scabrous, usually arcuate, 5-10 mm long; flowers solitary; swamps and bogs, rare. July-Aug. ....*G. trifidum* L.

120. **Caprifoliaceae** Vent. — Honeysuckle Family

1. Plants trailing; leaves roundish or oval, crenate, evergreen; flowers nodding in pairs; fruit ovoid, indehiscent, 1-seeded ....4. *Linnaea*
1. Erect or climbing shrubs, or herbs.
  2. Shrubs with erect or twining stems.
    3. Leaves pinnate; fruit berry-like, 3- to 5-seeded ....1. *Sambucus*
    3. Leaves simple.
      4. Flowers in compound cymes; fruit a 1-seeded drupe ....2. *Viburnum*
      4. Inflorescence otherwise.
        5. Leaves not serrate; fruit a berry or drupe.
          6. Flowers regular or nearly so; fruit a berry-like drupe with 2 nutlets ....3. *Symphoricarpos*

6. Flowers mostly irregular; fruit a few- to many-seeded berry ....5. *Lonicera*
5. Leaves serrate; flowers yellow; fruit a capsule ....6. *Diervilla*
2. Herbs; flowers axillary; leaves connate or sessile; fruit a drupe ....7. *Triosteum*

1. **Sambucus** L. — Elder

1. Inflorescence flat-topped, 10-40 cm broad; fruit black (rarely greenish-yellow) pith white; moist ground along roads, in woods or along streams and lakes, common throughout Ill. June-July. Common Elder ....*S. canadensis* L.
1. Inflorescence ovoid, 4-5 cm broad; fruit bright red (rarely yellow); pith brown; moist rocky woods, rare; known from Cook, La Salle, McHenry, and Winnebago counties. Apr.-May. Red Elder [*S. racemosa* sensu auth., non L.] ....*S. pubens* Michx.

2. **Viburnum** L. — Viburnum

1. Leaves not lobed.
  2. Leaves serrate or serrulate, the veins curving and anastomosing before reaching the margin; petioles flat or channelled and somewhat margined; cymes sessile or nearly so.
    3. Winter-buds scurfy-punctate, usually somewhat glossy; blades thin, acute or acuminate.
      4. Blades abruptly acuminate, sharply serrate; wet ground, chiefly in the northern half of the state. May-June. Nannyberry ....*V. lentago* L.
      4. Blades acute or obtuse at the apex, serrulate with incurved teeth; petioles glabrous or nearly so; moist woods, common. Apr. June. Blackhaw [*V. bushii* Ashe] ....*V. prunifolium* L.
    3. Winter-buds dull, porous, puberulent; blades firm, obtusish; petioles more or less reddish-tomentulose; wooded ravines, s. Ill., rare. May. Southern Blackhaw ....*V. rufidulum* Raf.
  2. Leaves coarsely dentate, the veins straight, ending in the teeth; petioles not margined; cymes peduncled.
    5. Leaves short-petioled, the petioles not more than 1 cm long; blades usually with 7-10 teeth on each side, softly pubescent beneath (or glabrous except on the veins in var. *affine* (Bush) House); fruit ellipsoid, the stone flattened, sulcate on both sides; woods, thickets, river banks, locally in the northern half of the state. May-June. [*V. pubescens* sensu auth., non Pursh; *V. affine* var. *hypomalacum* Blake] ....*V. rafinesquianum* Schultes
    5. Leaves longer-petioled, the petioles 1-4 cm long; blades usually with 10-20 teeth on each side.
      6. Leaves scarcely cordate at base, usually without stipules; fruit globose-ovoid, 6-8 mm long, the stone deeply sulcate ventrally, the back rounded; bark not exfoliat-

ing; woods, chiefly in the southern half of the state.
Arrow-wood [*V. pubescens* var. *deamii* Rehd.; *V.
pubescens* var. *indianense* Rehd.; *V.* dentatum var.
deamii (Rehd.) Fern.] ....*V. recognitum* Fern.

6. Leaves distinctly cordate, roundish-ovate, mostly with
linear stipules; fruit compressed-ellipsoid, 8-10 mm
long; bark gray, exfoliating; bluffs and rocky woods,
rare and local; Adams Co., *R. Brinker* in 1944; Peoria
Co., *V. H. Chase* in 1949. Kentucky Viburnum ....
....*V. molle* Michx.

1. Leaves palmately veined, usually 3-lobed.

7. Young twigs glabrous; petioles glabrous and with a pair of
glands; marginal flowers of the cyme neuter, with enlarged
flat corollas; fruit red; moist woods in the northern half of
the state. May-June. American Cranberry-bush [*V. opulus*
var. *americanum* (Mill.) Ait.] ....*V. trilobum* Marsh.

7. Young twigs pubescent; petioles pubescent, glandless; cyme
with all the flowers alike and perfect; fruit black; dry woods,
chiefly in the northern part of the state. May-June. Maple-
leaved Viburnum ....*V. acerifolium* L.

3. **Symphoricarpos** Duham. — Snowberry

1. Corolla 5-9 mm long; fruit white or greenish-white.

2. Stamens and style included; twigs and leaves glabrous; petioles
2-4 mm long; corolla 5-7 mm long; style 2 mm long, glabrous; fruits white, the larger ones 12-15 mm in diameter;
native of western N. Am. and commonly planted for ornament, but not established in Ill. Garden Snowberry [*S.
racemosus* sensu auth., non Michx.; *S. racemosus* var.
laevigatus Fern.] ....*S. rivularis* Suksd.

2. Stamens and style shortly exserted; twigs puberulent; leaves
pubescent; petioles 4-10 mm long; corolla 6-9 mm long;
style 4-8 mm long, pilose or glabrous; fruits pale greenish-
white, 6-8 mm in diameter; dry soil, rare; extending southward to Kankakee and Henry counties. June-July. Wolf-
berry ....*S. occidentalis* Hook.

1. Corolla 3-4 mm long; fruit red (rarely whitish), ellipsoid,
glaucous, 5-7 mm long; stamens and style included; style 2
mm long; petioles 2-4 mm long; river banks and woodland
pastures, common in the s. two-thirds of the state. July. Coral-
berry. Buckbrush [*S. vulgaris* Michx.] ....*S. orbiculatus* Moench

4. **Linnaea** L. — Twinflower

L. americana Forbes. Winnetka, Cook Co., *Vasey;* probably now
extinct in Ill. [*L. borealis* var. *americana* (Forbes) Rehd.].

5. Lonicera L. — Honeysuckle

1. Erect shrubs; leaves opposite, not connate-perfoliate; berries red.
  2. Young twigs and leaves pubescent or puberulent; peduncles not or scarcely longer than the flowers.
    3. Corolla more or less pubescent outside.
      4. Filaments pubescent below the middle; corolla strongly bilabiate, yellowish white, the upper lip 4-lobed, the lower one not lobed; bractlets much shorter than the ovaries; occasionally escaped from cult.; introd. from Eurasia. May. European Fly Honeysuckle. .... *L. xylosteum* L.
      4. Filaments glabrous; corolla scarcely bilabiate, the lobes nearly equal; bractlets pilose, longer than the ovaries; roadsides, etc., or persisting near dwellings; introd. from Asia. May-June. Morrow Honeysuckle. ....*L. morrowi* A.Gray
    3. Corolla and filaments glabrous; bractlets much longer than the ovaries; a garden hybrid, sometimes escaped and becoming established on rocky bluffs, in thickets, along railroads, or in woodland pastures in several localities in the northern half of Ill. May-July. Originated in Eur. [*L. morrowi* × *tatarica* Zabel] Belle Honeysuckle .... *L. bella* Zabel
  2. Twigs, leaves, and flowers glabrous; peduncles much longer than the white to pink flowers; often planted and sometimes escaped to roadsides and waste places; native of Asia. May-June. Tatarian Honeysuckle. .... *L. tatarica* L.
1. Stems twining or trailing.
  5. Flowers in terminal clusters; upper leaves connate-perfoliate.
    6. Corolla 2-lipped, the upper lip 4-lobed, the lower entire.
      7. Corolla-tube 6-10 mm long; filaments hirsute at base; leaves green above, glaucous beneath; rocky soil, local; known from Cook, Kane, and Lake counties. May-June. Glaucous Honeysuckle [*L. glauca* Hill; *L. parviflora* Lam.] .... *L. dioica* L.
      7. Corolla tube 10-14 mm long; filaments nearly glabrous; leaves glaucous on both sides; woods in the n. half of Ill., extending southw. to Cumberland Co. May-June. Sullivant's Honeysuckle [*L. sullivantii* A.Gray] ....*L. prolifera* (Kirchn.) Rehd.
    6. Corolla red, tubular, the short limb nearly equally 5-lobed; cultivated and sometimes escaped. May-Oct. Trumpet Honeysuckle ....*L. sempervirens* L.
  5. Flowers in pairs from the upper axils, white or pink, turning yellow, 2.5-4 cm long, fragrant; leaves ovate or oval, not connate-perfoliate; young branches villous; an aggressive woodland weed in the s. half of Ill.; native of Asia. May-July. Japanese Honeysuckle ....*L. japonica* Thunb.

6. Diervilla Mill. — Bush Honeysuckle

D. lonicera Mill. Rocky woods, n. Ill., extending southward to La Salle and Kankakee counties; an isolated station along Sangamon R. in Piatt Co. May-June. [*D. trifida* Moench].

7. Triosteum L. — Horse-gentian

1. Principal leaves usually with broadly dilated connate-perfoliate bases; corolla purplish or dull red, 12-15 mm long; sepals finely and evenly pubescent; stem softly short-pubescent, the hairs 0.5 mm long; woods and thickets. May-June. ....*T. perfoliatum* L.
1. Principal leaves narrowed to the sessile bases.
   2. Leaves ovate or oval; sepals finely and evenly pubescent; fruit 8-15 mm in diameter; corolla purplish-red.
      3. Stem glandular-puberulent and hirsute; sandy soil in open woods; n. and centr. Ill., extending southw. to Macoupin and Fayette counties. May-June ....*T. aurantiacum* Bickn.
      3. Stem rather sparsely hirsute with somewhat reflexed non-glandular hairs 1-2 mm long; rich woods, local. May-June ....*T. illinoense* (Wieg.) Rydb.
   2. Leaves lanceolate or oblanceolate; stem hirsute, not glandular; sepals ciliate, otherwise glabrous; corolla greenish-yellow; fruit 6-7 mm in diameter; alluvial soil, s. Ill., not common. May ....*T. angustifolium* L.

121. Campanulaceae Juss. — Bellflower Family

1. Leaves petioled or tapering at the base; flowers in a terminal inflorescence ....1. *Campanula*
1. Leaves sessile, clasping, cordate; flowers axillary, solitary, sessile ....2. *Specularia*

1. Campanula L. — Bellflower

1. Flowers in spikes or racemes.
   2. Corolla rotate; style declined; capsule clavate, with apical pores; moist woods, common throughout Ill. June-Sept. [*Campanulastrum americanum* (L.) Small; *Campanula illinoensis* Fresen.] ....*C. americana* L.
   2. Corolla campanulate; style straight; capsule globose, opening by basal pores; roadsides and waste places; escaped from cult.; introd. from Eur. June-Sept. ....*C. rapunculoides* L.
1. Flower in a loose panicle, or solitary; corolla campanulate.
   3. Corolla 5-12 mm long; leaves all linear or narrowly lanceolate; plants of wet ground.
      4. Leaves linear; corolla blue, 8-12 mm long; marshy ground, wet meadows, and lake shores in n. Ill., south. to Mason Co. July-Aug. ....*C. uliginosa* Rydb.
      4. Leaves lanceolate; corolla white, 5-8 mm long; wet meadows, local; chiefly in the northern half of the state, extending southw. to Cass Co. June-July ....*C. aparinoides* Pursh

3. Corolla 12-20 mm long; basal leaves ovate or cordate; plants of
sandy or rocky places in the n. counties; also Fountain Bluff,
Jackson Co. June-Aug. [*C. rotundifolia* sensu auth., non L.]
....*C. intercedens* Witasek

2. Specularia Fabr. — Venus' Looking-glass
(*Triodanis* Raf.)

1. Leaves cordate-clasping; capsules 4-6 mm long, ellipsoid, the
pores near the middle; sepals always 5; dry sandy soil, common throughout Ill. May-June ....*S. perfoliata* (L.) A.DC.
1. Leaves not clasping; capsules 6-10 mm long, cylindrical-fusiform,
the pores toward the apex; sepals of the lower flowers 3 or 4;
fields, roadsides, and waste places in s. Ill. May-June ....
....*S. biflora* (R. & P.) F. & M.

122. Lobeliaceae Dum. — Lobelia Family
1. Lobelia L. — Lobelia

1. Flowers red (rarely pink or white), 3-4 cm long; stem simple,
leafy, 50-120 cm tall; wet ground throughout Ill. July-Oct.
Cardinal-flower. A supposed hybrid with the next species has
been reported as *L. cardinalis* x *siphilitica* ....*L. cardinalis* L.
1. Flowers blue or whitish.
  2. Flowers 1-2.5 cm long, spicate-racemose; stem simple, leafy,
  30-100 cm tall.
    3. Stem and leaves sparsely hirsute to glabrous; flowers 2-2.5
    cm long; calyx-sinuses appendaged with large deflexed
    auricles; wet ground throughout Ill. Aug.-Oct. Blue
    Cardinal Flower ....*L. siphilitica* L.
    3. Stem finely pubescent; leaves puberulent; flowers 1.5-2 cm
    long; calyx-auricles small; dry or rocky woods, or in sandy
    ground in the s. counties. Aug.-Oct. Downy Lobelia [*L.
    puberula* var. *simulans* Fern.] ....*L. puberula* Michx.
  2. Flowers 6-10 mm long.
    4. Stem simple; flowers in an elongated spike-like raceme; leaves
    oblanceolate to elliptical, denticulate or repand.
      5. Calyx-lobes with 10 reflexed subulate appendages as long
      as the calyx-tube; dry soil, or in open woods, locally
      throughout Ill. June-Aug. ....*L. leptostachys* A. DC.
      5. Calyx-lobes not appendaged; open woods, or in dry sandy
      soil, common. June-Aug. Spiked Lobelia [*L. spicata*
      var. *hirtella* A. Gray] ....*L. spicata* Lam.
    4. Stem usually paniculately branched; flowers loosely racemose;
    sinuses of the calyx not appendaged.
      6. Leaves chiefly linear, entire or denticulate; plants glabrous;
      pods not inflated; wet meadows, often in calcareous
      soil, local; extending southward to Peoria and Wood-
      ford counties. July-Sept. Kalm's Lobelia ....*L. kalmii* L.

6. Leaves oblanceolate to elliptical, crenate to entire; stem pubescent; pods inflated, wholly inferior; fields or open woods, locally throughout Ill. June-Oct. Indian-tobacco .... *L. inflata* L.

123. **Valerianaceae** Batsch — Valerian Family

1. Perennial, strong-smelling, mostly tall herbs; some of the leaves pinnately divided; calyx-lobes becoming pappus-like; fruit 1-loculed ....1. *Valeriana*
1. Annual, dichotomously branched low herbs; leaves entire or dentate; sepals minute or lacking; fruit 3-loculed ....2. *Valerianella*

1. **Valeriana** L. — Valerian

1. Corolla 1-2 cm long; basal leaves cordate; stem-leaves thin, with 3-7 ovate, toothed leaflets; root fibrous; woods and alluvial banks, chiefly in the southern part of the state, extending northward to Vermilion Co. May-June ....*V. pauciflora* Michx.
1. Corolla 4-5 mm long; basal leaves spatulate; stem-leaves pinnately parted into 3-7 lanceolate or linear divisions; root fusiform; wet ground in the northern counties. May-June. [*V. edulis* sensu auth., non Nutt.] ....*V. ciliata* T. & G.

2. **Valerianella** Mill.

1. Corolla blue, 1.5-2 mm long; bracts ciliate, obtuse; fruits 2-4 mm long, laterally compressed, obliquely rhomboidal, wider than long, the dorsal side of the fertile cell with a thick corky mass; waste places and cultivated ground, occasional; introd. from Eur. Corn-salad [*V. locusta* (L.) Betcke] ....
....*V. olitoria* (L.) Poll.
1. Corolla white or pinkish; bracts acute, usually not ciliate; fruit longer than wide; native species.
    2. Fertile carpel of the fruit narrower than the combined width of the divergent sterile carpels; corolla 3-4 mm long.
        3. Fruit 3-3.5 mm long, 3 mm wide; sterile carpels divergent, the fruit becoming saucer-shaped; Ottawa, La Salle Co., *Skeels* ....*V. patellaria* (Sulliv.) Wood
        3. Fruit 2 mm long, 1.5-2 mm wide; sterile carpels inflated, curved together at the ends, forming a deep cavity; moist ground, not common; Kankakee and La Salle counties. May-June ....*V. umbilicata* (Sulliv.) Wood
    2. Fertile carpel of the fruit equalling or exceeding the width of the sterile carpels.
        4. Corolla 3-4 mm long, the tube as long as the limb; blades of the rosette-leaves oval, abruptly petioled; moist ground in the northern part of the state, not common; Kankakee Co., *Hill* in 1873; La Salle Co., *Greenman, Lansing, & Dixon 134;* Joliet, Will Co., *Hill* in 1907. May-June ....*V. intermedia* Dyal

4. Corolla 1.5-2 mm long, the tube shorter than the limb; rosette-leaves spatulate; moist ground, chiefly in the southern half of Ill. May-June ....*V. radiata* (L.) Dufr.

124. Dipsacaceae Lindl. — Teasel Family

1. **Dipsacus** L. — Teasel

1. Leaves entire; roadsides, fields, pastures, and waste places; nat. from Eur. July-Sept. ....*D. sylvestris* Huds.
1. Leaves pinnately lobed or divided; introd. from Eur.; used by florists in wreaths; reported from Cook and Jackson counties; Peoria, *V. H. Chase* ....*D. laciniatus* L.

125. **Compositae** P.F.Gmel. — Composite Family

(*Carduaceae* Neck.; *Cichoriaceae* Reichenb.; *Ambrosiaceae* Link)

1. Heads composed of ray- and disk-flowers, or of disk-flowers only; juice not milky ....Series I. TUBULIFLORAE, p. 233
1. Heads composed wholly of perfect flowers with ligulate corollas; herbs usually with milky juice; leaves alternate or sometimes all basal ....
....Series II. LIGULIFLORAE, p. 238

Series I. TUBULIFLORAE DC.

1. Pappus of capillary bristles.
   2. Heads radiate, *i.e.,* the outer flowers of the head with strap-shaped corollas. (Rays minute in *Dyssodia*.)
      3. Rays yellow (whitish in one species of *Solidago*).
         4. Bracts in one series, about equal in length (a few short basal ones sometimes present); pappus single.
            5. Leaves opposite, dissected into linear lobes; bracts bearing 3-7 conspicuous glands; pappus of 8-15 scales, each dissected into 5-10 bristles ....42. *Dyssodia*
            5. Leaves alternate and basal; bracts glandless; pappus of numerous capillary bristles ....51. *Senecio*
         4. Bracts in several series, unequal, overlapping.
            6. Heads numerous, small; pappus single ....16. *Solidago*
            6. Heads fewer, large, solitary, or corymbose.
               7. Leaves serrate; pappus single.
                  8. Leaves white-woolly beneath ....24. *Inula*
                  8. Leaves not white-woolly beneath ....15. *Haplopappus*
               7. Leaves entire or nearly so; pappus double.
                  9. Achenes of ray-flowers with capillary pappus ....13. *Chrysopsis*
                  9. Achenes of ray-flowers without pappus ....14. *Heterotheca*
      3. Rays not yellow.
         10. Bracts in 3-5 series; rays broad, few ....19. *Aster*
         10. Bracts usually in 1 or 2 series; rays usually narrow and numerous
         ....20. *Erigeron*
   2. Heads rayless (or apparently so), the flowers usually all tubular.
      11. Flowers white or whitish, or cream.
         12. Leaves prickly.
            13. Heads 1-flowered, in capitate clusters ....53. *Echinops*
            13. Heads many-flowered, distinct ....54. *Cirsium*
         12. Leaves not prickly.

14. Bracts scarious.
    15. Leaves mostly basal, spatulate or obovate, the stem-leaves small; plants perennial, stoloniferous, dioecious or polygamous ....22. *Antennaria*
    15. Leaves all or mostly cauline; plants annual or biennial, not stoloniferous or dioecious; all the flowers fertile, the central ones perfect, surrounded by pistillate ones .... 23. *Gnaphalium*
14. Bracts not scarious.
    16. Bracts with tips hooked; coarse biennial weeds with large ovate leaves; heads globose ....52. *Arctium*
    16. Bracts not hooked.
        17. Principal bracts in only one series (often with a few small bractlets at the base of the head).
            18. Pappus scabrous; flowers all perfect; plants perennial ....49. *Cacalia*
            18. Pappus smooth; marginal flowers pistillate, the disk-flowers perfect; plants annual, with strong odor ....50. *Erechtites*
        17. Bracts in more than one series.
            19. Leaves all or mostly opposite or whorled (or some of the upper ones alternate) ....7. *Eupatorium*
            19. Leaves alternate.
                20. Bracts striate, imbricated in 3 or more equal series; pappus plumose; achenes striate, nearly terete; leaves minutely resinous-dotted ....9. *Kuhnia*
                20. Bracts not striate, in 1-3 series; achenes flattened; pappus merely scabrous; leaves not resinous-dotted.
                    21. Heads racemose; outer bracts foliaceous; pappus copious, of soft bristles; achenes terete ....species of 19. *Aster*
                    21. Heads paniculate; bracts all narrow, not foliaceous; pappus-bristles short, brittle; achenes compressed ....species of 20. *Erigeron*
11. Flowers pink, purple, blue, or yellow (rarely white).
    22. Stems twining; leaves opposite, triangular-hastate; flowers pink ....8. *Mikania*
22. Stems not twining.
    23. Leaves opposite or whorled, not prickly; flowers purple, blue, or white ....7. *Eupatorium*
    23. Leaves alternate or basal.
        24. Leaves prickly.
            25. Heads 1-flowered, in capitate clusters ....53. *Echinops*
            25. Heads many-flowered, distinct.
                26. Pappus-bristles plumose ....54. *Cirsium*
                26. Pappus-bristles not plumose.
                    27. Receptacle bearing numerous bristles ....55. *Carduus*
                    27. Receptacle without bristles ....56. *Onopordum*
        24. Leaves not prickly.

28. Bracts of the involucre pectinate, or tipped with a rigid spine ....57. *Centaurea*
28. Bracts neither pectinate nor with a rigid spine.
  29. Bracts with hooked tips; coarse biennial weeds with large ovate chiefly basal leaves; heads globose; flowers purple (rarely white); receptacle bristly ....52. *Arctium*
  29. Bracts not hooked; receptacle not bristly.
    30. Flowers yellow; bracts in 1 series ....51. *Senecio*
    30. Flowers not yellow; bracts imbricated in 2-several series.
      31. Pappus-bristles plumose or barbellate; heads in long racemes or spikes; leaves narrow, entire, rigid ....10. *Liatris*
      31. Pappus-bristles not plumose.
        32. Pappus (in our species) double, the outer bristles short; heads many-flowered, in corymbose cymes; bracts imbricated in several series ....5. *Vernonia*
        32. Pappus-bristles approximately the same length, not in two series.
          33. Heads 2- to 5-flowered, aggregated into dense clusters subtended by foliaceous bracts; flowers all perfect and alike; bracts eight ....6. *Elephantopus*
          33. Heads many-flowered, corymbose; flowers of 2 kinds in the same head; bracts imbricated; plants camphor-scented ....21. *Pluchea*
1. Pappus not of capillary bristles, either of rigid awns, small chaffy scales, or reduced to a mere crown, or entirely lacking.
  34. Heads radiate.
    35. Rays yellow.
      36. Pappus of 2-several awns or bristles, these sometimes deciduous.
        37. Bracts of the involucre with recurved or hooked tips, often gummy; leaves alternate, sessile, dentate ....11. *Grindelia*
        37. Bracts not hooked or gummy.
          38. Pappus of 2 smooth awns ....35. *Verbesina*
          38. Pappus of 2-several barbed awns.
            39. Leaves alternate, linear ....12. *Gutierrezia*
            39. Leaves opposite or whorled, not linear ....38. *Bidens*
      36. Pappus none, or of few short teeth or scales.
        40. Leaves all or mostly opposite or whorled.
          41. Achenes thick, not at all, or scarcely flattened.
            42. Leaves thin, deeply angulate-lobed or lyrate-pinnatifid ....25. *Polymnia*
            42. Leaves thick, entire or serrate; rays conspicuous.
              43. Bracts obtuse; ray-flowers pistillate, fertile, papery and persistent on the achene ....28. *Heliopsis*
              43. Bracts acute or acuminate; ray-flowers neuter, deciduous ....34. *Helianthus*

41. Achenes flattened.
    44. Rays numerous; bracts thick, in several rows; coarse
        herbs with resinous sap; disk-flowers perfect but
        sterile ....26. *Silphium*
    44. Rays mostly 8; bracts in two series; disk-flowers
        fertile ....37. *Coreopsis*
40. Leaves alternate or basal.
    45. Leaves or some of them deeply lobed or divided; stem
        not winged.
        46. Receptacle conical to columnar.
            47. Achenes flattened, sharp-margined or winged ......
                ....32. *Ratibida*
            47. Achenes 4-sided, not at all margined or winged
                ....30. *Rudbeckia*
        46. Receptacle flat or convex; achenes flattened, 2-
            winged, notched at the apex ....26. *Silphium*
    45. Leaves serrate or entire.
        48. Stems scapose; leaves all basal.
            49. Leaves large, ovate, toothed, long-petioled; scapes
                2-3 m tall; heads several ....26. *Silphium*
            49. Leaves small, spatulate, entire; scapes 5-15 cm
                tall; heads solitary ....40. *Actinea*
        48. Stems leafy.
            50. Stems more or less winged by the decurrent bases
                of the leaves (except *Helenium tenuifolium*).
                51. Rays 3-lobed, 10-18; pappus of 5-8 acuminate
                    or aristate scales ....41. *Helenium*
                51. Rays entire or emarginate; pappus of 2 subu-
                    late awns ....35. *Verbesina*
            50. Stems not winged.
                52. Receptacle conical; pappus a mere crown, or
                    none; disk-flowers purple ....30. *Rudbeckia*
                52. Receptacle flat or convex; pappus of 2 decidu-
                    ous, translucent scales or awns; disk-flowers
                    yellow or brownish ....34. *Helianthus*
35. Rays not yellow.
    53. Leaves opposite; ray-flowers small, white.
        54. Leaves angulate-lobed, thin, dilated at the base; plants
            glandular-pubescent; corolla-tube of the ray-flowers
            pubescent ....25. *Polymnia*
    54. Leaves serrate.
        55. Leaves ovate, petioled ....33. *Galinsoga*
        55. Leaves lanceolate, sessile ....29. *Eclipta*
    53. Leaves alternate or basal.
        56. Leaves all basal, obovate; heads solitary; bracts about equal,
            obtuse, usually purplish; pappus a mere crown ....17. *Bellis*
        56. Leaves cauline and basal.
            57. Leaves dissected or incised; bracts scarious.
                58. Rays 4-6, short; heads numerous ....43. *Achillea*
                58. Rays 10-30; heads fewer.
                    59. Leaves cut into filiform divisions; receptacle
                    chaffy ....44. *Anthemis*

59. Leaves incised or coarsely and irregularly toothed
....46. *Chrysanthemum*
57. Leaves entire to serrate or dentate.
60. Rays purple, reflexed; receptacle conical or columnar.
60. Rays white or pink, not reflexed.
61. Rays many, lilac or white; leaves entire, lanceolate
....18. Boltonia
61. Rays 3-5, white, short.
62. Heads campanulate; pappus of 2 slender
awns; leaves entire to serrate ....
....35. *Verbesina*
62. Heads hemispheric; pappus of 2 or 3 inconspicuous scales; leaves dentate ....
....27. *Parthenium*
34. Heads rayless.
63. Flowers green or greenish.
64. Staminate and pistillate flowers in the same head, or flowers all
perfect.
65. Heads few or solitary; receptacle conical; bracts short, oval,
obtuse, scarious; leaves finely dissected, with pineapple
odor when crushed ....45. *Matricaria*
65. Heads numerous, in spikes, racemes, or panicles.
66. Heads in long terminal bracted spikes; receptacle bristly
or chaffy; leaves opposite, or the upper alternate,
entire or serrate ....1. *Iva*
66. Heads in panicles or racemes; receptacle smooth; leaves
alternate, mostly lobed or incised; plants bitter-aromatic
....48. *Artemisia*
64. Staminate and pistillate flowers in separate dissimilar heads.
67. Involucre of pistillate heads with hooked prickles ....
....4. *Xanthium*
67. Involucre of pistillate heads merely tuberculate, or with
straight spines.
68. Pistillate involucre with a single series of spines or
tubercles ....2. *Ambrosia*
68. Pistillate involucre with several series of spines or
tubercles ....3. *Franseria*
63. Flowers yellow (or yellowish) or white.
69. Flowers white.
70. Leaves alternate, pinnatifid ....39. *Hymenopappus*
70. Leaves opposite, entire to lobed ....36. *Melanthera*
69. Flowers yellow or yellowish; bracts green.
71. Leaves alternate or basal.
72. Leaves pinnately dissected ....47. *Tanacetum*
72. Leaves shallowly lobed, prickly-margined ....58. *Cnicus*
71. Leaves opposite.
73. Pappus none; achenes thick, not flattened; disk-flowers
perfect but sterile; plants glandular-pubescent, odorous
....25. *Polymnia*
73. Pappus of 2-4 awns or teeth; achenes flattened; disk-
flowers fertile; plants not glandular ....38. *Bidens*

Series II. LIGULIFLORAE DC.

1. Pappus none; annual herbs with alternate leaves and yellow flowers; bracts of the involucre about 8.
  2. Heads numerous; achenes 20-30-nerved; tall paniculately branched herbs with ovate, repand-dentate or lobed leaves ....59. *Lapsana*
  2. Heads few; achenes 8-10-ribbed; low glaucescent herbs with clasping entire or lobed leaves ....60. *Serinia*
1. Pappus present.
  3. Pappas composed of scales, or of scales and bristles, or of short bristles only.
    4. Flowers yellow; pappus double, the outer of short thin scales, the inner of bristles ....61. *Krigia*
    4. Flowers blue (sometimes white or pink); pappus a short crown of numerous small chaffy scales ....62. *Cichorium*
  3. Pappus consisting wholly of capillary bristles.
    5. Pappus plumose.
      6. Leaves grass-like ....65. *Tragopogon*
      6. Leaves not grass-like.
        7. Plants scapose ....63. *Hypochaeris*
        7. Plants leafy-stemmed ....64. *Picris*
    5. Pappus not plumose.
      8. Heads usually several on each stem; leaves not all basal.
        9. Achenes more or less flattened; leaves usually lobed and often somewhat soft-prickly.
          10. Achenes filiform-beaked, or if merely narrowed at the apex, the flowers not yellow ....66. *Lactuca*
          10. Achenes truncate at the apex, not beaked; flowers yellow, 50 or more in each head ....67. *Sonchus*
        9. Achenes cylindric or prismatic.
          11. Flowers whitish or purplish; heads pendent ....68. *Prenanthes*
          11. Flowers yellow; heads erect.
            12. Achenes beakless.
              13. Leaves entire or merely toothed ....69. *Hieracium*
              13. Leaves lobed ....70. *Crepis*
            12. Achenes filiform-beaked ....71. *Pyrrhopappus*
      8. Heads solitary; leaves all basal; flowers yellow.
        14. Achenes not muricate, 10-nerved; leaves (in our species)entire ....72. *Agoseris*
        14. Achenes not muricate near the apex, 4- to 5-nerved; leaves lobed ....73. *Taraxacum*

Tribe 1. *Ambrosieae*

1. **Iva** L. — Marsh-elder

1. Heads in bracted spikes; stem hispid; fields and roadsides, chiefly in the s. half of Ill. Aug.-Oct. ....*I. ciliata* Willd.
1. Heads spicate-paniculate; stem glabrous, or pilosulous above; roadsides, railroad yards, waste places, chiefly in the n. half of Ill. July-Sept. ....*I. xanthifolia* Nutt.

2. **Ambrosia** L. — Ragweed

1. Leaves pinnatifid or bipinnatifid.
  2. Leaves petioled, bipinnatifid; fruit with 5-7 sharp tubercles;

plants annual; fields and waste places, common. Aug.-Oct. Common Ragweed [*A. elatior* L.] *A. artemisiifolia* × *trifida* Rouleau is occasionally found ....*A. artemisiifolia* L.

2. Leaves sessile, pinnatifid; fruit unarmed or with blunt tubercles; plants perennial with a slender rhizome; roadsides and waste places. July-Oct. Western Ragweed [*A. psilostachya* sensu A.Gray, non DC.] ....*A. coronopifolia* T. & G.

1. Leaves 3-to 5-lobed or undivided; plants annual.

3. Leaves opposite, 3- to 5-lobed, or entire; stem stout, 1-4 m tall; staminate heads peduncled; fruit with 5-7 sharp tubercles; fields and waste places, common. July-Oct. Giant Ragweed ....*A. trifida* L.

3. Leaves chiefly alternate, lanceolate, hastately toothed at base; stem 30-90 cm tall, rough-hirsute; staminate heads sessile, the upper lobe of the involucre elongate, hispid; fruit with 4 teeth at the top; fields and waste places; chiefly in the southern half of Ill., extending northward to Menard Co. ....*A. bidentata* Michx.

3. Franseria Cav.

F. discolor Nutt. Adv. from the West; La Salle and McHenry counties.

4. Xanthium L. — Cocklebur

1. Leaves lanceolate, acute at each end, canescent beneath, each with a 3-parted spine at the base; waste ground, rare; adv. from trop. Am.; Alexander, Cook, and Pulaski counties. Aug.-Oct. Spiny Cocklebur ....*X. spinosum* L.

1. Leaves cordate or ovate, the axils without spines.

2. Bur ovoid to subglobose, less than twice as long as thick, merely glandular; bottomlands, rare; Illinois R., Tazewell Co., (type locality), *V. H. Chase;* Wayne Co., *M. Walker* in 1949 ....*X. chasei* Fern.

2. Bur ellipsoid, more than twice as long as thick.

3. Prickles numerous; body of the fruit and its prickles glandular-hispidulous; beaks hooked; waste places, cultivated ground, and river banks. Aug.-Oct. [*X. italicum* sensu auth., non Mor.; *X. saccharatum* sensu Widder, ex p.] ....*X. commune* Britt.

3. Prickles relatively few; body of fruit glabrous or merely glandular; beaks nearly straight; waste places, fields, and along rivers. Aug.-Oct. [*X. canadense* sensu auth., non Mill.; *X. pungens* Wallr.; *X. glabratum* Britt.; *X. pennsylvanicum* sensu auth., non Wallr.] ....*X. chinense* Mill.

Tribe 2. *Vernonieae*

5. Vernonia Schreb. — Ironweed

1. Leaves glabrous beneath or merely puberulent.

2. Leaves linear-lanceolate, puncticulate beneath; inflorescence dense, fastigiate; moist ground, locally throughout Ill. July-Aug. ....*V. fasciculata* Michx.
2. Leaves elliptic-lanceolate, puberulent beneath; inflorescence loose, the branches spreading; woods, fields, and roadsides throughout Ill. July-Oct. [*V. altissima* var. *brevipappa* Gleason; *V. altissima* var. *taeniotricha* Blake] ....
....*V. altissima* Nutt.
1. Leaves usually copiously tomentulose-pubescent beneath, not puncticulate.
   3. Bracts appressed, acute or obtuse; roadsides, pastures, and open woods, common. July-Sept. [*V. illinoensis* Gleason; *V. noveboracensis* sensu auth., non (L.) Michx.] ....
   ....*V. missurica* Raf.
   3. Bracts with acuminate, squarrose tips; open woods, locally in the southern half of the state. July-Sept..........*V. baldwini* Torr.

6. Elephantopus L. — Elephant's-foot

E. carolinianus Willd. Sandy soil in woods, and along roads, s. Ill., extending northward to Lawrence, Marion, and St. Clair counties. Aug.-Sept.

Tribe 3. *Eupatorieae*
7. Eupatorium L.

1. Leaves whorled.
   2. Each head with mostly 9-15 flowers; inflorescence flat-topped; moist ground; more frequent in the northern half of the state. July-Sept. [*E. purpureum* sensu auth., non L.].............
   ....*E. maculatum* L.
   2. Each head with 5-7 flowers; inflorescence convex.
      3. Stems purple only at the nodes, solid; woods throughout Ill. July-Aug. Joe-pye Weed [*E. trifoliatum* L.; *E. falcatum* Michx. ....*E. purpureum* L.
      3. Stems purple throughout, hollow; low wet ground, rare; Alexander Co., *J. R. Swayne 1152* in 1950 ....
      ....*E. fistulosum* Barratt
1. Leaves opposite, or the upper alternate.
   4. Flowers white (rarely purplish).
      5. Leaves connate-perfoliate, lanceolate, attenuate, crenate-serrate, rugose-reticulate, pubescent beneath; wet ground, common. Aug.-Oct. Boneset ....*E. perfoliatum* L.
      5. Leaves not connate-perfoliate.
         6. Stem pubescent; leaves lanceolate, 3-nerved, grayish-puberulent.
            7. Leaves conspicuously petioled, sharply serrate; heads 4-6 mm high, 7- to 15-flowered; moist ground, common. Aug.-Oct. Late Boneset........*E. serotinum* Michx.

7. Leaves sessile or nearly so, sparingly toothed above the middle, or entire; heads 6-8 mm high, about 5-flowered; woods near streams, and along roads. Aug.-Oct. Tall Thoroughwort ....*E. altissimum* L.
6. Stem glabrous or puberulent; leaves all opposite.
8. Leaves sessile, lanceolate, pinnately veined, serrate; heads about 5-flowered; woods, local. Aug.-Oct. Upland Boneset ....*E. sessilifolium* L.
8. Leaves petioled, ovate, triple-nerved, coarsely dentate (puberulent beneath in var. *tomentellum* (B. L. Robins.) Blake); heads 10- 30-flowered; woods, common. July-Sept. White Snakeroot [*E. ageratoides* L.f.; *E. urticaefolium* Reich.] ....*E. rugosum* Houtt.
4. Flowers purplish to blue; leaves ovate, petiolate, crenate-dentate, more or less puberulent.
9. Flowers pink to pale purple; receptacle flat; bracts acute, unequal, the outer less than half as long as the inner; woods, not common; Alexander and Pulaski counties, *E. J. Palmer* in 1919. Aug-Oct. Pink Eupatorium .... *E. incarnatum* Walt.
9. Flowers blue or violet; receptacle conical; bracts acuminate, nearly equal; moist ground in the southern half of the state, extending northward to Hancock and Vermilion counties. July-Oct. Mistflower [*E. coelestinum* f. *illinoense* Benke] .... *E. coelestinum* L.

8. Mikania Willd.

M. scandens (L.) Willd. Climbing Hempweed. In alluvial soil, not common; Alexander, Johnson, Lawrence, Pulaski, and Wabash counties. Aug.-Oct.

9. Kuhnia L. — False Boneset

K. eupatorioides L. Prairie soil, often along roads, common. Aug.-Oct. [*K. suaveolens* Fresen.].

10. Liatris Schreb. — Blazing Star

1. Pappus evidently plumose; heads few, racemose, cylindrical, 15- to 60-flowered, 1.5-2 cm high.
2. Heads with 10-60 flowers; corolla-lobes hairy within.
3. Stems and leaves glabrous or nearly so; bracts glabrous on the back, thin, appressed; roadsides, prairie soil, or on hillsides, nearly throughout Ill., except the most southerly counties. Aug.-Sept. ....*L. cylindracea* Michx.
3. Stems and leaves pubescent; bracts pubescent, lanceolate, acuminate, firm, rigid, more or less squarrose; dry soil, s. Ill. [*L. hirsuta* Rydb.] ....*L. squarrosa* (L.) Michx.
2. Heads with 4-6 flowers; corolla glabrous; adv. from the West; Du Page Co. .... *L. punctata* Hook.

1. Pappus merely barbellate or scabrous; heads numerous in elongate spikes.
  4. Heads ellipsoid, 3- to 15-flowered.
    5. Rachis of spike crisp-pubescent; bracts ciliate, acute, the tips spreading or recurved; prairie soil, common. July-Aug. [*L. bebbiana* Rydb.] A supposed hybrid with *L. squarrosa* from Richland Co., has been named *L. ridgwayi* Standl. .... *L. pycnostachya* Michx.
    5. Rachis of spike glabrous; bracts obtuse, appressed; prairies and interdunal flats, locally throughout Ill. July-Sept. .... *L. spicata* (L.) Willd.
  4. Heads hemispherical or campanulate, 15- to 45-flowered; rachis of inflorescence pubescent.
    6. Bracts entirely herbaceous, green, ciliolate, puberulent; woods and rocky slopes in s. Ill. (Pine Hills: type locality). Sept.-Oct. ....*L. scabra* (Greene) K. Schum.
    6. Bracts broadly scarious-margined, erose, colored, glabrous; roadsides, prairie soil, and open woods throughout Ill. Sept.-Oct. White-flowered plants are occasionally found. [*L. spheroidea* Michx.; *L. scariosa* sensu auth., non (L.) Willd.; *L.* × *nieuwlandii* (Lunell) Gaiser; *L. aspera* var. *intermedia* (Lunell) Gaiser] .... *L. aspera* Michx.

Tribe 4. *Astereae*

11. **Grindelia** Willd. — Gumweed

G. squarrosa (Pursh) Dunal. Waste ground, fields, and roadsides, occasional; adv. from western U.S. July-Aug. [*G. serrulata* Rydb.].

12. **Gutierrezia** Lag.

G. dracunculoides (DC.) Blake. Broomweed. Dry ground, roadsides, occasional; adv. from the West; known from St. Clair and Tazewell counties. Aug.-Sept.

13. **Chrysopsis** Nutt. — Golden-aster

C. camporum Greene. Sandy soil in the w. and s. parts of the state. June-Sept. [*C. mariana* of auth., not (L.) Ell.; *C. villosa* of auth., not (Pursh) Nutt.]

14. **Heterotheca** Cass.

H. subaxillaris (Lam.) Britt. & Rusby. Waste ground, occasional; Henry and Union counties; adv. from west of the Mississippi R.

15. **Haplopappus** Cass.

H. ciliatus (Nutt.) DC. Fields and roadsides; adv. from western U.S.; Jackson, Montgomery, Greene, and Union counties. Aug.-Sept. [*Prionopsis ciliata* Nutt.]

16. **Solidago** L. — Goldenrod

(*Euthamia* Nutt.; *Oligoneuron* Small)

1. Heads distinctly pedicellate; ray-flowers usually fewer than the disk-flowers; receptacle pitted; leaves not punctate.
   2. Heads in panicles, racemes, or axillary clusters; bracts of the involucre not longitudinally striate.
      3. Heads in small axillary clusters or short racemes.
         4. Stem pubescent or puberulent; achenes glabrous or nearly so at maturity.
            5. Rays cream or nearly white; involucres 3-5 mm high; wooded slopes and ridges, rare. Aug.-Oct. White Goldenrod. .... *S. bicolor* L.
            5. Rays orange-yellow; involucres 5-8 mm high.
               6. Leaves very unequal, the lower much larger than the middle and upper; basal rosettes of large leaves usually present; wooded slopes and ridges, rare, in Alexander and Jackson counties ....*S. hispida* Muhl.
               6. Leaves nearly uniform or only slightly decreasing in size upward; basal rosettes wanting.
                  7. Margin of leaves scabrous with short incurving hairs; inner phyllaries attenuate; rocky woods or bluffs, s. Ill., rare. Sept.-Oct. .... *S. petiolaris* Ait.
                  7. Margin of leaves with long spreading hairs; inner phyllaries obtuse to acute; bluffs, thickets, rocky woods, s. Ill., rare. Sept.-Oct. ....*S. buckleyi* T. & G.
         4. Stem glabrous; achenes pubescent; leaves mostly sharply serrate.
            8. Leaves unequal, the lower much larger; basal rosettes present; cliffs, rare; known from Carroll, Jo Daviess, La Salle, and Ogle counties. Sept. ......*S. sciaphila* Steele
            8. Leaves nearly uniform or only slightly decreasing in size upward; basal rosettes wanting.
               9. Leaves sessile, lanceolate; stem more or less glaucous, terete; woods throughout Ill., except the northwestern counties. Aug.-Oct. Woodland Goldenrod ....*S. caesia* L.
               9. Leaves with winged petioles, ovate or oval, sharply serrate; stem angled, not glaucous; woods throughout Ill. Aug.-Oct. Broad-leaved Goldenrod [*S. flexicaulis* L.] ....*S. latifolia* L.
   3. Heads mostly in terminal panicles or racemes.
      10. Stem below the inflorescence glabrous or nearly so.
         11. Branches of the inflorescence more or less pubescent or hirtellous.
            12. Branches of the panicle spreading or recurved, the heads distinctly secund.

13. Stem sharply angled, at least below; leaves thick,
with only 1 principal vein, rugulose and
glabrous beneath, strongly scabrous above;
achenes glabrous; wet ground, local. Aug.-
Oct. Spreading Goldenrod ....*S. patula* Muhl.
13. Stem terete; leaves thin, smooth (except the
margins), not rugulose; achenes pubescent.
14. Leaves with only one principal vein.
15. Leaves lanceolate, entire, smooth, glabrous, 10-40 cm long; stem 0.5-2 m
tall; inflorescence dense, terminal; adv.
in Chicago, *J. A. Steyermark* in 1947;
native along the e. coast of U.S. ....
.....................................*S. sempervirens* L.
15. Leaves elliptical, sharply serrate, pubescent beneath along the veins; stem 30-
90 cm tall.
16. Stems lacking basal rosettes of leaves;
involucral bracts linear, acute;
borders of woods, or wooded
slopes or ridges, common throughout Ill. Aug.-Oct. Elm-leaved
Goldenrod ....*S. ulmifolia* Muhl.
16. Basal rosettes present; involucral
bracts obtuse; woods, Pine Hills,
Union Co., *R. H. Mohlenbrock* in
1958 ....*S. strigosa* Small
14. Leaves more or less plainly 3-veined; inflorescence a dense pyramidal panicle; rays
7-15; moist ground, common. Aug.-Oct.
[*S. serotina* Ait. not Retz.; *S. gigantea*
var. *leiophylla* Fern.] Late Goldenrod ......
....*S. gigantea* Ait.
12. Branches of the panicle erect or ascending, the
heads not or scarcely secund.
17. Leaves mostly entire; heads 7-10 mm high;
panicle pyramidal; sandy or gravelly soil, or
in dry open woods. Aug.-Oct. Showy Goldenrod [*S. rigidiuscula* (T. & G.) Porter] ....
....*S. speciosa* Nutt.
17. Leaves serrate; heads about 5 mm high; panicle
narrow, dense, wand-like; bogs, swamps, and
meadows, locally in the northern third of Ill.
Aug.-Sept. Swamp Goldenrod [*S. uniligu-
lata* (DC.) Porter; *S. neglecta* T. & G.] ....
....*S. uliginosa* Nutt.
11. Branches of the inflorescence glabrous or nearly so.
18. Heads 4-5 mm high; plants strongly stoloniferous,

the stolons forming sterile branches; leaves more or less triple-veined, two of the lateral veins becoming more prominent than the others; prairie soil throughout Ill. Aug.-Sept. Prairie Goldenrod [*S. moritura* Steele; *S. missouriensis* of auth., not Nutt.] ....*S. glaberrima* Martens

18. Heads about 3 mm high; plants with rhizomes but not strongly stoloniferous; leaves with 1 principal vein; roadsides, fence-rows, open woods, fields throughout Ill. July-Aug. Early Goldenrod [*S. arguta* sensu auth., non Ait.]..............*S. juncea* Ait.

10. Stem hirsute or puberulent; branches of the inflorescence pubescent.

19. Leaves (at least the median and lower) more or less plainly 3-ribbed, two of the lateral veins becoming prominent (often only slightly so in the upper leaves).

20. Leaves lanceolate or oblanceolate.

21. Leaves lanceolate, acuminate or acute, sharply serrate or entire; bracts linear-lanceolate, thin; rays 9-15; involucre 2.5-4 mm high; stem 1-3 m tall; moist rich soil, chiefly along roads, and in thickets and woods, very common. Aug.-Oct. Tall Goldenrod [*S. gilvocanescens* (Rydb.) Smyth; *S. canadensis* sensu auth., non L.]..........*S. altissima* L.

21. Leaves oblanceolate or elliptical, dentate-crenate, the upper smaller, entire; outer bracts oval, obtusish, firm; rays 3-7, short; stem 30-100 cm tall; bluffs and dry soil, local; absent from the northern and eastern counties. Aug.-Oct. Rough Goldenrod ....
....*S. radula* Nutt.

20. Leaves broadly oval or ovate, sharply serrate, puberulent; bluffs, cliffs, or rocky woods along the Mississippi R., extending northw. to Pike Co. Sept.-Oct. Drummond's Goldenrod ....
....*S. drummondii* T. & G.

19. Leaves with 1 principal vein (i.e., not plainly 3-ribbed, the lateral veins, if present, weak).

22. Stem more or less hirsute, or the lower part almost glabrous; leaves lanceolate or elliptic-lanceolate, sharply serrate, sessile or nearly so, more or less rugulose, scaberulous above, short-hirsute on the veins beneath; moist ground, rare; Jackson, Lawrence, and Randolph counties. Aug.-Oct. Rough-leaved Goldenrod ....
....*S. rugosa* Mill.

22. Stem grayish-puberulent; leaves oblanceolate, crenate-dentate or entire, puberulent on both
sides, the lower long-petioled; fields, roadsides,
sand dunes, and open woods, common. Aug.-
Oct. Field Goldenrod [*S. longipetiolata* Mack.
& Bush] ....*S. nemoralis* Ait.
2. Heads in dense terminal compound corymbiform cymes; bracts
often longitudinally striate. (*Oligoneuron* Small).
23. Leaves oval or elliptical, scabrous on both sides, crenate;
stem pubescent or puberulent throughout; prairie soil,
mostly along roads throughout Ill., rare in the southern
counties. Aug.-Sept. Rigid Goldenrod ....*S. rigida* L.
23. Leaves lanceolate or linear, glabrous; stem glabrous, or
puberulent above.
24. Inflorescence pubescent or puberulent; stem-leaves entire, recurved, somewhat conduplicate, sheathing at
the base; moist ground, locally nearly throughout
Illinois except the s. counties. Aug.-Sept. Riddell
Goldenrod ....*S. riddellii* Frank
24. Inflorescence, as well as the rest of the plant, glabrous;
leaves flat; moist ground, rare; Cook, Kane, Lake,
McHenry, Peoria, and Woodford counties. Aug.-
Sept. Ohio Goldenrod ....*S. ohioensis* Riddell
1. Heads sessile or subsessile, in flat-topped corymbs; leaves puncticulate; ray-flowers more numerous than the disk-flowers; receptacle fimbriolate. (*Euthamia* Nutt.).
25. Stem and peduncles hirtellous; leaves minutely rough-
pubescent on veins and margins, the median leaves 3-8 mm
wide, 5-veined, i.e., with 3 prominent and 2 faint veins; rays
12-20; moist ground, common throughout Ill. Aug.-Oct. [*S.
graminifolia* of auth., not (L.) Salisb.; *S. lanceolata* of
auth., not L.; *E. nuttallii* Greene] ......*S. hirtella* (Greene) Bush
25. Stem glabrous; peduncles glabrous, glutinous; leaves scabrellous or glabrous, the median 2-4 mm wide, 1-veined, often
with a pair of more or less distinct lateral nerves; rays 6-12;
moist ground, common throughout Ill. Aug.-Oct. [*S. tenuifolia* of auth., not Pursh; *S. remota* (Greene) Friesn.; *S.
perglabra* Friesn.] ....*S. media* (Greene) Bush

17. Bellis L.

B. perennis L. English Daisy. Occasional in lawns and waste
ground; introd. from Eur. May-June.

18. Boltonia L'Her.

1. Stem-leaves conspicuously decurrent, 1-2 cm broad; achenes
2.5-3 mm long; phyllaries spatulate; alluvial bottoms along the
Illinois R. in Fulton, La Salle, Mason, Peoria, Tazewell, and
Woodford counties. .... *B. decurrens* (T. & G.) Wood

1. Leaves not decurrent; achenes 1.5-2 mm long; phyllaries linear-subulate.
    2. Leaves lanceolate to oblanceolate, 0.5-2 cm broad, the upper smaller; disk 5-8 mm broad; alluvial soil, river banks, or wet ground in woods, locally throughout Ill. Aug-Oct. [*B. asteroides* sensu auth., non (L.) L'Her.] ....
    .... *B. recognita* (Fern. & Grisc.) G. N. Jones
    2. Leaves linear, 1-5 mm wide, those of the branchlets subulate; disk 3-5 mm broad; dry soil in the southern part of the state, extending northward to St. Clair, Fayette, and Crawford counties. Aug.-Sept. [*B. diffusa* sensu auth., non Ell.]. ....
    .... *B. interior* (Fern. & Grisc.) G. N. Jones

19. **Aster** L. — Aster

1. Heads radiate; plants perennial.
    2. Lower leaves cordate or subcordate, long-petioled.
        3. Leaves nearly all sharply serrate.
            4. Heads corymbose; involucral bracts obtuse, the outer 1-2 mm wide, ciliolate and more or less puberulent; achenes linear.
                5. Peduncles (and involucres) more or less glandular; rays purple; dry open woods in Lake and Cook counties, not common. Aug.-Sept. Large-leaved Aster. ....
                .... *A. macrophyllus* L.
                5. Peduncles and involucres not glandular; rays white or lavender.
                    6. Heads 6-8 mm high; inflorescence forking; leaves pubescent beneath; wooded bluffs and ravines, locally in western and northern Ill., extending eastward and southward to McHenry, La Salle, Tazewell, and Calhoun counties. Aug.-Sept. Forked Aster. .... *A. furcatus* Burgess
                    6. Heads 8-10 mm high; inflorescence compact; leaves nearly glabrous; wooded ravines in Marshall, Peoria, and Tazewell counties. Aug.-Oct. [*A. schreberi* sensu Fern. ex. p., non Nees] Chase Aster .... *A. chasei* G. N. Jones
            4. Heads paniculate; bracts narrow, attenuate or acute, less than 1 mm wide, glabrous or nearly so on the back, or the margins sparsely ciliolate; achenes flattened.
                7. Bracts acute with conspicuous rhombic green tips; stem slender, often somewhat zigzag, glabrous or sparsely pubescent in decurrent lines above; leaves thin, cordate-ovate, sharply and conspicuously serrate, the lower surface sparsely pilosulous, at least along the veins, varying to nearly or quite glabrous, the petioles slightly or not at all margined; heads usually numer-

ous, small, the branches of the panicle spreading; dry woods, western and northern Ill., extending southward and eastward to Will and Macoupin counties. Aug.-Oct. [*A. cordifolius* var. *moratus* Shinners]. Blue Wood Aster ....*A. cordifolius* L.

   7. Bracts attenuate, with a median green line; leaves lanceolate to ovate-lanceolate, less serrate, the petioles margined; panicle-branches ascending.

      8. Stem glabrous, or sparsely pubescent along decurrent lines on the upper part; leaves glabrous to sparsely pubescent beneath; dry woods, common throughout Ill. Aug.-Oct. Arrow-leaved Aster ....
....*A. sagittifolius* Wedem.

      8. Stem evenly and often rather copiously short-pubescent throughout (except the base), varying to merely hirtellous-puberulent or nearly glabrous; lower surface of leaves finely and evenly short-pubescent throughout; dry open woods, common throughout Ill. Aug.-Oct. [*A. drummondii* var. *rhodactis* Benke]. Drummond Aster. ....*A. drummondii* Lindl.

  3. Leaves all or mostly entire or subentire, firm; rays purple.

    9. Bracts erect, appressed; involucre campanulate, 5-7 mm high; rays 12-15.

      10. Bracts and peduncles pubescent; stem nearly equally leafy throughout; leaves glabrous or nearly so above, sparingly pubescent beneath; rays 10-12 mm long; banks and dry open woods nearly throughout Ill. Aug.-Oct. [*A. shortii* f. *gronemanni* Benke].. *A. shortii* Lindl.

      10. Bracts glabrous, with conspicuous rhombic green tips; leaves thickish, firm, scabrous on both sides, those of the upper part of the stem and of the branches bract-like, linear, cuspidate; rays 6-8 mm long; sandy soil and in open woods nearly throughout Ill. Sept.-Oct. [*A. azureus* f. *laevicaulis* Fern.] .... *A. azureus* Lindl.

    9. Bracts spreading or recurved, scabrous-pubescent, lanceolate, acuminate; involucre hemispherical, 8-12 mm high; rays 30-45, 10-12 mm long; bluffs and rocky woods in and near the Mississippi valley northward to Hancock Co., and in the Illinois valley as far as Peoria and Woodford counties. Sept.-Oct. .... *A. anomalus* Engelm.

 2. Lower leaves not cordate.

   11. Stem leaves clasping or auricled at the base (only slightly in *A. oblongifolius*).

    12. Stem pubescent or puberulent throughout, or at least above.

      13. Leaves all entire or essentially so.

        14. Heads numerous, subcorymbose; involucre hemispherical, the bracts minutely glandular.

15. Leaves lanceolate, acuminate, 5-10 cm long, 1-2 cm wide, strongly clasping; bracts loose, linear-lanceolate, attenuate; involucre 6-10 mm high; peduncles copiously glandular-pubescent; rays 40-50; roadsides and moist ground, common. Aug.-Oct. New England Aster ....*A. novae-angliae* L.

15. Leaves elliptical-lanceolate, acute, 2-5 cm long, 4-10 mm wide (the upper ones slightly, if at all clasping); bracts appressed, linear-oblong, acute, firm; involucre about 5 mm high; peduncles hirtellous and minutely glandular; rays 20-30; wooded bluffs, local; Aug.-Oct...*A. oblongifolius* Nutt.

14. Heads few, scattered, solitary on slender peduncles beset with minute bract-like leaves; involucre turbinate, 1 cm high; bracts appressed, linear-oblanceolate, acuminate, ciliolate, sparsely pubescent on the back and minutely glandular; open woods, local; chiefly in s. Ill. Aug.-Oct. ....*A. patens* Ait.

13. Leaves, at least the lower, sharply toothed; bracts glabrous; involucre 8-10 mm high; moist ground, local. Aug.-Oct. ....*A. puniceus* L.

12. Stem glabrous or the upper part pubescent in lines; rays purple (rarely white).

16. Stem pubescent in lines; bracts of the involucre acuminate.

17. Stem-leaves sharply serrate, oblanceolate, abruptly contracted into winged entire auriculate-clasping petioles; moist ground, often along streams or ditches, Jo Daviess, Fulton, Peoria, and Henry counties. Sept.-Oct. ....*A. prenanthoides* Muhl.

17. Stem-leaves entire or nearly so.

18. Leaves lanceolate, 1-3 cm wide; stem 3-6 mm in diameter near base; moist ground, n.e. Ill., extending southw. to Menard Co. Aug.-Oct. ....*A. lucidulus* (A.Gray) Wieg.

18. Leaves linear-lanceolate, 5-10 mm wide; stem 1.5-3 mm in diameter near base; swampy ground, rare, n. Ill. Aug.-Sept. ....*A. longifolius* Lam.

16. Stem glabrous, often glaucous; leaves thick, lanceolate, mostly entire or nearly so; bracts acute, the tips green, rhombic; sandy soil in woods, usually near streams. Aug.-Oct. Smooth Aster ....*A. laevis* L.

11. Leaves not clasping.
   19. Leaves densely appressed silvery-silky on both sides; rays violet; sandy soil, often in open woods, local. Sept.-Oct. Silky Aster. ....*A. sericeus* Vent.
   19. Leaves not silvery-silky.
      20. Heads not in flat-topped corymbs.
         21. Involucre conspicuously turbinate, 8-12 mm high, the bracts linear-spatulate, obtuse, appressed, rounded on the back, imbricated in 5 or 6 series, green only near the apex; rays violet-blue; prairie soil, local, chiefly in the southern part of the state, but extending northward to Christian and Fulton counties. Sept.-Oct. ....*A. turbinellus* Lindl.
         21. Involucre hemispherical to campanulate; bracts not rounded on the back.
            22. Involucres 3-7 mm high.
               23. Bracts of the involucres (and uppermost leaves) minutely spinulose-tipped or evidently bristly ciliate; heads small, usually numerous, paniculate.
                  24. Stems pilose to glabrous; rays white.
                     25. Involucres 4-8 mm high.
                        26. Stem pilose; roadsides, fields, open woods, a b u n d a n t throughout Ill.; a plant of disturbed soil, hence much more common in recent years. Aug.-Oct. ....*A. pilosus* Willd.
                        26. Stem and leaves glabrous; dry sandy ridges, shore of Lake Michigan. Aug.-Oct. ....*A. pringlei* (A.Gray) Britt.
                     25. Involucres 3-4 mm high; disk florets 6-12; prairies and open woods in the northern half of Ill. Aug.-Oct. ....*A. parviceps* (Burgess) Mack. & Bush
                  24. Stems and branches copiously short-hirsute; bracts bristly ciliate; leaves linear, entire, 2-5 mm wide, hirsutulous, cuspidate; heads numerous; involucres 4-5 mm high.
                     27. Bracts acute, ascending, rays light blue or pink, about 5 mm long; stem pubescent; moist ground, rare; Champaign, Cook, Mc-

Lean, Peoria, and Winnebago counties. Sept. [*A. ericoides* ✕ *novae-angliae* Benke] ....✕ *A. amethystinus* Nutt.

27. Bracts with broad obtuse squarrose tips; rays white, 3-6 mm long.

  28. Stem with spreading or slightly reflexed hairs; bracts (at least the outer) hispidulous on the back; dry ground, prairie soil, often along roads, common. Sept.-Oct. ....*A. exiguus* (Fern.) Rydb.

  28. Stem with appressed or ascending short hairs, or the lower part glabrous; bracts smooth or nearly so on the back; in habitats similar to the preceding, but less common; in the northern half of Ill. July-Oct. [*A. multiflorus* Ait.; *A. stricticaulis* Rydb.] ....*A. ericoides* L.

23. Bracts thin, scarious, not subulate-tipped or bristly-ciliate.

  29. Rameal leaves linear, small, numerous, 1 mm wide.

    30. Rameal leaves very unequal; involucre 3-3.5 mm high; bracts thin, narrowly linear, with linear-oblanceolate green midrib; rays white, 3-6 mm long; fields, roadsides, s. Ill. Sept.-Oct. ....*A. vimineus* Lam.

    30. Rameal leaves uniform or nearly so; involucre 4-6 mm high; bracts with conspicuous rhombic green tips; rays pale lavender, 5-10 mm long; moist sandy soil in the northern half of Ill. Aug.-Sept. [*A. dumosus* var. *cordifolius* sensu Fern. quoad pl. Ill., non (Michx.) T. & G.] Bushy Aster ....*A. dumosus* L.

  29. Rameal leaves usually broader, fewer.

    31. Leaves linear, acuminate, ascending, 2-5 mm wide, entire, scabrous margined, otherwise gla-

brous; stem slender, 15-60 cm
tall; heads few; involucre 5-7
mm high, the bracts acute, slender, glabrous; rays 20-50, white
to pale lavender, 7-15 mm long;
wet ground and in bogs, rare,
n.e. Ill. Aug.-Sept. ....
.........................*A. junciformis* Rydb.

31. Leaves wider, mostly 1-3.5 cm wide
(except *A. praealtus,* with stout
stems 0.5-1.5 m tall, and numerous heads).

32. Stem-leaves soft, flat, thin, dark
green, widest near the middle,
tapering toward each end,
mostly 1-3.5 cm broad; rays
usually white.

33. Leaves finely and softly
short-pubescent over the
lower surface; rays 15-25;
roadsides, fields, river
banks, common through-
out Ill. Sept.-Oct. ....
..............*A. ontarionis* Wieg.

33. Leaves glabrous or nearly
so, or pubescent only on
the midrib beneath.

34. Leaves with midrib on
lower surface usually
short-pilose pubescent;
heads tending to be uni-
laterally racemose; in-
volucral bracts firm, linear-oblong, b l u n t o r
acute, with conspicuous
subspatulate green tips;
rays 9-15, each 4-7 mm
long; woods, common.
Sept.-Oct. ....
....*A. lateriflorus* (L.) Britt.

34. Leaves glabrous; panicle
large, with forking
branches; involucral
bracts narrowly linear,
a t t e n u a t e, with a
green median band;
rays 20-40, each 6-12
m m l o n g; m o i s t

ground, river banks, woods, common. Aug.-Oct. [*A. paniculatus* Lam., not Mill.; *A. tradescanti* of auth., not L.; *A. interior* Wieg.] ....
............*A. simplex* Willd.

32. Stem-leaves thick, firm, glossy, yellowish green, lanceolate, usually entire, 5-10 mm wide, the tips involute and indurated, the upper surface scabrous near the margins and toward the tip; branches and branchlets very leafy; rays lilac purple; involucre 4-6 mm high; moist ground, common throughout Ill. Sept.-Oct. [*A. salicifolius* Ait.] ......
...........................*A. praealtus* Poir.

22. Involucres 6-9 mm high.

35. Leaves numerous, linear, entire, sessile, 1-nerved, rigid, 1-3 cm long, 2-3 mm wide; rays 10-15, violet or rarely white, 7-10 mm long; sandy soil in woods in the northern half of the state. Sept.-Oct. [*Ionactis linariifolius* (L.) Greene]
....*A. linariifolius* L.

35. Leaves large, 15-60 cm long, coarse, elliptical, acuminate, all but the reduced upper ones serrate; stems stout, angular, 1-2 m tall; rays 15-20, purple, 1-1.5 cm long; cult., and occasionally escaped and persisting; native of E. Asia. Sept.-Oct. Tatarian Aster ....*A. tataricus* L.f

20. Heads in a flat-topped corymb; rays white or whitish; involucres 4-5 mm high.

36. Leaves rigid, linear-lanceolate, acute; rays about 8 mm long; sandy soil in the northern half of the state, extending southward to Kankakee and Menard counties. Aug.-Sept. [*A. lutescens* (Lindl.) T. & G.]; suggested by E. J. Hill in 1883 to be a hybrid between *A. ptarmicoides* and *Solidago riddellii* ....
...............................*A. ptarmicoides* (Nees) T. & G.

36. Leaves lanceolate, acuminate, not rigid; rays 4-6 mm long; pappus double, the outer bristles

shorter; achenes pubescent; moist ground in
the northern half of the state, local. Aug.-Oct.
[*Doellingeria umbellata* (Mill.) Nees]. Flat-top
Aster ....*A. umbellatus* Mill.

1. Heads rayless, campanulate, 8-12 mm broad; involucre 4-6 mm
high; pappus copious, soft; achenes appressed-pubescent; leaves
linear, entire, sessile, ciliolate, acutish; plants annual; roadsides and waste ground, local; adv. from w. U.S.; apparently
not coll. recently in Ill.; Cook Co., *Moffatt* in 1891; *Hill* in
1900, *Agnes Chase* in 1900. July-Sept. [*A. angustus* sensu auth.,
non Nees; *Brachyactis angustus* (Lindl.) Britt.] Rayless Aster.
.... *A. brachyactis* Blake

20. Erigeron L. — Fleabane

1. Rays conspicuous, longer than the pappus.
   2. Leaves clasping; rays lilac or purple; plants perennial.
      3. Heads few, 2.5-3.5 cm in diameter; rays 50-75, about 1 mm
      broad; peduncles hirsute; stem simple, rather leafless
      above; open woods, common. Apr.-June ....
      ....*E. pulchellus* Michx.
      3. Heads several, 1.5-2 cm in diameter; rays 150-200, about
      0.5 mm broad; peduncles strigose; stem branched, leafy;
      open woods, roadsides, and fields, common. May-June
      ....*E. philadelphicus* L.
   2. Leaves not at all clasping; rays white or pink-tinged; plants
   annual or biennial.
      4. Stem-leaves few, linear to narrowly lanceolate, strigose, usual-
      ly entire; stem softly strigose, 30-70 cm tall; basal leaves
      spatulate; roadsides, fields, or dry open woods, chiefly in
      the northern half of the state. May-July. Daily Fleabane
      [*E. ramosus* (Walt.) BSP.] ....*E. strigosus* Muhl.
      4. Stem-leaves more numerous, lanceolate, ciliate, sparsely hir-
      sute or glabrous, irregularly sharply toothed, or the upper
      ones entire; stem 60-150 cm tall, scabrous to hispidulous;
      basal leaves ovate, coarsely dentate, long-petioled, usually
      absent at flowering time; fields, roadsides, waste places, and
      open woods, very common throughout Ill. June-Oct.
      Whitetop ....*E. annuus* (L.) Pers.
1. Rays inconspicuous, scarcely, if at all, exceeding the pappus.
   5. Rays purplish; involucre about 2 mm high; stem diffusely or
   divaricately branched; leaves all linear, entire; dry soil, local.
   June-Sept. ....*E. divaricatus* Michx.
   5. Rays white; involucre 3-4 mm high; stem strict; lower leaves
   spatulate, toothed; common weed in cultivated ground and
   along roads. Aug.-Oct. Horseweed. Muletail ....
   ....*E. canadensis* L.

Tribe 5. *Gnaphalieae*

21. **Pluchea** Cass. — Marsh Fleabane
P. camphorata (L.) DC. Swamps and sloughs, not common, southern Ill. July-Oct.

22. **Antennaria** Gaertn. — Pussytoes. Ladies'-tobacco

1. Rosette leaves comparatively small, usually less than 3 cm long, 1-ribbed, or indistinctly 3-ribbed.
  2. Rosette leaves obovate, abruptly contracted below the middle into a petiole-like base; roadsides and open woods; De-Kalb and Henry counties. May-June. .... *A. neodioica* Greene
  2. Rosette leaves cuneate-spatulate, gradually tapering to the sessile base; fields, roadsides, and pastures, or open wooded slopes. Apr.-May. .... *A. neglecta* Greene
1. Rosette leaves larger, distinctly 3-ribbed, 3-12 cm long.
  3. Upper surface of leaves dark green and glabrous or nearly so from the beginning; involucres 7-11 mm high; upper part of stem usually with a few small glands; dry soil in open woods and on bluffs, locally throughout Ill., except the southern counties. May-June .... *A. parlinii* Fern.
  3. Upper surface of leaves arachnoid or tomentulose at first, tardily glabrate in age; stem glandless.
    4. Heads small, the involucres of the pistillate plants 5-7 mm high; wooded slopes, common throughout Ill. Apr.-May .... *A. plantaginifolia* (L.) Hook.
    4. Heads larger, the involucres of the pistillate plants 7-9 mm high.
      5. Rosette leaves rhombic-obovate, widest at or below the middle, usually acutish; pastures and open woods, common. May-June. [*A. occidentalis* Greene] .... *A. fallax* Greene
      5. Rosette leaves spatulate, widest above the middle, rounded at the apex; sandy ridges or open woods near Lake Michigan, rare; Lake Co., *F. C. Gates* in 1908 [*A. occidentalis* of auth., not Greene] .... *A. munda* Fern.

23. **Gnaphalium** L. — Cudweed

1. Heads in cymose or paniculate clusters; pappus-bristles not united.
  2. Stems 30-90 cm tall, simple below, bracts white; achenes smooth.
    3. Leaves not decurrent; plants not glandular; outer bracts obtuse; fields, roadsides, and open woods, common. Aug.-Oct. Sometimes mistaken for *Anaphalis margaritacea* (L.) A. Gray, which is not known to occur in Ill. Sweet Everlasting [*G. polycephalum* Michx.] .... *G. obtusifolium* L.

3. Leaves decurrent; stem glandular-pubescent; bracts acute; sandy soil in woods and fields, rare. July-Sept. ....
.... *G. macounii* Greene
2. Stems 5-25 cm tall, diffusely branched near the base; bracts brownish; achenes scabrous; dried mud, and along ditches, local; known from Cook and Lake counties. June-Aug. ....
.... *G. uliginosum* L.
1. Heads in a narrow spike-like panicle; pappus-bristles united at base, falling away in a ring; leaves glabrate above; fields and open woods, local. May-July. Early Cudweed ....
.... *G. purpureum* L.

Tribe 6. *Inuleae*
24. Inula L. — Elecampane

I. helenium L. Roadsides, fields, and open woods, occasional; introd. from Eur. July-Aug.

Tribe 7. *Heliantheae*
25. Polymnia L. — Leafcup

1. Leaves pinnately lobed; rays white, 2-5 mm long; achenes 3-5 mm long, angular; woods, common. June-Nov. ....
.... *P. canadensis* L.
1. Leaves palmately lobed; rays yellow, 1.5-2 cm long; achenes 6-8 mm long, black, flattened; woods and thickets, rare; known from Alexander, Hardin, Jackson, Pope, Pulaski, and Union counties. July-Sept. Bear's-foot ....*P. uvedalia* L.

26. Silphium L.

1. Stem 1-3 m tall, leafless or nearly so; leaves large, cordate, dentate, long-petioled; prairie soil, common. July-Sept. Prairie-dock .... *S. terebinthinaceum* Jacq.
1. Stem leafy throughout.
  2. Leaves pinnately parted, large, alternate; prairie soil, common. July-Aug. Compass-plant [*S. gummiferum* Ell.] ....
.... *S. laciniatum* L.
  2. Leaves toothed or entire, chiefly opposite.
    3. Leaves merely sessile, 7-10 cm long; stem nearly terete or obtusely angled; prairie soil, often along railroads, common. July-Aug. Rosinweed [*S. integrifolium* var. *deamii* Perry]. Occasional plants with some of the leaves whorled have been mistaken for *S. trifoliatum* L., which is not known to occur in Ill. .... *S. integrifolium* Michx.
    3. Leaves connate-clasping, perfoliate, 20-60 cm long; stem sharply 4-angled; alluvial soil, common. July-Aug. Cup-plant .... *S. perfoliatum* L.

27. Parthenium L.

1. Leaves simple, toothed; prairie soil, common. July-Sept. American Feverfew .... *P. integrifolium* L.

1. Leaves pinnatifid or pinnately dissected; adv. from trop. Am.; Cook Co. Aug.-Oct. Santa Maria .... *P. hysterophorus* L.

28. **Heliopsis** Pers.

H. helianthoides (L.) Sweet. Open woods, and along roads, common. July-Aug. [*H. scabra* Dunal; *H. laevis* Pers.].

29. **Eclipta** L.

E. alba (L.) Hassk. Shores, sloughs, and fields throughout Ill., except the northern counties. July-Sept.

30. **Rudbeckia** L. — Coneflower

1. Leaves clasping; along railroads, rarely adv. from w. U.S. ....
.... *R. amplexicaulis* Vahl
1. Leaves not clasping, usually petiolate.
    2. Peduncles glabrous; disk greenish-yellow; rays 2.5-5 cm long, soon drooping; lower leaves pinnately parted, the upper 3-lobed or entire; stem 1.5-3 m tall, glabrous; alluvial soil, common. July-Sept. Goldenglow .... *R. laciniata* L.
    2. Peduncles more or less pubescent; disk brown or purple; stem 30-150 cm tall.
        3. Chaff of the receptacle acuminate, glabrous; basal leaves ovate, coarsely serrate, long-petioled; lower stem-leaves, or some of them, 3-lobed or 3-parted, the upper lanceolate, entire or serrate; rays 8-12, orange-yellow, 1.5-2.5 cm long; woods, locally throughout Ill. Aug.-Oct. Brown-eyed Susan ....*R. triloba* L.
        3. Chaff obtuse or acutish, puberulent toward the tip.
            4. Stem (at least the upper part) tomentulose or puberulent; leaves thick, tomentulose beneath, the lower ones, or some of them frequently deeply 3-lobed or 3-parted; rays 15-20, 2-3 cm long; prairie soil, or in open woods, local. Aug.-Sept. Fragrant Coneflower ....
....*R. subtomentosa* Pursh
            4. Stem strigose or hirsute; leaves merely toothed, or entire.
                5. Leaves irregularly coarsely dentate, or serrate; stem hirsute; rays 2-4 cm long; plants perennial; moist ground, rare; Kankakee, Menard, Richland, Vermilion, and Wabash counties ....
....*R. sullivantii* Boynt. & Beadle
                5. Leaves denticulate or entire.
                    6. Stem sparsely strigose; rays orange-yellow, 1-1.5 cm long; stigmas obtuse; pappus a minute crown; plants perennial; dry open woods, rare; Herod, Pope Co., July 29, 1898, *G. P. Clinton*, also Monroe and Randolph counties. [*R. missouriensis* Engelm.] Orange Coneflower ....*R. fulgida* Ait.

6. Stem hirsute; rays bright yellow, 2-3.5 cm long; stigmas subulate; pappus none; plants annual or biennial; fields, roadsides, and open woods, common. June-Aug. [*R. serotina* Nutt.] Black-eyed Susan ....*R. hirta* L.

31. Echinacea Moench
(*Brauneria* Necker)

1. Leaves ovate to lanceolate, serrate or dentate, or the uppermost entire; stem usually branched above; woods and thickets, not common. July-Aug. Purple Coneflower..*E. purpurea* (L.) Moench
1. Leaves oblanceolate or narrowly elliptical, entire; stem simple; prairie soil, local. June-July. Pale Coneflower [*E. angustifolia* sensu auth., non DC.] ....*E. pallida* Nutt.

32. Ratibida Raf.

1. Rays spatulate-elliptical, 2.5-5 cm long; disk subglobose to short-ellipsoid, shorter than the rays, becoming 1-2 cm long and 1-1.5 cm thick in fruit; stigmas subulate; roadsides and prairie soil, common throughout Ill. July-Aug. Drooping Coneflower ....*R. pinnata* (Vent.) Barnh.
1. Rays oval, 1.5-2 cm long; disk cylindrical, equalling or exceeding the rays, becoming 2.5-4 cm long and 7-10 mm thick in fruit; stigmas short, obtuse; along railroads, occasional; adv. from w. U.S. [*R. columnaris* (Sims) D. Don] ....
................................*R. columnifera* (Nutt.) Wooton & Standl.

33. Galinsoga Ruiz & Pavon — Peruvian Daisy

1. Stem spreading-pubescent; rays conspicuously longer than the disk-flowers; pappus fimbriate and aristate, about as long as the corolla-tube; cultivated ground and waste places, first collected in Ill. at Chicago by W. S. Moffatt in 1891, now common throughout Ill.; nat. from trop. Am. June-Oct. [*G. parviflora* var. *hispida* DC.; *G. parviflora* of Ill. auth., not Cav.] Quickweed ....*G. ciliata* (Raf.) Blake
1. Stem glabrous or nearly so; rays short, not exceeding the disk-flowers; pappus fimbriate but not aristate, absent from the ray-flowers, as long or longer than the disk-flowers; cult. ground, occasional; nat. from S. Am.; Urbana, in September and October, 1951, *G. N. Jones,* and several later collections ....
....*G. parviflora* Cav.

34. Helianthus L. — Sunflower

1. Plants perennial.
   2. Stem scape-like; leaves mostly near the base of the stem, oval, long-petioled, the upper ones bract-like; sandy soil, chiefly in the northern half of the state. July-Sept. [*H. illinoensis* Gleason] ....*H. occidentalis* Riddell

2. Stem usually leafy to the inflorescence.
  3. Heads small, 1.5-3 cm broad, the rays about 1 cm long, the disk 6-10 mm broad; leaves lanceolate, acuminate, serrate, petiolate, more or less scabrous on both surfaces; stem glabrous or nearly so, often glaucous; sandy soil in open woods, local, s. Ill. Aug.-Oct. ....*H. microcephalus* T. & G.
  3. Heads large, 4-9 cm in diameter, the rays 2-5 cm long.
    4. Bracts acutish or obtuse, essentially glabrous on the back, ciliolate, shorter than the disk, erect, closely appressed; disk usually purple-brown; leaves opposite.
      5. Leaves lanceolate to rhombic-ovate; stems several, scabrous-puberulent; outer bracts of the involucre acutish or obtusish, ovate to ovate-lanceolate, conspicuously closely and evenly ciliolate; sandy or prairie soil, locally abundant. July-Sept. [*H. scaberrimus* Ell.] Prairie Sunflower ....*H. rigidus* (Cass.) Desf.
      5. Leaves rounded-ovate to cordate; stem solitary, villous-pubescent below; bracts oval to slightly obovate, broadly rounded and mucronulate at apex, minutely ciliolate, distinctly veined; rare, Cairo, Alexander Co., *O. Kuntze* in 1874 ....*H. silphioides* Nutt.
    4. Bracts lanceolate or linear-lanceolate, acuminate; disk-flowers yellow.
      6. Leaves linear to linear-lanceolate, entire, 1-veined, 4-10 mm wide, alternate, numerous.
        7. Stem glabrous and glaucous; leaves glabrous; bracts linear-lanceolate, glabrous, striate, ciliolate; waste ground, Cook Co., *J. A. Steyermark 80329;* adv. from w. U.S. [*H. orgyalis* DC.] ....*H. salicifolius* A.Dietr.
        7. Stem strigose to pilosulous; leaves often revolute-margined, dark green and scabrous above, paler beneath and closely pubescent; bracts lanceolate, strigillose; moist ground and thickets, occasionally in s. Ill. Aug.-Oct. ....*H. angustifolius* L.
      6. Leaves lanceolate to ovate, broader, more than 1 cm wide.
        8. Leaves sessile or subsessile.
          9. Stem hirsute or hispidulous; leaves ascending.
            10. Stem villous-hirsute; leaves finely and densely grayish-pubescent on both surfaces, ovate or ovate-lanceolate, acute, 3-veined above the slightly clasping base, all opposite; bracts copiously pubescent; heads solitary or few; rays 2-3 cm long; prairie soil, locally abundant. Aug.-Sept. [*H. canescens* Michx.; *H. doronicoides* sensu auth., non Lam.; *H. pubescens* Vahl] ....*H. mollis* Lam.

10. Stem more or less hispidulous or scabrous; leaves lanceolate, acuminate; heads several or many, panicled; waste places, particularly along railroads, occasional; adv. from w. U.S. July-Aug. Maximilian Sunflower ....
......................................*H. maximiliani* Schrad.

9. Stem glabrous or nearly so, glaucous, slender; leaves divaricate, lanceolate, acuminate, 3-veined from the rounded base, scabrous on both sides; roadsides and open woods, local. July-Sept. ....
......................................*H. divaricatus* L.

8. Leaves manifestly petioled.

11. Stem smooth or nearly so, glaucous.

12. Leaves triple-veined from near the base, chiefly opposite, at least below the inflorescence, abruptly contracted into margined petioles.

13. Leaves lanceolate, firm, serrate to entire, the lower surface hirsutulous or glaucous; roadsides and open woods, common. July-Sept. ....*H. strumosus* L.

13. Leaves elliptic-lanceolate, thin, usually conspicuously coarsely regularly serrate-dentate, the lower surface glabrous, scabrous, or puberulent; dry woods, local. Aug.-Oct. ....*H. decapetalus* L.

12. Leaves 1-veined or inconspicuously 3-veined, the upper alternate, remotely denticulate or nearly entire, the lower ones opposite (or sometimes whorled), coarsely serrate, all elongate-lanceolate, acuminate, scabrous above, finely shortly whitish-pubescent beneath; peduncles strigose; stem 2-4 m tall; prairie soil, roadsides, borders of fields, common. Aug.-Oct ....*H. grosseserratus* Martens

11. Stem scabrous or hispidulous; leaves triple-veined from near the base, chiefly opposite below the inflorescence.

14. Lower surface of leaves hispidulous or short-hirsute; stem scabrous-hirsute; roadsides and fields, local. Aug.-Sept. ....*H. hirsutus* Raf.

14. Lower surface of leaves rather copiously canescent-puberulent; stem hirsutulous or antrorsely scabrous-strigillose; rhizome short, often tuberous-thickened at apex; alluvial soil, common. July-Oct. [*H. tuberosus* of auth.; *H. subcanescens* (A.Gray) E.E.Wats.]
......................................*H. tomentosus* Michx.

1. Plants annual; leaves chiefly alternate; disk usually brownish-purple; stem hispid or strigose.
  15. Leaves lanceolate, usually entire; stem 30-90 cm tall; disk 1.5 cm broad; bracts lanceolate, densely scabrous; sandy soil, roadsides, waste-places, occasional; adv. from w. U.S. June-Sept. ....*H. petiolaris* Nutt.
  15. Leaves ovate, dentate; stem 1-4 m tall; disk 2.5-4 cm broad; bracts ovate-lanceolate, ciliate and hispid; fields and road-sides, and often cultivated; native west of the Mississippi R. Aug.-Sept. Garden Sunflower ....*H. annuus* L.

35. Verbesina L. — Crownbeard
(*Actinomeris* Nutt.)

1. Stem more or less winged, at least on the upper part, by the de-current bases of the leaves; plants perennial.
  2. Rays yellow, 2-3 cm long.
    3. Stem usually branched toward the summit, 1-2 m tall; heads several to many; rays 2-8; alluvial soil, open woods or along roads, common throughout Ill. Aug.-Sept. Yellow Ironweed. [*Actinomeris squarrosa* Nutt.; *A. alternifolia* (L.) DC.] ....*V. alternifolia* (L.) Britt.
    3. Stem simple, 60-90 cm tall; heads few (2-8); rays 8-15; open woods and along roads from Peoria and Vermilion counties southward. May-July. Yellow Crownbeard ....
    ....*V. helianthoides* Michx.
  2. Rays 3-4, white, 4-7 mm long; heads small, numerous; sandy or rocky soil, s. Ill., not common. July-Aug. Tickweed ....
  ....*V. virginica* L.
1. Stem wingless, 30-70 cm tall, cinereous-pubescent; leaves deltoid, petioled, canescent beneath; rays yellow, 1-2 cm long; plants annual; waste ground, St. Clair Co.; adv. from w. U.S. June-Aug. Golden Crownbeard ....*V. encelioides* (Cav.) Benth. & Hook.

36. Melanthera Rohr

M. hastata Michx. Flood-plain woods along Ohio R., Pulaski Co., *Mohlenbrock, Abney, & Dillard* in 1959; adv. from s. U.S.

37. Coreopsis L.

1. Leaves simple, entire or palmately cleft or divided; achenes wing-margined; plants perennial.
  2. Leaves entire, or rarely with 1 or 2 lateral lobes.
    3. Leaves mostly near the base of the stem; heads long-pe-duncled; sandy soil. June-July; [*C. lanceolata* var. *villosa* Michx.; *C. crassifolia* Ait.] .... *C. lanceolata* L.
    3. Stem leafy; plants pubescent; roadsides, fields, and woods; Jackson, Pope, St. Clair, and Washington counties ....
    .... *C. pubescens* Ell.

2. Leaves palmately cleft or divided, or the uppermost entire.
    4. Leaves petioled, 3-divided into elliptic-lanceolate segments;
        heads many; stem 1-3 m tall; rays entire; pappus none;
        open woods and along roads. Aug.-Sept. Tall Tickseed
        .... *C. tripteris* L.
    4. Leaves sessile, rigid, 3-cleft at or below the middle, the lobes
        linear-oblong; heads few or solitary; stem 30-90 cm tall;
        rays mostly 3-toothed; pappus of 2 short teeth, or none;
        roadsides and open woods. June-July ....*C. palmata* Nutt.
1. Leaves or most of them 1- to 2-pinnately parted.
    5. Heads 4-6 cm broad; rays 1.5-2 cm long, yellow throughout;
        disk yellow; achenes broadly winged; pappus of 2 short
        scales; plants perennial; roadsides and waste places, occa-
        sional; adv. from west-central U.S. June-Aug. ....
        .... *C. grandiflora* Hogg
    5. Heads 1.5-3 cm broad; rays 8-12 mm long, crimson-brown at
        base or throughout; disk brownish-purple; achenes linear,
        wingless; pappus a mere border, or absent; plants annual;
        roadsides, railroads, or waste places, occasional; adv. from
        the Great Plains, or sometimes escaped from cult. July-Sept.
        .... *C. tinctoria* Nutt.

38. **Bidens** L. — Beggar-ticks. Tickseed. Bur-marigold

1. Plants terrestrial; leaves not finely dissected; achenes flattened.
    2. Rays inconspicuous or none.
        3. Leaves pinnately parted or dissected.
            4. Achenes linear-fusiform, with 2-4 short-retrorsely barbed
                awns; rays yellowish-white; roadsides and open woods;
                chiefly in the southern half of Ill., but extending north-
                ward to Woodford and Henderson counties. Aug.-Sept.
                Spanish Needles .... *B. bipinnata* L.
            4. Achenes flat, 2-awned.
                5. Outer bracts 10-16; achenes brown, the awns down-
                    wardly barbed; involucres 10-12 mm high; roadsides,
                    fields, and woods, local. Aug.-Oct. ....
                    .... *B. vulgata* Greene
                5. Outer bracts 4-8; achenes black.
                    6. Awns of the achenes upwardly barbed.; wet ground,
                      not common. Aug.-Oct. ....
                    .... *B. discoidea* (T. & G.) Britt.
                  6. Awns downwardly barbed; roadsides, fields, wet
                    ground, and open woods. Aug.-Oct. ....
                    .... *B. frondosa* L.
        3. Leaves simple, lanceolate, toothed or lobed, sessile or peti-
        oled; awns of the pappus 3 or 4.
            7. Outer bracts rarely much exceeding the disk; achenes
                4-angled, 4-6 mm long; corollas 5-toothed; stamens ex-
                serted; wet ground throughout Ill. Sept.-Oct. Swamp
                Beggar-ticks ....*B. connata* Muhl.

7. Outer bracts foliaceous, 2-5 times the length of the disk; achenes flat, 7-9 mm long; corollas 4-toothed; stamens included; wet ground throughout Ill. Sept.-Oct. .... *B. comosa* (A.Gray) Wieg.
2. Rays present, conspicuous.
  8. Leaves simple, oblanceolate to linear-lanceolate, acuminate, serrate, connate at the base; heads nodding in fruit; achenes cuneate, 4-angled, the 4 awns retrorsely barbed; wet ground, local. July-Oct. [*B. chrysanthemoides* sensu auth., non Michx.; *B. filamentosa* Rydb.; *B. elliptica* (Wieg.) Gleason] .... *B. cernua* L.
  8. Leaves pinnately parted or dissected; achenes flat, upwardly ciliate.
    9. Outer bracts 6-12, ciliolate or glabrous, not exceeding the inner; (awns sometimes only 0.5 mm long).
      10. Achenes elliptic-obovate, more than 2 mm wide, the margins scarious; moist ground along roads, or in swales and fields throughout Ill. Aug.-Oct. [*B. aristosa* var. *mutica* A.Gray; *B. aristosa* var. *fritcheyi* Fern.] .... *B. aristosa* (Michx.) Britt.
      10. Achenes cuneate, 2 mm or less in width; moist ground throughout Ill. July-Oct. [*B. trichosperma* (Michx.) Britt.]. Plants with narrow leaf-segments have been named *B. coronata* var. *tenuiloba* (A.Gray) Sherff .... *B. coronata* (L.) Britt.
    9. Outer bracts 12-20, coarsely hispidulous, mostly longer than the inner; swampy ground, local. July-Sept. [*B. involucrata* (Nutt.) Britt., non Phil.] .... *B. polylepis* Blake
1. Plants aquatic, the immersed leaves finely dissected; uppermost leaves lanceolate, serrate; achenes terete, 1-1.5 cm long, the 3-6 awns divergent, barbed only toward the apex; ponds and slow streams, rare; Cook Co., *E. J. Hill* in 1878; Lake Co., *E. J. Hill* in 1898. Aug.-Sept. Water-marigold [*Megalodonta beckii* (Torr.) Greene] .... *B. beckii* Torr.

Tribe 8. *Helenieae*

39. **Hymenopappus** L'Her.

H. scabiosaeus L'Her. Open sandy woods, rare, Cass, Kankakee, and Mason counties. May-June. [*H. carolinensis* (Lam.) Porter].

40. **Actinea** Juss.

A. herbacea (Greene) B.L.Robins. Dry gravelly banks, stony fields, and limestone hills near Joliet, Will Co., *E. J. Hill,* May 9, and 27, 1902, June 8, 1907; *H. C. Cowles,* May 13, 1906; Manito, Mason Co., *J. Voss.* Also in Ottawa Co., Ohio, and s. Ontario, Canada. [*Tetraneuris herbacea* Greene; *Actinella scaposa* var. *glabra* A.Gray].

41. Helenium L. — Sneezeweed

1. Leaves lanceolate to elliptical, more or less decurrent on the angular stem; rays 1-2 cm long; plants perennial.
   2. Disk yellow; leaves lanceolate or oblanceolate, mostly dentate; ray-flowers fertile; low meadows, and along ditches, streams, and ponds, common. Aug.-Oct. [*H. latifolium* Mill.; *H. canaliculatum* Lam.; *H. altissimum* Link ex Rydb.] ....
   .... *H. autumnale* L.
   2. Disk brownish-purple; leaves linear-lanceolate, mostly entire; ray-flowers neutral, often brownish-purple at base; roadsides, meadows, and pastures, more common in the southern half of the state, but extending northward to Adams and Vermilion counties. June-Sept. [*H. polyphyllum* Small] ....
   .... *H. nudiflorum* Nutt.
1. Leaves narrowly linear, numerous, entire, not decurrent; rays 6-10 mm long; disk yellow; plants annual; dry ground, s. Ill., often abundant, extending northw. to Pike Co. Aug.-Oct. Bitterweed .... *H. tenuifolium* Nutt.

42. Dyssodia Cav. — Dogweed

D. papposa (Vent.) Hitchc. Roadsides and fields, not common. Sept.-Oct. [*D. chrysanthemoides* (Willd.) Lag.].

43. Achillea L. — Yarrow. Milfoil

1. Leaves and stems green, thinly villous; ultimate leaf-segments lanceolate; corymb flat-topped, up to 30 cm broad; roadsides, fields, lawns, etc., very common; nat. from Eur. May-Aug. Rays sometimes pink. [*A. occidentalis* Raf.] ....
   .... *A. millefolium* L.
1. Leaves and stems copiously grayish villous-tomentose; ultimate leaf-segments crowded, linear; corymb strongly convex, 2-8 cm broad; roadsides and fields, occasional; adv. from w. U.S. June-Aug. .... *A. lanulosa* Nutt.

44. Anthemis L.

1. Rays 10-18, white; achenes not flattened.
   2. Chaff of the receptacle subulate, stiff, subtending only the inner flowers; rays neuter; achenes sparsely glandular-tuberculate, 1-1.5 mm long; plants annual, ill-scented when fresh; fields and waste places, common; nat. from Eur. May-Sept. Dog-fennel or Mayweed [*Maruta cotula* (L.) DC.]
   .... *A. cotula* L.
   2. Chaff membranous or absent; rays fertile.
      3. Chaff broad, obtuse, or absent; achenes obtusely 3-angled, 1-1.5 mm long; plants perennial, tomentulose, pleasantly aromatic; cultivated, and occasionally spontaneous; introd. from Eur. June-Aug. Garden Chamomile ....
      .... *A. nobilis* L.

3. Chaff linear-lanceolate, cuspidate; achenes 10-ribbed, 1.5-2 mm long; plants annual; fields and waste places, rare; nat. from Eur. May-Aug. Field Chamomile .... *A. arvensis* L.
1. Rays 20-30, yellow, pistillate; achenes 4-angled and somewhat compressed; chaff lanceolate, acuminate, rigid; plants perennial, pubescent; fields and waste places; escaped from cult.; introd. from Eur. June-Sept. [*Cota tinctoria* (L.) J.Gay] .... *A. tinctoria* L.

45. Matricaria L.

1. Rays present, white; disk-corollas 5-lobed; roadsides and waste places, occasional; chiefly in the southern half of Ill.; nat. from Eur. May-Oct. Wild Chamomile ....*M. chamomilla* L.
1. Heads discoid; corollas 4-lobed; roadsides, farmyards, and waste places, common; nat. from the Pacific Coast. May-Aug. Pineapple-weed .... *M. matricarioides* (Less.) Porter

46. Chrysanthemum L.

1. Heads 3-5 cm broad, few or solitary; rays 20-30; fields, roadsides, and waste places, common; nat. from Eur. May-Aug. Ox-eye Daisy [*Leucanthemum vulgare* Lam.; *C. leucanthemum* var. *pinnatifidum* Lecoq. & Lamotte] .... *C. leucanthemum* L.
1. Heads 5-15 mm broad, corymbose; rays 10-15, or absent.
   2. Leaves pinnatifid; rays 3-8 mm long; roadsides, nat. from Eur.; Du Page, Lake, and Peoria counties. Feverfew .... *C. parthenium* (L.) Bernh.
   2. Leaves crenate; rays minute or absent; waste places; escaped from cult.; nat. from Eur. Sept.-Oct. Costmary ....*C. balsamita* L.

47. Tanacetum L. — Tansy

T. vulgare L. Waste places; escaped from cult.; nat. from Eur. July-Sept.

48. Artemisia L. — Wormwood

1. Leaves or their divisions linear to filiform, glabrous, or nearly so, green.
   2. Bracts of the involucre glabrous; heads 2-3 mm broad; disk-flowers sterile.
      3. Leaves simple, all entire, or the lower trifid; plants perennial; prairie soil, rare. July-Sept. [*A. cernua* Nutt.] ....*A. dracunculoides* Pursh
      3. Leaves 1- to 3-pinnately divided; plants biennial; sandy soil, local. July-Sept. ....*A. caudata* Michx.
   2. Bracts tomentulose; heads 3-4 mm broad; disk-flowers fertile; leaves 1- to 3-pinnately parted; plants perennial, shrubby; often cultivated, and sometimes persisting; introd. from Eur. Aug.-Sept. Southernwood .... *A. abrotanum* L.
1. Leaves or their divisions lanceolate to linear.

4. Plants more or less whitish-tomentose; perennials.
  5. Leaves lanceolate or the upper linear.
    6. Leaves regularly serrate, lanceolate, acuminate, green above, whitish-tomentose beneath; alluvial soil in the northern half of the state. Aug.-Sept. ....*A. serrata* Nutt.
    6. Leaves entire or few-toothed.
      7. Leaves dark green and glabrate above, tomentose beneath; waste ground, or along railroads, occasional. July-Sept. .... *A. ludoviciana* Nutt.
      7. Leaves whitish- or grayish-tomentose on both sides; along railroads, in waste ground, or sandy soil; more frequent than the preceding. Aug.-Oct. White-sage .... *A. gnaphalodes* Nutt.
  5. Leaves all pinnatifid.
    8. Leaves green and glabrate above, the lobes acute; heads 3-4 mm high; receptacle glabrous; waste places, occasional; escaped from cult.; native of Eur. July-Oct. .... *A. vulgaris* L.
    8. Leaves canescent on both sides, the lobes obtuse; heads very numerous, about 2 mm high; receptacle hairy; roadsides and waste places, occasional; escaped from cult.; native of Eur. July-Sept. Common Wormwood or Absinth .... *A. absinthium* L.
4. Plants glabrous, annual or biennial.
  9. Heads 2-3 mm high; leaf-divisions laciniate-dentate; plants biennial; cultivated ground, waste places, or along railroads in the n. half of the state. Aug.-Oct. Biennial Wormwood .... *A. biennis* Willd.
  9. Heads 1.5-2 mm high; leaf-segments 1-3 mm long; plants annual; roadsides and waste places, occasional; nat. from Eur. Aug.-Oct. Annual Wormwood .... *A. annua* L.

Tribe 10. *Senecioneae*
49. **Cacalia** L. — Indian-plantain

1. Heads 20- to 30-flowered; bracts 12-15; leaves hastate, dentate; woods, local. July-Aug. .... *C. suaveolens* L.
1. Heads 5-flowered; bracts 5.
  2. Leaves reniform or flabellate, lobed or sinuately dentate.
    3. Leaves green on both sides; stem conspicuously grooved; moist ground in woods. July-Sept. [*C. reniformis* Muhl., non Lam.] .... *C. muhlenbergii* (Sch.-Bip.) Fern.
    3. Leaves glaucous beneath; stem terete or nearly so; open woods. July-Oct. .... *C. atriplicifolia* L.
  2. Leaves oval, entire or denticulate, green on both sides; wet marly soil, local. June-Aug. .... *C. tuberosa* Nutt.

50. **Erechtites** Raf. — Fireweed

E. hieracifolia (L.) Raf. In moist woods, recently burned clearings, along roads, or in bogs, local. Aug.-Oct.

51. Senecio L. — Ragwort

1. Basal leaves crenate, dentate, or entire, the median stem-leaves often pinnatifid; stems leafy below, the median and upper leaves much reduced; plants perennial.
  2. Basal leaves with winged petioles; bluffs and open woods, not common; Champaign, Clark, and Vermilion counties. Apr.-June. Ill. plants belong to var. *rotundus* Britt. .... *S. obovatus* Muhl.
  2. Basal leaves slender-petioled.
    3. Basal leaves oblanceolate to oval, not cordate.
      4. Leaves and stems more or less floccose-tomentose, especially at the nodes, only tardily glabrate; peduncles tomentose; involucres 6-8 mm high, tomentose at base; prairie soil, and in dry ground in oak woods, locally throughout Ill. May-June. Prairie Ragwort .... *S. plattensis* Nutt.
      4. Leaves glabrous or nearly so; stem glabrous, or slightly floccose when young; peduncles glabrous or nearly so; involucres 4-5 mm high, glabrous or nearly so; roadsides and open woods in the northern two-thirds of the state. May-June. [*S. balsamitae* Muhl.] .... *S. pauperculus* Michx.
    3. Basal leaves more or less cordate or subcordate, long-petioled, mostly glabrous; wet ground, locally throughout Ill. Golden Ragwort [*S. semicordatus* Mack. & Bush] .... *S. aureus* L.
1. Leaves all pinnatifid or coarsely sinuate-dentate; stems nearly equally leafy throughout; plants annual.
  5. Rays 6-10 mm long; bracts not black-tipped; in fields, and in moist ground along streams, central and southern Ill., extending northward to Peoria Co. Apr.-June. Butterweed [*S. lobatus* Pers.] .... *S. glabellus* Poir.
  5. Rays none or up to 3 mm long; bracts often black-tipped.
    6. Stems glabrous at maturity; bracts black-tipped; rays none; waste places, occasional; nat. from Eur. June-July. Groundsel .... *S. vulgaris* L.
    6. Stems glandular-hairy; bracts not black-tipped; rays about 3 mm long; waste ground; nat. from Eur. July-Sept. .... *S. viscosus* L.

Tribe 11. *Cynareae*
52. Arctium L. — Burdock

1. Heads 1-2 cm broad, racemose; waste places, common; nat. from Eur. July-Sept. Common Burdock .... *A. minus* (Hill) Bernh.
1. Heads 2.5-4.5 cm broad, corymbose.
  2. Petioles solid; heads 3-4.5 cm broad; waste places, occasional; nat. from Eur. July-Oct. Great Burdock .... *A. lappa* L.
  2. Petioles hollow; heads 2.5-3 cm broad; waste places; nat. from Eur.; Cook and Morgan counties. June-Sept. .... *A. tomentosum* Mill.

53. Echinops L. — Globe Thistle

E. sphaerocephalus L. Roadsides and waste places, occasional; introd. from Eur.; apparently established in Kankakee Co., near Manteno, July 14, 1938, *Steyermark & Standley 1726;* s. of Peotone, Will Co., June 27, 1952, *H. E. Ahles 6334.*

54. Cirsium Mill. — Thistle

1. Heads large, more than 2 cm in diameter; flowers all perfect; plants biennial.
    2. Leaves bristly on the upper surface, grayish-arachnoid beneath, strongly decurrent; bracts of the involucre all spine-tipped; flowers violet-purple; fields, roadsides, and waste places, common; nat. from Eur. July-Aug. Bull Thistle [*C. lanceolatum* (L.) Hill] ....*C. vulgare* (Savi) Tenore
    2. Leaves not bristly on the upper surface; outer involucral bracts spine-tipped, the inner acuminate, soft, or all the bracts spineless.
        3. Leaves white-tomentose beneath.
            4. Leaves pinnately parted into linear lobes, persistently white-tomentose on both sides; flowers cream-color; sand dunes near Lake Michigan. June-July. Beach Thistle .... *C. pitcheri* (Torr.) T. & G.
            4. Leaves pinnately lobed or merely toothed.
                5. Leaves pinnately lobed, the margins revolute; rich soil along roads, in fields or in woods throughout Ill. Aug.-Sept. Field Thistle .... *C. discolor* (Muhl.) Spreng.
                5. Leaves merely toothed, or shallowly lobed, the margins flat; woods, locally throughout Ill. Aug.-Sept. Tall Thistle .... *C. altissimum* (L.) Spreng.
        3. Leaves not white-tomentose.
            6. Heads 5-10 cm broad; stem stout, 30-60 cm tall; bracts spine-tipped and with a prominent glutinous midvein; gravelly soil, extending southward to Coles, Sangamon, and Adams counties. June-July. Hill's Thistle [*C. pumilum* sensu auth., non (Nutt.) Spreng.] ....*C. hillii* (Canby) Fern.
            6. Heads 2-3 cm broad; stem 1-2.5 m tall; bracts without prickle-points; wet ground, chiefly in the northern half of Ill., extending southward to Macoupin and Wabash counties. Aug.-Sept. Swamp Thistle....*C. muticum* Michx.
1. Heads smaller, 1.5-2.5 cm high and 1-1.5 cm in diameter; plants dioecious; perennials with spreading rhizomes.
    7. Leaves deeply pinnately lobed, strongly prickly; fields and waste places; nat. from Eur. June-Aug. Canada Thistle ....*C. arvense* (L.) Scop.
    7. Leaves almost entire or slightly lobed, weakly prickly; occasional in fields and waste places; nat. from Eur. June-Aug. [*C. arvense* var. *integrifolium* Wimm. & Grab.] ....*C. setosum* (Willd.) Bieb.

55. **Carduus** L. — Musk Thistle

C. nutans L. An occasional weed in waste places; introd. from Eur. May-Sept.

56. **Onopordum** L. — Scotch Thistle

O. acanthium L. Roadsides and waste places, occasional; nat. from Eur.; Champaign and Cook counties. July-Aug.

57. **Centaurea** L. — Star Thistle

1. Bracts of the involucre not spiny.
    2. Heads large, few or solitary, the involucre 3.5-4.5 cm high; flowers purple, the marginal ones enlarged, sterile; waste ground, occasionally escaped from cult. but not established in Ill.; native of western U.S. June-Aug. American Basket Flower ....*C. americana* Nutt.
    2. Heads smaller, the involucre 0.5-2.5 cm high.
        3. Bracts entire; leaves linear-lanceolate, sessile, the basal pinnatifid; flowers rose; perennial with deep horizontal black roots; occasional in fields and waste places; nat. from the region of the Caucasus. June-Aug. Russian Knapweed ....*C. repens* L.
        3. Bracts pectinate.
            4. Lower bracts pectinate or fringed to the middle or below; leaves entire or toothed.
                5. Bracts lanceolate, pale, without dilated tips; flowers blue, purplish, pink, or white, the marginal ones enlarged; plants annual; waste places, escaped from cult.; native of Eur. July-Sept. Bachelor's Button ....
                ....*C. cyanus* L.
                5. Bracts with abruptly dilated tips; flowers rose-purple; plants perennial.
                    6. Flowers all alike, discoid, not enlarged; bracts regularly pectinate-fringed; fields and roadsides, occasional; adv. from Eur. July-Sept. Black Knapweed ....*C. nigra* L.
                    6. Marginal flowers enlarged, showy; bracts irregularly lacerate to entire; fields and roadsides, occasional; adv. from Eur. June-Sept. Brown Knapweed ....
                    ....*C. jacea* L.
            4. Lower bracts pectinate only near the dark-colored tip.
                7. Leaves lanceolate, entire or toothed, only the lower ones lyrate; heads about 4 cm in diameter; flowers rose-purple; plants perennial; waste ground, occasional; adv. from Eur. Aug.-Oct. ....*C. vochinensis* Bernh.
                7. All but the uppermost leaves pinnatifid with linear segments; heads 2-2.5 cm broad; flowers white to purple; plants annual or biennial; roadsides and waste places in the northern counties; nat. from Eur. July-Sept. Spotted Knapweed ....*C. maculosa* Lam.

1. Bracts of the involucre tipped with a rigid spine; plants annual.
   8. Spines of the bracts 1-2.5 cm long.
      9. Flowers purple; stem wingless; heads sessile; waste places,
        occasional; adv. from Eur. June-Oct. ....*C. calcitrapa* L.
      9. Flowers yellow; stem winged by the decurrent leaf-bases;
        heads peduncled; waste places, occasional; adv. from Eur.
        July-Sept. Barnaby's Thistle ....*C. solstitialis* L.
   8. Bracts pectinate, the spine weak, 1-2 mm long; flowers whitish
     or pink; stems angular; heads peduncled, numerous; road-
     sides and waste places, occasional; native of Eurasia. July-
     Sept. ....*C. diffusa* Lam.

58. Cnicus L.

C. benedictus L. Escaped from gardens; introd. from s. Eur.

Tribe 12. *Cichorieae*
59. Lapsana L.

L. communis L. Nipplewort. Occasional weed along roads and
in waste places; nat. from Eur. June-Sept.

60. Serinia Raf.

S. oppositifolia (Raf.) Ktze. Moist sandy soil, s. Ill. Mar.-Apr.

61. Krigia Schreb.

1. Plants perennial; pappus of 10-15 minute scales, and 15-20 long
   bristles.
   2. Plants with a solitary head on a leafless scape; involucre 10-15
     mm high; plant bearing a small globose tuber; open woods
     in the southern half of Ill. Apr.-May ....*K. dandelion* (L.) Nutt.
   2. Plants with 1-3 clasping stem-leaves, and several heads; in-
     volucre 8-10 mm high; plant without a tuber; wooded slopes
     and ridges. May-Sept. [*K. amplexicaulis* (Michx.) Nutt.]
     ....*K. biflora* (Walt.) Blake

62. Cichorium L. — Chicory

C. intybus L. Roadsides and fields, common; nat. from Eur. June-
Nov. There are occasional white-flowered plants.

63. Hypochaeris L.

H. radicata L. Waste ground, rare. Champaign Co., *M. L. Briggs*
in 1950.

64. Picris L.

1. Outer bracts of the involucre large, ovate, bristly-ciliate; achenes
   long-beaked; adv. from Eur.; reported from Hancock Co. ....
   ....*P. echioides* L.
1. Outer bracts of the involucre linear-lanceolate, strigose; achenes
   short-beaked; adv. from Eur.; reported from Menard Co. ....
   ....*P. hieracioides* L.

65. **Tragopogon** L. — Oyster-plant. Salsify

1. Flowers purple; bracts longer than the flowers; peduncle thickened below the head; fruiting involucre 3-5 cm long; roadsides and fields, occasional; nat. from Eur. June-Aug. Vegetable Oyster. (*T. porrifolius* x *pratensis* is reported from Kane Co. by E. E. Sherff) ....*T. porrifolius* L.
1. Flowers yellow.
    2. Bracts usually 13, longer than the pale lemon-yellow flowers; peduncles thickened beneath the fruiting head; fruiting involucres 4.5-6 cm long; roadsides and fields, common; nat. from Eur. May-Oct. ....*T. dubius* Scop.
    2. Bracts usually 8 or 9, equalling or shorter than the chrome-yellow flowers; peduncles slender, scarcely thickened beneath the head; fruiting involucres 3-4 cm long; roadsides and fields, common; nat. from Eur. May-Oct. Yellow Goats-beard ....*T. pratensis* L.

66. **Lactuca** L. — Lettuce

1. Achenes slender-beaked; pappus white.
    2. Achenes light brown, 5- to 7-ribbed, the beak filiform, longer than the body; stem 30-60 cm tall; flowers yellow.
        3. Leaves elliptical in outline, pinnatifid, or merely spinulose-denticulate in f. *integrifolia* (Bogenh.) G. Beck, tending to turn edgewise in a vertical position, the margins and midribs spinulose; panicle open, with spreading branches; waste places, fields, and roadsides, common; nat. from Eur. July-Sept. Prickly Lettuce ....*L. scariola* L.
        3. Leaves linear-lanceolate, or pinnatifid, their margins and midrib not spinulose; panicle narrow, with short ascending branches; roadsides and waste places, occasional; nat. from Eur. July-Aug. Willow Lettuce ....*L. saligna* L.
    2. Achenes dark brown, 1-nerved, transversely rugulose, the beak about as long as the body or shorter; stem 1-3 m tall; native species.
        4. Leaves entire to pinnatifid, not spinulose-toothed; flowers yellow; open woods, fields, roadsides, common. June-Aug. Wild Lettuce. A supposed hybrid between this and the following species has been collected in Cook Co. ....*L. canadensis* L.
        4. Leaves spinulose-toothed, the midvein on the lower surface somewhat setose; flowers pale lilac; prairie soil, rare. July. [*L. campestris* Greene] ....*L. ludoviciana* (Nutt.) Riddell
1. Achenes beakless or short-beaked; flowers not yellow.
    5. Pappus white; flowers lavender or blue.
        6. Heads 6-10 mm in diameter, the involucres 10-13 mm high; leaves varying from dentate to usually lyrate-pinnatifid with the triangular terminal lobe larger; plants biennial

or annual; woods, common throughout Ill. July-Sept.
[*L. villosa* Jacq.] Woodland Lettuce ..*L. floridana* (L.) Gaertn.

6. Heads 1-2 cm in diameter, the involucres 16-20 mm high; leaves linear-lanceolate, entire or dentate to lobed or pinnatifid, those of the stem partly clasping; plants perennial, adv. from western U.S.; an occasional migrant along railroads in the northern counties. July-Aug. Blue Lettuce
....*L. pulchella* (Pursh) DC.

5. Pappus brown; flowers cream or bluish; leaves pinnatifid or merely sinuate; alluvial soil in woods, occasional. Aug.-Sept. Tall Blue Lettuce ....*L. biennis* (Moench) Fern.

67. Sonchus L. — Sow Thistle

1. Plants perennial; heads 4-5 cm in diameter, the flowers bright yellow; involucre 1.5 cm high; achenes striate and papillose.
2. Involucres and peduncles glandular-setose; fields and waste places in a few scattered localities in the northern half of the state; first coll. in Cook Co., by E. J. Hill in 1882; nat. from Eur. July-Sept. ....*S. arvensis* L.
2. Involucres and peduncles glabrous; fields and waste places, first reported for Ill. in 1934; recently spread with remarkable rapidity almost throughout the northern half of the state, where it is now an abundant weed; nat. from Eur. July-Sept. [*S. arvensis* var. *glabrescens* Guenth., Grab. & Wimm.] ....*S. uliginosus* Bieb.
1. Plants annual; heads 1-2.5 cm in diameter, pale yellow; involucre 1 cm high.
3. Leaves runcinate-pinnatifid, scarcely prickly, the terminal segment commonly large and triangular; upper leaves clasping by an acute, sagittate base; achenes longitudinally striate and papillose; fields and waste places; nat. from Eur. June-Nov. Common Sow Thistle ....*S. oleraceus* L.
3. Leaves toothed or more or less curled or lobed, harshly prickly, the basal auricles rounded; achenes longitudinally ribbed, otherwise smooth; fields and waste places; nat. from Eur. May-Aug. Spiny Sow Thistle ....*S. asper* (L.) Hill

68. Prenanthes L. — Rattlesnake-root

1. Involucre glabrous.
2. Heads about 2 mm thick, 5- to 7-flowered; pappus straw-colored; plants not glaucous; oak woods, locally in the eastern and southern counties; absent from the western part of the state. Aug.-Sept. ....*P. altissima* L.
2. Heads 3-5 mm thick, 8-12-flowered; pappus reddish-brown; plants glaucous; woods in the northern half of the state. Aug.-Sept. ....*P. alba* L.
1. Involucre pubescent.
3. Stem usually simple; heads 12- to 16-flowered.

4. Stem and leaves glabrous; flowers purplish; moist ground, nearly throughout Ill. Aug.-Sept. ....*P. racemosa* Michx.
4. Stem and lower surface of leaves scabrous-pubescent; flowers light yellow; prairie soil, locally throughout Ill. Aug.-Sept. [*P. illinoensis* Pers.] ....*P. aspera* Michx.
3. Stem corymbosely branched above; heads 20- to 35-flowered; flowers cream; banks of streams and edges of woods, locally throughout Ill., except the extreme northern counties. Aug.-Oct. ....*P. crepidinea* Michx.

69. Hieracium L. — Hawkweed

1. Plants with stolons and slender rhizomes.
  2. Flowers orange-red; fields and meadows, occasional; nat. from Eur.; Lake and Ogle counties. June-July. Orange Hawkweed ....*H. aurantiacum* L.
  2. Flowers yellow; nat. from Eur.; Cook Co.......*H. pratense* Tausch
1. Plants with short stout erect rhizomes; stolons none; flowers yellow.
  3. Heads medium or small, 1-2 cm in diameter; leaves entire or denticulate.
    4. Leaves and lower part of stem densely long villous-hirsute with brownish or whitish hairs 1-2 cm long; achenes fusiform; fields and open woods, local. July-Sept. ....*H. longipilum* Torr.
    4. Leaves and stem with shorter pubescence.
      5. Inflorescence with foliaceous bracts, the heads 40-50-flowered, on stout peduncles; achenes columnar, truncate, 2-2.5 mm long; dry woods and fields, locally throughout Ill. Aug.-Sept. [*H. scabrum* var. *intonsum* Fern. & St.John] ....*H. scabrum* Michx.
      5. Inflorescence with small subulate bracts, the heads 15-20-flowered, on slender peduncles; achenes fusiform, tapering toward the apex, 3-3.5 mm long; dry soil in woods, local. July-Sept. ....*H. gronovii* L.
  3. Heads large, 2.5-4.5 cm in diameter; leaves dentate.
    6. Stem leafless or nearly so; basal leaves elliptical, dentate toward the base, the petioles villous; peduncles and bracts with stalked glands; pappus white; fields and waste places; adv. from Eur.; Springfield, Sangamon Co., *G. D. Fuller & Lola Carter* in 1947. June-Aug. Golden Hieracium ....*H. murorum* L.
    6. Stem leafy; leaves numerous, lanceolate, sessile; peduncles tomentulose; pappus brownish; dry woods and thickets in the northern counties. Aug.-Sept. Canada Hawkweed ....*H. canadense* Michx.

70. Crepis L. — Hawksbeard

C. capillaris (L.) Wallr. Occasionally found in waste places, or in lawns; adv. from Eur. June-July.

71. Pyrrhopappus DC. — False Dandelion

P. carolinianus (Walt.) DC. Dry soil in s. Ill., extending northward to Hancock, Sangamon, and Crawford counties. May-June.

72. Agoseris Raf.

A. cuspidata (Pursh) D.Dietr. Dry soil, rare, in the northern half of the state, southward to Tazewell and Champaign counties. May-June.

73. Taraxacum Zinn — Dandelion

1. Achenes greenish-brown; heads usually 3-5 cm in diameter, 150- to 200-flowered, the flowers orange-yellow; outer involucral bracts reflexed; leaves usually sinuate to coarsely pinnatifid, the terminal lobe large; waste places, fields, roadsides, lawns, etc., very common; nat. from Eur. Mar.-Nov. Common Dandelion [*Leontodon taraxacum* L.; *L. vulgaris* Lam.] ....
....*T. officinale* Wiggers
1. Achenes red or reddish-brown; heads 2-3 cm in diameter, 75- to 125-flowered, the flowers sulphur-yellow; leaves deeply pin-natifid, the terminal lobe small; waste places, less frequent than the preceding; nat. from Eur. Apr.-June. Red-seeded Dandelion [*T. laevigatum* of auth., not (Willd.) DC.; *Leon-todon erythrospermum* (Andrz.) Eichw.] ....
....*T. erythrospermum* Andrz.

Class II. Monocotyledoneae (Juss.) DC.

126. Alismaceae DC. — Water-plantain Family

1. Flowers numerous, small, perfect, in a compound panicle; leaves oval or ovate; stamens usually 6; carpels flattened, arranged in a ring on a small flat receptacle ....1. *Alisma*
1. Flowers in whorls, fewer; stamens 9-many; carpels in a head on a convex receptacle.
    2. Leaves cordate or ovate, with 5-7 veins from the base; flowers perfect, 3-9 or more in each whorl; plants annual ....2. *Echinodorus*
    2. Leaves sagittate or lanceolate, more than 7-veined; plants perennial ....
    ....3. *Sagittaria*

1. Alisma L. — Water-plantain

1. Petals 1-2 mm long; achenes 1.5-2 mm long; ditches and margins of ponds, common. July-Sept. [*A. plantago-aquatica* Am. auth., non L.] ....*A. subcordatum* Raf.
1. Petals 3-5 mm long; achenes 2.2-3 mm long; in similar habitats, but apparently less common. [*A. plantago* var. *americanum* R. & S.; *A. brevipes* Greene] ....*A. triviale* Pursh

2. Echinodorus Rich. — Burhead

1. Leaves linear-lanceolate; scape 3-10 cm tall; stamens 9; achenes 10-15, black, merely apiculate; muddy shores, rare; Cass, Mason, and St. Clair counties. [*E. tenellus* (Mart.) Buch.] ......
....*E. parvulus* Engelm.

1. Leaves ovate to cordate; stamens 12-21; achenes 40 or more, brown, beaked.
    2. Scape erect, 10-30 cm tall; stamens 12; style longer than the ovary; shores of ponds, rare. June-July [*E. cordifolius* sensu auth., non (L.) Griseb.] ......*E. rostratus* (Nutt.) Engelm.
    2. Scape prostrate, proliferous; stamens about 20; style shorter than the ovary; swamps, rare. June-July [*E. radicans* (Nutt.) Engelm.] ....*E. cordifolius* (L.) Griseb.

3. Sagittaria L. — Arrowhead
(*Lophotocarpus* T.Durand)

1. Fruiting pedicels thickened, spreading or recurved; sepals suborbicular, surrounding the mature fruit; lower flowers perfect, the upper staminate with 9-15 stamens; leaves sagittate; shallow water, rare or local. [*L. calycinus* (Engelm.) J.G.Sm.] ......
....*S. calycinus* Engelm.
1. Fruiting pedicels not thickened, ascending; sepals spreading or reflexed in fruit; lower flowers pistillate, the upper staminate with numerous stamens.
    2. Leaves sagittate; stamens with glabrous filaments.
        3. Bracts of the inflorescence ovate, obtusish; beak of the achene horizontal; shallow water. July-Sept. Common Arrowhead ....*S. latifolia* Willd.
        3. Bracts lanceolate, acuminate; beak erect.
            4. Achenes 2 mm long, with thick equal wings on both margins, the beak 0.5 mm long; shallow water. July-Sept. ....*S. cuneata* Sheld.
            4. Achenes 2.5-3 mm long, with thin, unequal wings; beak 1-1.5 mm long; muddy shores, or in ditches, common. July-Sept. ....*S. brevirostra* Mack. & Bush
    2. Leaves linear, lanceolate, or oval (rarely sagittate) ; filaments more or less glandular-pubescent.
        5. Achenes 3 mm long, the beak 1.5 mm long; pedicels very short, the pistillate flowers nearly sessile; ditches or muddy shores. June-Oct. ....*S. rigida* Pursh
        5. Achenes 2 mm long, the beak less than 1 mm long; pedicels of the pistillate flowers equalling those of the staminate; shallow water or margins of ponds and ditches. June-Sept. ....*S. graminea* Michx.

127. Juncaginaceae Lindl. — Arrow-grass Family

1. Flowers numerous, greenish, in a long spike-like raceme; leaves all basal
....1. *Triglochin*
1. Flowers few, white, in a loose raceme ....2. *Scheuchzeria*

1. Triglochin L. — Arrow-grass

1. Carpels usually 6, in fruit ellipsoid, 3-6 mm long; sandy or marly swales, or in swamps or along ditches, not common; Cook,

Lake, McHenry, and Peoria counties. June-July ....
.... *T. maritima* L.
1. Carpels 3, in fruit clavate, 7-8 mm long; calcareous soil, rare;
Cook, Kane, Kankakee, Lake, McHenry, Peoria, and Tazewell
counties. July-Sept. .... *T. palustris* L.

2. Scheuchzeria L.

S. americana (Fern.) G.N.Jones. Bogs, rare; Fulton, Lake,
McHenry, and Menard counties. June-July. [*S. palustris* sensu Am.
auth., non L.; *S. palustris* var. *americana* Fern.]. On the basis of shape
and size of follicles, our plants appear specifically distinct from the
European *S. palustris* L.

128. Naiadaceae Lindl. — Naiad Family
1. Naias L. — Naiad

1. Fruit glossy, with 30-50 longitudinal lines; style 1-2 mm long;
leaves with 20-30 minute teeth on each margin; ponds and slow
streams throughout Ill. June-Aug. ......*N. flexilis* (Willd.) R. & S.
1. Fruit dull, with 10-20 rows of distinct reticulations; style 0.2-
0.6 mm long; leaves with 40-50 minute teeth on each margin;
ponds and shallow lakes, rare; Lake, Macoupin, Peoria, and
Williamson counties. July-Sept. ....
.... *N. guadalupensis* (Spreng.) Magnus

129. Potamogetonaceae Engler — Pondweed Family
(*Zosteraceae* Dumort.)

1. Flowers perfect, in spikes; leaves alternate, or the upper sometimes opposite
....1. *Potamogeton*
1. Flowers unisexual, axillary; leaves opposite, filiform, 1-veined, entire ....
....2. *Zannichellia*

1. Potamogeton L. — Pondweed

1. Leaves uniform, all submerged.
  2. Leaves linear to filiform.
    3. Stipules free from the petioles and blades.
      4. Leaves 9- to 35-veined; fruits 3.5-5 mm long; lakes, chief-
      ly in Cook, Kankakee, Lake, McHenry, Menard,
      and Winnebago counties. [*P. compressus* Am. auth.,
      non L.] .... *P. zosteriformis* Fern.
      4. Leaves 1- to 7-veined; fruits 1.5-3 mm long.
        5. Leaves 5- to 7-veined, with a pair of basal glands;
        stagnant water, rare; Cook, Jackson, and Lake
        counties. [*P. mucronatus* Schrad.] .... *P. friesii* Rupr.
        5. Leaves 1- to 3-veined.
          6. Blades usually without basal glands; fruiting spikes
          subcapitate, 2-8 mm long; ponds, ditches, and
          streams, chiefly in the northern half of Ill. ....
          .... *P. foliosus* Raf.

6. Blades usually with a pair of small translucent glands at the base.
  7. Leaves gradually tapering to a bristle tip, revolute, rigid; shallow water, Wolf Lake, Cook Co., *A. Chase* ....*P. strictifolius* Benn.
  7. Leaves not bristle-tipped.
    8. Peduncles filiform, 3-8 mm long; stipules partly connate; lakes, etc. [*P. panormitanus* Biv.] ......
    ....*P. pusillus* L.
    8. Peduncle 0.5-3 cm long; stipules not connate; ditches, rare; Lake Co. ....*P. berchtoldi* Fieber
3. Stipules adnate to the base of the leaves.
  9. Leaves filiform, less than 0.6 mm wide, entire; lakes and ponds, locally abundant .... *P. pectinatus* L.
  9. Leaves linear, 2-ranked, 3-6 mm wide, the margin microscopically serrulate; lakes, rare; Lake Co. ....
  .... *P. robbinsii* Oakes
2. Leaves lanceolate to elliptical or ovate.
  10. Leaves clasping the stem.
    11. Leaves slightly clasping at base, cucullate at the apex, mostly 8-30 cm long; fruits 4-5 mm long; lakes in Cook, Lake, and McHenry counties ....*P. praelongus* Wulfen
    11. Leaves mostly 2-8 cm long, strongly clasping at the base, the apex flat, not cucullate; fruits 2.5-4 mm long; lakes in Cook, Kankakee, Lake, and McHenry counties ....
    ....*P. richardsonii* (A.Benn.) Rydb.
  10. Leaves sessile, not clasping, linear-elliptical, 5-12 mm wide, obtuse, undulate or crisped, 3-5-nerved; ponds and streams, not common; introd. from eastern U.S.; nat. from Eur. May-Sept. .... *P. crispus* L.
1. Leaves of two kinds, broader floating ones, and narrower submerged ones.
  12. Submerged leaves lanceolate to elliptical, more than 5 mm wide.
    13. Stem usually black-spotted; principal floating leaves somewhat cordate at base; fruit 3-3.5 mm long; shallow water in Mason, Menard, and St. Clair counties ....
    ....*P. pulcher* Tuckerm.
    13. Stem not black-spotted; leaves tapering at the base, or rounded.
      14. Floating leaves with 30 or more principal veins; lakes and ditches, local; Cook, Du Page, Lake, and Wabash counties .... *P. amplifolius* Tuckerm.
      14. Floating leaves with fewer veins.
        15. Mature spikes 4-6 cm long.
          16. Floating leaves elliptical, not mucronate, 4-9 cm broad; submerged leaves lanceolate; style prominent on the fruit; streams and ponds

in the northern half of the state; first collected near Oquawka, Henderson Co., by H.
N. Patterson .... *P. illinoensis* Morong
16. Floating leaves oval, mucronate, 1-3 cm wide;
    submerged leaves narrowly lanceolate; fruit
    tipped by the nearly sessile stigma; ponds,
    ditches, and streams, not uncommon. [*P.
    nodosus* Poir. (?)] .... *P. americanus* C. & S.
15. Mature spikes 1-2 cm long; floating leaves oval, 1-3
    cm wide; submerged leaves lanceolate, acumi-
    nate or cuspidate; ponds or slow streams, chief-
    ly in the eastern part of the state ....
    .... *P. gramineus* L.
12. Submerged leaves linear or filiform, not more than 5 mm
    wide.
17. Submerged leaves linear, 2-5 mm wide, conspicuously
    reticulate along the midvein; ponds and lakes, not
    common; Fulton, Hancock, and Lake counties ....
    .... *P. epihydrus* Raf.
17. Submerged leaves filiform, 1-2 mm wide.
18. Spikes of 2 kinds: one emersed, cylindrical, many-
    flowered, the other submerged, globose, few-
    flowered; ditches and slow streams, not uncom-
    mon; chiefly in the w. and s. counties. [*P. hybridus*
    of Michx. and Am. auth.] ....*P. diversifolius* Raf.
18. Spikes all alike, cylindrical.
19. Blades of the floating leaves less than 1.5 cm long,
    equalling or longer than the petioles; spikes less
    than 1 cm long; lakes, rare; McHenry Co. ....
    .... *P. vaseyi* Robbins
19. Blades of the floating leaves 2.5 cm or more in
    length, mostly shorter than the petioles; spikes 1.5
    cm or more in length; lakes, ponds, and ditches,
    not uncommon .... *P. natans* L.

2. Zannichellia L. — Horned Pondweed

Z palustris L. Ditches and ponds, not common; Fulton, Henderson, Henry, Menard, Peoria, and Winnebago counties.

130. Liliaceae Adans. — Lily Family

1. Stem leafy (bearing one or more leaves).
  2. Flowers large, 4-10 cm long; leaves alternate or whorled; fruit a capsule
  ....11. *Lilium*
  2. Flowers smaller.
    3. Leaves whorled.
      4. Flowers several; leaves in usually two whorls, parallel-veined ....
      ....23. *Medeola*
      4. Flowers solitary; leaves in one whorl, net-veined ....24. *Trillium*
    3. Leaves alternate.

5. Flowers axillary or terminal, solitary or few, or in umbels.
  6. Leaves reduced to scales with filiform short branchlets appearing like leaves about 1 cm long in the axils; flowers axillary, small, greenish, nodding, on slender, jointed pedicels; berry red, 3-seeded ....16. *Asparagus*
  6. Leaves foliaceous.
    7. Flowers in axillary umbels, unisexual; leaves net-veined; fruit a berry ....25. *Smilax*
    7. Flowers not in umbels.
      8. Stem simple; perianth-segments united below the middle; flowers greenish; fruit a berry ....20. *Polygonatum*
      8. Stem forked above; perianth-segments free; flowers yellowish; fruit a capsule ....19. *Uvularia*
5. Flowers in a terminal raceme or panicle.
  9. Leaves linear; styles 3, separate.
    10. Stem puberulent above; perianth-segments clawed, and (in our species) bearing a pair of glands; plants with a rhizome ....5. *Melanthium*
    10. Stem glabrous; plants from a bulb.
      11. Perianth-segments lanceolate, acuminate, glandless; panicle many-flowered ....1. *Stenanthium*
      11. Perianth-segments bearing a large obcordate gland; raceme simple or sparingly branched, few- or several-flowered ....2. *Zigadenus*
  9. Leaves not linear.
    12. Leaves 2 or 3, cordate at base; perianth-segments 4, white; stamens 4; fruit a berry ....18. *Maianthemum*
    12. Leaves several, lanceolate or oblanceolate; perianth-segments 6.
      13. Plants not dioecious.
        14. Flowers (in our species) greenish-purple; leaves strongly veined; fruit a capsule ....6. *Veratrum*
        14. Flowers white; fruit a berry ....17. *Smilacina*
      13. Plants dioecious; flowers white; fruit a capsule ....4. *Chamaelirium*
1. Leaves all or mostly basal, or apparently so, rarely absent at flowering time; fruit a capsule.
15. Flowers very large, over 5 cm long.
  16. Flowers orange or yellow ....9. *Hemerocallis*
  16. Flowers blue or whitish ....10. *Hosta*
15. Flowers smaller.
  17. Flower solitary, nodding; leaves 2 (or 1); plants from deep-seated corms ....12. *Erythronium*
  17. Flowers several or many.
    18. Flowers in racemes or panicles.
      19. Inflorescence a large panicle; flowers large (3-5 cm long); leaves stiff, long-pointed, filamentous on the margins ....22. *Yucca*
      19. Inflorescence a raceme; flowers smaller; leaves soft, not filamentous.
        20. Flowers white; plants with rhizomes.
          21. Sepals and petals nearly distinct throughout ....3. *Tofieldia*

21. Sepals and petals united nearly to apex ....
....21. *Convallaria*
20. Flowers lavender or blue; plants with bulbs.
22. Sepals and petals nearly distinct throughout ....
....13. *Camassia*
22. Sepals and petals united nearly to apex ....
....14. *Muscari*
18. Flowers in a corymb or umbel; plants with bulbs.
23. Flowers in a corymb, greenish-white; filaments flattened at
the base; midvein of leaves whitish ....15. *Ornithogalum*
23. Flowers in an umbel.
24. Plants with the odor and taste of onions (alliaceous);
flowers pink or white, often replaced by bulblets; seeds
1 or 2 in each locule of the capsule ....7. *Allium*
24. Plants not alliaceous; flowers yellowish; seeds several in
each locule ....8. *Nothoscordum*

1. **Stenanthium** (A. Gray) Kunth

S. gramineum (Ker) Morong. Woods, and moist ground along
creeks, rare; s. Ill., extending northward to Richland, Macoupin,
Fayette, and Pike counties. June-Aug.

2. **Zigadenus** Michx. — Death Camas

Z. glaucus Nutt. Limestone bluffs and crevices of rocks, rare;
known from Jo Daviess and Kane counties. July-Aug.

3. **Tofieldia** Huds. — Asphodel

T. glutinosa (Michx.) Pers. Bogs in Cook, Lake, and McHenry
counties. June-July.

4. **Chamaelirium** Willd.

C. luteum (L.) A.Gray. Woods, rare; Hardin and Massac counties.

5. **Melanthium** L. — Bunchflower

M. virginicum L. Meadows, in the w. and centr. part of the state,
rare. June-July.

6. **Veratrum** L.

V. woodii Robbins. Moist wooded ravines, rare; known from eight
counties chiefly in the central part of Ill. July-Sept.

7. **Allium** L. — Onion

1. Leaves linear, terete or flat, present at flowering time.
2. Umbel nodding, 2-bracted, not bulblet-bearing; perianth rose,
4-6 mm long; ovary and capsule crested; stamens exserted;
outer bulb-coat membranous; banks, n. Ill. July-Sept. Nodding Onion .... *A. cernuum* Roth
2. Umbel erect.
3. Umbels commonly bulblet-bearing.

4. Bracts below the umbel 3; leaves flat, soft, slightly keeled, 2-8 mm wide; stamens about as long as the perianth; outer bulb-coat fibrous; meadows, roadsides, woods, common. May-June. Wild Onion .... *A. canadense* L.
4. Bract one; stamens exserted; bulb-coat membranous.
    5. Leaves hollow, about 2 mm wide; umbels rather lax, usually with bulblets only; roadsides, meadows, and fields, common; nat. from Eur. June-July. Field Garlic. .... *A. vineale* L.
    5. Leaves flat, 8-15 mm wide; umbels dense; waste places, occasional; native of Eur. June-July. Garlic .... *A. sativum* L.
3. Umbels not bulblet-bearing.
    6. Leaves flat.
        7. Leaves 2-4 mm broad; bracts of the umbel 2 or 3.
            8. Stamens exserted; outer bulb-coat membranous, finely reticulate; ovary and capsule crested; rocky slopes, s.w. Ill. July-Aug. ....*A. stellatum* Ker
            8. Stamens included; outer bulb-coat fibrous; ovary and capsule not crested; prairie soil, borders of woods, or calcareous bluffs, occasionally in s. and w. Ill. May-June .... *A. mutabilis* Michx.
        7. Leaves 2.5-4 cm broad, keeled; flowers numerous in a dense terminal umbel, subtended by a single, acuminate bract; plant stout, biennial, 60-90 cm tall; a cultigen, sometimes escaped but not established in Ill.; native of Eurasia. Leek .... *A. porrum* L.
    6. Leaves hollow; bracts 2 or 3, reflexed; scape 30-90 cm tall, hollow, longer than the leaves; flowers numerous, lilac; gardens and waste places, occasional; native of western Asia. Onion ....*A. cepa* L.
1. Leaves 2, elliptical-lanceolate, 3-6 cm wide, disappearing before flowering time; perianth-segments white, obtuse, 6-7 mm long; filaments subulate, equalling the perianth; capsule strongly 3-lobed; woods in the northern half of Ill. June-Aug. Wild Leek .... *A. tricoccum* Ait.

8. Nothoscordum Kunth — False Garlic

N. bivalve (L.) Britt. Meadows, roadsides or woodlands in the southern half of the state, not common. Apr.-May.

9. Hemerocallis L. — Day Lily

1. Flowers 8-12 cm long, orange, not fragrant; margins of perianth-segments undulate; leaves 1-3 cm wide; a sterile triploid not forming seeds; commonly cult. and extensively naturalized, spreading vegetatively to roadsides, waste places, and moist woods and fields, common; native of China. June-Aug. Orange Day Lily .... *H. fulva* L.

1. Flowers 6-8 cm long, lemon-yellow, fragrant; margins of perianth-
segments flat; leaves 5-10 mm wide; capsules 2-3 cm long;
cult. and occasionally escaped; native of temperate eastern Asia.
May-July. Yellow Day Lily. .... *H. flava* L.

10. Hosta Tratt. — Plantain Lily

H. lancifolia (Thunb.) Engler. Waste ground, Mississippi Palisades
State Park, Carroll Co., *R. H. Mohlenbrock* in 1956; escaped from
cult.; native of Asia. [*H. japonica* (Thunb.) Voss, not Tratt.]

11. Lilium L. — Lily

1. Leaf-axils not bulblet-bearing.
    2. Flowers erect; perianth-segments with oval or lanceolate blades
    and a slender claw; leaves mostly alternate, linear, 2-7 mm
    wide; dry open woods in the northern half of Ill. June-July.
    [*L. philadelphicum* var. *andinum* (Nutt.) Ker] Wood Lily
    .... *L. umbellatum* Pursh
    2. Flowers nodding; perianth-segments oblanceolate, not clawed,
    recurved; leaves mostly whorled, elliptic-lanceolate, 1-3 cm
    wide; moist woods, thickets, meadows. June-Aug. [*L. cana-
    dense* and *L. superbum* of auth., not L.] Turk's-cap Lily
    .... *L. michiganense* Farw.
1. Leaves scattered, the upper axils usually bulblet-bearing; stem
pubescent above; perianth-segments recurved from the base;
rarely escaped from cult., but not established; native of eastern
Asia. July-Aug. Tiger Lily ....*L. tigrinum* Ker

12. Erythronium L. — Trout Lily

1. Perianth yellow; style clavate, the stigmas erect, united; woods;
apparently absent from the western part of Ill. Apr-May ....
.... *E. americanum* Ker
1. Perianth white or pale lavender; style 3-cleft, the recurved stigmas
1-3 mm long; alluvial soil in woods, common. Apr. ....
.... *E. albidum* Nutt.

13. Camassia Lindl. — Camas

C. scilloides (Raf.) Cory. Wild Hyacinth. Moist woods or meadows, locally throughout Ill. Apr.-June. [*C. esculenta* sensu auth., non
(Raf.) Lindl.; *C. fraseri* Torr.]. Including *C. angusta* (Engelm. &
Gray) Blankinship, a late-flowering plant with deeper colored shorter
perianth. Macon Co.: *V. H. Chase* 11900; Peoria Co.: *Schoenbeck.*

14. Muscari Mill. — Grape Hyacinth

1. Leaves overtopping the scape; open woods, rare, escaped from
cult.; Piatt Co. Native of Armenia. April ....
.... *M. armeniacum* Leichtl.

1. Leaves not longer than the scape.
 2. Leaves erect, flat, 4-8 mm broad; flowers globose, odorless, pale blue; roadsides and woods, occasional, escaped from cult.; Jackson, Union, Edgar, and Hardin counties ....
 .... *M. botryoides* (L.) Mill.
 2. Leaves recurved, 1-3 mm broad, almost terete; flowers ellipsoid, fragrant, dark blue; occasionally along roads and in fields, escaped from cult. and spreading; native of Eur.; Monroe and Montgomery counties. ....
 .... *M. racemosum* (L.) Mill.

15. Ornithogalum L.

O. umbellatum L. Star-of-Bethlehem. Roadsides, edges of fields, locally abundant; escaped from cult.; nat. from Eur. Apr.-May.

16. Asparagus L.

A. officinalis L. Garden Asparagus. Roadsides and fields, common; nat. from Eur. May-June.

17. Smilacina Desf. — False Solomon's-seal

1. Flowers numerous in a panicle; perianth-segments 1-2 mm long; woods, common. May-June .... *S. racemosa* (L.) Desf.
1. Flowers few in a raceme; perianth-segments 3-5 mm long; woods, common, extending southward to Macoupin and Wabash counties. Apr.-May .... *S. stellata* (L.) Desf.

18. Maianthemum Weber — False Lily-of-the-Valley

M. canadense Desf. Moist woods, n. Ill. May-June. Our plants belong to var. *interius* Fern.

19. Uvularia L. — Bellwort

1. Leaves perfoliate, puberulent beneath; capsules obtusely 3-angled, rounded or retuse at the apex; moist woods, not uncommon. Apr.-May .... *U. grandiflora* Sm.
1. Leaves sessile, glabrous; capsules sharply 3-angled, acutish at each end; woods in s. Ill., rare. Apr.-May ....
 .... *U. sessilifolia* L.

20. Polygonatum Mill. — Solomon's-seal

1. Leaves puberulent on the veins beneath; lowest leaf a papery bract, leaving a ring-like scar on the stem; peduncles commonly 2-flowered; woods, n.e. Ill.; known from Cook, Du Page, Kankakee, Lake, and Winnebago counties. May-June. [*P. biflorum* sensu auth., non (Walt.) Ell.] ....*P. pubescens* (Willd.) Pursh
1. Leaves glabrous; lowest leaf persistent; peduncles bearing 2-5 or more flowers.

2. Stem slender, 30-50 cm tall, 2-4 mm thick at base; median and lower leaves when mature usually 6-10 cm long, 1.5-3 cm wide; berries paired or solitary, 7-9 mm in diameter; seeds 2.5-3.5 mm long; plants presumably diploid (n = 10); woods, s. Ill., not common. May. [*P. canaliculatum* (Muhl.) Pursh] ....*P. biflorum* (Walt.) Ell.

2. Stem stout, becoming 60-120 cm tall and 1-1.5 cm thick toward the base; median and lower leaves 10-15 cm long, 5-8 cm wide; berries 5-8 on the lower peduncles, each 10-14 mm in diameter when fresh; seeds 9-11, subglobose, 4-5 mm in diameter; plants presumably tetraploid (n = 20); rich soil in woods throughout Ill. May-June. [*P. giganteum* Dietr.; *P. canaliculatum* sensu Fern., probably not *Convallaria canaliculata* Muhl.] ....*P. commutatum* (Schultes) Dietr.

21. Convallaria L. — Lily-of-the-valley

C. majalis L. Persisting near old dwellings; when planted in cemeteries often forming large patches from which the mature fruits are scattered by birds. Native of Eur.

22. Yucca L. — Common Yucca

Y. filamentosa L. Cemeteries, roadsides, old gardens; frequently cultivated, and often persisting, or occasionally escaped; native of southeastern U.S. June.

23. Medeola L. — Indian Cucumber-root

M. virginiana L. Wooded ravines, rare; Evanston, Cook Co., *L. N. Johnson* in 1889; Ottawa, La Salle Co., *G. D. Fuller* in 1939.

24. Trillium L. — Trillium

1. Flowers sessile; petals purple or green.
  2. Leaves definitely petioled, the petioles 1-2.5 cm long; sepals reflexed, acuminate, 1.5-3 cm long; rhizome slender, horizontal; woods, common throughout Ill. Apr.-May. Purple Trillium. Wake Robin. Yellow-flowered plants with purple stamens (f. *luteum* Clute) or yellow stamens (f. *shayi* Palmer & Steyerm.) are found occasionally ....
    ....*T. recurvatum* Beck
  2. Leaves sessile; sepals not reflexed; rhizome short, stout.
    3. Petals purple; sepals 2-3 cm long; stem smooth; moist woods, locally nearly throughout Ill., but not common. Apr.-May. Sessile Trillium ....*T. sessile* L.
    3. Petals greenish; sepals 4-6 cm long; stem often minutely hirtellous at summit; woods, rare; Jackson, Macoupin, Pike, and Union counties. Apr.-May. Green Trillium ....*T. viride* Beck
1. Flowers peduncled; petals white (or purple).

4. Leaves sessile or essentially so; fruit 6-angled, 6-winged.
  5. Petals 4-6 cm long, obovate or oblanceolate, white, turning pink with age; stigmas straight or nearly so; peduncle 3-10 cm long, erect or ascending; woods, locally in the northern half of Ill. Apr.-May. Large Trillium ....
....*T. grandiflorum* (Michx.) Salisb.
  5. Petals 2-4 cm long, oval; stigmas recurved or coiled.
    6. Peduncle 4-6 cm long, usually horizontal or declined; petals usually white (purple in f. *walpolei* (Farw.) Deam); filaments about one-third as long as the anthers; woods, locally nearly throughout Ill. Apr.-May ....*T. gleasoni* Fern.
    6. Peduncle 1-3 cm long, deflexed; filaments two-thirds as long as the anthers; woods, rare; Ringwood, McHenry Co., *Vasey;* Wolf Lake, Chicago, Cook Co., *E. J. Hill* in 1891 ....*T. cernuum* L.
4. Leaves short-petioled; petals white, 1.5-3 cm long; peduncle erect; fruit 3-lobed, not winged; wooded slopes, locally in the northern half of Ill., extending southward to Jersey, Sangamon, and Coles counties. Mar.-Apr. Snow Trillium
....*T. nivale* Riddell

25. Smilax L.

1. Stems woody, usually more or less prickly, at least on the lower part; ovules solitary in each locule of the ovary.
  2. Leaves glaucous on the lower surface, ovate; umbels 6- to 12-flowered; open woods and sandy soil in s. Ill. May-June. Sawbrier ....*S. glauca* Walt.
  2. Leaves green on both surfaces.
    3. Leaves more or less contracted near the middle or 3-lobed, commonly deltoid-hastate, often spinulose on the margins and veins beneath; umbels 15- to 45-flowered; fruit mostly 1-seeded; thickets in s. Ill. May-June. Fringed Greenbrier ....*S. bona-nox* L.
    3. Leaves ovate, cordate, or roundish.
      4. Branchlets terete or nearly so; prickles black, terete (upper branches often without prickles); peduncles longer than the petioles; fruit black, not glaucous, usually 1-seeded; woods and thickets, common throughout Ill. May-June. Common Greenbrier ....*S. hispida* Muhl.
      4. Branchlets angular; prickles flattened, green; peduncles shorter than the petioles; fruit glaucous, 2- or 3-seeded; dry woods in s. Ill. May-June ....*S. rotundifolia* L.
1. Plants herbaceous, not bristly or prickly; ovules two in each locule.
  5. Leaves puberulent and green and glossy beneath; stem climbing; fruit black; wooded slopes in the s. half of Ill. May ....
....*S. pulverulenta* Michx.

    5. Leaves glaucous beneath; fruit bluish, glaucous, 2- to 5-seeded.
      6. Stem climbing, 1-3 m long; tendrils present; umbels 25-
        to 100-flowered; peduncles in the axils of leaves; woods,
        common. Apr.-June. Carrion Flower [*S. herbacea* sensu
        auth., non L.] ....*S. lasioneura* Hook.
      6. Stem erect, 40-60 cm tall; tendrils usually absent; umbels
        with fewer than 25 flowers; peduncle in the axil of a
        bract below the leaves; moist woods, locally throughout
        Ill. except the southern counties. Apr.-May ....
        ....*S. ecirrhata* (Engelm.) Wats.

131. Juncaceae Vent. — Rush Family

1. Capsule many-seeded, 1- or 3-loculed, with axial or parietal placentae; plants glabrous ....1. *Juncus*
1. Capsule 3-seeded, 1-loculed, with basal placentae; plants often sparsely pilose ....2. *Luzula*

1. Juncus L. — Rush

1. Inflorescence appearing lateral, the involucral bract erect, terete, simulating a continuation of the stem; leaves reduced to sheaths.
    2. Stamens 3; perianth 2-3 mm long; anthers shorter than the filaments; stems densely tufted; ditches and marshy ground. Common Rush ....*J. effusus* L.
    2. Stamens 6; perianth 3-4.5 mm long; anthers much longer than the filaments; stems usually arising singly from the rhizome and growing in a row; shores and wet ground in n. Ill. ....*J. balticus* Willd.
1. Inflorescence terminal.
    3. Leaves flat (or involute), not septate.
      4. Flowers borne singly on the branches of the inflorescence, not in heads.
        5. Annual; stem branched, the inflorescence more than half the height of the plant; sandy soil, roadsides, or ditches throughout Ill. June-Oct. Toad Rush ....*J. bufonius* L.
        5. Perennials; inflorescence less than half the length of the plant.
          6. Capsule longer than the perianth; leaves nearly terete.
            7. Capsule greenish, usually slightly longer than the perianth; seeds cylindrical, the caudate appendages half as long as the body; damp shores, rare; Ringwood, McHenry Co., *Vasey* (type coll.) ; Cook Co., *Bebb;* Winnebago Co. July-Aug.......*J. vaseyi* Engelm.
            7. Capsule reddish or castaneous, glossy, much exceeding the perianth; seeds ellipsoid, merely short-pointed, or obtuse; sandy soil, rare, n.e. Ill. ....
            ....*J. greenei* Oakes & Tuckerm.
          6. Capsule shorter than or equalling the perianth, greenish or pale brown; leaves flat or involute.

8. Inflorescence distinctly secund; dry soil, rare; Jackson, Pope, and Saline counties.....*J. secundus* Beauv.

8. Inflorescence not secund.

9. Auricles at the summit of the sheaths thin, scarious, hyaline, conspicuously prolonged 1-3 mm beyond the point of insertion; fields, roadsides, paths, open woods, very common. May-Sept. Path Rush ....*J. tenuis* Willd.

9. Auricles firm, not conspicuously prolonged beyond the point of insertion.

10. Sheaths and auricles membranous, hyaline; perianth appressed to the capsule, 3-4 mm long; sandy soil, common. May-Aug. ....*J. interior* Wieg.

10. Sheaths and auricles cartilaginous, yellowish, rigid, glossy; perianth somewhat divergent, 4-5 mm long; meadows, common. May-Aug. ....*J. dudleyi* Wieg.

4. Flowers in heads (glomerules).

11. Heads few (2-20), commonly 5- to 10-flowered; stamens not persistent; meadows or ditches, not common. June-Sept. ....*J. marginatus* Rostk.

11. Heads numerous (20-100), commonly 2- to 6-flowered, stamens persistent, exserted; wet sandy soil, local ....*J. biflorus* Ell.

3. Leaves terete, hollow, more or less septate.

12. Stamens 6.

13. Involucral leaf longer than the short-branched inflorescence; filaments longer than the anthers.

14. Heads 7-10 mm in diameter; flowers 3-4 mm long, the petals equalling or exceeding the sepals; wet ground, rare in n. Ill. July-Aug. ....*J. nodosus* L.

14. Heads 1-1.5 cm in diameter; flowers 4-5 mm long, the petals much shorter than the sepals; ditches, common. July-Aug. ....*J. torreyi* Coville

13. Involucral leaf much shorter than the long-branched inflorescence; filaments about as long as the anthers.

15. Branches of the inflorescence widely divergent; sepals acuminate; sandy shores; Cook, Kane, Lake, McHenry, and Menard counties. July-Aug. ....*J. articulatus* L.

15. Branches of the inflorescence erect or closely ascending; sepals obtuse or mucronate; wet soil; Cook, Kane, Lake, and McHenry counties. July-Aug. ....*J. richardsonianus* Schult.

12. Stamens usually 3.

16. Seeds caudate.

17. Perianth 3-4 mm long, the segments acuminate;
heads 5- to 50-flowered; wet ground, locally
throughout Ill. Aug.-Oct. ....*J. canadensis* J.Gay
17. Perianth 2-2.5 mm long, the segments obtuse; heads
3- to 5-flowered; wet ground in the northern and
central counties. July-Sept. ....
.......................*J. brachycephalus* (Engelm.) Buch.
16. Seeds not caudate; perianth-segments acuminate.
18. Capsule twice as long as the perianth; wet ditches,
rare; Jackson Co. ....*J. diffusissimus* Buckl.
18. Capsule equalling to one-third longer than the
perianth.
19. Capsule acuminate or subulate, longer than the
perianth; heads 2-30, each 15- to 40-flowered;
perianth 2.5-3 mm long; wet sandy soil in the
northern half of Ill. July-Sept. ....
....*J. scirpoides* Lam.
19. Capsule obtuse or merely acute at the apex,
about equalling or shorter than the perianth.
20. Capsule about two-thirds the length of the
perianth; sepals longer than the petals; wet
ground. June-Aug. ....
....................................*J. brachycarpus* Engelm.
20. Capsule about equalling the perianth; sepals
and petals nearly equal.
21. Heads 1-50; branches of the inflorescence
ascending; perianth 3-3.5 mm long; wet
ground, throughout Ill. May-Aug. ......
....................................*J. acuminatus* Michx.
21. Heads more numerous; branches of the
inflorescence widely divergent; perianth
2-2.5 mm long; swampy ground, not
common. June-July. [*J. robustus* sensu
auth., non Wats.] ....*J. nodatus* Coville

2. Luzula DC. — Woodrush

1. Flowers solitary (rarely 2) at the tips of the slender ascending or
loosely spreading peduncles; inflorescence an umbel; perianth
3-4.5 mm long, pale brown, shorter than the capsule; wooded
banks, rare; La Salle and Ogle counties. [*L. acuminata* Raf.
(?)] ....*L. saltuensis* Fern.
1. Flowers subsessile, crowded in small head-like clusters.
2. Rays of the inflorescence erect or ascending; perianth 2-3 mm
long; heads mostly cylindrical.
3. Base of plant commonly with small corms; perianth about
2.5 mm long, slightly shorter than the capsule; stem-leaves
2-4 mm wide; sandy soil in open woods, local. Apr.-May
....*L. bulbosa* (Wood) Rydb.

3. Plant not cormose; perianth about 3 mm long, slightly exceeding the capsule; stem-leaves 4-8 mm wide; dry open woods, locally throughout Ill. Apr.-May ....
.............................,..*L. multiflora* (Retz.) Lej.
2. Rays of the inflorescence unequal, becoming strongly divergent; plant without corms; perianth 3-4 mm long, much longer than the capsule; open woods, not common. Apr.-May ....
....*L. echinata* (Small) Hermann

132. **Xyridaceae** Lindl. — Yellow-eyed Grass Family

1. **Xyris** L. — Yellow-eyed Grass

X. torta Sm. Moist sandy soil, not common; known from Cook, Iroquois, Kankakee, Mason, Will, and Winnebago counties. July-Aug. [*X. flexuosa* sensu auth., non Muhl.]

133. **Commelinaceae** Reichenb. — Spiderwort Family

1. Petals equal; perfect stamens 6; filaments pilose ....1. *Tradescantia*
1. Petals more or less unequal; perfect stamens 3; filaments glabrous ....
....2. *Commelina*

1. **Tradescantia** L. — Spiderwort

1. Leaves lanceolate, 1.5-5 cm broad, not glaucous, the margins ciliolate; sepals sparsely pilose or glabrous; cymes axillary and terminal; stems 40-80 cm tall; woods, common in the central and southern part of the state. June-Aug. [*T. pilosa* Lehm.]
....*T. subaspera* Ker
1. Leaves linear or linear-lanceolate; cymes terminal.
    2. Leaves glaucous; sepals glabrous, or pilose at the tip; petals 12-16 mm long; stems usually 40-90 cm tall; prairies, roadsides, open woods, common. May-Sept. [*T. canaliculata* Raf.] ....*T. ohiensis* Raf.
    2. Leaves not glaucous; petals 16-20 mm long; stem 10-30 cm tall.
        3. Sepals and pedicels pubescent with non-glandular hairs; petals blue; meadows, roadsides, open woods, and thickets, common. May-June ....*T. virginica* L.
        3. Sepals and pedicels copiously glandular-villous; petals rose or blue; prairie soil, rare, w. Ill.; Morgan Co., Mrs. *J. M. Mulligan* in 1869; Mason Co., *R. T. Rexroat* in 1953
        ....*T. bracteata* Small

2. **Commelina** L. — Dayflower

1. Margins of the spathe united at the base; native perennial species; seeds smooth, farinose.
    2. All three petals blue; leaf-sheaths fringed with long, erect, ferruginous bristle-like hairs; leaves lanceolate, 1-4 cm wide; wet woods, s. Ill., rare. July-Sept. ....*C. virginica* L.

2. One petal white, smaller; leaf-sheaths ciliate with short whitish hairs; leaves linear-lanceolate to lanceolate; sandy soil in the western and northern parts of the state. July-Sept. ....*C. erecta* L.
1. Margins of the spathe not united; stems decumbent, rooting at the lower nodes; species nat. from Asia.
    3. All three petals blue; anthers 5; capsules 3-loculed, 5-seeded; seeds 2-3 mm long, reticulate; plants perennial; moist ground, locally in s. Ill., often as a cornfield weed; a widespread species of trop. and subtrop. regions ....*C. diffusa* Burm.f.
    3. One petal white, smaller; anthers 6; capsules 2-loculed, 4-seeded; seeds 3.5-4 mm long, gray, rugose; plants annual; moist shaded ground, common. June-Oct. Dayflower ....
    ....*C. communis* L.

134. **Pontederiaceae** Dumort. — Pickerelweed Family

1. Flowers 2-lipped; stamens 6; leaves large, cordate to lanceolate; fruit a 1-seeded utricle ....1. *Pontederia*
1. Flowers regular, salverform; stamens 3; leaves either reniform or linear; fruit a many-seeded capsule ....2. *Heteranthera*

1. **Pontederia** L. — Pickerelweed

P. cordata L. Margins of ponds and streams, local. June-Sept.

2. **Heteranthera** Ruiz & Pavon

1. Leaves linear, grass-like; flowers yellow; stamens equal; shallow water or muddy shores in the northern half of the state. July-Sept. Water star-grass ....*H. dubia* (Jacq.) MacM.
1. Leaves not linear; flowers blue or white; stamens unequal.
    2. Leaves reniform; flowers white or pale blue; spathe 3- to 6-flowered; style pubescent; shallow water or muddy shores in s. Ill. Aug.-Sept. ....*H. reniformis* Ruiz & Pavon
    2. Leaves oval to lanceolate; flowers blue; spathe 1-flowered; style glabrous; ponds and sloughs; St. Clair Co., *Eggert; G. D. Fuller* ....*H. limosa* (Sw.) Willd.

135. **Amaryllidaceae** Lindl. — Amaryllis Family

1. Bulbous herbs.
    2. Flowers solitary or several, the tubular or annular corona separate from the filaments; stamens included ....1. *Narcissus*
    2. Flowers umbellate, subtended by long bracts, the membranous corona formed by the expanded filaments; stamens long-exserted ....
    ....2. *Hymenocallis*
1. Plants not bulbous.
    3. Flowers in a long spike or spike-like raceme; leaves basal.
        4. Perianth greenish-yellow; leaves thick, succulent; anthers versatile ......
        ....3. *Agave*
        4. Perianth white (in our species); leaves thin, flat, lanceolate; anthers not versatile ....4. *Aletris*

3. Flowers solitary or sub-umbellate, bright yellow; low mostly pubescent herbs with grass-like leaves ....5. *Hypoxis*

1. Narcissus L.

N. pseudo-narcissus L., Daffodil, with solitary yellow flowers, is extensively planted and often persists, but is scarcely established in Ill. *N. poeticus* L., Poet's Narcissus, with solitary white flowers, and *N. jonquilla*, Jonquil, with 2-6 yellow flowers, sometimes are briefly persistent after cultivation; all are native of Eur.

2. Hymenocallis Salisb. — Spider Lily

H. occidentalis (Le Conte) Kunth. Stream banks and moist ground in woods; known from Jackson, Johnson, Pulaski, Union, and Wabash counties.

3. Agave L.

A. virginica L. American Aloe. Sandy soil, or in rocky open woods in s. Ill. June-Aug.

4. Aletris L. — Colic-root

A. farinosa L. Sandy woods; known from Cook, Iroquois, Kankakee, and Lake counties. July-Aug.

5. Hypoxis L. — Stargrass

H. hirsuta (L.) Coville. Meadows, sandy soil, open woods, common. Apr.-June.

136. Iridaceae Lindl. — Iris Family

1. Leaves more than 1 cm wide; flowers large; plants with rhizomes.
  2. Flowers blue, yellow, or reddish; seeds flattened or angular; style-branches broad, petal-like, opposite the anthers ....1. *Iris*
  2. Flowers orange, mottled with purple; seeds globose, black, shining, succulent; style-branches filiform, alternate with the anthers ....
  ....2. *Belamcanda*
1. Leaves less than 7 mm wide; flowers small; plants without rhizomes ....
  ....3. *Sisyrinchium*

1. Iris L. — Iris

1. Flowers blue or yellow.
  2. Flowers yellow; escaped from cult.; native of Eur. ....
  ....*I. pseudacorus* L.
  2. Flowers blue, variegated with yellow and white.
    3. Perianth-tube as long as or longer than the sepals; streambanks, woods in Hardin and Union counties. Apr.-May. Dwarf Crested Iris ....*I. cristata* Ait.
    3. Perianth-tube much shorter than the sepals.
      4. Leaves somewhat glaucous; sepals 5-8 cm long; capsule obscurely 3-lobed, 1.5 cm thick; ditches, wet meadows, moist woods, banks of streams, ponds, and sloughs, common. May-June. Blue Iris [*I. versicolor* sensu auth., ex p., non L.] ....*I. shrevei* Small

4. Leaves green, not glaucous; sepals 8-10 cm long; capsule
   strongly 6-angled, 2 cm thick; meadows, swamps, and
   borders of woods in the western half of Ill., from Tazewell to Pulaski counties. May-June ....*I. brevicaulis* Raf.
1. Flowers dull reddish-brown, variegated with blue and green;
   leaves pale green and somewhat glaucous; sepals 3-5 cm long;
   swamps, Alexander, Pulaski, and Union counties. May. Red
   Iris ....*I. fulva* Ker

2. Belamcanda Adans. — Blackberry-lily

B. chinensis (L.) DC. Roadsides and banks, scattered nearly
throughout Ill.; escaped from cult. Native of Asia. June-July.

3. Sisyrinchium L. — Blue-eyed Grass

1. Spathes and flowers arising directly from apex of stem; leaves
   and stems glaucous, 1-2 mm broad, the margins smooth, entire.
   2. Spathes usually 2, with a single outer leaf-like bract; perianth
      usually white, or sometimes purple; ovary often minutely
      glandular; capsules 3-5 mm long, straw-colored; prairie soil,
      and meadows, common throughout Ill. May-June ....
      ....*S. albidum* Raf.
   2. Spathe solitary; perianth bluish-purple; stem 0.5-1.5 mm wide;
      capsules 2.5-3 mm long; prairie soil, roadsides, open woods,
      sandy banks, common throughout the western part of the
      state from Winnebago to Macoupin counties. Apr.-June.
      [*S. mucronatum* sensu auth., non Michx.; *S. montanum*
      sensu auth., non Greene] ....*S. campestre* Bickn.
1. Spathes and flowers peduncled from the axil of a leaf-like bract;
   perianth bluish-purple.
   3. Leaves 3-4 mm wide, dark green, not glaucous, drying darker;
      stems broadly winged, minutely serrulate, almost straight, 3-4
      mm wide; inner bract of spathe 1.5-3 cm long; capsules
      blackish, 4-6 mm long; moist meadows or wooded areas
      throughout Ill. May-June. [*S. gramineum* Lam.; *S. angusti-
      folium* Mill.; *S. graminoides* Bickn.] ....*S. bermudiana* L.
   3. Leaves 1-3 mm wide, pale green or glaucous; stem slender,
      narrowly winged, curved or flexuous; inner bract of spathe
      1-1.5 cm long; capsules 3-4 mm long; sandy soil, local;
      known from Kankakee Co., *R. A. Schneider* ....
      ....*S. atlanticum* Bickn.

137. Dioscoreaceae Lindl. — Yam Family
1. Dioscorea L. — Yam

1. Petioles glabrous or nearly so at the insertion of the blade; mature capsules 1.5-2.3 cm long; all the leaves alternate (or the
   three lowest close together or indefinitely whorled); blades
   glabrous or puberulent beneath; seeds (exclusive of the wing)

3-4.5 mm broad; rhizome mostly 5-8 mm thick (when dry), simple, or rarely branched; thickets or open woods, common. May-July. [*D. paniculata* Michx.] ....*D. villosa* L.
1. Petioles puberulent at the insertion of the blade; mature capsules 2.5-3 cm long; lower leaves in whorls of 4-9 (usually 6) ; lower surface of blades glabrous or puberulent, glaucous or green; seeds (exclusive of the wing) 5-6.5 mm broad; rhizome stout, irregularly knotted, 1-1.5 cm thick; woods, s. Ill. May-June ....*D. quaternata* (Walt.) Gmel.

138. **Hydrocharitaceae** Aschers. — Frogbit Family

1. Leaves cordate, petioled ....1. *Limnobium*
1. Leaves neither cordate nor petioled.
  2. Leaves basal, ribbon-like, elongated, floating ....2. *Vallisneria*
  2. Leaves small, whorled or opposite, sessile, pellucid, 1-veined; stems elongated, leafy, floating ....3. *Elodea*

1. **Limnobium** Rich. — Frogbit

L. spongia (Bosc) Steud. Sponge-plant. Shallow water or mud, rare; Alexander and Union counties. June-Aug.

2. **Vallisneria** L. — Tapegrass

V. americana Michx. "Wild Celery." Ponds and slow streams in the northern half of the state. July-Aug.

3. **Elodea** Michx. — Waterweed
(*Anacharis* Rich.)

1. Leaves three in each whorl, 1-2 cm long; flowers 3-6 mm in diameter, solitary in the spathe.
  2. Leaves elliptical or oblong, obtusish, 1.5-4 mm wide; slow streams, widely distributed. July-Aug. Canadian Waterweed ....*E. canadensis* Michx.
  2. Leaves linear, acute, mostly 1-1.5 mm wide; ponds and slow streams, apparently more common in Ill. than the preceding species. July-Aug. Common Waterweed. [*E. nuttallii* (Planch.) St.John] ....*E. occidentalis* (Pursh) St.John
1. Leaves six in each whorl, 2-4 cm long, 3-5 mm wide, the stem densely leafy; flowers 1.5-2 cm in diameter, usually 3 in a spathe; used in aquaria and rarely found as an escape from cult.; introd. from S. Am. Brazilian Waterweed....*E. densa* Planch.

139. **Burmanniaceae** Blume — Burmannia Family
1. **Thismia** Griff.

T. americana N.E.Pfeiff. "Chicago, Ill., in open prairie," *Norma E. Pfeiffer;* known only from the original collection; type, herb. Chicago Nat. Hist. Mus.; isotype, herb. Univ. of Ill. Discovered in Aug. 1912, now almost certainly extinct.

140. Orchidaceae Lindl. — Orchid Family

1. Lip large, inflated, moccasin-shaped; leaves plaited; fertile anthers 2 ....
   ....1. *Cypripedium*
1. Lip concave or flat, not moccasin-shaped; fertile anther 1.
   2. Plants with ordinary green foliage at flowering time.
      3. Flowers distinctly spurred, the spur 2 mm or more in length.
         4. Flowers bicolored, the lip white and the sepals and petals purple;
            leaves 2, basal, oval ....2. *Orchis*
         4. Flowers concolored ....3. *Habenaria*
      3. Flowers spurless.
         5. Flowers large (more than 1 cm broad), solitary or few.
            6. Leaves grass-like; flowers several, racemose, pink-purple ....
               ....4. *Calopogon*
            6. Leaves not grass-like.
               7. Flowers axillary; lip not crested ....5. *Triphora*
               7. Flowers terminal, solitary or few; lip fringed and crested ....
                  ....6. *Pogonia*
         5. Flowers smaller, several to many, in spikes or racemes (flowers large
            in *Epipactis*).
            8. Flowers white or greenish-white.
               9. Inflorescence more or less twisted spirally; leaves alternate or
                  basal, not variegated, often soon withering ....7. *Spiranthes*
               9. Inflorescence not spiral; leaves basal, often whitish-variegated
                  ....8. *Goodyera*
            8. Flowers racemose, greenish or purplish.
               10. Leaves 1-2.
                  11. Leaf solitary near the middle of the stem, ovate or oval,
                      clasping; flowers many, greenish, 2-3 mm long ....
                      ....9. *Malaxis*
                  11. Leaves two, basal; flowers larger ....10. *Liparis*
               10. Leaves several, clasping, lanceolate to ovate, acuminate or
                   acute; flowers purplish, pendulous in a long, often 1-sided
                   raceme ....11. *Epipactis*
   2. Leaves absent at flowering time, or a single basal withered one per-
      sisting.
      12. Inflorescence spirally twisted; flowers white or greenish-white; plants
          with 1-several elongate or tuberous-thickened roots ....7. *Spiranthes*
      12. Inflorescence not spirally twisted.
         13. Stem cormose at base, with a solitary basal oval leaf usually with-
             ering or absent at flowering time; capsules reflexed.
            14. Flowers spurless; leaf green beneath ....12. *Aplectrum*
            14. Flowers with a long spur; leaf purplish beneath ......13. *Tipularia*
         13. Stem from a cluster of coral-like rhizomes; leaves reduced to scales.
            15. Lip with a callus on each side of the midrib near the base;
                pollinia 4, in two pairs ....14. *Corallorhiza*
            15. Lip with 5 or 6 prominent ridges down the middle; pollinia
                8, united ....15. *Hexalectris*

1. Cypripedium L. — Lady's Slipper

1. Flowering stem leafy.
   2. Sepals oval, not twisted, shorter than the white lip, which is 3-4
      cm long, tinged with purple; wet woods or springy places,

n. Ill., rare. Showy Lady's Slipper [*C. spectabile* Salisb.] ....
....*C. reginae* Walt.
2. Sepals lanceolate, attenuate, twisted, equalling or exceeding the lip.
  3. Lip yellow, 2-5 cm long; wooded hillsides, or in ravines, or bogs, rare. May-June. Yellow Lady's Slipper [*C. pubescens* Willd.; *C. parviflorum* var. *pubescens* (Willd.) Knight] ....*C. parviflorum* Salisb.
  3. Lip white or cream, 2-2.5 cm long.
    4. Sepals and petals solid madder-purple; lip creamy white; near Spring Bay, Woodford Co., *V. H. Chase 4024.* [*C. candidum* X *parviflorum* A.M.Fuller] ....
....X *C. andrewsii* A.M.Fuller
    4. Sepals and petals greenish-yellow, usually purple-lined; lip waxy-white; bogs, swamps, or wet ground on "original prairie" in the northern half of Ill. May-June. White Lady's Slipper ....*C. candidum* Muhl.
1. Flowering stem leafless; basal leaves 2; woods, Cook Co., rare; May ....*C. acaule* Ait.

2. Orchis L.

O. spectabilis L. Showy Orchis. Woods, occasional. May-June.

3. Habenaria Willd.

1. Lip not fringed or deeply lobed; flowers greenish.
  2. Stem with one to several leaves.
    3. Leaves several; bracts mostly longer than the flowers.
      4. Lip not entire, 6-8 mm long.
        5. Lip 3-toothed at apex; spur shorter than lip; rich woods, rare, n. Ill., extending southward to Peoria Co. May-June. Long-bracted Orchid ....
....*H. bracteata* (Muhl.) R.Br.
        5. Lip with a median tubercle and a tooth on each side near the base; spur longer than the lip; wet ground, rare; Cook, Hancock, Kankakee, Lake, Ogle, Peoria, St. Clair, Tazewell, and Wabash counties. June-July. Tubercled Orchid ....*H. flava* (L.) R.Br.
      4. Lip entire, shorter than the slender spur; swamps, rare; Cook, Kane, Lake, Peoria, Tazewell, and Woodford counties. June-July. [*H. hyperborea* sensu Am. auth.. non *Orchis hyperborea* L.] ....
....*H. huronensis* (Nutt.) Spreng.
    3. Leaves 1 or 2; bracts shorter than the flowers; lip entire at base, cuneate, truncate, 3-5 mm long; wet ground, rare; Cass, Cook, Kankakee, and Lake counties. July-Aug. Wood Orchid ....*H. clavellata* (Michx.) Spreng.

2. Stem scapiform; leaves basal, orbicular, 3-10 cm broad; lip lanceolate, entire, about 1 cm long; flowers yellowish-green; rich woods; Cook and Lake counties. June-July. Round-leaved Orchid ....*H. hookeri* Torr.
1. Lip fringed or deeply lobed; flowers large and showy.
   6. Flowers orange-yellow; lip oval, about 1 cm long, the conspicu-ous fringe 3-5 mm long; wet ground, rare, Cook Co. Yellow Fringed Orchid ....*H. ciliaris* (L.) R.Br.
   6. Flowers whitish, greenish, or purplish; lip more or less 3-lobed, each lobe fringed or denticulate.
      7. Petals entire; flowers greenish; lobes of the lip narrow, few-fringed; swamps, rare; Cook, Kane, Kankakee, Lake, Vermilion, and Winnebago counties. June-July. Green Fringed Orchid ....*H. lacera* (Michx.) Lodd.
      7. Petals denticulate; lobes of the lip fan-shaped.
         8. Lip deeply fringed and 3-parted, the fringe 2-5 mm long.
            9. Flowers creamy-white, fragrant, the spikes relatively few-flowered; wet meadows, rare. June-July. White Fringed Orchid ....*H. leucophaea* (Nutt.) A.Gray
            9. Flowers lilac or purplish, crowded in the spike; mead-ows and swamps, rare; Cook, Lake, and Winnebago counties. July-Aug. Small Purple Fringed Orchid ....*H. psycodes* (L.) Spreng.
         8. Lip toothed but not fringed; flowers violet-purple; moist woods, occasional; s. Ill. July-Aug. Fringeless Purple Orchid ....*H. peramoena* A.Gray

4. Calopogon R.Br. — Grass-pink Orchid

C. pulchellus (Salisb.) R.Br. Meadows, chiefly in the northern half of Ill. May-July.

5. Triphora Nutt. — Nodding Pogonia

T. trianthophora (Sw.) Rydb. Woods, not common. Aug.-Sept. [*Pogonia trianthophora* (Sw.) BSP.].

6. Pogonia Juss.

P. ophioglossoides (L.) Ker. Swamps and meadows, not common; Cook, Lake, Lee, McHenry, and Will counties. June-July.

7. Spiranthes Rich. — Ladies' Tresses

1. Raceme loosely-flowered, the flowers usually in a single row, spirally twisted or merely secund.
   2. Rachis of inflorescence and stem glabrous; leaves basal, oval, petioled, soon withering and usually absent at flowering time.
      3. Perianth 3 mm long; lip entirely white; root solitary; dry woods and bluff tops; Jackson, Pope, Randolph, and Union counties. July-Sept. [*S. tuberosa* Raf., nom. dub.; *S. beckii* sensu auth.] ....*S. grayi* Ames

3. Perianth 4-6 mm long; lip with a median green stripe; rachis twisted; roots usually several; dry open woods, local. July-Sept. Slender Ladies' Tresses [*S. lacera* Raf., nom. dub.; *S. beckii* Lindl., nom. illegit.] ....*S. gracilis* (Bigel.) Beck

2. Rachis of inflorescence and usually the upper part of stem pubescent; leaves linear-lanceolate, not distinctly petioled, commonly present at flowering time; perianth 8-10 mm long; lip ovate, yellowish, pubescent beneath, 5-7 mm long; Effingham, Menard, and St. Clair counties. May-Sept. ....*S. vernalis* Engelm. & Gray

1. Raceme closely flowered, the flowers apparently in 2 or 3 spirals; rachis and upper part of stem puberulent or pubescent.

4. Raceme slender, 8-12 mm thick; perianth 3-7 mm long.

5. Lip white, puberulent, ovate, 4-5 mm long with 2 slender incurved callosities; Pulaski, Sangamon, and Union counties. Sept.-Oct. [*S. montanum* Raf., nom. dub.] ....*S. ovalis* Lindl.

5. Lip with a median yellow stripe, glabrous, elliptical-quadrate; callosities none or very small; springy bog in wooded pasture, near Marley, Will Co., June 22, 1897, *Agnes Chase;* Hancock Co., *Mead* in 1844. May-July. Shining Ladies' Tresses [*S. latifolia* Torr.; *S. plantaginea* (Raf.) Torr., non Lindl.] ....*S. lucida* (H.H.Eaton) Ames

4. Raceme stout, 1.5-2.5 cm thick; perianth 8-10 mm long; lip white, pubescent; meadows and swamps, occasional. Aug.-Oct. Nodding Ladies' Tresses ....*S. cernua* (L.) Rich.

8. Goodyera R.Br. — Rattlesnake-plantain

G. pubescens (Willd.) R.Br. Woods, rare; chiefly in n. and s.e. Ill. July-Sept.

9. Malaxis Soland. ex Sw. — Adder's-mouth Orchid

M. unifolia Michx. Woods, rare; Hancock, Henderson, Kane, and Menard counties. May-Aug.

10. Liparis Rich.

1. Flowers few, greenish; lip about 5 mm long, shorter than the petals; capsules ellipsoid, about twice the length of the pedicels; wet ground in the n. half of the state, rare. June-July ....*L. loeselii* (L.) Rich.

1. Flowers numerous, purple; lip 10-12 mm long, about equalling the petals; capsules clavate, equalling or shorter than the pedicels; woods, not common. June-July ....*L. lilifolia* (L.) Rich.

11. Epipactis Sw. — Helleborine

E. helleborine (L.) Crantz. Moist woods near Barrington, Lake Co., *J. A. Steyermark* 76351; native of Eur.

12. Aplectrum Nutt. — Puttyroot

A. hyemale (Muhl.) Torr. Rich woods, occasional. May-June.

13. **Tipularia** Nutt. — Cranefly Orchid

T. discolor (Pursh) Nutt. Deep mesophytic beech-maple woods, rare. Jackson Hollow and Belle Smith Spring, Pope Co., *R. H. Mohlenbrock & J. W. Voigt* in 1958.

14. **Corallorhiza** Chat. — Coralroot

1. Lip with two prominent basal lobes, white, conspicuously crimson-spotted; mature capsules 10-18 mm long; woods, rare; Cook, Jo Daviess, La Salle, Peoria, and Winnebago counties. July-Aug. Spotted Coralroot ....*C. maculata* Raf.
1. Lip entire or denticulate, or crenulate.
   2. Lip 4-5 mm long, entire or denticulate, white, with crimson spots; mature capsules 6-7 mm long; moist woods, rare. Aug.-Oct. Late Coralroot ....*C. odontorhiza* (Willd.) Nutt.
   2. Lip 5-7 mm long, crenulate, notched at apex, white, with purple spots; mature capsules 9-11 mm long; woods in the southern half of Ill. Apr.-May. Wister's Coralroot ....
   ....*C. wisteriana* Conrad

15. **Hexalectris** Raf. — Crested Coralroot

H. spicata (Walt.) Barnh. Woods, rare; Jackson, Pope, and Randolph counties. July-Aug.

141. **Araceae** Necker — Arum Family

1. Leaves with 3-11 leaflets; spathe conspicuous, convolute at least below, enveloping the cylindrical or slightly flattened spadix which is flower-bearing near the base; plants monoecious or dioecious; perianth none; plant cormose ....1. *Arisaema*
1. Leaves simple, or absent at flowering time.
   2. Leaves sagittate or cordate, or absent; spadix terminal.
      3. Spathe ovoid, fleshy, greenish or yellowish, purple-mottled; spadix globose, covered by the perfect flowers; perianth of 4 hooded sepals; leaves appearing later, large, ovate, cordate; plant with a very fetid odor ....2. *Symplocarpus*
      3. Spathe narrow, elongate, convolute, green; spadix cylindrical, bearing staminate flowers above and pistillate below; perianth none; leaves sagittate ....3. *Peltandra*
   2. Leaves linear, erect, equitant; spathe merely a foliaceous prolongation of the scape; spadix cylindrical, borne laterally on the leaf-like, 3-angled scape; perianth with 6 membranous concave divisions; rhizomes and leaves aromatic ....4. *Acorus*

1. **Arisaema** Mart.

1. Leaflets usually 3; spadix terete, club-shaped, obtuse, overarched by the green or purple-striped spathe; moist woods, common. Apr.-May. Jack-in-the-pulpit. Indian Turnip. [*A. atrorubens* of some recent auth.] Smaller plants with the spathe dark purple (var. *pusillum* Peck) have been collected in s. Ill. ....
....*A. triphyllum* (L.) Schott

1. Leaflets 7-11; spadix slender, projecting beyond the green spathe; moist woods, common. May-June. Green Dragon. Dragonroot
....*A. dracontium* (L.) Schott

2. Symplocarpus Salisb. — Skunk-cabbage
S. foetidus (L.) Nutt. Swamps, local; chiefly in n.e. and central Ill., extending southward to Jasper Co. Feb.-Apr.

3. Peltandra Raf.
P. virginica (L.) Kunth. Muddy margins of ditches and ponds, or in shallow water, or swamps, local; extending northward to Kankakee and Peoria counties. May-June.

4. Acorus L. — Sweetflag
A. calamus L. Swamps or wet ground along streams, locally nearly throughout Ill. June-Aug. Probably native in Ill. and elsewhere in U.S., although introd. into Eur. as early as 1557.

142. Lemnaceae Dumort. — Duckweed Family
1. Plants with roots.
  2. Root solitary, without vascular tissue ....1. *Lemna*
  2. Roots 2-several, each with a vascular bundle ....2. *Spirodela*
1. Plants without roots.
  3. Plants thick, ellipsoid to subglobose ....3. *Wolffia*
  3. Plants thin, ligulate ....4. *Wolffiella*

1. Lemna L. — Duckweed
1. Plants paddle-shaped, 6-10 mm long, remaining connected, wholly submerged; ponds and ditches, local ....*L. trisulca* L.
1. Plants oval or roundish, 2-5 mm long, soon separating, floating.
  2. Plants narrowly elliptical, often somewhat falcate, 0.5-1.5 mm wide, obscurely 1-veined, smooth; ponds and swamps, rare, s. Ill. [*L. cyclostasa* of auth.] ....*L. valdiviana* Phil.
  2. Plants suborbicular to ovate, 2-5 mm in diameter.
    3. Plant-body asymmetrical; root-tip pointed; seeds orthotropous; ponds and streams, local ....*L. perpusilla* Torr.
    3. Plant-body symmetrical or nearly so; root-tip rounded; seeds amphitropous; stagnant water and slow streams; probably the most prevalent species in Ill. [incl. *L. minima* of auth.] ....*L. minor* L.

2. Spirodela Schleid.
1. Plants roundish-obovate, 3-8 mm long, 5-11-nerved; roots 6-18; ponds, ditches, slow streams, locally abundant ....
....*S. polyrhiza* (L.) Schleid.
1. Plants elliptical, 2-4 mm long, obscurely nerved; roots usually 2 or 3 (rarely 6); Horseshoe Lake, Alexander Co., *E. H. Daubs 545,*

802; also in Missouri. Native of trop. Asia ....
....*S. oligorhiza* (Kurz) Hegelm.

3. **Wolffia** Horkel

1. Plants globose or ellipsoid, not flattened, 0.5-1 mm long, loosely
cellular, not punctate, floating somewhat beneath the surface;
locally abundant in stagnant water ....*W. columbiana* Karst.
1. Plants flattened on the upper surface, brown-punctate, compactly
cellular, floating at the surface of the water.
  2. Plants 1-1.5 mm long, rounded ovate, strongly gibbous, the
upper surface with a central conical papilla; in permanent
pools of stagnant water, rare; Wabash Co., *Schneck;* Union
Co., *Swayne 1890* ....*W. papulifera* C. H. Thompson
  2. Plants 0.5-0.8 mm long, ellipsoid, slightly gibbous, symmetrical,
the upper surface flat or slightly convex, gradually rising to
the acute apex; stagnant water, rare; Hancock, Jackson,
Menard, and Sangamon counties ....*W. punctata* Griseb.

4. **Wolffiella** Hegelm.

W. floridana (J.D.Sm.) C.H.Thompson. Stagnant water, rare;
Alexander and Union counties.

143. **Typhaceae** J. St. Hil. — Cat-tail Family
1. **Typha** L. — Cat-tail

1. Leaves 1-2.5 cm wide, light green, nearly flat; staminate and pistillate parts of the spike usually contiguous, the latter becoming
2-3 cm in diameter at maturity; pollen grains in fours; stigma
spatulate; marshes, margins of ponds, and along ditches, common throughout Ill. June-July. Common Cat-tail ....
....*T. latifolia* L.
1. Leaves 4-8 mm wide, dark green, convex on the back; staminate
and pistillate parts of the spike separated by a short interval,
the pistillate part only 10-18 mm in diameter; pollen grains
simple; stigma linear; marshes, less common than the preceding
species. June-July. Narrow-leaved Cat-tail ....*T. angustifolia* L.

144. **Sparganiaceae** J. G. Agardh — Bur-reed Family
1. **Sparganium** L. — Bur-reed

1. Achenes obpyramidal, truncate at the summit, sessile; stigmas
usually 2; ditches and margins of ponds. June-July. Giant Bur-
reed ....*S. eurycarpum* Engelm.
1. Achenes fusiform, stipitate; stigma 1.
  2. Pistillate heads all strictly axillary, 2-2.5 cm in diameter at
maturity; beak of the mature achene 2-3 mm long; leaves 6-
12 mm wide.
    3. Inflorescence branched; stigmas 2-4 mm long; ditches, rare
....*S. androcladum* (Engelm.) Morong

3. Inflorescence usually simple; stigmas 1-2 mm long; ditches; Cook, Du Page, McHenry, and Winnebago counties ....
....*S. americanum* Nutt.
2. Pistillate heads usually supra-axillary; leaves 3-7 mm wide; ditches and ponds, not common; Cook Co., *J. A. Steyermark 40920;* Union Co., *G. Dillard & S. Abney* in 1959 ....
....*S. chlorocarpum* Rydb.

145. Cyperaceae J. St. Hil. — Sedge Family

1. Spikelets all alike; flowers of the spikelet, or at least one of them, perfect.
   2. Glumes of the spikelet 2-ranked; spikelets flattened or subterete.
      3. Perianth bristles none; spikelets in umbellate clusters; stems mostly triangular ....1. *Cyperus*
      3. Perianth of 6-9 bristles; inflorescence axillary; stem terete, hollow; achenes beaked ....2. *Dulichium*
   2. Glumes spirally imbricated.
      4. Spikelets with several to many perfect flowers.
         5. Base of the style swollen, persistent as a tubercle on the achene.
            6. Spikelet solitary; bristles usually present; stems leafless ....
            ....3. *Eleocharis*
            6. Spikelets several; bristles none; leaves filiform, the sheaths pubescent ....4. *Bulbostylis*
         5. Base of style deciduous, sometimes enlarged.
            7. Flowers with a perianth of 3 stalked sepals, or of 1 or 2 hyaline glumes.
               8. Bristles 3; bracteoles 0 ....5. *Fuirena*
               8. Bristles 0; bracteoles 1-2.
                  9. Flowers with a single minute inner scale (bracteole) ....
                  ....6. *Hemicarpha*
                  9. Flowers with 2 convolute inner scales ....7. *Lipocarpha*
            7. Flowers without a perianth.
               10. Style swollen at the base; bristles none ....8. *Fimbristylis*
               10. Style not at all or only slightly thickened at base; bristles usually present.
                  11. Bristles few (0-8), short, not long and silky ....9. *Scirpus*
                  11. Bristles numerous, long, slender, silky ....10. *Eriophorum*
      4. Spikelets 1- to 4-flowered, polygamous.
         12. Base of the style persistent as a tubercle on the achene; perianth bristles usually present; style 2-cleft or entire ....
         ....11. *Rhynchospora*
         12. Style wholly deciduous; bristles 0; style 3-cleft ....12. *Cladium*
1. Spikelets usually unisexual; plants monoecious, or rarely dioecious.
   13. Achenes white, bony, globose, usually supported on a disk, not enclosed in a sac (perigynium); pistillate spikes 1-flowered ....13. *Scleria*
   13. Achenes not bony, enclosed in a perigynium ....14. *Carex*

1. Cyperus L.*

1. Achenes lenticular; stigmas 2.

---
* Revised by R. H. Mohlenbrock.

2. Spikelets 1-flowered; inflorescence of 1-3 sessile heads; plants
   with a strong sweet odor; moist ground, chiefly along streams
   and ditches in Alexander, Jackson, Massac, Pope, and
   Wabash counties. Aug.-Oct. [*Kyllinga pumila* Michx.] ....
   ....*C. densicaespitosus* Mattf. & Kükenth.

2. Spikelets 5- to 35-flowered; inflorescence of 1-several radiating
   sessile spikelets and usually 1-several rays; plants essentially
   inodorous.

   3. Achenes black, nearly as broad as long, with transverse wrin-
      kles; scales stramineous; wet ground, rare; Coles, Jackson,
      Peoria, Pope, and Union counties. Aug.-Oct. [*C. poae-
      formis* Pursh] ....*C. flavescens* L.

   3. Achenes drab or gray, longer than broad, without transverse
      wrinkles; scales usually suffused with purple.

      4. Styles cleft nearly to the base, persistent and conspicuously
         exserted to 4 mm from the scales; marshy ground, or
         margins of streams, local; Henry, Jackson, McHenry,
         Mason, Peoria, St. Clair, and Winnebago counties. Aug.-
         Oct. Low Cyperus ....*C. diandrus* Torr.

      4. Styles cleft to about the middle, early deciduous, included
         or projecting to 2 mm from the scales.

         5. Scales closely imbricate, strongly suffused with purple;
            moist ground, chiefly in the northern half of Ill. Aug.-
            Oct. Shining Cyperus ....*C. rivularis* Kunth

         5. Scales with tips somewhat spreading, the spikelets ap-
            pearing serrate, stramineous or purple only on the
            margins; roadside ditch, De Soto, Jackson Co., *J.
            W. Voigt 391* ....*C. filicinus* Vahl

1. Achenes trigonous; stigmas 3.

   6. Scales with strongly reflexed acuminate tips; plants when dry
      with fragrance of slippery elm; wet sandy soil along streams
      or ditches throughout Ill. June-Sept. Awned Cyperus [*C. in-
      flexus* Muhl.] ....*C. aristatus* Rottb.

   6. Scales with tips either appressed or slightly spreading.

      7. Spikes spherical or globose, with spikelets radiating in all
         directions.

         8. Scales appressed but with the tips shortly excurved; spikes
            to 8 mm across.

            9. Perennial; achene narrowly lanceolate to linear; wet
               ground, rare; s. Ill. July-Sept. Marsh Cyperus ....
               ....*C. pseudovegetus* Steud.

            9. Annual; achene oblong; wet soil throughout Ill. July-
               Sept. ....*C. acuminatus* Torr. & Hook.

         8. Scales appressed to spreading, their tips straight; some of
            the heads over 1 cm across.

            10. Scales appressed; spikelets 2- to 3-flowered; sandy
                borders of woods, or in old fields, chiefly in s. Ill.,

but extending northward to Peoria Co. June-Sept.
Round-headed Sedge [*C. wolfii* Wood] ....

....*C. ovularis* (Michx.) Torr.

10. Scales spreading; spikelets 5- to several-flowered; sand
prairies, rare; Mason and Whiteside counties. Aug.-
Oct. ....*C. grayioides* Mohlenbrock

7. Spikes hemispherical, cylindrical, ellipsoidal, or lanceolate,
but not globose or spherical.

11. Spikelets arising from a central axis.

12. Scales with a mucro 0.5-1.5 mm long; achenes 2.2-3.3
mm long; sandy soil chiefly in the northern part of
the state. Aug.-Oct. [*C. houghtonii* of auth., not
Torr.] ....*C. schweinitzii* Torr.

12. Scales acute or with a mucro to 0.5 mm long; achenes
usually 1.2-2.1 mm long; some spikelets spreading
or slightly reflexed; dry sandy soil ....*C. filiculmis* Vahl

11. Spikelets produced pinnately along the axis.

13. Scales 1.0-1.5 mm long; achene 0.8-1.0 mm long;
along streams and ditches, and in fields. July-Sept.
...............................*C. erythrorhizos* Muhl.

13. Scales 1.5-4.5 mm long; achene 1.0-2.8 mm long.

14. Scales very remote, the tip of one just reaching
the base of the one above it, giving the spikelet
a zig-zag appearance; wet ground, local; Alexander, Lake, McHenry, St. Clair, and Union
counties. Aug.-Oct. ....*C. engelmannii* Steud.

14. Scales approximate and overlapping.

15. Some or all the mature spikelets reflexed;
spikelets subterete; moist ground, rare; Massac and Pulaski counties ....

...............................*C. lancastriensis* Porter

15. None of the spikelets (except sometimes the
lowest pair) reflexed; spikelets flattened.

16. Rhizomes scaly and usually ending in a
tuber; scales at the tips of the spikelets
rather blunt, giving the spikelets an obtuse appearance; moist ground, common.
Aug.-Oct. Chufa or Nut Sedge ....

...............................*C. esculentus* L.

16. Rhizomes absent or merely becoming hard
and corm-like.

17. Plants annual; scales ferruginous or
golden-brown; achenes obovoid-ob-
long, 1.0-1.7 mm long; wet ground,
not uncommon. July-Oct. [*C. speci-
osus* sensu auth., non Vahl; *C. ferax*
sensu Britt., non Rich.] ....

...............................*C. ferruginescens* Boeck.

17. Plants perennial; scales stramineous;
achenes linear, 1.3-2.2 mm long;
moist meadows and alluvial soil, common. Aug.-Oct. ...._C. strigosus_ L.

2. Dulichium Rich.

D. arundinaceum (L.) Britt. Wet ground, chiefly along borders of
streams and ponds, local.

3. Eleocharis R. Br. — Spike Rush

1. Spikelet linear, scarcely thicker than the stem; glumes of the
    mature spikelet persistent; plants aquatic, about 1 m tall.
    2. Stems terete, conspicuously nodose; achenes 2-2.5 mm long (in-
        cluding the style-base); shallow water, rare, n.e. Ill. Wolf
        Lake, _Hill_ in 1890. [_E. interstincta_ sensu auth., non R. & S.]
        ...._E. equisetoides_ (Ell.) Torr.
    2. Stems sharply 4-angled, continuous, not septate; achenes 2.5-4
        mm long, including the beak (1 mm long); shallow water,
        not common. Wolf Lake, _Hill;_ St. Clair Co., _Brendel._ [_E.
        mutata_ sensu auth., non R. & S.] ....
        ...._E. quadrangulata_ (Michx.) R. & S.
1. Spikelet usually much thicker than the stem; glumes persistent.
    3. Style 2-cleft; achenes lenticular or biconvex.
        4. Perennials with rhizomes.
            5. Sheaths loose, hyaline and scarious at the summit; glumes
                hyaline-margined; wet soil, rare. Wolf Lake, Chicago,
                Hill, and other localities ...._E. olivacea_ Torr.
            5. Sheaths close, not hyaline at the summit.
                6. Basal glumes of the spikelets usually 2 or 3 below the
                    thinner fertile glumes.
                    7. Tubercle elongate, much longer than broad; achenes
                        narrowly obovoid or pyriform; stems subterete,
                        rather firm; ponds, swamps, and marshes, n. Ill.
                        Creeping Spike Rush ...._E. palustris_ (L.) R. & S.
                    7. Tubercle depressed-deltoid, umbonate, as broad as or
                        broader than long; achenes broadly obovoid or
                        roundish.
                        8. Stems firm, nearly terete; fertile glumes ascending,
                            oval, acuminate; marshes, ditches, shores, locally
                            throughout Ill. ...._E. smallii_ Britt.
                        8. Stems soft, compressed; fertile glumes appressed,
                            obtusish; wet ground, not common; chiefly in the
                            southern half of the state, extending northward
                            to Menard Co. ...._E. mamillata_ Lindb.
                6. Basal glume solitary, spathiform, usually encircling the
                    base of the spikelet; wet ground, local ...._E. calva_ Torr.
        4. Tufted annuals, with fibrous roots.

9. Tubercle flattened or saucer-shaped; mature achenes black, 1 mm long; wet ground. [*E. capitata* R.Br.; *E. caribaea* (Rottb.) Blake; *E. dispar* E.J.Hill] ....*E. geniculata* (L.) R. & S.

9. Tubercle conical or deltoid, acute; mature achenes pale brownish.

  10. Tubercle conical, narrower than the top of the achene; wet ground in the northern half of the state ....*E. ovata* (Roth) R. & S.

  10. Tubercle depressed-deltoid, as wide as the top of the achene.

    11. Bristles longer than the achene; tubercle one-third or more the length of the body of the achene; spikelets ovoid; wet ground throughout Ill., not uncommon. Blunt Spike Rush ....*E. obtusa* (Willd.) Schult.

    11. Bristles about equalling the achene, or rudimentary; tubercle less than one-fourth the length of the body of the achene; spikelets cylindrical-ellipsoid; muddy shores and along ditches, local. Engelmann's Spike Rush ....*E. engelmanni* Steud.

3. Style usually 3-cleft; achenes trigonal or turgid.

 12. Tubercle plainly distinguishable from the achene; achenes less than 2 mm long.

  13. Achenes cancellate and striate.

    14. Spikelet flattened, 3-9-flowered, the glumes 2-3-ranked; bristles 3-4, fugacious; stems very slender, not more than 0.5 mm in diameter, 5-20 cm long; wet ground and shallow water. Needle Spike Rush ....*E. acicularis* (L.) R. & S.

    14. Spikelet terete, the glumes many-ranked; bristles 0; stems about 1 mm in diameter; wet ground; Fulton, Peoria, Stark, and La Salle counties. Discovered at Canton by J. Wolf ....*E. wolfii* (A.Gray) Patterson

  13. Achenes papillose or pitted.

    15. Tubercle depressed; achene about 1 mm long; perennials with rhizomes.

      16. Stems filiform, about 0.5 mm wide, angular; glumes obtuse; wet ground, local. [*E. elliptica* Kunth; *E. capitata* var. *borealis* Svens.] Slender Spike Rush ....*E. tenuis* (Willd.) Schult.

      16. Stem flattened, 1 mm or more in width; glumes acuminate, often bifid; moist ground throughout Ill. [*E. acuminata* (Muhl.) Nees] ....*E. compressa* Sulliv.

15. Tubercle conical-subulate; achenes 1.5 mm long
(incl. the tubercle); glumes obtuse; tufted annuals with filiform stems; muddy shores, not
common ....*E. intermedia* (Muhl.) Schult.
12. Tubercle confluent with the top of the achene, long-conical;
achenes 2-3 mm long.
17. Stems flattened, 1-2 mm wide, 30-60 cm long; marshes
and shores, not common ....*E. rostellata* Torr.
17. Stems somewhat 3-angled, filiform, less than 1 mm wide,
5-30 cm tall; marshes and shores, n.e. Ill. ....
....................*E. pauciflora* (Lightf.) Link

4. **Bulbostylis** [Kunth] C.B.Clarke

B. capillaris (L.) C.B.Clarke. Sandy soil, locally nearly throughout Ill. [*Stenophyllus capillaris* (L.) Britt.].

5. **Fuirena** Rottb. — Umbrella Sedge

F. pumila Torr. Shores, swamps, and wet meadows, n.e. Ill. [*F.
squarrosa* sensu auth., non Michx.].

6. **Hemicarpha** Nees & Arn.

1. Spikelets 2-4 mm long; glumes elliptical, the tips somewhat recurved; wet sandy soil, local ....*H. micrantha* (Vahl) Pax
1. Spikelets 4-7 mm long; glumes broadly ovate, appressed; wet
sandy soil, n. Ill. ....*H. drummondii* Nees

7. **Lipocarpha** R.Br.

L. maculata (Michx.) Torr. Dry margins of ponds, rare; Mason
Co., *R. T. Rexroat* in 1957.

8. **Fimbristylis** Vahl

1. Perennial with rhizomes; stems 20-60 cm tall; leaves puberulent;
achenes lenticular, about 1 mm long; style 2-cleft; moist sandy
soil, local; known from Cook, Hancock, Henderson, Kankakee,
and Lake counties. [*F. puberula* (Michx.) Vahl] ....
....................*F. drummondii* Boeckl.
1. Annual with fibrous roots.
2. Style 2-cleft; achene lenticular; lumber yard, Metropolis, Massac Co., *H. E. Ahles* ....*F. baldwiniana* (Schultes) Torr.
2. Style 3-cleft; achene trigonous; moist sandy or alluvial soil,
locally nearly throughout Ill. [*F. mucronulata* (Michx.)
Blake] ....*F. autumnalis* (L.) R. & S.

9. **Scirpus** L. — Bulrush

1. Involucral bract usually solitary, appearing like a continuation of
the stem, or lacking.
2. Spikelets solitary, rarely two.

3. Bract 1-5 cm long, twice the length of the cylindrical or ovoid spikelet; shallow water, Wolf Lake, Chicago, Cook Co., July 26, 1890, *E. J. Hill;* swamp, Waukegan, Lake Co., *R. A. Harper* in 1891 ....*S. subterminalis* Torr.
3. Bract shorter than or equalling the spikelet; Ringwood, McHenry Co., *Vasey* ....*S. cespitosus* L.
2. Spikelets usually more than one.
　4. Spikelets few, appearing lateral.
　　5. Stems terete, or obtusely 3-angled; plants annual, tufted; bristles minute or absent, or equalling or exceeding the achene.
　　　6. Spikelets solitary or rarely 2, the glumes boat-shaped, keeled, strongly convex; stems filiform, 0.2-0.3 mm thick; low wet ground, rare; Alexander Co., *H. E. Ahles* in 1951. [*S. carinatus* (H. & A.) A.Gray, not Sm.] ....*S. koilolepis* (Steud.) Gleason
　　　6. Spikelets more than one, usually several; glumes flat or nearly so; stems 0.7-2 mm thick.
　　　　7. Achenes strongly transversely rugose; low sandy places in Cass, Mason, and Menard counties ....*S. hallii* A.Gray
　　　　7. Achenes obscurely ridged, or smooth.
　　　　　8. Stems subterete with rounded sides; spikelets acutish; involucral bract always erect; achenes glossy, black, plano-convex; wet shores, rare ....*S. smithii* A.Gray
　　　　　8. Stems obtusely 3-angled with concave sides; spikelets blunt; involucral bract usually divaricate at maturity; achenes dull, unequally biconvex, or lenticular; wet soil, rare; Hancock, Lawrence, and Mason counties. [*S. debilis* of auth., not Lam.] ....*S. purshianus* Fern.
　　5. Stems sharply 3-angled; plants perennial, with rhizomes.
　　　9. Bristles longer than the trigonal achenes; glumes yellowish-brown, entire, mucronate; St. Clair Co., *G. Engelmann* ....*S. torreyi* Olney
　　　9. Bristles not longer than the plano-convex achenes; glumes reddish-brown, awn-tipped; shores and marshy ground throughout Ill. Three-square ....*S. americanus* Pers.
　4. Spikelets in compound umbels.
　　10. Achenes trigonal, 2.5 mm long; spikelets ovoid to cylindrical, 7-15 mm long, usually solitary on the slender branches; shallow water, rare; known in Ill. from Henderson, Menard, and St. Clair counties ....*S. heterochaetus* Chase
　　10. Achenes biconvex; spikelets 2-several on the slender branches.

11. Achenes 2 mm long; glumes 2-2.5 mm long, nearly glabrous, slightly spotted; inflorescence lax; spikelets ovoid, 5-10 mm long; stems soft, easily compressed; marshes and shallow water, throughout Ill. ....*S. validus* Vahl

11. Achenes 2.5 mm long; glumes 3-4 mm long, more or less viscid-puberulent, brown-spotted; inflorescence condensed; spikelets ellipsoid, 1-2 cm long; stems firm and hard; shallow water, local. [*S. occidentalis* (Wats.) Chase] ....*S. acutus* Muhl.

1. Involucral bracts several, foliaceous; stem more or less 3-angled, leafy; plants perennial.

12. Spikelets 1-4 cm long; achenes 2.5-4 mm long.

13. Achenes strongly 3-angled, 4-5 mm long; bristles 6, well-developed; wet ground, local ....
....*S. fluviatilis* (Torr.) A.Gray

13. Achenes more or less compressed or obtusely 3-angled, 3-4.5 mm long; bristles 2-6, usually weakly-developed; wet ground, rare, Cook Co.; adv. from w. U.S. ....
....*S. paludosus* A.Nels.

12. Spikelets numerous, 3-8 mm long, umbellate or paniculate; achenes about 1 mm long.

14. Spikelets in dense glomerules in stiff-rayed decompound umbels; bristles retrorsely minutely barbed, at least at apex, rarely absent.

15. Spikelets 2.5-3 mm long, commonly proliferous; leaves 4-6 mm wide; bristles much longer than the achene, flexuous; wet ground in woods in the southern half of the state ....*S. polyphyllus* Vahl

15. Spikelets 3-9 mm long; leaves 6-16 mm wide; bristles straight, or none.

16. Style usually 3-cleft; bristles about equalling the achene or shorter, or absent, barbed only above the middle; along ditches, streams, lake shores, or in wet woods throughout Ill. [*S. georgianus* Harper] ....*S. atrovirens* Willd.

16. Style usually 2-cleft; bristles usually 4, barbed nearly to the base, equalling or slightly exceeding the achene; lower sheaths red-banded; swamps, rare; Lake Co., *F. C. Gates 2270, 3059* ....
....*S. rubrotinctus* Fern.

14. Spikelets in loose clusters in larger drooping panicles; bristles smooth, flexuous, much longer than the achene.

17. Spikelets cylindrical, 5-8 mm long; leaves 4-7 mm wide; bristles not exceeding the glumes; wet ground in woods, or along ditches, common ....
....*S. lineatus* Michx.

17. Spikelets subglobose, 3-5 mm long; leaves 6-10 mm wide; bristles at maturity much longer than the glumes; wet ground, locally abundant, sometimes covering large areas. [*S. rubricosus* Fern.; *S. pedicellatus* Fern.] ....*S. cyperinus* (L.) Kunth

10. Eriophorum L. — Cotton Sedge

1. Glumes with 1 prominent midrib; spikelets 2-10; bristles bright white; achenes 2-2.5 mm long; stamens 3; bogs, n.e. Ill. [*E. gracile* sensu Ill. auth., non Koch; *E. tenellum* sensu auth. quoad pl. Ill., non Nutt.] ....*E. angustifolium* Nutt.
1. Glumes prominently 3-5-nerved; spikelets crowded into a head; bristles tawny or copper-colored; achenes 3-3.5 mm long; stamen 1; tamarack bogs, Lake Co. ....*E. virginicum* L.

11. Rhynchospora Vahl — Beaked-rush

1. Style entire or slightly 2-toothed, persistent as a long subulate beak on the achene; bristles upwardly scabrellous; wet ground, rare, s. Ill. ....*R. corniculata* (Lam.) A.Gray
1. Style 2-cleft, only its base persistent as a tubercle on the achene.
    2. Bristles downwardly barbed, or sometimes smooth.
        3. Glumes whitish; bristles 9-15; bogs; Lake Co., *Gleason & Shobe 137;* Peoria, *Brendel* ....*R. alba* (L.) Vahl
        3. Glumes brown; bristles 6.
            4. Leaves filiform, less than 0.5 mm wide; spikelets 3-6 in a terminal cluster; bogs and springy ground, n.e. Ill., rare ....*R. capillacea* Torr.
            4. Leaves linear, 2-7 mm wide; spikelets numerous in clusters or heads; lake shores, and moist ground, rare [incl. *R. glomerata* of auth., not (L.) Vahl] ....*R. capitellata* (Michx.) Vahl
    2. Bristles upwardly barbed; leaves flat, 1-4 mm wide; spikelets ovoid, sessile, in erect, cymose clusters; wet sandy soil, Kankakee Co., *Hill* in 1871. [*R. cymosa* of auth.] ....*R. globularis* (Chapm.) Small

12. Cladium P. Br. — Twig-rush

C. mariscoides (Muhl.) Torr. Bogs, marshes, or wet shores, Cook, Lake, and McHenry counties.

13. Scleria Berg. — Nut-rush

1. Spikelets in terminal clusters; achenes supported by a basal disk (hypogynium).
    2. Achenes smooth, ovoid, 3 mm long, the hypogynium covered with a rough white crust; leaves glabrous, 3-9 mm wide; moist sandy soil in the northern half of the state, rare ....*S. triglomerata* Michx.

2. Achenes papillose, subglobose, 1.5-2 mm long; leaves puberulent, 1-2 mm wide; dry ground, s. Ill., rare ....
....*S. pauciflora* Muhl.
1. Spikelets in an interrupted spike; hypogynium absent; achenes transversely wrinkled and reticulate; leaves glabrous, 1 mm or less in width; moist meadows, locally in the northern half of the state ....*S. verticillata* Muhl.

14. **Carex** L. — Sedge

ARTIFICIAL KEY TO GROUPS

1. Perigynia glabrous.
   2. Stigmas two; achenes lenticular or plano-convex.
      3. Spikes of one kind, bearing both pistillate and staminate flowers; lateral spikes sessile.
         4. Spikes androgynous, i.e., with the staminate flowers at the apex ....
         ....GROUP I
         4. Spikes gynecandrous, i.e., with the staminate flowers at the base or middle of the spike ....GROUP II
      3. Spikes usually of two kinds, the terminal commonly staminate, the lower entirely or mostly pistillate ....GROUP III
   2. Stigmas three; achenes trigonal.
      5. Spike solitary, terminal, small, few-flowered, androgynous ....GROUP IV
      5. Spikes two or more.
         6. Beak of the perigynium (if present) small, entire or emarginate, or if bidentulate the short teeth soft and thin ....GROUP V
         6. Beak of the perigynium sharply bidentate ....GROUP VI
1. Perigynium more or less pubescent or puberulent; stigmas 3; achenes trigonal ....GROUP VII

GROUP I

Spikes of one kind, bearing both pistillate and staminate flowers, the staminate occurring at the apex; lateral spikes sessile; stigmas 2; achenes lenticular or plano-convex; perigynia glabrous.

1. Stems arising singly from long rhizomes or prostrate old stems.
   2. Inflorescence 1.5-6 cm long; leaves 2-4 mm wide.
      3. Perigynia ellipsoid, widest near the middle, 3-4 mm long, 1.5 mm wide, the beak 1-1.5 mm long; rhizomes long, stout, black, fibrillose; moist prairie soil, chiefly along railroads, in De Kalb and Winnebago counties ....
      ....*C. praegracilis* W.Boott
      3. Perigynia lanceoloid, widest near the base, 2.5-3 mm long, 1-2 mm wide, the gradually tapering beak about 1 mm long; rhizomes slender; marshes and bogs in the northern half of the state ....*C. sartwellii* Dewey
   2. Inflorescence subcapitate, 5-15 mm long; leaves involute, 0.5-1 mm wide; perigynia ellipsoid, 3 mm long, the beak 0.5-1 mm long; old stems elongate, decumbent, producing new stems from the leaf-axils; sphagnum bogs, Lake and McHenry counties ....*C. chordorrhiza* L.f.

1. Stems tufted.
  4. Perigynia subulate-lanceolate.
    5. Perigynia 4-5 mm long, the beak about the length of the
       body; swamps and wet meadows ....*C. stipata* Muhl.
    5. Perigynia 5-7 mm long.
      6. Perigynium about 5 mm long, tapering gradually from base
        to apex; inflorescence 2.5-6 cm long; leaves 3-6 mm
        wide; swampy woods ....*C. laevivaginata* (Kükenth.) Mack.
      6. Perigynium 6-7 mm long, abruptly enlarged below into a
        disc-like base; inflorescence 7-17 cm long; leaves 5-10
        mm wide; swampy ground ....*C. cruscorvi* Shuttlw.
  4. Perigynia oval, ovate-lanceolate, ovoid or ellipsoid.
    7. Spikes usually fewer than 12; inflorescence often capitate.
      8. Leaves 1-4 mm wide; sheaths close.
        9. Perigynia spongy-thickened at the base.
          10. Perigynium with a minute beak 0.2 mm or less in
            length; bogs, n.e. Ill. ....*C. disperma* Dewey
          10. Perigynium with a distinct beak 0.6-1 mm long.
            11. Beak entire-margined; glumes acuminate or cus-
              pidate.
              12. Body of the perigynium broadly ovate, deep
                green, abruptly short-beaked; dry woods,
                not common ....*C. retroflexa* Muhl.
              12. Body of the perigynium ovate-lanceolate, light
                green, tapering to the beak; dry woods, s.
                Ill. ....*C. texensis* (Torr.) Bailey
            11. Beak minutely scrrulate along the edges.
              13. Broadest leaves 1-2 mm wide; perigynium
                tapering into the beak; stigmas long, slen-
                der, usually not twisted; woods and thickets,
                common ....*C. rosea* Schk.
              13. Broadest leaves 2-3 mm wide; perigynium
                abruptly contracted into the beak; stigmas
                short, stout, contorted, red; dry woods,
                common ....*C. convoluta* Mack.
        9. Perigynia not spongy-thickened at the base.
          14. Heads mostly 1.5-3.5 cm long; leaves and stems stiff
            and wiry; perigynia oval, 3-3.5 mm long, 2.5 mm
            wide, the beak 0.5 mm long, serrulate; sandy soil,
            often in open woods, in the northern half of Ill.
            [Incl. *C. austrina* (Small) Mack.] ....
            ....*C. muhlenbergii* Schk.
          14. Heads mostly 8-15 mm long; leaves and stems soft;
            perigynia 2-3 mm long.
            15. Perigynia oval, 1-1.5 mm wide, the serrulate beak
              1 mm long; open woods or along roads, fre-
              quent ....*C. cephalophora* Muhl.

15. Perigynia ovate, truncate at base, 2 mm wide, the beak 0.5 mm long, entire or nearly so; meadows and open woods, not common ....
....*C. leavenworthii* Dewey
8. Leaves 4.5-8 mm wide; sheaths loose.
16. Stem about 2 mm in diameter below the head, soft and wing-angled, flattened when pressed and dry.
17. Beak of the perigynium about half the length of the body, which is strongly nerved dorsally; sheaths rugose ventrally; woods and thickets, local ....
....*C. conjuncta* Boott
17. Beak about as long as the body of the faintly nerved perigynium; sheaths not rugose; meadows, n. Ill., not common ....*C. alopecoidea* Tuckerm.
16. Stem 1 mm in diameter below the head, not winged.
18. Inflorescence elongate, interrupted, 3-9 cm long; beak of the perigynium shorter than the body; glumes acute; woods and thickets chiefly in the northern half of the state ....*C. sparganioides* Muhl.
18. Inflorescence short, compact, 1-3 cm long.
19. Beak of the perigynium equalling the body; glumes acute; woods and thickets ....
....*C. cephaloidea* Dewey
19. Beak of the perigynium shorter than the body.
20. Glumes aristate, nearly as long as the perigynia; river banks, meadows, edges of woods, roadsides, common. [*C. lunelliana* Mack.] ....*C. gravida* Bailey
20. Glumes ovate, acuminate, shorter than the perigynia; woods and meadows, rare ....
....*C. aggregata* Mack.
7. Spikes numerous (10 or more).
21. Beak of the perigynium much shorter than the body.
22. Leaves 5-8 mm wide; sheaths red-dotted; swamps, rare; Pulaski and Union counties ....
....*C. decomposita* Muhl.
22. Leaves 2-4 mm wide; sheaths not red-dotted.
23. Perigynia 2.5-3.5 mm long, 1.6-2.4 mm broad; beak prominently notched; meadows, fields, pastures in the n. counties, not common ....
....*C. annectens* Bickn.
23. Perigynia 2.2-2.7 mm long, 1.5-1.8 mm broad; beak obscurely notched; fields and pastures, occasionally throughout Ill. ....*C. brachyglossa* Mack.
21. Beak equalling the body.
24. Glumes awned; leaves 2-5 mm wide; swampy ground, often along ditches; common throughout Ill. ....
....*C. vulpinoidea* Michx.

24. Glumes acute; leaves 1-3 mm wide.
  25. Perigynium 2-2.5 mm long, glossy, not concealed by the glume; wet meadows; Fulton, Peoria, and Stark counties ....*C. diandra* Schrank
  25. Perigynium 2.5-3.5 mm long, dull, nearly concealed by the glume; wet meadows, n. Ill. ....
  ....*C. prairea* Dewey

GROUP II

Spikes of one kind, gynecandrous (or variable in *C. sterilis* and *C. interior*), bearing both pistillate and staminate flowers, the staminate occurring at the base or the middle of the spike; lateral spikes sessile; stigmas two; achenes lenticular or plano-convex; perigynia glabrous.
1. Perigynia without winged margins.
  2. Perigynia 4-5 mm long; beak serrulate, bidentate, 1.5-2 mm long; wet ground in Boone, Cook, De Kalb, and La Salle counties ....*C. bromoides* Schk.
  2. Perigynia 2-4 mm long.
    3. Beak of the perigynium entire or emarginate, not more than 0.5 mm long; perigynium oval, plano-convex; spikes 2 or 3, each 2- to 5-flowered; tamarack swamp, Lake Villa, Lake Co., *Gleason & Shobe* ....*C. trisperma* Dewey
    3. Beak of the perigynium bidentate, serrulate, 0.5-1 mm long.
      4. Perigynia ovate-deltoid; glumes acute; spikes 4-6; anthers 1-2 mm long; swampy meadows ....*C. sterilis* Willd.
      4. Perigynia flattened, ellipsoid; glumes obtuse; spikes 2-3; anthers 0.7-0.9 mm long; damp soil. [*C. scirpoides* Schk., ex p.] ....*C. interior* Bailey
1. Perigynia thin- or wing-margined.
  5. Plants strongly stoloniferous, the stems arising from an elongated rhizome; spikes 6-12, the lowest pistillate, the middle staminate, the terminal gynecandrous; sandy soil, rare; Kankakee Co., *Hill;* Peoria Co., *Brendel* ....*C. siccata* Dewey
  5. Plants not stoloniferous, the stems tufted; spikes usually all gynecandrous.
    6. Perigynia 1-2 mm wide.
      7. Perigynia elongate-lanceolate, 2½ - 6 times longer than wide.
        8. Spikes 15-25 mm long, tapering at each end; perigynia 7-10 mm long; wet ground in woods, local ....
        ....*C. muskingumensis* Schw.
      8. Spikes 4-15 mm long; perigynia 3-6 mm long.
        9. Leaves 1-3 mm wide; spikes glossy, acute; leaf-sheaths white-hyaline ventrally; marshes and wet meadows, common ....*C. scoparia* Schk.
        9. Leaves 3-7 mm wide; spikes obtuse; leaf-sheaths green-striate nearly to auricle.

10. Tips of the perigynia appressed or ascending; inflorescence compact, stiff; spikes 7-12 mm long;
meadows and ditches, common. [*C. tribuloides*
var. *sangamonensis* Clokey] ....
....*C. tribuloides* Wahl.
10. Tips of the perigynia spreading; spikes 4-8 mm
long.
    11. Inflorescence compact; spikes globose, echi-
nate; stems stiff; perigynia 3-4 mm long;
meadows, roadside ditches, and thickets,
chiefly in the northern half of the state.
[*C. cristata* Schw., non Clairv.] ....
....*C. cristatella* Britt.
    11. Inflorescence loose, flexuous, elongate; stems
slender, weak; perigynia 4-5 mm long;
moist ground, rare; Jackson and Menard
counties ....*C. projecta* Mack.
7. Perigynia oval or ovate-lanceolate to suborbicular, seldom
more than twice as long as wide.
    12. Perigynium-body oval, finely nerved on the inner sur-
face; leaf-sheaths ventrally white-hyaline.
        13. Perigynia brownish; spikes closely aggregated into
a head 1-2.5 cm long, not clavate at the base;
marshes and ditches chiefly in the n. half of Ill.
....*C. bebbii* Olney
        13. Perigynia green; spikes contiguous to widely sep-
arate, usually more or less clavate at the base;
inflorescence at maturity 2.5-5 cm long.
            14. Leaves 3-4 mm wide; moist ground along roads
or in open woods, common. [*C. mirabilis*
Dewey, non Host] ....*C. normalis* Mack.
            14. Leaves 1.5-2.5 mm wide; open woods ....
....*C. tenera* Dewey
    12. Perigynium-body ovate-orbicular, nerved on both sur-
faces.
        15. Perigynia 4-5.5 mm long, spreading-ascending;
spikes straw-colored or ferrugineous; leaf-sheaths
white-hyaline ventrally; woods and roadsides, not
infrequent ....*C. festucacea* Schk.
        15. Perigynia 3.5-4 mm long, closely appressed; spikes
grayish-green turning dull brown; leaf-sheaths
green-striate; open woods, local. [*C. straminea*
sensu auth., non Willd.] ....*C. albolutescens* Schw.
6. Perigynia 2.5-4 mm wide.
    16. Perigynia 3-5 mm long.
        17. Leaf-sheaths green-striate nearly to the auricle.
            18. Glumes aristate; spikes 4-8 in a flexuous inflores-
cence; perigynia nerved ventrally; Athens,

Menard Co., *E. Hall* in 1861 ....
....................................*C. richii* (Fern.) Mack.
18. Glumes acute; perigynia nerveless or nearly so
ventrally.
19. Perigynia 3-4 mm long, widest above the
middle; spikes 5-25, densely aggregated;
peaty margin of oak woods near St. Anne,
Kankakee Co., *R. A. Schneider 1654* ....
.........................*C. cumulata* (Bailey) Mack.
19. Perigynia 4-5 mm long, widest at the middle;
spikes 2-5, ovoid, acute, yellowish-brown or
reddish-brown, 7-12 mm long; wet ground,
Cook, Kankakee, and Will counties ....
.........................*C. suberecta* (Olney) Britt.
17. Leaf-sheaths conspicuously hyaline ventrally; spikes 5-
8 mm long, roundish, greenish; roadsides and open
woods, common [*C. molesta* Mack.] ....
....*C. brevior* (Dewey) Mack.
16. Perigynia 5.5-6.5 mm long, 3-4 mm wide, flat, thin, translucent, prominently nerved on each face; dry soil in
the northern half of Ill. ....*C. bicknellii* Britt.

GROUP III

Stigmas 2; achenes lenticular; perigynia short-beaked or beakless;
spikes normally unisexual, i.e., the terminal spike commonly staminate,
the lower spikes entirely or mostly pistillate.

1. Perigynia obovoid or subglobose, beakless, yellowish or brownish,
plump, nerved, about 2 mm in length, longer than the obtuse,
pale brown glumes; wet ground, Lake Co. ....*C. aurea* Nutt.
1. Perigynia compressed, short-beaked, the beak less than 0.5 mm
long.
2. Midvein of pistillate glumes prolonged 5-10 mm beyond the
glume; marshy ground, rare ....*C. crinita* Lam.
2. Midvein of pistillate glumes not conspicuously exserted.
3. Glumes obtuse, approximately equalling the perigynia.
4. At least the lower pistillate spikes drooping; beak of perigynium twisted at maturity; in and along streams or
rarely in swamps, s. Ill. ....*C. torta* Boott
4. All the pistillate spikes erect or ascending; beak of perigynium not twisted.
5. Perigynium 2.7-3.2 mm long, strongly flattened; stems
strongly phyllopodic, the dried-up leaves of the previous year persistent; wet ground, n. Ill. [*C. aquatilis*
of auth., not Wahl.] ......*C. substricta* (Kükenth.) Mack.
5. Perigynium 2-2.7 mm long; stems aphyllopodic; leaves
of the previous year not persistent; swamps in the n.
two-thirds of Ill. ....*C. stricta* Lam.

3. Glumes acuminate or acute, longer than the perigynia; stems
   aphyllopodic.
   6. Perigynia 2-2.5 mm long, turgid; moist ground in woods
      in the n. counties ....*C. haydenii* Dewey
   6. Perigynia 1.5-1.7 mm long, flattened; moist ground in
      woods, rare ....*C. emoryi* Dewey

GROUP IV

Spike solitary, terminal, small, few-flowered, androgynous; perigynia glabrous; stigmas three; achenes trigonal.

1. Perigynia 2.5-3.5 mm long, beakless, ellipsoid; leaves 0.5-1.5 mm
   wide; glumes obtuse; bogs and wet meadows .... *C. leptalea* Wahl.
1. Perigynia 5-6 mm long, globose, with a roughened entire beak 3
   mm long; leaves 2-3 mm wide; glumes aristate, foliaceous; dry
   woods ....*C. jamesii* Schw.

GROUP V

Stigmas three; achenes trigonal; spikes two or more; perigynia glabrous, the beak (if present) small, entire, emarginate, or bidentulate.

1. Leaves 1-3 cm wide; beak of the perigynium curved or bent.
   2. Cauline sheaths bladeless, red-tinged; woods, rare ....
      ....*C. plantaginea* Lam.
   2. Cauline sheaths with well developed blades.
      3. Perigynia sharply triangular; pistillate glumes acute to acu-
         minate.
         4. Perigynia 5-6.5 mm long; rich woods, locally in eastern
            and southern Ill. ....*C. careyana* Torr.
         4. Perigynia 3-4.5 mm long; open woods, not common ....
            ....*C. platyphylla* Carey
      3. Perigynia obtusely triangular; pistillate glumes obtuse; woods,
         not uncommon ....*C. albursina* Sheldon
1. Leaves usually less than 1 cm wide.
   5. Leaves capillary, 0.5 mm wide; perigynia 2 mm long, minutely
      straight-beaked or beakless; glumes obtuse; rocky soil, or
      sandy thickets, rare, in the northern half of Ill. ....
      ....*C. eburnea* Boott
   5. Leaves 1-9 mm wide.
      6. Perigynium beakless, or the straight beak not more than 0.5
         mm long.
         7. Mature perigynia conspicuously nerved or ribbed.
            8. Spikes drooping on slender peduncles.
               9. Lateral spikes 3-6, linear-cylindrical, 2-3 mm thick;
                  perigynia twice the length of the obtuse glumes;
                  leaves 3-7 mm wide; moist woods and meadows,
                  common ....*C. gracillima* Schw.

9. Lateral spikes 1-2, ellipsoid, 5-8 mm thick; perigynia nearly equalling the acute or mucronate glumes; bogs; Peoria and Tazewell counties, *Brendel,* and in the n.e. counties ....*C. limosa* L.
8. Spikes ascending or erect.
  10. Terminal spike gynecandrous; leaves and base of stem usually more or less pubescent.
    11. Perigynia beakless, 2-3.5 mm long; leaves 1.5-4 mm wide.
      12. Perigynia appressed-ascending, much wider than thick, obtuse; dry woods and meadows throughout Ill. ....*C. hirsutella* Mack.
      12. Perigynia spreading, nearly as thick as wide, acute.
        13. Sheaths glabrous or nearly so; low, wet woods, local ....*C. caroliniana* Schw.
        13. Sheaths pubescent; meadows and woods; s. Ill. ....*C. bushii* Mack.
    11. Perigynia 3.5-6 mm long, ellipsoid, ascending, the beak short; glumes acuminate to awned; leaves 3-8 mm wide.
      14. Glumes awned; mature perigynia 5 mm long; roadside ditches and alluvial soil in woods, frequent ....*C. davisii* Schw. & Torr.
      14. Glumes acuminate; perigynia 3.5-4 mm long, swampy woods, Union Co., *R. H. Mohlenbrock & J. W. Voigt* in 1955 ....
...............................*C. oxylepis* Torr. & Hook
  10. Terminal spike staminate.
    15. Perigynia tapering at the base, triangular in cross-section.
      16. Pistillate glumes mucronate or awned; stems phyllopodic; stolons deep-seated; plants of open marly or sandy soil.
        17. Pistillate spikes cylindrical, 3-4.5 mm thick; sandy soil, n. Ill. ....
....*C. tetanica* Schk.
        17. Pistillate spikes ellipsoid, 5-8 mm thick; meadows and prairies chiefly in the northern half of Ill. ....*C. meadii* Dewey
      16. Pistillate glumes obtuse; pistillate spikes 3-4 mm thick; stems aphyllopodic; stolons superficial; woodland plants, rare ....
....*C. woodii* Dewey
    15. Perigynia rounded at the base, nearly terete in cross-section.

18. Plants loosely stoloniferous, the stems solitary, 10-30 cm tall; leaves often folded, 1.5-3 mm wide; sandy soil, n.e. Ill. ....
....*C. crawei* Dewey

18. Plants tufted, 30-60 cm tall; leaves 3-9 mm wide; moist meadows and woods, common. [*C. rectior* Mack.; *C. haleana* Olney] ....
....*C. granularis* Muhl.

7. Mature perigynia faintly impressed-nerved or nerveless; spikes erect or ascending.

19. Terminal spike staminate; pistillate glumes mucronate or awned.

20. Sheaths and lower blades pubescent; perigynia 2.5-3 mm long; moist ground, rare; "N. Illinois", *Vasey* ....*C. pallescens* L.

20. Plants glabrous; perigynia 3.5-5.5 mm long.

21. Perigynia 1.5 mm wide; bract-sheaths with serrulate margins; peduncles of the pistillate spikes scabrous; meadows and ditches in the n. half of Ill., not common ....*C. conoidea* Schk.

21. Perigynia 2-2.5 mm wide; bract-sheaths and peduncles smooth or nearly so.

22. Pistillate spikes 3- to 12-flowered; leaves thin, soft, not glaucous.

23. Perigynia 4.5-5.5 mm long; stems brownish at base; leaves 4-8 mm wide; woods, thickets, and meadows, common ....*C. grisea* Wahl.

23. Perigynia 3.5-4.5 mm long; stems reddish at base; leaves 2-4 mm wide; dry banks and wooded hillsides, rare; Cook, Du Page, and Stark counties ....
.................................*C. amphibola* Steud.

22. Pistillate spikes 12- to 35-flowered; leaves glaucous, thick, firm; awn of the pistillate glumes smooth; woods, local [*C. glaucodea* Tuckerm.] (Although not closely related, *C.* x *fulleri* Ahles, Rhodora 58: 320, 1956, from Winnebago Co. might be sought here.) ....*C. flaccosperma* Dewey

19. Terminal spike gynecandrous, or at least with some pistillate flowers.

24. Perigynia elliptical, light green, granular, much shorter than the purplish-black cuspidate glumes; leaves 1.5-4 mm wide; plants stoloniferous, growing in bogs and marshy ground in n. Ill. ....
....*C. buxbaumii* Wahl.

24. Perigynia obovate-orbicular, slightly wrinkled, about equalling the reddish-brown acute or obtuse glumes; leaves 4-9 mm wide; plants cespitose, growing in moist woods, thickets, and roadside ditches, common ....*C. shortiana* Dewey

6. Beak of the perigynium curved, or if straight 0.7-1 mm long; glumes mucronate or aristate, or sometimes merely acutish.

25. Beak oblique or abruptly curved, 0.3-0.5 mm long.

26. Staminate spikes sessile or nearly so; woods, common ....*C. blanda* Dewey

26. Staminate spikes long-peduncled.

27. Stems reddish-tinged at base; woods, not uncommon ....*C. gracilescens* Steud.

27. Stems green or brown at base; rich woods, rare; Panther's Den, Union Co., *R. R. MacMahon* in 1959 ....*C. striatula* Michx.

25. Beak straight, 0.7-1 mm long; perigynia 40-50-nerved.

28. Sheaths pubescent; perigynia 4-5 mm long; leaves 3-7 mm wide; wooded hillsides, rare; near Peoria, Peoria Co., *Brendel, McDonald;* Stark Co., *V. H. Chase* ....*C. hitchcockiana* Dewey

28. Sheaths glabrous; perigynia 3-4 mm long; leaves 2-4.5 mm wide; dry woods in the northern half of the state ....*C. oligocarpa* Schk.

GROUP VI

Stigmas three; achenes trigonal; spikes two or more; perigynia glabrous, the beak sharply bidentate.

1. Staminate spike solitary or none, sometimes bearing some pistillate flowers.

2. Mature perigynia 1-2 cm long.

3. Pistillate spikes globose, the ellipsoid perigynia widely radiate-spreading; beak of the perigynium 1.5-2.5 mm long; swampy woods, rare ....*C. intumescens* Rudge

3. Pistillate spikes ellipsoid to cylindrical, the ovoid-lanceoloid perigynia ascending; beak of the perigynium 5-10 mm long.

4. Leaves 3-5 mm wide; perigynia 10-12 mm long, the beak smooth, not serrulate; pistillate spikes subglobose-ellipsoid, 2-3.5 cm long; staminate spike 2-2.5 mm wide; stems solitary or few from elongate rhizomes; achenes longer than wide, the angles not prominently thickened; wet ground in woods, s. Ill. [*C. halei* sensu Carey, non Dewey] ....*C. louisianica* Bailey

4. Leaves 5-15 mm wide; perigynia 13-20 mm long; pistillate spikes ellipsoid-cylindrical, 2-8 cm long; staminate spike 3-5 mm wide; stems cespitose.

5. Beak of the perigynium serrulate; achenes longer than wide, the angles not thickened; swamps, common ....*C. lupulina* Muhl.

5. Beak of the perigynium smooth; achenes as wide as long, the angles prominently thickened; wet ground, local ....*C. lupuliformis* Sartw.

2. Mature perigynia not more than 1 cm long.

  6. Leaves involute-filiform; pistillate spikes 1 or 2, sessile, globose, few-flowered; perigynia ovoid, turgid, glossy, 4-7 mm long, nearly twice the length of the obtuse glumes; bogs; Lake Co., *Hill* in 1908 ....*C. oligosperma* Michx.

  6. Leaves flat.

    7. Perigynia obovoid, 4-5 mm long, truncate above and abruptly subulate-beaked; terminal spike often mostly pistillate.

      8. Perigynia shorter than the serrulate, linear-subulate glumes; ditches and swamps; northward to McLean and Adams counties ....*C. frankii* Kunth

      8. Perigynia much longer than the glumes.

        9. Perigynia squarrose; glumes acute to mucronate; style strongly curved near the ovary; swampy ground and roadside ditches, common ....*C. squarrosa* L.

        9. Perigynia ascending; glumes obtusish or acutish; style straight throughout; swamps and roadside ditches; chiefly in the southern half of Ill., extending northward to Macon Co. [*C. typhinoides* Schw.] ....*C. typhina* Michx.

    7. Perigynia lanceoloid, ellipsoid, or ovoid.

      10. Glumes with a serrulate awn.

        11. Perigynia lanceoloid, strongly ribbed, soon reflexed, 5-7 mm long, the beak equalling or exceeding the body; teeth strongly divergent, 1-2 mm long; swamps and ditches, local. [*C. pseudocyperus* of auth.] ....*C. comosa* Boott

        11. Perigynia ellipsoid or ovoid, often inflated, 5-9 mm long.

          12. Perigynia 15- to 20-nerved, 1.5-2 mm thick, the beak 2 mm long; wet ground, common; chiefly in the northern half of the state ....*C. hystricina* Muhl.

          12. Perigynia 8- to 10-nerved, 2.5-3 mm thick, the beak 3-4 mm long; swamps, wet meadows, and ditches, common ....*C. lurida* Wahl.

      10. Glumes not serrulate.

        13. Beak of the perigynium 0.5-1 mm long, minutely bidentate.

14. Perigynia 2-3.5 mm long; lake shores and river banks, locally in n.e. Ill. ....*C. viridula* Michx.

14. Perigynia 5.5-6.5 mm long; open woods, rare; Hardin Co., *R. H. Mohlenbrock* in 1954 ....*C. debilis* Michx.

13. Beak of the perigynium 2-2.5 mm long, equalling or exceeding the body.

15. Pistillate spikes erect, sessile; perigynia spreading or reflexed, 2-3 times as long as the glumes; wet meadows in n.e. Ill. ....*C. cryptolepis* Mack.

15. Pistillate spikes pendulous on slender peduncles; perigynia spreading-ascending, slightly longer than the glumes; beak smooth; alluvial soil in the northern half of the state. [*C. longirostris* sensu Torr., non Krock.] ....*C. sprengelii* Dewey

1. Staminate spikes two or more; perigynia ovoid to ellipsoid, often more or less inflated.

16. Teeth of the perigynium short, usually not more than 0.5 mm long.

17. Perigynia ascending, fusiform or narrowly ellipsoid, short-beaked, the beak not more than 1 mm long.

18. Mature perigynia strongly-nerved; stems aphyllopodic, purplish and filamentose at base; swamps and ditches, local ....*C. lacustris* Willd.

18. Mature perigynia finely impressed-nerved; stems phyllopodic, light brownish at base; ditches, and wet ground in woods, local ....*C. hyalinolepis* Steud.

17. Perigynia spreading or reflexed, ovoid-lanceoloid, inflated, papery, strongly nerved, the beak 2-3 mm long; swampy ground, local ....*C. retrorsa* Schw.

16. Teeth of the perigynium 0.5-2 mm long.

19. Perigynium 5-6 mm wide, 7-10 mm long, the teeth 0.5-1 mm long; wet ground in woods; Cook, Lake, Winnebago, and Hancock counties ....*C. tuckermani* Dewey

19. Perigynium 2-3 mm wide.

20. Teeth 1-3 mm long; perigynium dull; style straight.

21. Sheaths and blades pubescent; prairie sloughs, rare; Winnebago Co., *E. W. Fell* ....*C. atherodes* Spreng.

21. Sheaths and blades glabrous; marshy ground, locally in the northern half of the state ....*C. laeviconica* Dewey

20. Teeth 0.5-1 mm long; perigynia glossy; style flexuous or abruptly bent.

22. Lower perigynia reflexed or widely spreading; stems scattered, obtusely angled; plants stoloniferous; leaves 4-12 mm wide; ditches and shores, rare; Henderson and Winnebago counties ....
....*C. rostrata* Stokes

22. Perigynia ascending; stems cespitose, sharply angled; leaves 3-5 mm wide; swamps, and wet ground in woods, local ....*C. vesicaria* L.

GROUP VII

Perigynia more or less pubescent or puberulent (sometimes only slightly so); stigmas 3; achenes trigonal.

1. Perigynia beakless (or the beak less than 0.4 mm long).
  2. Terminal spike staminate throughout; perigynia 2-3 mm long.
    3. Perigynia ellipsoid, 3-12 in a spike, longer than, or equalling the glumes; leaves 2.5-5 mm wide; woods and thickets in the northern half of Ill. ....*C. digitalis* Willd.
    3. Perigynia obovoid, 10-25 in a spike, shorter than the obtuse, hyaline-margined glumes; leaves 2-2.5 mm wide; sandy or rocky barrens, rare; Hancock, Lake, Menard, Peoria, and Winnebago counties ....*C. richardsonii* R.Br.
  2. Terminal spike with some pistillate flowers.
    4. Perigynia about 4 mm long, puberulent to glabrate, obovoid, angular; leaves persistent, 2-5 mm wide, usually longer than the slender stems; dry woods, n. Ill., rare ....
....*C. pedunculata* Muhl.
    4. Perigynia 2-2.5 mm long.
      5. Stems usually shorter than the leaves; pistillate spikes ellipsoid; perigynia obovoid; woods and roadsides, not common ....*C. swanii* (Fern.) Mack.
      5. Stems usually longer than the leaves; pistillate spikes cylindrical; perigynia ellipsoid; woods, n.e. Ill. ....
....*C. virescens* Muhl.
1. Perigynium beaked; terminal spike (or spikes) wholly staminate.
  6. Mature perigynia 12-18 mm long; leaves 5-15 mm wide; moist woods, common ....*C. grayii* Carey
  6. Perigynia shorter.
    rigynia 9-10 mm long; leaves 3-8 mm wide; wet meadows the n. half of Ill. ....*C. trichocarpa* Muhl.
    ynia 2.5-5 mm long.
      e (or all) the spikes half hidden among the tufted leaf-
es; plants densely tufted, 5-15 cm tall; pistillate spikes
mm long; perigynia plump, stipitate, 2-keeled, 2.5-
m long; dry sandy or gravelly soil, local ....
....*C. umbellata* Schk.
    ikes near the summit of the stem.

9. Leaves pubescent; woods, common nearly throughout
   Ill. [*C. pubescens* Muhl., non Poir.] ....
   ....*C. hirtifolia* Mack.
9. Leaves glabrous.
   10. Pistillate spikes 3-12 mm long; plants flowering in
       early spring.
       11. Staminate spike stout, 2-4 mm thick; body of the
           perigynium suborbicular, about as long as
           wide; plants strongly stoloniferous, the stolons
           slender, reddish, fibrillose, scaly; dry open
           woods, common. [*C. heliophila* Mack.] ....
           ....*C. pensylvanica* Lam.
       11. Staminate spike 0.5-2 mm thick; plants forming
           small tufts, never stoloniferous.
           12. Mature leaves 3-5 mm wide; dry woods in
               the northern part of the state ....
               ....*C. communis* Bailey
           12. Mature leaves 1-2.5 mm wide; dry woods,
               locally throughout Ill. [*C. varia* of Muhl.,
               not Lumn., or Host] ....*C. artitecta* Mack.
   10. Pistillate spikes 1-7 cm long.
       13. Leaves involute-filiform, 1-2 mm wide; stems ob-
           tusely triangular, smooth; swamps and bogs in
           the northern half of Ill. ....*C. lasiocarpa* Ehrh.
       13. Leaves flat, 2-6 mm wide; stems sharply triangu-
           lar, rough above.
           14. Perigynia 2.5-3.5 mm long, the beak 1 mm
               long; pistillate spikes 5-8 mm thick; style
               straight, jointed with the achene; swamps,
               chiefly in the northern and central parts of
               the state ....*C. lanuginosa* Michx.
           14. Perigynium 5 mm long, the beak 1.5 mm
               long; pistillate spikes 8-12 mm thick; style
               flexuous, continuous with the achene;
               marshy alluvial soil, Cowford Bridge,
               Macon Co., June 18, 1915, *I. W. Clokey*
               2338, type collection. [*C. impressa* $\times$
               lanuginosa Clokey] ......*C. subimpressa* Clokey

146. Gramineae Juss. — Grass Family
KEY TO THE TRIBES

1. Spikelets usually more or less laterally compressed, 1-many-flowered, usually
   articulating above the persistent glumes. (Subfamily I. *Poacoideae*)
   2. Plants woody; stems perennial; leaf-blade (short-) petioled and articu-
      lated with the sheath ....Tribe 1. *Bambuseae*
   2. Plants herbaceous; stems annual; leaf-blade continuous with the sheath.
      3. Spikelets several-flowered.
         4. Inflorescence a panicle, this sometimes contracted and spike-like.

    5. Lemmas longer than the glumes, awnless or with a straight
       apical awn ....Tribe 2. *Festuceae*
    5. Lemmas usually shorter than the glumes.
      6. Florets essentially uniform, the lemmas usually with a bent
         awn arising from the back ....Tribe 4. *Aveneae*
      6. The two lower florets sterile or staminate, unlike the single
         fertile floret; spikelets awned or not ....Tribe 7. *Phalarideae*
   4. Inflorescence of solitary, racemose, or digitate spikes or racemes,
    the spikelets sessile or nearly so.
      7. Spikelets solitary, or in clusters of 2-6, arranged alternately on
         opposite sides of the axis; spike solitary, terminal ....
         ....Tribe 3. *Hordeae*
      7. Spikelets in one-sided spikes or racemes, the spikes or racemes
         solitary or several ....Tribe 6. *Chlorideae*
  3. Spikelets 1-flowered.
    8. Glumes 2; stamens 3 or 1 ....Tribe 5. *Agrostideae*
    8. Glumes none; stamens 6 ....Tribe 8. *Oryzeae*
1. Spikelets more or less dorsally compressed with only one perfect terminal
  floret whose lemmas resemble glumes; articulation below the spikelets,
  these falling entire. (Subfamily II. *Panicoideae*)
  9. Stamens and pistils in the same inflorescence, usually in the same spike-
    let or floret.
    10. Spikelets essentially uniform ....Tribe 9. *Paniceae*
    10. Spikelets in pairs or threes, one sessile and fertile, the others pedi-
       celled and staminate or neuter, or rarely absent or reduced to a
       pedicel ....Tribe 10. *Andropogoneae*
  9. Staminate and pistillate spikelets in different parts of the same spike, or
    in different inflorescences, the staminate above the pistillate ones ....
    ....Tribe 11. *Tripsaceae*

KEY TO THE GENERA
Subfamily 1. **Poacoideae**
Tribe 1. BAMBUSEAE. — Bamboo Tribe

One genus in Illinois ....1. *Arundinaria*

Tribe 2. FESTUCEAE. — Fescue Tribe

1. Plants 2-4 m tall; rachilla plumose; panicles large ....14. *Phragmites*
1. Plants less tall; rachilla not plumose.
  2. Plants dioecious, the staminate and pistillate flowers unlike ....18. *Distichlis*
  2. Plants with perfect flowers in uniform spikelets.
    3. Lemmas prominently 3-nerved.
      4. Lemmas more or less villous on the nerves.
        5. Stem-nodes glabrous; palet not ciliate ....16. *Tridens*
        5. Stem-nodes pubescent; palet conspicuously ciliate ....17. *Triplasis*
      4. Lemmas glabrous, or merely scabrous on the nerves.
        6. Callus of lemma heavily bearded ....13. *Redfieldia*
        6. Callus of lemma not bearded.
          7. Lemmas less than 5 mm long ....9. *Eragrostis*
          7. Lemmas about 8 mm long; the upper 2-4 lemmas empty ....
          ....10. *Diarrhena*
    3. Lemmas 5- to many-nerved (the nerves sometimes indistinct).
      8. Spikelets with sterile lemmas above or below the fertile florets.

9. Spikelets 8-20-flowered, green, nodding on long slender pedicels, the lower 1-5 lemmas sterile ....11. *Uniola*
9. Spikelets 2- or 3-flowered, short-pedicelled, the uppermost 1-3 sterile lemmas much smaller ....15. *Melica*
8. Spikelets without sterile lemmas.
  10. Lemmas awned.
    11. Lemmas bifid at apex, awned just below the apex or behind the teeth.
      12. Ovary pubescent at apex; grain furrowed, adnate to the palet; stigmas sessile, arising below the apex of the ovary; sheaths closed ....2. *Bromus*
      12. Ovary glabrous; grain smooth, free; styles terminal; sheaths split ....3. *Schizachne*
    11. Lemmas entire, with an apical point or awn ....4. *Festuca*
  10. Lemmas awnless, or mucronate, or short-awned in *Dactylis*.
    13. Spikelets nodding, as broad as long, on capillary pedicels in open panicles; lemmas papery, imbricated, scarious-margined, cordate at base, the apex obtuse or acutish ......
    ....8. *Briza*
    13. Spikelets not as above in all respects.
      14. Spikelets strongly flattened, crowded in 1-sided clusters at the ends of long branches; keels of the glumes and lemmas hispid-ciliate ....12. *Dactylis*
      14. Spikelets neither strongly flattened, nor in 1-sided clusters.
        15. Lemmas with cobwebby hairs at base ....7. *Poa*
        15. Lemmas without cobwebby hairs.
          16. Nerves of the lemma parallel.
            17. Lemmas faintly 5-nerved; stigmas sessile, the style none; sheaths open; annual or perennial halophytes ....5. *Puccinellia*
            17. Lemmas prominently 5-9-nerved; styles short, distinct; sheaths closed; tall marsh perennial grasses ....6. *Glyceria*
          16. Nerves of the lemma converging at the apex (sometimes indistinct).
            18. Lemmas 8-11 mm long; spikelets large ....
            ....2. *Bromus*
            18. Lemmas less than 8 mm long.
              19. Lemmas keeled on the back, the apex obtuse or acute ....7. *Poa*
              19. Lemmas convex on the back or subcarinate, acute or awn-tipped (obtusish in *F. obtusa*) ....4. *Festuca*

Tribe 3. HORDEAE. — Barley Tribe

1. Spikelets solitary at each joint of the rachis.
  2. Spikelets placed edgewise to the rachis; first glume of the lateral spikelets absent ....26. *Lolium*
  2. Spikelets placed flatwise to the rachis; glumes 2.
    3. Spikelets cylindrical, awned, sunk in the thickened rachis ....21. *Aegilops*
    3. Spikelets compressed.
      4. Glumes 1-nerved; spikelets with 2 perfect flowers ....22. *Secale*
      4. Glumes 3- to several-nerved.

     5. Glumes lanceolate to linear ....19. *Agropyron*
     5'. Glumes ovate ....20. *Triticum*
1. Spikelets 2-6 at each joint of the rachis.
     6. Spikelets 3 at each joint, 1-flowered, the lateral pair usually aborted; glumes awn-like ....25. *Hordeum*
     6. Spikelets usually in pairs, 2- to 6-flowered.
        7. Spike loosely flowered, the spikelets widely spreading; glumes obsolete or bristle-like ....24. *Hystrix*
        7. Spike densely flowered, the spikelets ascending; glumes well-developed ....23. *Elymus*

Tribe 4. AVENEAE. — Oat Tribe

1. Spikelets more than 5 mm long.
     2. Lemmas awned from the back, or awn absent.
        3. Spikelets more than 1 cm long; plants annual ....31. *Avena*
        3. Spikelets less than 1 cm in length; lower floret long-awned, the upper one usually awnless; plants perennial ....32. *Arrhenatherum*
     2. Lemmas awned from between the apical teeth ....33. *Danthonia*
1. Spikelets not more than 5 mm long.
     4. Spikelets disarticulating above the glumes.
        5. Inflorescence contracted, spike-like; glumes unequal; plants of dry habitats ....27. *Koeleria*
        5. Inflorescence a spreading panicle; lemmas awned from the middle or below; plants of moist habitats.
           6. Lemmas truncate and erose at summit ....29. *Deschampsia*
           6. Lemmas 2-toothed at summit ....30. *Aira*
     4. Spikelets disarticulating below the glumes.
        7. Florets awnless, all perfect; glumes exceeded by the upper floret ....28. *Sphenopholis*
        7. Lower spikelet perfect, awnless, the upper staminate and bearing a hooked awn; glumes longer than the florets ....34. *Holcus*

Tribe 5. AGROSTIDEAE. — Timothy Tribe

1. Lemmas of more delicate texture than the glumes, not at all indurated.
     2. Inflorescence dense, spike-like; glumes keeled.
        3. Lemma awnless.
           4. Glumes short-awned; leaves flat ....41. *Phleum*
           4. Glumes awnless.
              5. Tall perennials; florets bearing a tuft of hairs at base ....36. *Ammophila*
              5. Low annuals; florets without hairs at base ....44. *Heleochloa*
        3. Lemma awned; glumes awnless ....40. *Alopecurus*
     2. Inflorescence an open or somewhat spike-like panicle; glumes not keeled.
        6. Grain permanently enclosed in the lemma and palet; pericarp adherent to the grain.
           7. Palet 1-nerved, 1-keeled; stamen 1; tall perennials with flat leaves and nodding panicles ....39. *Cinna*
           7. Palet 2-nerved and 2-keeled; stamens 3.
              8. Lemma with long hairs at the base.
                 9. Lemma and palet membranous; rachilla prolonged beyond the palet, bristle-like ....35. *Calamagrostis*
                 9. Lemma and palet chartaceous; rachilla not prolonged beyond the palet ....37. *Calamovilfa*

8. Lemma without a tuft of hairs at the base.
  10. Lemma awnless or with a dorsal awn ....38. *Agrostis*
  10. Lemma with a terminal awn, or mucronate at apex ....
    ....42. *Muhlenbergia*
6. Grain not permanently enclosed in the lemma and palet, readily •
  separating from the pericarp ....43. *Sporobolus*
1. Lemma indurated when mature, closely enveloping the grain.
  11. Lemma awnless ....46. *Milium*
  11. Lemma awned.
    12. Lemma 3-awned ....49. *Aristida*
    12. Lemma 1-awned.
      13. Awn twisted or bent ....48. *Stipa*
      13. Awn not twisted or bent.
        14. Lemma broad, the awn deciduous ....47. *Oryzopsis*
        14. Lemma narrow, the tip awned or mucronate.
          15. Rachilla not prolonged behind the palet ....
          .... 42. *Muhlenbergia*
          15. Rachilla prolonged into a bristle behind the palet ....
          ....45. *Brachyelytrum*

Tribe 6. CHLORIDEAE. — Grama Tribe

1. Plants monoecious or dioecious ....50. *Buchloë*
1. Plants with perfect flowers.
  2. Spikelets with more than 1 perfect floret; plants annual.
    3. Spikes numerous, slender, racemose ....54. *Leptochloa*
    3. Spikes few, digitate.
      4. Rachilla prolonged beyond the spikelets ....52. *Dactyloctenium*
      4. Rachilla not prolonged ....51. *Eleusine*
  2. Spikelets with only one perfect floret.
    5. Spikelets with one or more modified florets above the perfect one.
      6. Spikes digitate ....58. *Chloris*
      6. Spikes racemose ....59. *Bouteloua*
    5. Spikelets without additional modified florets.
      7. Spikelets falling entire, the rachilla articulated below the glumes.
        8. Spikelets narrow; glumes unequal ....57. *Spartina*
        8. Spikelets globose; glumes equal ....56. *Beckmannia*
      7. Spikelets with the rachilla articulated above the glumes, these therefore persistent.
        9. Spikes digitate ....53. *Cynodon*
        9. Spikes racemose ....55. *Schedonnardus*

Tribe 7. PHALARIDEAE. — Canary Grass Tribe

1. First and second lemmas oval.
  2. Glumes nearly equal; lower florets staminate; spikelets brown, glossy
  ....60. *Hierochloë*
  2. Glumes very unequal; lower florets consisting of sterile lemmas ....
  ....61. *Anthoxanthum*
1. First and second lemmas bristle-like ....62. *Phalaris*

Tribe 8. ORYZEAE. — Rice Tribe

1. Spikelets perfect; stamens 1-3 ....63. *Leersia*
1. Spikelets unisexual; stamens 6 ....64. *Zizania*

Tribe 9. Paniceae. — Millet Tribe

1. Spikelets with an involucre of bristles or spine-bearing valves.
    2. Spikelets subtended by bristles; inflorescence a dense, spike-like panicle
    ....72. *Setaria*
    2. Spikelets in a spiny involucre ....73. *Cenchrus*
1. Spikelets not involucrate.
    3. Glumes awned or awn-pointed ....71. *Echinochloa*
    3. Glumes not awned.
        4. Glumes 2 ....68. *Paspalum*
        4. Glumes 3.
            5. Spikelets in slender, 1-sided racemes ....65. *Digitaria*
            5. Spikelets in panicles or racemes.
                6. Spikelets covered with long, silky, silvery hairs ....66. *Trichachne*
                6. Spikelets not with silky, silvery hairs.
                    7. Margins of lemma hyaline, flat ....67. *Leptoloma*
                    7. Margins of lemma not hyaline, more or less inrolled.
                        8. Spikelets placed with the back of the fruit turned away from
                        the rachis of the racemes ....70. *Eriochloa*
                        8. Spikelets placed with the back of the fruit turned toward the
                        rachis ....69. *Panicum*

Tribe 10. Andropogoneae. — Sorghum Tribe

1. Spikelets in slender racemes, these single or 2 or 3 together, not panicled
    ....74. *Andropogon*
1. Spikelets in open or contracted panicles.
    2. Panicle densely pubescent; spikelets all perfect.
        3. Rachis continuous; leaves about 1 cm broad ....75. *Miscanthus*
        3. Rachis jointed; leaves 1.2-2 cm broad ....76. *Erianthus*
    2. Panicle not densely pubescent.
        4. Pedicelled spikelets staminate or neuter; panicle open; awns deciduous
        ....77. *Sorghum*
        4. Pedicelled spikelets reduced to a hairy pedicel; panicle narrow; awns
        persistent ....78. *Sorghastrum*

Tribe 11. Tripsaceae. — Corn Tribe

1. Pistillate and staminate spikelets in different parts of the same inflores-
    cence, the pistillate below ....79. *Tripsacum*
1. Pistillate spikelets in thick, axillary, solitary spikes ("cobs"); staminate
    spikelets in terminal paniculate spikes, forming the "tassel" ....80. *Zea*

Tribe 1. Bambuseae — Bamboo Tribe
1. **Arundinaria** Michx. — Cane

A. gigantea (Walt.) Muhl. River banks and swamps, s. Ill., often
forming extensive colonies ("cane-brakes"). April-June; rarely flowering.

Tribe 2. Festuceae — Fescue Tribe
2. **Bromus** L. — Brome Grass

1. Plants perennial.
    2. First glume 1-nerved (or 3-nerved in *B. kalmii*); second glume
    3-nerved; lemmas not keeled.

3. Spikelets awnless or nearly so, 2-3.5 cm long, nearly terete;
   panicle erect, 10-20 cm long, the branches spreading;
   plants with rhizomes; fields and roadsides; nat. from Eur.
   May-June. Smooth or Hungarian Brome ....*B. inermis* Leyss.
3. Spikelets conspicuously awned; native species.
   4. Lemmas pubescent on the margins and sometimes near the
      base, otherwise glabrous; second glume 3-nerved; first
      glume 1-nerved; hillsides and open woods. June-Aug.
      ....*B. ciliatus* L.
   4. Lemmas evenly pubescent.
      5. Second glume 3-nerved; first glume 1-nerved.
         6. Sheaths (except the lower one or two) shorter than
            the internodes; blades scarcely auriculate at base;
            meadows, woods, and banks throughout Ill. June-
            Aug. Canada Brome ....*B. purgans* L.
         6. Sheaths longer than the internodes, densely villous
            at the summit; blades somewhat auriculate at base;
            meadows and open woods, chiefly in the n. half
            of the state. July-Sept. [*B. altissimus* Pursh, non
            Gilib.; *B. incanus* (Shear) Hitchc.] ....
            ....*B. latiglumis* (Shear) Hitchc.
      5. Second glume 5-7-nerved.
         7. Spikelets 3-4 cm long; first glume 1-nerved; panicle
            12-20 cm long; awns of the lemmas 6-8 mm long;
            known in Ill. from three coll. by V. H. Chase:
            Wady Petra, Stark Co., in 1900, Woodford Co., in
            1946, and Peoria Co., in 1953....*B. nottowayanus* Fern.
         7. Spikelets 1.5-2.5 cm long; first glume 3-nerved;
            panicle 7-10 cm long; awns of the lemmas 1-3 mm
            long; dry ground in open woods in the n. half of
            the state. June-July ....*B. kalmii* A. Gray
2. First glume 3-5-nerved, the second with 5-7 nerves; lemmas
   keeled; adv. from w. U.S.; waste ground, Cook and Kane
   counties. June-Aug. ....*B. marginatus* Nees
1. Annual weedy species, nat. from Eur.
   8. Lemmas awnless or the awn not more than 2 mm long; leaves
      pubescent.
      9. Panicle loose, 1-sided, the spikelets few, ovate, nodding, 1.5-
         2.5 cm long; lemmas ovate, awnless, scarious; fields and
         waste places, occasional. June-July. Rattlesnake Grass ......
         ....*B. brizaeformis* Fisch. & Mey.
      9. Panicle-branches ascending, the spikelets 2-3.5 cm long;
         lemmas lanceolate, the awn not more than 2 mm long;
         cult. in s. U.S. and occasionally adv. northward; weed
         along railroad, Urbana, Champaign Co., *H. E. Ahles* in
         1953. Rescue Grass [*B. catharticus* Vahl, nom. dub.] ....
         ....*B. willdenowii* Kunth
   8. Lemmas awned.

10. First glume 3-nerved; second glume 5- or 7-nerved; lemmas
broad, obtuse.
   11. Panicle open, the branches ascending or drooping.
      12. Sheaths glabrous; awns shorter than the lemmas;
         fields and waste places. May-July. Cheat ....
         ....*B. secalinus* L.
      12. Sheaths pilose.
         13. Awns straight, 7-10 mm long.
            14. Lemmas 7-8 mm long; spikelets 3-4 mm
               wide; anthers 4 mm long; waste places,
               Adams, Fulton, and Jersey counties ....
               ....*B. arvensis* L.
            14. Lemmas 9-11 mm long; spikelets 6-7 mm
               wide; anthers 1.5-2 mm long; fields and
               waste places. May-July ....
               ....*B. commutatus* Schrad.
         13. Awns flexuous, divergent at maturity, 9-12 mm
            long; waste places; nat. from Eurasia. May-
            July. Japanese Chess ....*B. japonicus* Thunb.
   11. Panicle small, dense, erect or nearly so, 5-10 cm long;
      sheaths pubescent.
      15. Lemmas glabrous, 7 mm long; roadsides and waste
         places. June-Aug. ....*B. racemosus* L.
      15. Lemmas pubescent, 9-10 mm long; roadsides, waste
         places, and fields. May-July. Soft Chess ..*B. mollis* L.
10. First glume 1-nerved; second glume 3-nerved; sheaths
pubescent; awns longer than the acuminate lemmas.
   16. Awns 10-17 mm long; lemmas pubescent; panicle
      dense; roadsides and fields. May-July. Downy Cheat
      ....*B. tectorum* L.
   16. Awns 2-3 cm long; lemmas scabrous; panicle loose;
      waste places. May-July ....*B. sterilis* L.

3. **Schizachne** Hack.

S. purpurascens (Torr.) Swallen. Moist wooded slope, Apple River
Canyon, near Stockton, Jo Daviess Co., June 16, 1937, *F. J. Hermann*
8829.

4. **Festuca** L. — Fescue Grass
(*Vulpia* K.C.Gmel.)

1. Leaves 3-8 mm wide, flat.
   2. Panicle narrow, erect; lemmas (including the awn) 5-10 mm
      long; meadows, roadsides, fields, waste places; nat. from
      Eur. June-July. Meadow Fescue. Var. *arundinacea* (Schreb.)
      Wimm. [*F. arundinacea* Schreb.] Tall Fescue, a larger and
      stouter plant with wider leaves, is collected occasionally,
      Peoria and Tazewell counties, *V. H. Chase* in 1953; Piatt
      Co., *G. N. Jones* in 1957 ....*F. elatior* L.
   2. Panicle open; lemmas 4-5 mm long.

3. Panicle branches elongate, slender, spreading, spikelet-bearing toward the ends or above the middle; woods, local. May-July. Nodding Fescue [*F. nutans* Spreng., non Moench] ....*F. obtusa* Bieler

3. Panicle more compact, the few shorter branches spikelet-bearing from near the middle, the spikelets somewhat aggregate; woods, rather rare. June. [*F. shortii* Kunth] ....*F. paradoxa* Desv.

1. Leaves involute, not more than 1 mm wide.

    4. Perennial, tufted; spikelets 4-5-flowered; stamens 3.

        5. Lemmas 4-5 mm long, short-awned, the awns 1.5-3 mm long; fields and waste places, open woods; nat. from Eur. May-June. Sheep Fescue ....*F. ovina* L.

        5. Lemmas 3 mm long, awnless, or the short mucro 0.5 mm long; lawns and waste places, nat. from Eur. Hair Fescue ....*F. capillata* Lam.

    4. Annual, not tufted; spikelets 5-13-flowered; stamen 1; sandy soil. May-June. Slender Fescue [*F. tenella* Willd.] ....
....*F. octoflora* Walt.

5. Puccinellia Parl. — Alkali Grass

P. distans (L.) Parl. Railroad yards, Northlake, Cook Co., *Glassman & Thieret* in 1957; adv. in Ill.; native of Eur. June-Oct.

6. Glyceria R.Br. — Manna Grass

1. Spikelets linear, nearly terete, 1-2 cm long; panicles narrow, erect.

    2. Lemmas scaberulous over the back on and between the nerves; spikelets 12-30 mm long; first glume 2-3 mm long; leaves 4-9 mm wide; in shallow water or wet soil, locally nearly throughout Ill. May-Aug. [*G. arkansana* Fern.] ....
....*G. septentrionalis* Hitchc.

    2. Lemmas glabrous between the minutely scaberulous nerves; spikelets 10-18 mm long; first glume 1.5-2 mm long; leaves 2-4 mm wide; in shallow water, or at the edges of streams or ponds, n. Ill., not common ....*G. borealis* (Nash) Batch.

1. Spikelets more or less compressed, not more than 8 mm long; panicles usually nodding.

    3. Lemmas broadly ovate, evidently but not prominently nerved; spikelets 3-4 mm wide; wet ground in the n. part of the state, rare; Cook and Peoria counties. June-July ....
....*G. canadensis* (Michx.) Trin.

    3. Lemmas elliptical, the nerves prominent; spikelets 1-2.5 mm wide.

        4. Spikelets 4-7 mm long.

            5. Stems erect, stout, 1-1.5 m tall; panicle 15-40 cm long, diffuse, often purple; leaves 6-15 mm wide; second glume 1-nerved, acute; wet ground, n. Ill., rare. June-Aug.
....*G. grandis* S.Wats.

5. Stems slender, ascending from a decumbent base; panicle 5-15 cm long, the branches ascending, pale green; leaves 4-8 mm wide; second glume 3-nerved, obtuse; swampy ground, s. Ill., rare. June-July ......*G. pallida* (Torr.) Trin.
4. Spikelets 2-3 mm long, 1.5-2 mm wide, usually 3-5-flowered; leaves 2-6 mm wide; glumes 1-nerved, 0.5 mm long; wet ground, the common species throughout Ill. May-July ....*G. striata* (Lam.) Hitchc.

7. **Poa** L. — Blue Grass.   Meadow Grass

1. Perennials; stem 30-120 cm tall.
  2. Plants with conspicuous horizontal rhizomes.
    3. Stems terete, 30-120 cm tall; leaves bright green; panicle open, 5-20 cm long, the ascending or spreading branches in whorls of 3-5; lemmas 3 mm long, copiously webbed at base; roadsides, lawns, fields, and woods, very common. May-June. Kentucky Blue Grass ....*P. pratensis* L.
    3. Stems compressed above, 30-40 cm tall; leaves bluish green; panicle narrow, 3-8 cm long; lemmas 2-2.5 mm long, scarcely webbed; roadsides, cultivated ground, waste places, common; nat. from Eurasia. June-July. Canada Blue Grass ....*P. compressa* L.
  2. Plants without horizontal rhizomes.
    4. Lemmas glabrous, except the webbed base; damp woods, n. Ill., rare; Cook and Jo Daviess counties. June-Aug. ....*P. languida* Hitchc.
    4. Lemmas puberulent or pubescent, at least on the keel and marginal nerves.
      5. Lemmas webbed, i.e., with a tuft of soft hairs at base.
        6. Lemmas apparently 3-nerved, the intermediate nerves obscure or obsolete.
          7. Panicles 5-10 cm long, the lower branches mostly in pairs; ligule 1-1.5 mm long; wet ground, n.e. Ill., rare ....*P. paludigena* Fern. & Wieg.
          7. Panicle 10-30 cm long, the lower branches mostly fascicled; damp meadows, locally in the n. half of Ill. July-Aug. ....*P. palustris* L.
        6. Lemmas distinctly 5-nerved.
          8. Spikelets 3-4 mm long; lemmas 2-3 mm long.
            9. Lemmas glabrous except the keel; panicle-branches ascending with numerous crowded spikelets; roadsides, waste places, occasional; Stark Co., *V. H. Chase* in 1907; Cook Co., *E. K. Chord* in 1948 ....*P. trivialis* L.
            9. Lemmas pilosulous on the marginal nerves and keel; panicle with slender divaricate branches bearing a few spikelets above the middle; woods and

thickets, common nearly throughout Ill. May-July. Woodland Blue Grass ......*P. sylvestris* A.Gray

8. Spikelets 5-6 mm long; lemmas 3.5-4 mm long, glabrous between the nerves; known in Ill. only from three nineteenth-century collections; Fulton and Peoria counties, *Brendel;* Hancock Co., *Mead* ....*P. wolfii* Scribn.

5. Lemmas not webbed, 5-nerved, pubescent on the nerves and between them; spikelets 5-7 mm long; moist woods, rare ....*P. autumnalis* Muhl.

1. Low tufted annuals; stems 5-25 cm tall.

10. Lemmas distinctly 3-nerved, the other nerves obscure; lemmas webbed at the base; anthers 0.2-0.3 mm long; fields and roadsides, locally abundant nearly throughout Ill. Apr.-June ....*P. chapmaniana* Scribn.

10. Lemmas 5-nerved, not webbed at the base; anthers 0.7-1 mm long; common in waste places, lawns, cultivated ground; nat. from Eurasia. Apr.-Oct. Annual Blue Grass ....*P. annua* L.

8. **Briza** L. — Quaking Grass

B. maxima L. Fields and waste places, rarely escaped from cult.; adv. from Eurasia; Cook Co.

9. **Eragrostis** Beauv.

1. Stems creeping, rooting at the nodes, the flowering branches erect; plants annual.

2. Lemmas 1.5-2 mm long; anthers 0.2-0.3 mm long; flowers perfect; sandy, gravelly, or muddy shores. July-Oct. Pony Grass ....*E. hypnoides* (Lam.) BSP.

2. Lemmas 3-4 mm long; anthers 1.5-2 mm long; plants dioecious; sandy soil, not common ....*E. reptans* (Michx.) Nees

1. Stems erect or ascending, not rooting at the nodes.

3. Spikelets 2- to 7-flowered, 2-4 mm long.

4. Panicle about as long as wide, the branches elongated, capillary; plants branched at the base; dry ground in open woods. July- Sept. ....*E. capillaris* (L.) Nees

4. Panicle much longer than broad, the branches short; plants branched from above the base; sandy soil and roadsides. Aug.-Oct. ....*E. frankii* C.A.Mey.

3. Spikelets 5- to 35-flowered, 3-15 mm long.

5. Plants perennial, erect, 30-120 cm tall.

6. Panicle-branches spreading at maturity; spikelets 6- to 12-flowered; lemmas 1.5-2 mm long; sandy soil. July-Oct. Tumble Grass. [*E. pectinacea* sensu auth., non (Michx.) Nees] ....*E. spectabilis* (Pursh) Steud.

6. Panicle-branches erect or ascending; spikelets 4- to 6-flowered; lemmas 2.5-3 mm long; sandy soil, chiefly in centr. and w. Ill. [*E. pilifera* Scheele] ....
....*E. trichodes* (Nutt.) Wood

5. Plants annual, usually 10-50 cm tall, decumbent at base.

7. Keels of glumes and lemmas (and margins of leaves) with minute glands; spikelets 8- to 35-flowered.

8. Spikelets 2.5-3 mm wide; waste places and cultivated ground; nat. from Eur. June-Sept. Stink Grass [*E. megastachya* Link] ....*E. cilianensis* (All.) Lut.

8. Spikelets 1.5-2 mm wide; waste places and cultivated ground; nat. from Eur. [*E. minor* Host] ....
....*E. poaeoides* (L.) Beauv.

7. Keels of glumes and lemmas glandless, scaberulous; spikelets usually 3- to 9-flowered, 1-1.5 mm wide; fields, waste places, roadsides, and cultivated ground, common. July-Sept. [*E. purshii* Schrad.; *E. pilosa* sensu auth., non (L.) Beauv.] ....*E. pectinacea* (Michx.) Nees

10. Diarrhena Beauv.

D. americana Beauv. Woods, locally nearly throughout Ill. June-Sept.

11. Uniola L. — Spike Grass.   Sea Oats

U. latifolia Michx. Open woods in s. and central Ill., extending northward to Menard and Cook counties. June-Oct.

12. Dactylis L. — Orchard Grass

D. glomerata L. Fields and roadsides, very common; nat. from Eur. May-June.

13. Redfieldia Vasey

R. flexuosa (Thurb.) Vasey. Adv. from w. U.S. Carthage, Hancock Co., *Alice L. Kibbe.* July-Aug.

14. Phragmites Trin. — Common Reed

P communis Trin. Marshy ground, locally in the n. and central counties; formerly more abundant. Aug.-Sept.

15. Melica L. — Melic Grass

1. Glumes nearly equal and almost as long as the 2-flowered spikelet; leaves glabrous above, pubescent beneath; rocky woods and bluffs, not common. May-June ....*M. mutica* Walt.
1. Glumes unequal, shorter than the usually 3-flowered spikelet; leaves pubescent above and glabrous or scabrous beneath; rocky woods, somewhat more common than the preceding species. May-June ....*M. nitens* (Scribn.) Nutt.

16. **Tridens** R. & S.
(*Triodia* R.Br. in part)

1. Panicle loose, open, often glandular, the branches more or less spreading; glumes shorter than the lower lemmas; spikelets purplish, 7-8 mm long; 3 nerves of the lemma shortly excurrent; sandy soil in open woods nearly throughout Ill., except the n. counties. July-Sept. Purpletop. [*Triodia flava* (L.) Smyth] ....*T. flavus* (L.) Hitchc.
1. Panicle dense, spike-like, 1-2.5 cm broad, the branches erect or ascending; glumes nearly as long as the spikelet; spikelets pale, 4-6 mm long; only the midrib of the lemma excurrent; moist ground, roadsides, abandoned fields, and waste places, not common; adv. from s. U.S. in Franklin, Peoria, and Williamson counties. Sept.-Nov. [*Triodia stricta* (Nutt.) Benth.] ....*T. strictus* (Nutt.) Nash

17. **Triplasis** Beauv.

T. purpurea (Walt.) Chapm. Sand Grass. Dry sand, local. Aug.-Sept.

18. **Distichlis** Raf.

D. stricta (Torr.) Rydb. Salt Grass. Waste places, occasional; adv. from w. U.S. Champaign and Cook counties.

Tribe 3. Hordeae. — Barley Tribe

19. **Agropyron** Gaertn. — Wheat Grass

1. Spikelets ascending or appressed, the glumes several-nerved, not conspicuously keeled.
   2. Lemmas glabrous or scabrous.
      3. Plants tufted, not stoloniferous; glumes scabrous on nerves and margins.
         4. Lemmas awnless or mucronate; spikes slender, lax; glumes 10-12 mm long; dry ground, rare; Cook Co., *Agnes Chase* in 1899. [*A. tenerum* Vasey; *A. pauciflorum* (Schw.) Hitchc.] ....*A. trachycaulum* (Link) Malte
         4. Lemmas distinctly awned; spikes dense; glumes 7-9 mm long; woods, roadsides, meadows, occasional in the n. counties. July-Aug. [*A. trachycaulum* var. *unilaterale* (Cassidy) Malte] ....*A. subsecundum* (Link) Hitchc.
      3. Plants with horizontal rhizomes, forming a sod; glumes smooth, except on the keel.
         5. Leaves green; spikelets mostly 4-6-flowered, 1-1.5 cm long; waste ground and fields, common; nat. from Eur. June-July. Quack Grass ....*A. repens* (L.) Beauv.
         5. Leaves glaucous; spikelets 7-13-flowered, 1.5-2.5 cm long; along railroads, adv. from w. U.S. June-July. Bluestem ....*A. smithii* Rydb.

2. Lemmas and glumes pubescent; along railroad, Du Page Co.,
June 26, 1897, *Moffatt* 231; adv. from w. U.S. [*A. dasy-
stachyum* of auth., not (Hook.) Scribn.] ....
....*A. molle* (Scribn. & Smith) Rydb.
1. Spikelets pectinately spreading, crowded in a flattened spike;
glumes keeled, awned, glabrous; spikelets 3-flowered; introd.
from Eurasia, and occasionally spontaneous.
6. Spikelets 8-12 mm long with awns 2-3 mm long; waste ground,
Cook Co., *J. W. Thieret* in 1956 ....
....*A. desertorum* (Fisch.) Schultes
6. Spikelets 5-7 mm long, the awns 2-5 mm long; waste places,
occasional. Crested Wheat Grass ......*A. cristatum* (L.) Gaertn.

20. Triticum L. — Wheat

T. aestivum L. Roadsides and fields; occasionally spontaneous but
not persisting; of Eurasian origin.

21. Aegilops L. — Goat Grass

A. cylindrica Host. Waste places; an occasional railroad migrant;
introd. from Eur.

22. Secale L. — Rye

S. cereale L. Occasionally spontaneous in fields and waste ground;
often planted as a soil binder along new roads and sometimes briefly
persisting; native of Eurasia. May-July.

23. Elymus L. — Wild Rye

1. Lemmas awnless; spike erect, dense, 7-25 cm long; sand dunes
along L. Michigan; native of Eur. June-July. Dune Grass [*E.
mollis* sensu auth., non Trin.] ....*E. arenarius* L.
1. Lemmas usually awned.
2. Glumes subulate, 0.5-1 mm wide.
3. Spikes 10-25 cm long, loose; spikelets 2-4-flowered; palet 7-8
mm long; chiefly alluvial soil, occasional. July-Sept. ....
....*E. riparius* Wieg.
3. Spikes 5-15 cm long, compact; spikelets 1-2-flowered; palet
5-7 mm long; woods, common. June-Aug. Slender Wild
Rye ....*E. villosus* Muhl.
2. Glumes lanceolate, 2- to several-nerved, 2 mm or more in width.
4. Awn of lemma straight, about 1 cm long; spike usually erect;
glumes strongly bowed out at base; roadsides and woods,
common and variable. July-Aug. ....*E. virginicus* L.
4. Awn of lemma curved when dry, 2-4 cm long; spike nodding;
glumes not bowed out at base; roadsides and edges of
woods, common. July-Aug. Nodding Wild Rye ....
....*E. canadensis* L.

24. Hystrix Moench — Bottlebrush Grass

H. patula Moench. Woods, common throughout Ill. June-July.

25. **Hordeum** L. — Barley

1. Rachis of spike becoming disjointed.
   2. Spikes nodding, 6-16 cm long; awns 2-6 cm long; tufted perennials.
      3. Blades 2-4 mm wide; awns 3-6 cm long; roadsides and fields, common. June-Aug. Squirrel-tail Grass ....*H. jubatum* L.
      3. Blades 5-8 mm wide; awns 2-3.5 cm long; open woods, hillsides, prairie soil; Marshall, Peoria, and Stark counties, *V. H. Chase*. June-Aug. Said to be a sterile F$_1$ hybrid of *H. jubatum* and *Elymus canadensis*. [*H. pammeli* Scribn. & Ball] ....*H. montanense* Scribn.
   2. Spikes erect, 2-6 cm long; awns less than 1.5 cm long; blades 2-4 mm wide; plants annual; roadsides and fields. May-June. Small Wild Barley ....*H. pusillum* Nutt.
1. Rachis of spike not disarticulating; blades flat, 5-15 mm wide; plants annual; cult., and sometimes spontaneous; introd. from Eur. Barley ....*H. vulgare* L.

26. **Lolium** L. — Rye Grass

1. Glume shorter than the spikelet; plants perennial.
   2. Lemmas awned; spikelets mostly 10- to 20-flowered; lawns, roadsides, and fields; nat. from Eur. June-Aug. Italian Rye Grass ....*L. multiflorum* Lam.
   2. Lemmas awnless or short-awned; spikelets mostly 5- to 10-flowered; meadows, lawns, roadsides; nat. from Eur. June-Aug. English Rye Grass ....*L. perenne* L.
1. Glume as long or longer than the spikelet; plants annual; lemmas awned; waste places and wheat fields, rare; not recently coll. in Ill.; adv. from Eur. June-Aug. Darnel ....*L. temulentum* L.

Tribe 4. AVENEAE. — Oat Tribe

27. **Koeleria** Pers. — June Grass

K. cristata (L.) Pers. Sandy soil, local. June-July [*K. gracilis* Pers.]

28. **Sphenopholis** Scribn. — Wedge Grass

1. Second glume firm, rounded and somewhat cucullate at apex, 2 mm long, nearly as wide; first glume linear; anthers 0.4-0.8 mm long; panicles erect or nearly so, compact; prairie soil, and in open woods. May-June ....*S. obtusata* (Michx.) Scribn.
1. Second glume thin, acute or apiculate; panicles lax, nodding.
   2. Lemmas not scabrous; spikelets 2.5 mm long; first glume linear, 0.2 mm wide; second glume 2-2.5 mm long; anthers 0.3-0.5 mm long; woods, fields, roadsides, frequent nearly throughout Ill. May-June ....*S. intermedia* Rydb.
   2. Lemmas scabrous-papillate; spikelets about 3 mm long; first glume narrowly elliptical, 0.8 mm wide; second glume nearly 3 mm long; anthers 1-2 mm long; woods, not common in Ill. May-June ....*S. nitida* (Spreng.) Scribn.

29. Deschampsia Beauv. — Hair Grass

D. cespitosa (L.) Beauv. Moist soil along streams, rare; Kane and Kankakee counties.

30. Aira L. — Silver Hairgrass

A. caryophyllea L. Dry soil, rare; Piatt Co., *H. E. Ahles 2429*.

31. Avena L. — Oat

1. Lemmas bearing stiff brownish hairs, at least at base; awn stout, geniculate, strongly twisted; spikelets mostly 3-flowered; fields and waste places; nat. from Eur. May-July. Wild Oat ....
....*A. fatua* L.
1. Lemmas glabrous; awn small, usually straight, or absent; spikelets mostly 2-flowered; commonly cultivated; occasionally spontaneous. May-July. Oat ....*A. sativa* L.

32. Arrhenatherum Beauv. — Tall Oat Grass

A. elatius (L.) Mert. & Koch. Fields, roadsides, and waste places; nat. from Eur. June-July.

33. Danthonia Lam. & DC. — Curly Grass

D. spicata (L.) Beauv. Common throughout Ill. in thin soil in open woods, particularly on black oak and white oak ridges, forming small dense clumps of curled leaves. May-July.

34. Holcus L. — Velvet Grass

H. lanatus L. Roadsides and fields, occasional; introd. or adv. from Eur., but scarcely established in Ill. June-Aug.

Tribe 5. AGROSTIDEAE. — Timothy Tribe
35. Calamagrostis Adans.

1. Panicle narrow but loose, becoming somewhat open; spikelets 3-3.5 mm long; blades flat, 4-8 mm wide; marshy ground. June-July. Blue-joint Grass ....*C. canadensis* (Michx.) Beauv.
1. Panicle contracted, spike-like; spikelets 4-4.5 mm long; blades involute, scabrous, 2-4 mm wide; moist ground, n. Ill., Cook and Jo Daviess counties. June-Aug. Northern Reed Grass ....
....*C. inexpansa* A.Gray

36. Ammophila Host

A. breviligulata Fern. Beach Grass. Sand dunes along L. Michigan. July-Aug. [*A. arenaria* sensu auth., non Link].

37. Calamovilfa Hack. — Sand Reed Grass

C. longifolia (Hook.) Scribn. Sand dunes along L. Michigan and in sandy areas in the valleys of the Illinois and Mississippi rivers. Aug.-Sept.

38. Agrostis L. — Bent Grass

1. Lemma awnless.
  2. Palet half the length of the lemma or longer; spikelets 2-2.5 mm long.
    3. Panicles open, the branches ascending; stems erect or somewhat decumbent at base, with strong horizontal rhizomes but no conspicuous stolons; leaves 4-10 mm wide; roadsides, fields, lawns, very common; nat. from Eur. June-Aug. Redtop ....*A. alba* L.
    3. Panicles contracted, the branches appressed; stems strongly decumbent, rooting at the nodes and developing long stolons; leaves mostly 2-5 mm wide; roadsides, fields, cult. ground, occasional; nat. from Eur. June-Aug. Creeping Bent Grass ....*A. palustris* Huds.
  2. Palet lacking or minute.
    4. Panicle very diffuse, 15-60 cm long, often purplish at maturity, the capillary branches scabrous, 5-15 cm long, spikelet-bearing only near the tips.
      5. Spikelets 1.5-2 mm long; anthers 0.2 mm long; glumes spreading in fruit and exposing the grain; roadsides and fields, common throughout Ill. May-July. Common Tickle Grass ....*A. hyemalis* (Walt.) BSP.
      5. Spikelets 2-2.5 mm long; anthers 0.5 mm long; glumes connivent in fruit, covering the grain; sandy soil in the n. counties. June-Aug. Northern Tickle Grass ....
      ....*A. scabra* Willd.
    4. Panicle open but not diffuse, 10-20 cm long, usually greenish at maturity, the branches smooth; spikelets 2-2.5 mm long; woods, locally throughout Ill. Aug.-Oct. Autumn Bent Grass ....*A. perennans* (Walt.) Tuckerm.
1. Lemma usually with a slender delicate awn about 5 mm long; leaves about 1 mm wide; slender annual 10-30 cm tall; fields and open woods in the s. half of Ill. May-June ....
....*A. elliottiana* Schult.

39. Cinna L.

1. Spikelets 5 mm long, the awn 0.5-1 mm long; panicle rather dense, the branches ascending; moist woods and borders of streams. July-Sept. Wood Reed ....*C. arundinacea* L.
1. Spikelets 3-4 mm long, the awn 1-2 mm long; panicle loose, the branches spreading or drooping; moist woods, n.e. Ill., not common. July-Sept. ....*C. latifolia* (Trev.) Griseb.

40. Alopecurus L. — Foxtail

1. Spikelets 5-6 mm long; fields and waste ground, occasional; introd. from Eur. Meadow Foxtail ....*A. pratensis* L.
1. Spikelets 3-4 mm long.

2. Awn scarcely exceeding the glumes; shallow water and wet
banks. May-July. ....*A. aequalis* Sobol.
2. Awn bent, exserted from the spikelet 2 mm or more; ditches
and fields. May-June. ....*A. carolinianus* Walt.

41. **Phleum** L. — Timothy

P. pratense L. Roadsides and fields, very common; nat. from Eur.
June-July.

42. **Muhlenbergia** Schreb.

1. Panicles narrow, not diffuse or spreading.
  2. First glume obsolete or nearly so, the second minute, truncate;
  lemma long-awned.
    3. Second glume 0.2-0.5 mm long; awn as long as or twice as
    long as the lemma; fields and dry woods, common. July-
    Oct. Nimble Will ....*M. schreberi* J.F.Gmel.
    3. Second glume 1.5-2 mm long; awn half as long as the lemma;
    Champaign Co., *Clinton* in 1892. Type collected in Ill. by
    J. Wolf in 1881 ....*M. curtisetosa* (Scribn.) Bush
  2. Glumes half the length of the lemma, or longer.
    4. Plants with conspicuous scaly rhizomes.
      5. Lemma awnless or nearly so; anthers 0.5-1 mm long.
        6. Glumes lanceolate or oval, cuspidate, about half or two-
        thirds the length of the lemma; dry or rocky woods.
        July-Oct. ....*M. sobolifera* (Muhl.) Trin.
        6. Glumes subulate.
          7. Glumes equalling the lemma, or somewhat shorter,
          awnless or short-awned.
            8. Internodes of the stem glabrous.
              9. Panicles usually well exserted; woods in Christian,
              Menard, Peoria, and Sangamon counties. Aug.-
              Oct. ....*M. brachyphylla* Bush
              9. Panicles shortly exserted or partly included in the
              sheath; fields, roadsides, waste places, common.
              Aug.-Sept. ....*M. frondosa* (Poir.) Fern.
            8. Internodes of the stem puberulent.
              10. Lemma short-pilose at base (on the callus);
              moist woods and thickets. Aug.-Oct. [*M.
              foliosa* sensu auth.] ....*M. mexicana* (L.) Trin.
              10. Lemma not pilose at base; woods, chiefly in the
              s. and central parts of the state ....
              ....*M. glabriflora* Scribn.
          7. Glumes much longer than the lemma, awned; panicle
          dense, somewhat interrupted; wet ground. Aug.-
          Sept. ....*M. racemosa* (Michx.) BSP.
      5. Lemma long-awned.
        11. Spikelets 3-4 mm long; glumes lanceolate, awn-pointed,
        shorter than the lemma; anthers 1-1.5 mm long; rocky
        woods. July-Oct. ....*M. tenuiflora* (Willd.) BSP.

11. Spikelets 2-2.5 mm long; glumes subulate-lanceolate, somewhat shorter than or nearly equalling the lemma; anthers 0.3-0.6 mm long; moist woods. Aug.-Oct. ....*M. sylvatica* Torr.
4. Plants without scaly rhizomes; glumes lanceolate, shorter than the awnless lemma; anthers 1-1.5 mm long; dry ground, n. Ill. July-Sept. [*Sporobolus brevifolius* (Nutt.) Scribn.] ......
....*M. cuspidata* (Torr.) Rydb.
1. Panicles open, the slender branches widely spreading.
12. Spikelets 3-4 mm long, the awns 5-15 mm long; stems 60-100 cm tall, tufted; rhizomes none; sandy soil, s. Ill. Sept.-Oct.
....*M. capillaris* (Lam.) Trin.
12. Spikelets 1.5-2 mm long, awnless; stems 10-40 cm tall; plants with creeping scaly rhizomes; sandy soil, n. Ill. June-Sept. [*Sporobolus asperifolius* Nees & Mey.] ....
...................................*M. asperifolia* (Nees & Mey.) Parodi

43. Sporobolus R.Br. — Dropseed

1. Plants perennial; leaf-blades much longer than the sheaths.
2. Spikelets 1.5-2.5 mm long; panicle either free and spreading at maturity or remaining partly or wholly included in the sheath; leaf-sheaths with a conspicuous tuft of whitish hairs at summit; sandy soil. Aug.-Sept. Sand Dropseed ....
....*S. cryptandrus* (Torr.) A.Gray
2. Spikelets 4-8 mm long.
3. Second glume shorter than the lemma; panicle contracted, more or less included in the sheath.
4. Lemma glabrous, glossy; spikelets 5-6 mm long; dry sandy soil. Sept.-Oct. ....*S. asper* (Michx.) Kunth
4. Lemma pubescent at base; spikelets 6-8 mm long; sandy soil, local. Aug.-Sept. [*S. canovirens* Nash] ....
...................................*S. clandestinus* (Bieler) Hitchc.
3. Second glume slightly longer than the glabrous lemma; spikelets 4-6 mm long; panicle long-exserted at maturity; dry soil. Aug.-Sept. Prairie Dropseed ....*S. heterolepis* A.Gray
1. Plants annual; sheaths enclosing the lateral panicles; leaf-blades short, scarcely longer than the sheaths.
5. Lemma pubescent; spikelets 3.5-6 mm long; dry sandy soil. Sept.-Oct. ....*S. vaginiflorus* (Torr.) Wood
5. Lemma glabrous; spikelets 2-3 mm long; dry sandy soil. Sept.-Oct. ....*S. neglectus* Nash

44. Heleochloa Host

H. schoenoides (L.) Host. Waste places, occasional; introd. from Eur.; Cook Co., *Moffatt* in 1893; St. Clair Co., *J. Neill* in 1947.

45. Brachyelytrum Beauv.

B. erectum (Schreb.) Beauv. Woods, locally throughout Ill. June-Aug.

46. Milium L. — Wild Millet

M. effusum L. Moist woods; Kane Co., *Vasey;* Tazewell Co., *Brendel;* probably now extinct in Ill. May-July.

47. Oryzopsis Michx. — Rice Grass

1. Leaves narrow, involute; spikelets (excluding the awns) 3-4 mm long; dry soil, rare, or probably now extinct in Ill. ....
   ....*O. pungens* (Torr.) Hitchc.
1. Leaves flat, 4-15 mm wide; spikelets (excluding the awns) 6-8 mm long.
   2. Leaves scattered along the stem, the upper surface pubescent; panicle 15-30 cm long; rocky woods, rare; La Salle Co., *McDonald* in 1919, Peoria Co., *Alice Heading* in 1882, Vermilion Co., *A. B. Seymour* in 1884. Aug.-Sept. ....
      ....*O. racemosa* (Sm.) Ricker
   2. Leaves mostly basal, merely scabrous above; panicle 5-8 cm long; Cook Co., *Shipman* in 1877 ....*O. asperifolia* Michx.

48. Stipa L. — Spear Grass

1. Awn 10-25 cm long; glumes 1.5-4 cm long.
   2. Glumes 1.5-2.8 cm long; grain 1-1.5 cm long; Winnebago Co., *E. W. & G. B. Fell* ....*S. comata* Trin. & Rupr.
   2. Glumes 2.8-4 cm long; grain 2-3 cm long; sandy ground or prairie soil, locally in the n. half of Ill. May-June. Porcupine Grass ....*S. spartea* Trin.
1. Awn 2-3 cm long; lemma 5-6 mm long; glumes 7-10 mm long; Kane Co., *Benke* in 1916; McHenry Co., *V. H. Chase* in 1948. Green Needlegrass ....*S. viridula* Trin.

49. Aristida L. — Three-awned Grass

1. Awns jointed to the lemma.
   2. Awns united in a spiral column 6-15 mm or more in length; sandy soil in the n. half of Ill. Aug.-Sept. .....*A tuberculosa* Nutt.
   2. Awn-column about 2 mm long; sandy soil, not common; Cass, Mason, and Morgan counties ....*A. desmantha* Trin. & Rupr.
1. Awns distinct, not jointed to the lemma.
   3. Central awn much longer than the lateral awns, these erect.
      4. Central awn spirally coiled at base.
         5. Second glume 7-9 mm long, equalling or slightly longer than the first; roadsides and fields, chiefly in central and s. Ill. Aug.-Oct. ....*A. dichotoma* Michx.
         5. Second glume 10-15 mm long, much longer than the first.
            6. Lateral awns 1-2 mm long, straight, erect; dry ground, not common. Sept.-Oct. ....*A. curtissii* (A.Gray) Nash
            6. Lateral awns 2-7 mm long, spreading; dry ground, scattered ....*A. basiramea* Engelm.
      4. Central awn not coiled, but with a semicircular bend at base.

7. Lemma 4-5 mm long; fields and roadsides, chiefly in the s.
and w. parts of the state. [*A. gracilis* Ell.] ....
....*A. longespica* Poir.
7. Lemma 2-3 cm long; fields and roadsides in the s. half of
the state. Aug.-Sept. ....*A. ramosissima* Engelm.
3. Central awn subequal in length with the lateral ones.
   8. Glumes 5-14 mm long; awn not over 2.5 cm long.
      9. Perennial; first glume 8-14 mm long, exceeding the second;
         sandy soil, local. Aug.-Sept. ....*A. purpurascens* Poir.
      9. Annual; first glume 5-9 mm long, shorter than the second;
         sandy soil; Henry, Lake, and Lee counties. Aug.-Sept.
         ....*A. intermedia* Scribn. & Ball
   8. Glumes 2-3 cm long; awns 3-7 cm long; fields, open woods,
      and roadsides. Aug.-Oct. ....*A. oligantha* Michx.

Tribe 6. Chlorideae. — Grama Tribe
50. Buchloe Engelm. — Buffalo Grass

B. dactyloides (Nutt.) Engelm. Apparently a relic on soil never in
cultivation, Peoria, *V. H. Chase* in 1956.

51. Eleusine Gaertn. — Goose Grass

E. indica (L.) Gaertn. Waste places, roadsides, and cultivated
ground; nat. from Eurasia. July-Oct.

52. Dactyloctenium Willd. — Crowfoot Grass

D. aegypticum (L.) Beauv. Waste ground and fields, rare in Ill.;
nat. from Old World tropics. St. Clair Co., without locality, Aug. 1876,
H. Eggert.

53. Cynodon Rich. — Bermuda Grass

C. dactylon (L.) Pers. Fields, roadsides, and waste places; nat.
from Eur. June-Aug.

54. Leptochloa Beauv. — Sprangletop Grass

1. Sheaths pubescent; spikelets 1.5-2 mm long; sandy soil, s. Ill.
Aug.-Sept. [*L. attenuata* (Nutt.) Steud.] ....
....*L. filiformis* (Lam.) Beauv.
1. Sheaths glabrous; spikelets 6-10 mm long; wet meadows and along
ditches, of scattered distribution; also one collection as a railroad weed in Cook Co. [*Diplachne fascicularis* (Lam.) Beauv.]
....*L. fascicularis* (Lam.) A.Gray

55. Schedonnardus Steud.

S. paniculatus (Nutt.) Trel. Hancock Co., *Mead* in 1845; probably now extinct in Ill. "It was found on the original prairie, especially
around salt licks."—Mosher.

56. Beckmannia Host — Slough Grass

B. 'syzigachne (Steud.) Fern. Wet ground, rare; Cook Co., *L. M. Umbach;* Lake Co., *R. A. Evers* in 1957.

57. Spartina Schreb. — Cord Grass

S. pectinata Link. Along ditches, moist ground along roads, in marshes, etc.; formerly more abundant. July-Oct. [*S. michauxiana* Hitchc.]

58. Chloris Sw. — Windmill Grass

C. verticillata Nutt. Sandy soil, or along roads, occasional; adv. from w. of the Mississippi R. June-July.

59. Bouteloua Lag. — Grama Grass

1. Spikes 1-4, usually curved, of 25 or more densely crowded spikelets.
   2. Rachis of spike projecting beyond the uppermost spikelet in a prominent point; keel of the second glume papillose-hispid; prairie soil, w. and n.w. Ill. July-Sept. ....*B. hirsuta* Lag.
   2. Rachis not projecting; keel of second glume glabrous or with few hairs, these without papillose bases; Jo Daviess Co., *H. S. Pepoon* 173, in 1908 ....*B. gracilis* (HBK.) Lag.
1. Spikes numerous (12 or more), each with 4-12 spikelets; prairie soil, local; chiefly in the n. half of Ill., extending southward to Kankakee, Woodford, and Menard counties, and along the Mississippi R. to s. Ill. July-Sept. Side-oats Grama ....
   ....*B. curtipendula* (Michx.) Torr.

Tribe 7. PHALARIDEAE. — Canary Grass Tribe

60. Hierochloe J. G. Gmel. — Sweet Grass

H. odorata (L.) Beauv. Moist meadows, fields, and roadsides in the n. counties. May-June.

61. Anthoxanthum L. — Sweet Vernal Grass

A. odoratum L. Meadows, roadsides, waste places; nat. from Eurasia; Cook and Lake counties. May-July.

62. Phalaris L. — Canary Grass

1. Panicle 8-15 cm long; spikelets 5-6 mm long, the glumes not winged; marshes and wet meadows. May-July. Reed Canary Grass ....*P. arundinacea* L.
1. Panicle ovoid, 1-4 cm long; spikelets 6-8 mm long, the glumes winged; roadsides and waste places; nat. from Eur. June-July. Canary Grass ....*P. canariensis* L.

Tribe 8. ORYZEAE. — Rice Tribe
63. Leersia Sw.

1. Spikelets broadly oval, densely imbricate, 3-4 mm wide; stem terete; moist ground, locally throughout Ill. except the n. counties. Aug.-Oct. Catchfly Grass ....*L. lenticularis* Michx.
1. Spikelets elliptical, 1-2 mm wide.
  2. Spikelets 3-3.5 mm long; stamens 1 or 2; leaves nearly smooth; stem compressed; moist woods. July-Sept. White Grass ....
  ....*L. virginica* Willd.
  2. Spikelets 4-4.5 mm long; stamens 3; leaves very rough; stem terete; wet ground. Aug.-Sept. Cut Grass ....
  ....*L. oryzoides* (L.) Sw.

64. Zizania L. — Wild Rice

Z. aquatica L. Borders of streams, ponds, and lakes, usually in shallow water, chiefly in n.e. Ill., and in the valley of the Illinois and Mississippi rivers; formerly more common. July-Sept. [*Z. interior* (Fassett) Rydb.].

Subfamily II. Panicoideae

Tribe 9. PANICEAE. — Millet Tribe
65. Digitaria Heist.

1. Rachis winged, 0.7-1 mm wide; stems spreading, often rooting at the lower nodes.
  2. Sheaths pilose; pedicels 3-angled, scabrous; spikelets 3 3.5 mm long; a common weed in cultivated ground, lawns, and waste places; nat. from Eur. July-Oct. Common Crab Grass ....
  ....*D. sanguinalis* (L.) Scop.
  2. Sheaths glabrous; pedicels terete or nearly so; spikelets 2 mm long; fields, meadows, waste ground, roadsides, common; nat. from Eurasia. July-Oct. Smooth Crab Grass ....
  ....*D. ischaemum* (Schreb.) Muhl.
1. Rachis of the racemes wingless, about 0.3 mm wide; spikelets 1.6-2 mm long; lower sheaths pilose, the upper ones glabrous; stems usually erect; sandy soil, infrequent, chiefly in the w. central counties. Sept.-Oct. Finger Grass. [*D. villosa* (Walt.) Pers.]
....*D. filiformis* (L.) Koel.

66. Trichachne Nees

T. insularis (L.) Nees. Sour Grass. Roadsides, Williamson Co., *J. W. Voigt* in 1954; adv. from s.e. U.S.

67. Leptoloma Chase

L. cognatum (Schultes) Chase. Fall Witch Grass. Sandy soil, locally throughout Ill. July-Sept.

68. Paspalum L.

1. Rachis of the spikes dilated, thin, more than 2 mm broad, with membranous margins.
    2. Spikelets pubescent, 1-1.5 mm long; blades 6-15 mm wide; muddy banks or in shallow water in s. and w. Ill. Aug.-Oct. ....*P. fluitans* (Ell.) Kunth
    2. Spikelets glabrous, 2 mm long; blades 2-5 mm wide; in ditches or along muddy or sandy shores, s. Ill.; Perry, Pulaski, and St. Clair counties ....*P. dissectum* L.
1. Rachis narrow, less than 2 mm broad; spikelets glabrous.
    3. Spikelets 1.4-2.8 mm long; plant often with 1-several axillary peduncles from the upper sheath.
        4. Spikelets orbicular; blades sparsely pilose and ciliate; sandy soil, roadsides, etc. July-Sept. ....*P. stramineum* Nash
        4. Spikelets oval or somewhat obovate; blades glabrous or softly pubescent on both sides.
            5. Blades glabrous; sandy soil or open woods in the centr. counties ....*P. ciliatifolium* Michx.
            5. Blades softly pubescent; sandy soil; nearly throughout Ill. July-Sept. [*P. muhlenbergii* Nash] ....*P. pubescens* Muhl.
    3. Spikelets 2.8-4 mm long; plant simple.
        6. Spikelets orbicular, arranged singly in 2 rows; wet ground, chiefly in the s. half of the state. July-Sept. ....
        ....*P. circulare* Nash
        6. Spikelets oval or slightly obovate, borne in pairs and appearing as if in 3 or 4 rows.
            7. Spikelets 3-3.2 mm long; ditches, s. Ill., rare. Aug.-Sept. [*P. pubiflorum* var. *glabrum* Vasey; *P. laeviglume* Scribn.] ....*P. geminum* Nash
            7. Spikelets 3.6-4 mm long; moist soil in Perry and Williamson counties. [*P. floridanum* Michx. var. *glabratum* Engelm.] ....*P. glabratum* (Engelm.) Mohr

69. Panicum L. — Panic Grass

1. Spikelets glabrous (sparsely pubescent in *P. depauperatum*).
    2. Spikelets 3 mm or more in length.
        3. Plants glabrous, perennial, with rhizomes; panicle 15-50 cm long; spikelets 4-4.5 mm long; roadsides and fields, common. July-Sept. Switch Grass ....*P. virgatum* L.
        3. Plants more or less pubescent (except *P. anceps* and a var. of *P. depauperatum*).
            4. Spikelets 4-5 mm long; panicles often drooping at maturity; waste places; cultivated and occasionally spontaneous; native of the Old World. Broomcorn Millet ....
            ....*P. miliaceum* L.
            4. Spikelets 3-3.8 mm long, lanceoloid, pointed; panicles erect.

5. Plants annual; panicles 10-30 cm long; blades 2-5 mm
wide; sandy soil, local. July-Oct. ....
....*P. flexile* (Gatt.) Scribn.
5. Plants perennial.
  6. Panicle loose, open, 20-50 cm long; blades 6-10 mm
wide; plants with long scaly rhizomes; along ditches,
or in moist soil, or woods in the s. and w. parts of
Ill., extending northward to Peoria and Henderson
counties. July- Sept. ....*P. anceps* Michx.
  6. Panicle 3-8 cm long, not much exceeding or shorter
than the leaves, few-flowered; blades 2-5 mm wide,
often involute in drying; open woods. May-June
....*P. depauperatum* Muhl.
2. Spikelets less than 3 mm long.
  7. Sheaths glabrous.
    8. First glume not more than one-fourth the length of the
spikelets, rounded at the apex; plants annual, mostly
glabrous; spikelets 2.5-3 mm long; fields and waste
places, common. Aug.-Oct. Fall Panicum ....
....*P. dichotomiflorum* Michx.
    8. First glume more than one-fourth the length of the spike-
let; plants perennial.
      9. Spikelets 1.5-1.6 mm long; blades 10-12 cm long, 8-15
mm wide, ciliate at base, otherwise glabrous; panicle
8-12 cm long; stem-nodes densely bearded with reflexed hairs; wet ground, s. Ill. June-Aug ....
....*P. microcarpon* Muhl.
      9. Spikelets 2-2.5 mm long.
        10. Pedicels about half the length of the spikelets; pan-
icles 10-30 cm long, the spikelets subsecund; plants
in dense tufts; moist ground, locally throughout
Ill. except the n. counties. July-Oct. Munro Grass
....*P. agrostoides* Spreng.
        10. Pedicels longer than the spikelets, which are not at
all secund; panicles 4-12 cm long.
          11. Sheaths bearing pale glandular spots, the margins
glabrous; blades 8-11 mm wide; spikelets 2.3-
2.5 mm long, pointed; moist woods and thickets, s. Ill. June-July ....*P. yadkinense* Ashe
          11. Sheaths not spotted, the margins pubescent;
blades 4-8 mm wide; spikelets 2 mm long, not
pointed; open woods, more common in s. Ill.,
but extending northward to Peoria Co. May-
July. [*P. barbulatum* Michx.] ....
....*P. dichotomum* L.
  7. Sheaths pubescent.
    12. Spikelets lanceoloid, acuminate, 2-3 mm long; panicle

diffuse, often half the length of the plant; sheaths copiously villous; fields, roadsides, and waste places, common. July-Oct. Witch Grass ....*P. capillare* L.

12. Spikelets elliptical, obtuse, 1.3-2.2 mm long.

13. Panicles 12-20 cm wide, delicate, relatively few-flowered; blades 2-6 mm wide, villous on both sides; roadsides and waste places, local. July-Oct. [*P. tuckermani* Fern.] ....*P. philadelphicum* Bernh.

13. Panicles narrower; blades 6-10 mm wide, nearly or quite glabrous; plants much branched, with many axillary panicles; moist sandy soil, along roads, in fields, or along streams; s. and central Ill., extending northward to Henry Co. Sept.-Oct. ....
....*P. gattingeri* Nash

1. Spikelets pubescent or puberulent (occasionally only sparsely so).

14. Spikelets 3 mm or more in length; sheaths more or less pubescent or ciliate.

15. Blades 1.5-4 cm wide, ciliate, otherwise glabrous or nearly so.

16. Spikelets 3.4-3.8 mm long; nodes glabrous or puberulent; rocky or sandy woods. May-Aug. ....
....*P. latifolium* L.

16. Spikelets 4-4.5 mm long; nodes retrorsely bearded; woods throughout Ill., except the n.e. counties. May-July ....*P. boscii* Poir.

15. Blades 6-13 mm wide; spikelets 3-4 mm long.

17. Sheaths with appressed or ascending hairs; spikelets sparsely pubescent to nearly glabrous; blades glabrous or nearly so above, puberulent beneath; sandy soil, local. May-June ....*P. oligosanthes* Schult.

17. Sheaths with spreading hairs, or nearly glabrous.

18. Spikelets sparsely short-pubescent to nearly glabrous; blades glabrous or nearly so; sandy soil, common. May-July ....*P. scribnerianum* Nash

18. Spikelets pilose; blades more or less papillose-hirsute on both surfaces, or glabrous above; dry sandy soil, occasional. June-July ....
....*P. leibergii* (Vasey) Scribn.

14. Spikelets less than 3 mm long.

19. Sheaths glabrous or nearly so, or merely ciliate (or the lower internodes and sheaths sometimes pubescent in *P. lindheimeri*).

20. Spikelets 2.1-2.9 mm long.

21. Blades 12-25 mm wide, cordate at base; spikelets short-pubescent, 2.7-2.9 mm long; woods, s. Ill. May-June ....*P. commutatum* Schult.

21. Blades 7-12 mm wide, not cordate; spikelets sparsely pilose to nearly glabrous, 2-2.2 mm long; Lake Co., *Fuller & Graham 9400* ....*P. boreale* Nash
20. Spikelets 1.3-1.9 mm long, puberulent or nearly glabrous.
   22. Blades usually 1.5-2.5 cm wide, ciliate toward the base, otherwise glabrous; nodes glabrous or nearly so; panicle 8-25 cm long, not more than half as wide as long; moist ground, chiefly in s. Ill. but extending northward to Peoria Co. ....
   ....*P. polyanthes* Schult.
   22. Blades 4-14 mm wide; panicle often about as wide as long.
      23. Ligule of conspicuous hairs 3-5 mm long; sandy soil in open woods. June-Sept. ....
      ....*P. lindheimeri* Nash
      23. Ligule obsolete or nearly so; sandy soil in the s. half of Ill. June-July ....*P. sphaerocarpon* Ell.
19. Sheaths pubescent.
24. Sheaths conspicuously pilose, the hairs either retrorse or horizontally spreading.
   25. Spikelets 1.9-2 mm long; wooded slopes nearly throughout Ill. May-July ....*P. xalapense* HBK.
   25. Spikelets 2-2.5 mm long; sandy soil, locally in the n. half of Ill. ....*P. villosissimum* Nash
24. Sheaths not retrorsely pilose.
   26. Spikelets 2.7-3 mm long.
      27. Blades 12-30 mm wide; stems 50-120 cm tall; panicle 7-15 cm long; sandy soil. June-Aug. Deer-tongue Grass ....*P. clandestinum* L.
      27. Blades 2-6 mm wide; stems 8-40 cm tall; panicles 2-8 cm long.
         28. Blades copiously pilose on both surfaces; panicles 2-4 cm long; dry ground, n.w. Ill.; Carroll, Whiteside, and Winnebago counties ....*P. wilcoxianum* Vasey
         28. Blades scabrellous above, pilose beneath; panicles 4-8 cm long, some of them usually more or less concealed among the basal leaves; dry soil in the n. counties. June-July ....*P. perlongum* Nash
   26. Spikelets less than 2.7 mm long.
      29. Sheaths with spreading hairs.
         30. Spikelets 2.2-2.6 mm long.
            31. Blades 2-4 mm wide, 10-30 cm long; spikelets sparsely pilosulous or nearly glabrous; dry woods, local. May-July ....*P. linearifolium* Scribn.

31. Blades 5-10 mm wide, 6-10 cm long; ligule 4-5 mm long; dry sandy soil. June-July. [*P. euchlamydeum* Shinners] ....*P. pseudopubescens* Nash
30. Spikelets 1.3-1.9 mm long; ligule 3-5 mm long.
    32. Upper surface of blades glabrous or with a few long hairs toward the base, the lower surface glabrous or puberulent; moist ground, local. June-July ....
        ....*P. tennesseense* Ashe
    32. Upper surface of blades not glabrous.
        33. Upper surface of blades pilose, the hairs 3-5 mm long.
            34. Stems conspicuously villous with horizontal hairs 4-5 mm long; dry soil; chiefly in the n. half of the state. June-July ....
            ......*P. praecocius* Hitchc. & Chase
            34. Stems with shorter hairs.
                35. Axis of panicle pilose; the lowest panicle branches often tangled or implicate; wet meadows, swamps, or woods, local. June-July ....
                ....*P. implicatum* Scribn.
                35. Axis of panicle puberulent; branches ascending, not tangled; sandy soil in n. part of Ill. June-July ....
                ....*P. meridionale* Ashe
        33. Upper surface of blades with somewhat appressed hairs 1-2 mm long; meadows and open woods, common. May-Sept. ....*P. huachucae* Ashe
29. Sheaths with appressed or ascending hairs; ligule 1-1.5 mm long; blades glabrous or nearly so on the upper surface, puberulent beneath; spikelets 1.8-2 mm long; sandy or gravelly soil in the n. part of Ill. June-July ....
....*P. tsugetorum* Nash

70. **Eriochloa** HBK. — Cup Grass

1. Pedicels and rachis copiously villous; spikelets about 5 mm long; fields and waste places, occasional; native of e. Asia. Livingston Co., *Winterringer & Hoegger;* Peoria, *V. H. Chase* 16782 ....*E. villosa* (Thunb.) Kunth

1. Pedicels and rachis pilosulous.
   2. Fruit 2-2.5 mm long, the awn only 1 mm long; panicle contracted, the racemes appressed; roadsides and along ditches, occasional, Jackson and Union counties; adv. in Ill. from s.w. U.S. July-Oct. ....*E. contracta* Hitchc.
   2. Fruit about 3 mm long, apiculate; panicle-branches ascending or spreading; fields, Union Co., *R. A. Evers.* Adv. from s.w. U.S. ....*E. gracilis* (Fourn.) Hitchc.

71. **Echinochloa** Beauv.

1. Sheaths glabrous or nearly so; spikelets ovoid.
   2. Racemes 2-10 cm long, crowded and fascicled; spikelets 3-4 mm long, awned or nearly awnless; fields, roadsides, waste ground, river banks, common; nat. from Eurasia. July-Sept. Barnyard Grass. [*E. muricata* (Michx.) Fern.; *E. pungens* (Poir.) Rydb.]. Japanese Millet or Billion-dollar Grass, var. *frumentacea* (Roxb.) Wight, with awnless spikelets and dense purple or brown panicles, occurs occasionally ....
   ....*E. crusgalli* (L.) Beauv.
   2. Racemes 8-18 mm long, distant; spikelets 2.5-3 mm long, merely apiculate, crowded in about four regular rows; moist ground, occasional; adv. from the s. states; Chicago, *F. A. Swink* in 1947. Jungle-rice ....*E. colonum* (L.) Link
1. Sheaths, at least the lower ones, usually strongly papillose-hirsute, or rarely merely papillose; panicle dense, the ellipsoid spikelets conspicuously long-awned, purple at maturity, the awns 1.5 cm long; wet ground, local. Aug.-Oct. ....
   ....*E. walteri* (Pursh) Heller

72. **Setaria** Beauv.

1. Plants perennial with short branched rhizomes; bristles below each spikelet 8-12, yellowish or purplish, upwardly scabrous; waste ground, occasional; Fayette, Jackson, Marion, and Mason counties ....*S. geniculata* (Lam.) Beauv.
1. Plants annual.
   2. Bristles retrorsely scabrous, 3-6 mm long; weed in waste ground, chiefly about towns; nat. from Eur. July-Sept. Bristly Foxtail ....*S. verticillata* (L.) Beauv.
   2. Bristles antrorsely scabrous.
      3. Leaves loosely pubescent above; spikelets 2.7-3 mm long; panicles curved, nodding, 2-3 cm thick, 10-17 cm long; a serious weed in fields and along roads; recently nat. from Asia. July-Oct. Giant Foxtail ....*S. faberii* Herm.
      3. Leaves glabrous on both sides.
         4. Spikelets about 2 mm long; panicles erect or nearly so, 3-10 cm long; a common weed throughout Ill.; nat from Eur. June-Sept. Green Foxtail ....
         ....*S. viridis* (L.) Beauv.

4. Spikelets 3 mm long.
   5. Bristles 1-3; panicle thick, lobed or interrupted, purplish or yellowish; cult. and sometimes spontaneous; introd. from Eurasia. July-Sept. Italian Millet or Hungarian Grass ....*S. italica* (L.) Beauv.
   5. Bristles 5-15 at the base of each spikelet; panicles straight, about 1 cm thick, 5-10 cm long; a common weed in waste ground and along roads; nat. from Eur. June-Sept. Yellow Foxtail [*S. glauca* sensu auth., non (L.) Beauv.] ....
   ....*S. lutescens* (Weigel) F.T.Hubb.

73. Cenchrus L. — Sandbur

C. pauciflorus Benth. Sandy soil, cult. ground, or roadsides. July-Sept. [*C. longispinus* (Hack.) Fern.]

Tribe 10. ANDROPOGONEAE — Sorghum Tribe
74. Andropogon L.

1. Racemes usually borne singly on the few to many branches, 3-6 cm long; joints of the rachis clavate; sandy or prairie soil and open woods. Aug.-Oct. Little Bluestem ....
   ....*A. scoparius* Michx.
1. Racemes in fascicles of 2-7, the common peduncle enclosed in a bract-like sheath or spathe; joints of the rachis not clavate.
   2. Pedicellate spikelet staminate, as large as the sessile spikelet; racemes 5-13 cm long, exserted on a naked peduncle, the uppermost sheath inconspicuous, not inflated; rachis straight, the hairs inconspicuous and shorter than the spikelets; stamens 3; prairie soil. July-Sept. Big Bluestem [*A. gerardi* Vitm. (?)] ....*A. furcatus* Muhl.
   2. Pedicellate spikelet reduced to 1 or 2 empty glumes or a mere pedicel; racemes 1.5-4 cm long; stamen 1.
      3. Upper sheaths inflated, spathe-like; awns coiled at the base; sessile spikelets 4-4.5 mm long; open woods, s. Ill., rare ....*A. elliottii* Chapm.
      3. Upper sheaths not inflated; awns straight or somewhat curved; sessile spikelets 3-3.5 mm long; fields and roadsides in the s. half of the state. Sept.-Oct. Broom-sedge ....*A. virginicus* L.

75. Miscanthus Anderss.

M. sacchariflorus (Maxim.) Hack. Cultivated for ornament, rarely persisting; introd. from Asia; Du Page and Rock Island counties.

76. Erianthus Michx.

1. Spikelets awned; open woods, s. Ill. Plume Grass [*E. divaricatus* (L.) Hitchc.] ....*E. alopecuroides* (L.) Ell.
1. Spikelets awnless; cultivated for ornament; native of Eur. Ravenna Grass ....*E. ravennae* (L.) Beauv.

77. Sorghum Pers.

1. Perennial with creeping rhizomes; spikelets readily deciduous at maturity; pedicellate spikelet usually staminate; fields and waste places; escaped from cult.; introd. from Eur. June-Oct. Johnson Grass ....*S. halepense* (L.) Pers.
1. Annual; spikelets persistent at maturity; pedicellate spikelet usually neuter, shorter than the sessile one; waste places, occasionally escaped from cult.; resembling *Zea mays* when not in bloom. Sorghum. [*S. saccharatum* Moench]. More robust plants with loose panicles are known as *S. drummondii* Nees ....*S. vulgare* Pers.

78. Sorghastrum Nash — Indian Grass

S. nutans (L.) Nash. Prairies, open woods, roadsides, common. Aug.-Oct.

Tribe 11. Tripsaceae — Corn Tribe

79. Tripsacum L. — Gama Grass

T. dactyloides L. Wet ground, local; chiefly in the s. half of the state, but extending northward to Hancock, Fulton, and Tazewell counties. May-Sept.

80. Zea L. — Maize. Indian Corn

Z. mays L. Cultivated; but rarely spontaneous along roads or in waste places. July-Sept.

ILLINOIS COUNTIES

Adams 50	Ford 26	Livingston 27	Randolph 82
Alexander 100	Franklin 91	Logan 45	Richland 76
Bond 70	Fulton 37	McDonough 36	Rock Island 15
Boone 4	Gallatin 95	McHenry 5	Saint Clair 80
Brown 49	Greene 66	McLean 40	Saline 94
Bureau 18	Grundy 22	Macon 56	Sangamon 54
Calhoun 67	Hamilton 90	Macoupin 65	Schuyler 48
Carroll 13	Hancock 35	Madison 69	Scott 52
Cass 47	Hardin 96	Marion 78	Shelby 63
Champaign 42	Henderson 34	Marshall 28	Stark 30
Christian 55	Henry 17	Mason 38	Stephenson 2
Clark 60	Iroquois 25	Massac 102	Tazewell 39
Clay 77	Jackson 92	Menard 46	Union 99
Clinton 79	Jasper 73	Mercer 16	Vermilion 41
Coles 61	Jefferson 85	Monroe 81	Wabash 88
Cook 7	Jersey 68	Montgomery 64	Warren 33
Crawford 74	Jo Daviess 1	Morgan 53	Washington 83
Cumberland 62	Johnson 98	Moultrie 57	Wayne 86
De Kalb 10	Kane 9	Ogle 11	White 89
De Witt 44	Kankakee 24	Peoria 31	Whiteside 14
Douglas 58	Kendall 21	Perry 84	Will 23
Du Page 8	Knox 32	Piatt 43	Williamson 93
Edgar 59	Lake 6	Pike 51	Winnebago 3
Edwards 87	La Salle 20	Pope 97	Woodford 29
Effingham 72	Lawrence 75	Pulaski 101	
Fayette 71	Lee 12	Putnam 19	

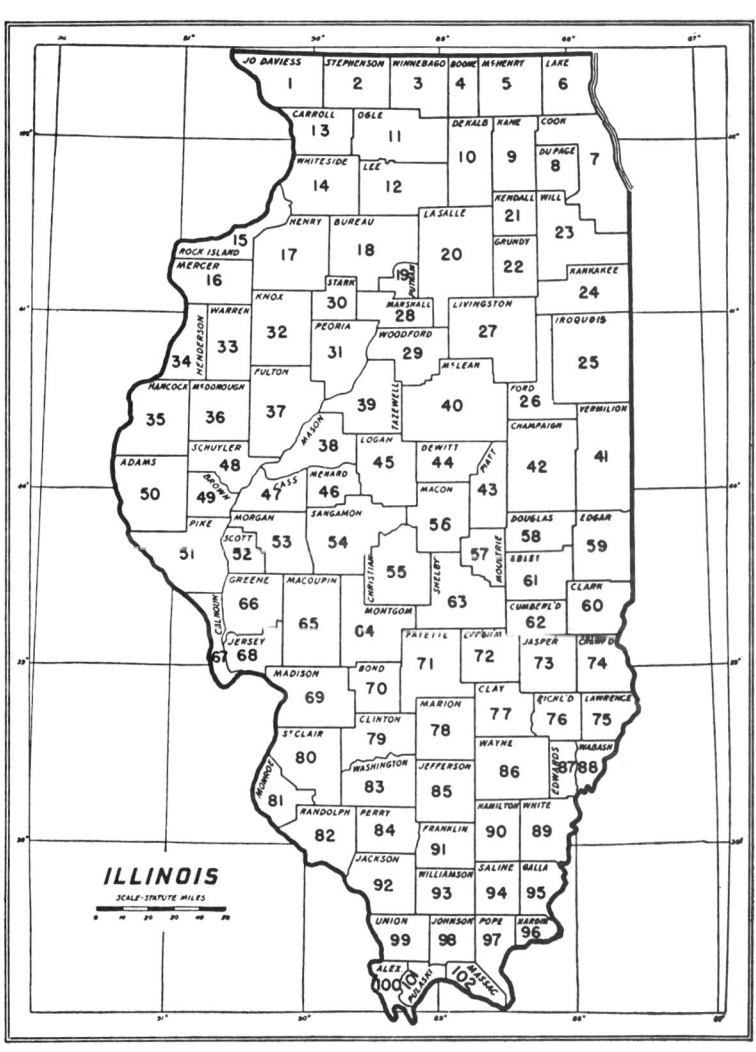

ILLINOIS

SCALE-STATUTE MILES

Glossary

ACAULESCENT. Stemless or apparently so.

ACHENE. A small dry, hard, unilocular, indehiscent, 1-seeded fruit in which the pericarp and seed-coat are not fused.

ACICULAR. Needle-shaped.

ACTINOMORPHIC. Radially symmetrical; regular; capable of being divided vertically into similar halves through two or more planes.

ACUMINATE. Tapering at the apex, and ending in a point or angle of about forty-five degrees.

ACUTE. Sharp-pointed; ending in a point or angle of about ninety degrees.

ADNATE. United with a dissimilar part, as the calyx-tube to the ovary, or stamens to the corolla, etc.

ADVENTIVE (adv.). Transient, not native or fully naturalized.

ALTERNATE. An arrangement of leaves or other parts not opposite or whorled; placed singly at different heights on the axis or stem.

ANASTOMOSING (veins). Connecting by cross-veins and forming a network.

ANDROGYNOUS. Having both staminate and pistillate flowers in the same inflorescence; in *Carex,* with the staminate flowers above the pistillate.

ANNUAL. Of one year's growth; a plant that completes its life-cycle in one season.

ANNULAR. In the form of a ring.

ANNULUS. A ring of thick-walled cells partly surrounding the sporangium of some ferns.

ANTHER. The pollen-bearing part of the stamen.

ANTHERIFEROUS. Anther-bearing.

ANTHESIS. The time at which a flower opens; or the act of expansion of a flower.

APETALOUS. Without petals.

APHYLLOPODIC. With the basal leaves rudimentary or bladeless, as in species of *Carex.*

APICULATE. With a small point or apiculus.

APOPETALOUS. Having the corolla composed of several distinct petals; equivalent to the more common term *polypetalous.*

APPRESSED. Pressed close to the surface but not fused with it.

AQUATIC. Living in water; said of plants which live in water, either floating at the surface or completely submerged.

ARACHNOID. Cobwebby; with fine, grayish entangled hairs.

ARCUATE. Curved or bent like a bow.

AREOLA. A small angular space marked upon a surface; the meshes of cellular tissue.

ARIL. An appendage or an outer covering of a seed, growing out from the hilum or funiculus; sometimes it appears as a pulpy covering.

ARISTATE. Awned; tipped by a bristle.

ASCENDING. Growing somewhat obliquely and curving upward.

ATTENUATE. Tapering to a narrow point.

AURICULATE. With ear-shaped appendages (auricles); said of leaves having a pair of short obtuse projections at base.

AWN. A bristle-like appendage.

AXIAL (axile). With the placentae in the axis or center of the ovary.

AXIL. The upper angle formed by a leaf or branch with the stem.

AXILLARY. Situated in an axil.

BARBELLATE. With small fine barbs or bristles.

BASIFIXED. Attached or fixed by the base, as an anther upon the filament.

BEAK. A narrowed or prolonged tip; applied particularly to fruits and carpels.

BERRY. A pulpy indehiscent fruit, formed from a single pistil, usually containing one or more seeds.

BICONVEX. Convex on both sides; doubly convex, as a lens; lenticular.

BIDENTATE. Having two teeth.

BIDENTULATE. Minutely bidentate.

BIENNIAL. Of two years' duration; a plant requiring two growing seasons to complete its life cycle.

BIFID. Two-cleft.

BILABIATE. Two-lipped, referring especially to the corolla (or calyx).

BIPINNATE. Twice pinnate.

BIPINNATIFID. Twice pinnatifid, that is, having the primary divisions of the leaves again pinnatifid.

BRACT. A reduced or more or less modified leaf, usually subtending a flower or a cluster of flowers.

BRACTLET. A small bract, particularly if borne on a secondary axis, as on a pedicel or even on a petiole; a bracteole.

BRANCHLET. A small branch or twig.

BULB. A short thick bud or modified stem, usually underground, bearing fleshy scale-like leaves that are stored with reserve food.

BULBOUS. Resembling a bulb.

BUNDLE-SCARS. Scars left in leaf-scars at time of leaf-fall by the breaking of the vascular bundles that pass from the stem into the petiole.

CADUCOUS. Falling off early, or prematurely, as the sepals of the poppy; in distinction from deciduous, or persistent.

CALYX. The outer perianth of the flower; a collective term for the sepals.

CAMPANULATE. Bell-shaped.

CANCELLATE. Marked like lattice, with lines crossing each other.

CANESCENT. With gray or whitish pubescence.

CAPILLARY. Fine, slender, hair-like.

CAPITATE. Aggregated in a dense or compact head, or head-like cluster.

CAPSULE. A dry dehiscent fruit composed of two or more carpels.

CARPEL. A simple pistil or a member of a compound pistil; the ovuliferous organ of a flower.

CATKIN. A bracteate, spike-like inflorescence bearing staminate or pistillate apetalous flowers; the catkin usually falls as a whole.

CAUDATE. Bearing a tail-like appendage.

CAUDEX. A short stem or trunk, usually the persistent woody base of a perennial herb.

CAULESCENT. Having a manifest stem above ground.

CAULINE. Pertaining or belonging to the stem.

CESPITOSE. Growing in tufts; forming mats.

CHAFF. A small thin scale or bract; particularly on the receptacle of Compositae.

CHARTACEOUS. Papery; having the texture of writing paper.

CHLOROPHYLL. The green coloring matter of plants, occurring chiefly in chloroplasts.

CILIATE. Bearing cilia, a marginal fringe of hairs.

CILIOLATE. Minutely ciliate.

CINEREOUS. Ash-colored; light gray.

CLASPING (leaf). With the base partly or completely surrounding the st

CLAVATE. Club-shaped; gradually thickened upward.

CLAW. The narowed base of the petals of some flowers.

CLEISTOGAMOUS (flowers). Small, closed, self-pollinated flowers, as in some violets and other plants; they are often underground.

*CLIMBING. Said of plants that ascend by means of tendrils, or by twining the stem or petiole around a support, or sometimes by other means.

COMA. The hairs at the end of some seeds, as in *Epilobium,* or *Asclepias.*

COMPLETE (leaf). One consisting of blade, petiole, and stipules.

COMPOUND (leaf). One composed of two or more leaflets on a common petiole or rachis.

CONCOLORED. Of one color throughout; not variegated.

CONDUPLICATE. Folded together lengthwise.

CONNATE. Similar parts fused together, *e.g.,* a pair of leaves united by their bases.

CONVOLUTE. Rolled up longitudinally.

CORDATE. Heart-shaped.

CORIACEOUS. Leathery.

CORM. A short, erect, often globose underground stem.

CORMOSE. Resembling a corm.

COROLLA. The inner cycle of the perianth, composed of petals.

CORONA. A structure occurring in some flowers between the corolla and the stamens, as in *Narcissus,* and in *Asclepias.*

CORYMB. A flat-topped or convex indeterminate inflorescence with the pedicels arising from different points on the axis, the outer flowers opening first.

CORYMBOSE (corymbiform). Like a corymb.

CREEPING (stem). Growing along the surface of the ground and rooting from the nodes.

CRENATE. Toothed with rounded shallow teeth.

CRENULATE. Finely crenate.

CUCULLATE. Hooded, or hood-shaped.

CULTIGEN. A plant or taxon known only in cultivation.

CUNEATE. Wedge-shaped; broad at one end and tapering to a point at the other.

CUSPIDATE. Sharp-pointed; ending in a sharp point or cusp.

CYATHIUM. The specialized inflorescence of *Euphorbia,* consisting of a cup-like involucre bearing the flowers within.

CYME. A convex or flat flower-cluster of the determinate type, the central flowers opening first.

CYMOSE. Arranged in cymes; cyme-like.

DECIDUOUS. Falling off at maturity, or at the end of the season.

DECLINED. Bent downward or aside; applied to stamens or style when turned to one side of the flower.

DECOMPOUND. More than once compound.

DECUMBENT (stem). Reclining, but with apex ascending.

DECURRENT (leaf). Extending down the stem below the insertion.

DEFLEXED. Deflected, or turned abruptly downward.

DEHISCENT. Splitting open along definite lines at maturity.

DELTOID. Triangular, shaped like the Greek letter Δ, as in the leaves of species of poplar.

DENTATE. Coarsely toothed, with the teeth directed outward.

DENTICULATE. Minutely dentate.

DETERMINATE (inflorescence). One in which the terminal flower is the oldest and therefore the first to open, the order of flowering proceeding from the top downward.

DIADELPHOUS. Having the stamens united by their filaments in two sets, as in almost all papilionaceous flowers.

DIFFUSE. Loosely spreading or branching.

DIGITATE. Compound leaves with the leaflets arising from the apex of the petiole.

DIMORPHOUS. Occurring in two forms.

DIOECIOUS. Having the staminate and pistillate flowers on different plants.

DISCOID. Resembling a disk; a discoid head (in Compositae) is one without ray-flowers.

DISK. A development of the receptacle about the base of the pistil; the common receptacle of the heads of Compositae.

DISSECTED. Divided into many narrow segments.

DISTINCT. Separate; not united with parts of the same series; not connate.

DIVARICATE. Spreading; widely divergent.

DIVIDED. Separated to the base or to the midvein.

DOUBLE. Said of flowers that have more than the usual number of petals.

DRUPE. A succulent indehiscent fruit with a bony, usually one-seeded endocarp; a stone-fruit, such as a plum.

DRUPELET. A little drupe, such as the individual carpels which together form the blackberry and similar fruits.

ECHINATE. Beset with prickles or bristles.

ELLIPSOID. A solid body elliptical in longitudinal section.

ELLIPTICAL. Having the form of an ellipse; nearly oblong.

EMARGINATE. Deeply notched at the apex.

ENDOCARP. The inner layer of the pericarp.

ENTIRE. With smooth margins, not toothed or lobed.

EPIGYNOUS. Borne on the ovary; applied to petals and stamens when the ovary is inferior.

EPIPETALOUS. Borne upon the corolla.

EPISEPALOUS. Borne upon the calyx,

EQUITANT. Said of conduplicate leaves which alternately enfold each other as in *Iris,* the upper part of the leaf being flat and vertical.

EROSE. With jagged margin, as if gnawed.

ESCAPE. Escaping from cultivation, and maintaining itself.

EVANESCENT. Soon disappearing.

EVERGREEN. Remaining green in the dormant season; applied to plants whose leaves persist throughout the year.

EXFOLIATING. Peeling off in thin layers.

EXSERTED. Prolonged beyond the surrounding organs, as stamens from the corolla; not included.

EXSTIPULATE (or ESTIPULATE). Lacking stipules.

FALCATE. Sickle- or scythe-shaped.

FARINOSE. Covered with mealy powder.

FASCICLE. A compact cluster or bundle.

FASTIGIATE. With stems or branches erect and close together.

FERRUGINOUS.   Rust-colored.

FILAMENT.   The stalk of a stamen, usually bearing an anther at its apex.

FILIFORM.   Thread-like; slender and terete.

FIMBRIATE.   Fringed.

FIMBRILLATE.   Minutely fringed.

FLABELLATE.   Fan-shaped.

FLEXUOUS.   Having a more or less zigzag form.

FLOCCOSE.   With tufts of soft woolly hairs.

FLORET.   Individual flower of Compositae and grasses.

FLORICANE.   A biennial stem in its second year, bearing flowers and fruits. (Rubus).

FOLIACEOUS.   Having the form or texture of a leaf; leafy.

FOLLICLE.   A simple, dry, dehiscent fruit, producing several or many seeds and composed of one carpel, which splits along one suture.

FREE.   Said of floral organs which are not united with other floral organs.

FUGACIOUS.   Falling or withering away very early; ephemeral.

FUNNELFORM.   Said of a corolla with the tube gradually widening upward into the spreading limb.

FUSIFORM.   Spindle-shaped, narrowed toward the ends from an enlarged middle.

GENICULATE.   Bent abruptly like a knee.

GIBBOUS.   Swollen on one side.

GLABRATE.   Nearly glabrous, or becoming glabrous.

GLABROUS.   Not hairy; free from epidermal hairs.

GLANDULAR.   Bearing glands or gland-like appendages or trichomes.

GLAUCESCENT.   Becoming glaucous.

GLAUCOUS.   Covered with a "bloom"; bluish white or bluish gray.

GLOMERULE.   An inflorescence condensed in the form of a small head or cluster.

GLUME.   A chaff-like bract; particularly one of the two empty bracts at the base of the spikelet in grasses, or the single bract of sedges.

GLUTINOUS.   Sticky; mucilaginous; covered with a sticky exudate.

GRAIN.   The dry, unilocular, 1-seeded, indehiscent, superior fruit of grasses, in which the thin pericarp is adherent throughout to the seed; a caryopsis.

GRANULAR, GRANULOSE.   Composed of or appearing as if covered with minute grains.

GYNECANDROUS.   Having staminate and pistillate flowers in the same spike, as in sedges, the upper flowers pistillate and the lower staminate.

HALBERD-SHAPED.   Hastate.

HASTATE.   Halberd-shaped; like an arrowhead, but with the basal lobes pointing outward nearly at right angles.

HEAD.   A type of inflorescence in which numerous small flowers are crowded upon a common receptacle; the inflorescence or capitulum of Compositae; a compact inflorescence.

HERB.   A plant that has no perennial woody stem above ground, thus distinguished from a shrub or tree.

HIRSUTE.   Pubescent with rather coarse or stiff hairs.

HIRSUTULOUS.   Slightly hirsute.

HIRTELLOUS.   Minutely hirsute.

HISPID. Beset with rigid hairs or bristles.

HISPIDULOUS. Minutely hispid.

HYALINE. Thin and translucent.

HYBRID. A plant (or animal) derived from the crossing of two distinct varieties or species; plants that appear to be intermediate between given or assumed parents.

HYPANTHIUM. The cup-shaped or tubular receptacle on which the perianth and the stamens are inserted.

HYPOGYNIUM. A structure supporting the ovary in some sedges.

HYPOGYNOUS. Borne on the receptacle beneath the ovary; said of stamens and petals.

IMBRICATE. Overlapping, as shingles on a roof.

INCISED. Sharply and more or less deeply and irregularly cut.

INCLUDED. Not at all exserted or protruded, as stamens not projecting from the corolla.

INDEHISCENT. Not opening regularly.

INDURATE. Hardened.

INDUSIUM. The covering of the sori of some ferns.

INFERIOR. Said of an ovary when the other floral parts appear to be inserted upon it.

INFLORESCENCE. The arrangement of the flowers on the stem.

INTERNODE. The portion of the stem between the nodes.

INTRODUCED. Brought intentionally from another country or region.

INVOLUCEL. A secondary involucre; that subtending the umbellets in the Umbelliferae.

INVOLUCRE. A whorl or group of bracts surrounding or subtending a single flower, or the collection of bracts aggregated at the base of an inflorescence, as the heads of Compositae, or in the umbels of Umbelliferae.

INVOLUTE. A type of vernation, in which the margins are rolled inward or toward the upper side.

IRREGULAR (flower). See Zygomorphic.

KEEL. A central dorsal ridge like the keel of a boat; the structure formed by the two lower united petals of a papilionaceous flower; the midvein of a compressed floral bract in grasses and sedges.

LACINIATE. Cut into narrow pointed lobes.

LANCEOLATE. Lance-shaped; much longer than broad, widening above the base, and tapering to the apex.

LANCEOLOID. A solid body lanceolate in longitudinal section.

LEAFLET. One of the blades of a compound leaf.

LEGUME. The fruit of certain Leguminosae, a pod formed from a simple pistil, and dehiscent along both sutures.

LEMMA. The lower of two bracts enclosing the flower in grasses.

LENTICULAR. Lentil-shaped, that is, with the shape of a biconvex lens.

LIGULATE. Provided with or resembling a ligule.

LIGULE. A thin, often scarious projection from the top of the leaf-sheath in grasses and similar plants; the principal part of the corolla of ray-florets in numerous Compositae; the membranous structure on the adaxial surface of the leaf of *Isoetes* and *Selaginella*.

LINEAR. Long and narrow with nearly parallel margins.

LIP. Either of the divisions of a bilabiate corolla; the peculiar upper (apparently lower) petal in orchids.

LOBE. Any part or segment of an organ; specifically, a part of a corolla, calyx, or leaf that represents a division to about the middle.

LOBULATE. With small shallow lobes.

LOCAL. Species of restricted or infrequent occurrence, but the number of individuals may vary from one to many.

LOCULE. One of the cavities or compartments of a pistil or anther.

LOMENT. A jointed legume, usually constricted between the seeds, and at maturity breaking transversely into 1-seeded, indehiscent segments.

LUNATE. Crescent- or half-moon-shaped.

LYRATE. Lyre-shaped; descriptive of a pinnatifid leaf having a large, rounded terminal lobe, and the lateral lobes becoming gradually smaller toward the base.

MEGASPORE. The larger of two kinds of spores of a plant, usually giving rise to a female gametophyte.

MEMBRANOUS. Thin, soft, pliable, sometimes more or less translucent.

MICROSPORE. The smaller of two kinds of spores of a plant, usually giving rise to a male gametophyte.

MICROSPOROPHYLL. A sporophyll that bears microspores.

MONADELPHOUS. Said of stamens when the filaments are united into one tube.

MONILIFORM. Resembling a string of beads, as the rhizome of certain species of *Scutellaria*.

MONOECIOUS. Having stamens and pistils in separate flowers on the same plant.

MUCRONATE. Tipped with a short abrupt point or mucro.

MUCRONULATE. Minutely mucronate.

MULTIPLE FRUIT. A cluster of matured ovaries produced by separate flowers.

MURICATE. Roughened with short hard points.

NATURALIZED (nat.). Although not native in the region, growing spontaneously and well established as a component of the flora.

NEUTER. Devoid of stamens and functional pistil.

NODOSE. Provided with knots or internal transverse partitions, as the leaves of some species of *Juncus*, and *Eleocharis*.

NODE. The joint of a stem where the leaves are inserted.

NUT. An indehiscent, dry, one-seeded, hard-walled fruit, produced from a compound ovary.

NUTLET. A little nut; one of the achene-like parts of the fruit of Boraginaceae, Verbenaceae, Labiatae, etc.

OB—. A Latin prefix, usually signifying inversion, as obcordate (inversely heart-shaped), oblanceolate (inversely lanceolate), obovate (inversely ovate), etc.

OBTUSE. Blunt, rounded.

OPPOSITE. Inserted on opposite sides of an axis, as leaves, when there are two at one node.

ORBICULAR. Circular; round in outline.

Oval. Broadly elliptical, with the width more than half the length.

Ovary. The basal part of the pistil containing the ovules; the immature fruit.

Ovate. Having an outline like the median longitudinal section of a hen's egg, the broader end downward.

Ovoid. A solid body ovate in longitudinal section.

Ovule. The primordium of a seed in the ovary; the organ which may develop after fertilization into the seed.

Palet. The upper bract which with the lemma encloses the flower in grasses.

Palmate (leaf). Radiately lobed or divided, with three or more veins arising from one point.

Panicle. A compound raceme.

Paniculate. Borne in panicles, or resembling a panicle.

Pannose. Having the appearance or texture of felt or woollen cloth.

Papilionaceous. Referring to the peculiar irregular corolla of many Leguminosae, consisting of a larger upper petal (*standard*), two oblique lateral petals (*wings*), and the two lower ones connivent into a *keel*.

Papillose. Covered with papillae, which are small protuberances.

Pappus. The modified limb of the calyx in Compositae, forming a crown of variable structure at the summit of the achene.

Parasite. An organism which derives nourishment from another living organism.

Parietal. Borne on or pertaining to the wall of the ovary or fruit.

Pectinate. Comb-like; pinnatifid with narrow, closely set segments.

Pedate. Palmately divided or parted, with the lateral divisions two-cleft.

Pedicel. The stalk of a single flower in a cluster.

Peduncle. The primary flower stalk which supports either a cluster of flowers, or a single flower.

Pellucid. Clear, transparent, or translucent.

Peltate. Shield-shaped; said of a leaf when the petiole is attached to the under side away from the margin or usually not far from the center.

Pendent. Hanging down; pendulous.

Penicillate. Bearing a little tuft of hairs, especially at the tip.

Perennial. A plant, or part of a plant, which persists for more than two seasons.

Perfect (flower). Having both stamens and carpels; bisexual.

Perfoliate. Said of a leaf when the stem appears to pass through its base.

Perianth. The floral envelope; consisting of calyx and corolla; a term commonly used when there is no clear distinction between calyx and corolla.

Pericarp. The wall of the ripened fruit.

Perigynium. The inflated sac (bract) enclosing the pistillate flower in *Carex*.

Perigynous. Borne around the ovary and not at its base, as in flowers in which perianth and stamens are borne on the rim of the hypanthium.

Petal. One of the parts of an apopetalous corolla.

Petaliferous. Petal-bearing.

Petiolate. Having a petiole.

Petiole. A leaf-stalk.

Petiolulate. Having a petiolule.

Petiolule. Stalk of a leaflet.

Phyllopodic. The basal leaves of the fertile stems normally blade-bearing, as in species of *Carex*.

Pilose. Pubescent with soft long trichomes.

Pilosulous. Minutely pilose.

PINNA. A primary division of a pinnate leaf.

PINNATE (leaf). Compound, with the leaflets on each side of a common petiole or rachis.

PINNATIFID. Cleft or divided in a pinnate manner, the sinuses or lobes narrow or acute.

PINNULE. One of the smaller subdivisions of the primary divisions of a compound leaf, especially of ferns.

PISTIL. The ovule-bearing part of a flower, comprising ovary, style, and stigma; consisting of a single carpel (simple pistil) or of two or more partly or wholly fused carpels (compound pistil).

PISTILLATE FLOWER. A flower with a pistil but no stamens.

PLACENTA. Any part of the interior of the ovary which bears the ovules.

PLANO-CONVEX. Plane on one side and convex on the other.

PLICATE. Folded like a fan.

PLUMOSE. Feathery; furnished with long hairs as the beak of the achene in *Clematis,* or the pappus of some Compositae.

POLLEN. Microspores, or partially developed male gametophytes, formed in the anthers of seed plants; the powdery contents of an anther.

POLYGAMOUS. Bearing unisexual and bisexual flowers on the same plant.

POLYPETALOUS. With petals separate.

POME. An accessory fruit composed of the pericarp and enlarged receptacle, as in the apple.

PRICKLE. A sharp-pointed outgrowth of the cortex and epidermis of a stem or leaf, as in rose, blackberry, etc.

PRIMOCANE. A biennial stem in its first (vegetative) season. (Rubus).

PROCUMBENT (stem). Trailing on the ground, but not rooting at the nodes.

PROLIFEROUS. Producing offshoots, sometimes abnormal, as when carpels or stamens give rise to leafy shoots.

PROSTRATE. Lying flat on the ground.

PUBERULENT. Minutely pubescent.

PUBESCENT. Covered with pubescence, an indument of hairs (trichomes).

PULVERULENT. Appearing as if covered with powder or dust.

PUNCTATE. Marked with small dots or translucent glands.

PUNCTICULATE. Minutely punctate.

PUNGENT. Terminating in a rigid sharp point; also of acrid flavor.

PYRIFORM. Pear-shaped.

QUADRIFOLIATE. Four-leaved.

QUADRIFOLIOLATE. Having four leaflets.

RACEME. An indeterminate inflorescence with pedicellate flowers on a more or less elongated axis.

RACEMOSE. In a raceme, or resembling a raceme.

RACHILLA. A secondary axis or rachis; in the grasses and sedges the axis that bears the flowers.

RACHIS. An axis bearing flowers or leaflets.

RADIATE. Spreading from a common center; in the Compositae, a head with ray-flowers.

RAY. The branch of an umbel; the marginal flowers (ray-flowers) of an inflorescence if differentiated; the strap-shaped part of the corolla of the ray-flowers in Compositae.

RECEPTACLE. The more or less expanded portion of an axis bearing the organs of a flower or the collected flowers of a head.

REGULAR (flower). See Actinomorphic.

RENIFORM. Kidney-shaped; having the width greater than the length, and a wide sinus at the base.

REPAND. With a slightly sinuate margin.

RETICULATE. In the form of a network; net-veined.

RETRORSE. Turned backward or downward.

RETUSE. Slightly notched at the rounded apex.

REVOLUTE. Rolled backward from the margin or apex.

RHIZOME. A more or less elongated, usually underground, horizontal or ascending stem modified for food storage and asexual reproduction.

RHOMBIC. Having the shape of a rhomb; oval, but somewhat angular at the sides; obliquely four-sided.

ROTATE (corolla). Wheel-shaped; with a flat and circular limb, and a very short tube.

RUGOSE. Wrinkled.

RUGULOSE. Minutely rugose.

RUNCINATE. Pinnatifid; cut into sharp triangular lobes, the points directed backward.

SAGITTATE. Shaped like an arrowhead, with the basal lobes directed downward.

SALVERFORM (flower). With the slender corolla-tube abruptly expanded in a flat limb.

SAMARA. A dry indehiscent, one-seeded, winged fruit, such as that of elm, ash, or maple.

SAPROPHYTE. A plant which derives its food from non-living organic matter.

SCABRELLOUS. See Scabrid.

SCABRID. Slightly rough to touch.

SCABROUS. Rough to the touch.

SCALE. A term applied to several kinds of small usually appressed leaves or bracts.

SCAPE. A leafless peduncle arising from the ground; it may bear scales or bracts, and may be one- or several-flowered.

SCAPIFORM. Scape-like; having the form of a scape.

SCAPOSE. Having a scape.

SCARIOUS. Dry, thin, scale-like; membranous; not green.

SCORPIOID. Applied to inflorescences which are circinately coiled in the bud, unrolling as the flowers expand, as in Boraginaceae.

SECUND. Turned to one side, as the flowers of an inflorescence.

SEPAL. One of the parts or lobes of a calyx.

SEPTATE. Divided by septa, or partitions.

SEPTICIDAL. Dehiscing along or in the partitions; said of a fruit that opens between the locules.

SEPTUM. A partition.

SERICEOUS. Silky; pubescent with soft, shining, usually appressed hairs.

SERRATE. Saw-toothed; having small, forwardly-directed sharp teeth on the margin.

SERRULATE. Finely serrate.

SESSILE. Not stalked.

SETACEOUS. Bristle-like.

SETOSE. Beset with bristles.

SETULOSE. Finely setose.

SHEATH.   The basal part of a leaf of a grass; any long and more or less tubular structure surrounding an organ or part.

SHRUB.   A woody plant which does not become tree-like and usually produces several stems from a common base.

SIMPLE (stem).   Unbranched or without branches. (Leaf), with the blade composed of one piece, not divided into separate leaflets; not compound. (Pistil), of one carpel.

SINUATE.   With a strongly wavy margin.

SORUS.   One of the fruit-dots or clusters of sporangia on the leaves of ferns.

SPADIX.   A thick or fleshy spike of certain plants, as the Araceae, surrounded or subtended by a spathe.

SPATHACEOUS.   Resembling a spathe; spathe-bearing.

SPATHE.   A large protecting bract, often colored or membranous, enclosing the flower or inflorescence, especially of certain Monocotyledons.

SPATULATE.   Spatula-shaped; gradually narrowed from a rounded summit.

SPIKE.   An indeterminate simple inflorescence with sessile flowers on an elongated axis.

SPIKELET.   A small spike; the unit of inflorescence of grasses and sedges.

SPINE.   A sharp-pointed structure; a thorn.

SPINESCENT.   Becoming spiny; with short spine-like branchlets.

SPINULOSE.   Minutely spiny.

SPONTANEOUS (spont.).   Growing as native; appearing by itself without having been planted.

SPORANGIUM.   The spore-sac, especially in ferns, in which spores are produced.

SPOROCARP.   A pod-like structure containing one or more sporangia, as in Marsileaceae.

SPOROPHYLL.   A specialized spore-bearing leaf, usually more or less modified and unlike the normal leaves.

SPUR.   A sac-like or tubular extension of some part or parts of the perianth, usually nectariferous; a short branchlet with much shortened internodes, usually bearing a cluster of leaves.

SPURRED.   Provided with a spur.

SQUARROSE.   Spreading at the tip, at a right angle or more.

STAMEN.   The pollen-bearing male organ of the flower.

STAMINATE FLOWER.   A flower which bears stamens but no carpels.

STAMINODE.   A sterile stamen, or a structure resembling such and borne in the staminal part of the flower; in some flowers staminodia are petal-like.

STANDARD.   The upper broad petal of a papilionaceous flower.

STELLATE.   Star-shaped; said of trichomes with radiating branches, or of a cluster of radiating trichomes.

STIGMA.   The part of the pistil, usually the apex, which receives pollen and upon which pollen grains germinate.

STIPE.   The stalk of a pistil or similar organ.

STIPEL.   A minute stipule on the petiolule of a leaflet.

STIPITATE.   Having a stipe.

STIPULE.   One of a pair of lateral appendages at the base of the petiole of many leaves.

STIPULATE (leaf).   Possessing stipules.

STOLON.   In flowering plants, a slender modified stem or basal branch trailing along the ground and rooting at the nodes; a "runner."

STOLONIFEROUS.   Bearing stolons.

STRAMINEOUS.   Straw-like, especially of the color of straw.

STRIATE.   Marked with fine longitudinal lines.

STRIGILLOSE. Minutely strigose.

STRIGOSE. With appressed straight and stiff hairs.

STYLE. The usually attenuated part of the pistil between the ovary and the stigma.

SUB—. A Latin prefix, usually signifying somewhat, or slightly.

SUBULATE. Awl-shaped; slender, and tapering to a point.

SUCCULENT. Juicy; fleshy; soft and thickened.

SUFFRUTICOSE. Applied to a perennial plant that is low and somewhat shrubby, with only the lower part of the stem or branches woody and persistent.

SUPERIOR (ovary). Borne above the insertion of the perianth and free from it.

SYMPETALOUS. Having the petals united into one piece by their margins.

SYNGENESIOUS. Stamens with united anthers but separate filaments, as in Compositae.

SYNSEPALOUS. Having the sepals more or less united.

TAWNY. Tan color, or yellowish brown.

TAXON. A term for any taxonomic category of any rank.

TENDRIL. A filiform organ used for climbing, and representing a modified leaflet, or leaf, or stipules, or branch.

TERETE. Circular in transverse section.

THALLOID. Resembling or consisting of a thallus; said of Lemnaceae, a family of monocotyledonous aquatic plants distinguished by the absence of a distinct stem or foliage.

THORN. A woody sharp-pointed structure formed from a modification of a branch of a stem.

TOMENTOSE. Densely woolly or pubescent; with matted soft wool-like hairiness.

TOMENTULOSE. Closely and finely tomentose.

TORULOSE. Diminutive of torose, cylindrical, swelling in knobs at intervals, somewhat moniliform, or like a string of beads.

TRAILING. A plant unable to support itself, prostrate but not rooting at the nodes.

TREE. A woody perennial plant, usually with an evident trunk, and attaining a height at maturity of not less than five meters.

TRICHOME. An outgrowth from the epidermis of plants, as hair, scale, bristle, or prickle.

TRIFID. Divided into three parts; three-cleft.

TRIGONAL. Triangular; the same as trigonous.

TRIPINNATIFID. Thrice pinnatifid.

TRUNCATE. Ending abruptly, as if cut off.

TUBER. Enlarged, fleshy, underground stem, commonly borne at the end of a rhizome.

TUBERCLE. A small swelling, or a little tuber-like body; the persistent base of the style in certain Cyperaceae; the grain-like corky growths on the valves of *Rumex;* enlargements on the roots of leguminous plants produced by symbiotic bacteria.

TUBERCULATE. Having tubercles.

TUBULAR (corolla). Prolonged into a tube, without much spreading at the border.

TURBINATE. Inversely conical; top-shaped.

TWIG. A small shoot or branchlet of a tree or shrub, particularly that of the current season's growth.

TWINING. Climbing by twisting spirally around another stem or other support.

Umbel. An indeterminate inflorescence with branches (rays) arising from a common point, resembling the framework of an inverted umbrella; characteristic of the Umbelliferae.

Umbellate. Borne in umbels.

Umbellet. A small umbel formed at the end of one of the rays of a compound umbel.

Uncinate. Hooked at the tip.

Undulate. With wavy surface or margin.

Unisexual. Of one sex, either staminate or pistillate.

Urceolate. Urn-shaped; ovoid or shortly cylindrical and contracted or constricted at the mouth.

Utricle. A fruit consisting of a single seed enveloped in a thin pericarp and enclosed by the persistent calyx.

Valve. The pieces into which a capsule splits or divides; of anthers which open by flaps or lids; the three inner accrescent sepals of *Rumex*.

Velutinous. Velvety.

Venation. Arrangement of veins, or vascular bundles.

Vernation. The arrangement of leaves in bud.

Versatile. Attached by the middle so as to swing freely, as an anther.

Verticillate. Arranged in a whorl.

Villous. Provided with long and soft, not matted, hairs; shaggy.

Villosulous. Minutely villous.

Virgate. Wand-like; with straight, stiff, erect branches.

Viscid. Clammy; sticky; glutinous.

Whorl. An arrangement of three or more leaves or other organs in a circle around the axis.

Zygomorphic. Bilaterally symmetrical; irregular; applied to flowers capable of being bisected into similar halves along only one plane.

Conspectus of Classification

Division I. PTERIDOPHYTA
   Class Lycopsida
      Order lycopodiales
         Family 1. Lycopodiaceae
      Order selaginellales
         Family 2. Selaginellaceae
      Order isoetales
         Family 3. Isoetaceae

   Class Sphenopsida
      Order equisetales
         Family 4. Equisetaceae

   Class Filicopsida
      Order ophioglossales
         Family 5. Ophioglossaceae
      Order filicales
         Family 6. Hymenophyllaceae
              7. Osmundaceae
              8. Polypodiaceae
              9. Marsileaceae
            10. Salviniaceae

Division II. SPERMATOPHYTA
   Subdivision 1. Gymnospermae
      Order coniferales
         Family 1. Taxaceae
              2. Pinaceae
              3. Taxodiaceae
              4. Cupressaceae

   Subdivision 2. Angiospermae
      Class 1. Dicotyledoneae
         Subclass 1. Archichlamydeae
            Order ranales
               Families:

1. Magnoliaceae	6. Nelumbonaceae
2. Annonaceae	7. Ceratophyllaceae
3. Ranunculaceae	8. Berberidaceae
4. Cabombaceae	9. Podophyllaceae
5. Nymphaeaceae	10. Menispermaceae

            Order papaverales
               Families:

11. Violaceae	15. Droseraceae
12. Cistaceae	16. Resedaceae
13. Papaveraceae	17. Capparidaceae
14. Fumariaceae	18. Cruciferae

Order HYPERICALES
Families:

19. Hypericaceae   20. Elatinaceae

Order SARRACENIALES
Family 21. Sarraceniaceae

Order MALVALES
Families:

22. Tiliaceae   23. Malvaceae

Order CARYOPHYLLALES
Families:

24. Caryophyllaceae   26. Aizoaceae
25. Portulacaceae

Order CHENOPODIALES
Families:

27. Chenopodiaceae   30. Phytolaccaceae
28. Amaranthaceae   31. Nyctaginaceae
29. Illecebraceae

Order POLYGONALES
Family 32. Polygonaceae

Order PIPERALES
Family 33. Saururaceae

Order GERANIALES
Families:

34. Rutaceae   39. Limnanthaceae
35. Simarubaceae   40. Zygophyllaceae
36. Geraniaceae   41. Balsaminaceae
37. Linaceae   42. Polygalaceae
38. Oxalidaceae

Order EUPHORBIALES
Family 43. Euphorbiaceae

Order SAPINDALES
Families:

44. Celastraceae   48. Aquifoliaceae
45. Sapindaceae   49. Anacardiaceae
46. Staphyleaceae   50. Aceraceae
47. Hippocastanaceae

Order RHAMNALES
Families:

51. Rhamnaceae   52. Vitaceae

Order ROSALES
Family 53. Rosaceae

Order LEGUMINALES
Family 54. Leguminosae

Order HAMAMELIDALES
Families:

55. Hydrangeaceae
56. Escalloniaceae
57. Grossulariaceae
58. Hamamelidaceae
59. Platanaceae

60. Crassulaceae
61. Penthoraceae
62. Saxifragaceae
63. Parnassiaceae
64. Adoxaceae

Order FAGALES
Families:

65. Fagaceae

66. Betulaceae

Order JUGLANDALES
Families:

67. Juglandaceae

68. Myricaceae

Order SALICALES
Family 69. Salicaceae

Order URTICALES
Families:

70. Ulmaceae
71. Moraceae

72. Cannabinaceae
73. Urticaceae

Order LAURALE3
Families:

74. Lauraceae
75. Lythraceae

76. Thymelaeaceae
77. Elaeagnaceae

Order PASSIFLORALES
Family 78. Passifloraceae

Order CACTALES
Family 79. Cactaceae

Order LOASALES
Family 80. Loasaceae

Order CUCURBITALES
Family 81. Cucurbitaceae

Order MYRTALES
Families:

82. Melastomaceae
83. Onagraceae
84. Haloragaceae

85. Callitrichaceae
86. Hippuridaceae

Order ARISTOLOCHIALES
Family 87. Aristolochiaceae

Order SANTALALES
Families:

88. Santalaceae   89. Loranthaceae

Order UMBELLALES
Families:

90. Cornaceae   92. Umbelliferae
91. Araliaceae

Subclass 2. METACHLAMYDEAE

Order ERICALES
Family 93. Ericaceae

Order EBENALES
Families:

94. Ebenaceae   96. Sapotaceae
95. Styracaceae

Order PRIMULALES
Family 97. Primulaceae

Order OLEALES
Family 98. Oleaceae

Order GENTIANALES
Families:

 99. Apocynaceae   102. Gentianaceae
100. Asclepiadaceae   103. Menyanthaceae
101. Loganiaceae

Order POLEMONIALES
Families:

104. Polemoniaceae   106. Hydrophyllaceae
105. Convolvulaceae   107. Solanaceae

Order SCROPHULARIALES
Families:

108. Scrophulariaceae   112. Lentibulariaceae
109. Bignoniaceae   113. Orobanchaceae
110. Acanthaceae   114. Martyniaceae
111. Plantaginaceae

Order LAMIALES
Families:

115. Boraginaceae   117. Phrymaceae
116. Verbenaceae   118. Labiatae

Order RUBIALES
Families:

119. Rubiaceae   120. Caprifoliaceae

Order CAMPANALES
Families:
121. Campanulaceae   122. Lobeliaceae

Order ASTERALES
Families:
123. Valerianaceae   125. Compositae
124. Dipsacaceae

Class 2. MONOCOTYLEDONEAE

Order ALISMALES
Families:
126. Alismaceae   128. Naiadaceae
127. Juncaginaceae   129. Potamogetonaceae

Order LILIALES
Families:
130. Liliaceae   131. Juncaceae

Order XYRIDALES
Families:
132. Xyridaceae   134. Pontederiaceae
133. Commelinaceae

Order AMARYLLIDALES
Families:
135. Amaryllidaceae   137. Dioscoreaceae
136. Iridaceae

Order HYDROCHARITALES
Family 138. Hydrocharitaceae

Order ORCHIDALES
Families:
139. Burmanniaceae   140. Orchidaceae

Order ARALES
Families:
141. Araceae   142. Lemnaceae

Order PANDANALES
Families:
143. Typhaceae   144. Sparganiaceae

Order GRAMINALES
Families:
145. Cyperaceae   146. Gramineae

Index to Plant Names*

* Family names appear in caps and small caps; synonyms are indicated by italic type. In genera with fewer than ten species the latter have not been indexed.

INCHES 1 2 3 4 5 6

METRIC 1 2 3 4 5 6 7 8 9 10 11 12 13 14 15